CARAVAN

CARAVAN

THE ASSEMBLED TALES

OF

JOHN GALSWORTHY

NEW YORK
CHARLES SCRIBNER'S SONS
1926

823.91

G13c

13013

To

MY WIFE

FOREWORD

Like some long caravan bearing merchandise of sorts, the tales of a writer wind through the desert of indifference towards the oasis of public favour. Whether they ever arrive, or drift to death among the shifting sands of popular taste, lies on the knees of the gods—their author has no say. When he has mustered and sent them forth, he may retire and squat afresh on the carpet of vision, having done all he can.

In assembling for this 'Caravan' all my tales falling short of the novel in length, written between the years 1900 and 1923 inclusive, I have roped them two by two, an early tale behind and a late tale in front. Taking 1914 as the dividing year, I have thus paired forty-six out of these fifty-six tales. The five remaining pairs belong entirely to the last ten years, more prolific than the first fourteen. In selecting each tandem, I have tried to find tales which have some likeness to each other in theme, or mood, so that any reader who has the curiosity can mark such difference as Time brings to technique or treatment.

Ten of the tales thus paired are what one calls "long-short," ranging from 30,000 to 8,000 words—no one of the rest exceeds, I think, 6,000.

The fiction market is supposed to require of short stories a certain pattern full of "pep" and sting in the tail. The scorpion, it is said, if sufficiently irritated, will sting itself to death. So will the short story when worried by the demands of editors. The inveterately independent will resist these blandishments, go their own ways, imitate no one. They may achieve results as little to the taste of the market as are these tales, but at least they will fail after their own hearts and probably end by getting very high prices for their merchandise.

"Ev'yone that talk about Heav'n ain't goin' there!" and those who dutifully confection the short story to the sacred pattern of the hour may well become of the company which shakes its tambourines in hell. Independence is the state best worth having in life, and such as believe they can achieve it in their later tales by servitude to fashion in their youthful efforts are doomed, I fear, to the drinking of bitter waters. If the writer of the short tale submit himself to the discipline demanded by the crisp and clear expression of his genuine fancies and his genuine moods, he has submitted to quite enough.

As the untaught spider spins his delicate rose-window and assures it against wind and rain by sheer adjustment—not a thread too many or too few—so let us writers of short tales try to spin out of our own instinct and vision the round and threaded marvel. If in it we catch some hopeful editor and hold him to ransom—all the better for us; but if we don't we have none the less fulfilled our being, and that is our real end in life.

Far be it from this writer to think that he has achieved that end, but he has tried; and in this 'Caravan' the assembly of his differing and indifferent efforts sets forth.

JOHN GALSWORTHY.

ALGERIA,
February 5, 1925.

CONTENTS

CARAVAN

SALVATION OF A FORSYTE

I

SWITHIN FORSYTE lay in bed. The corners of his mouth under his white moustache drooped towards his double chin. He panted: "My doctor says I'm in a bad way, James."

His twin-brother placed his hand behind his ear. "I can't hear you. They tell me I ought to take a cure. There's always a cure wanted for something. Emily had a cure."

Swithin replied: "You mumble so. I hear my man, Adolph. I trained him. . . . You ought to have an ear-trumpet. You're getting very shaky, James."

There was silence; then James Forsyte, as if galvanized, remarked: "I s'pose you've made your will. I s'pose you've left your money to the family; you've nobody else to leave it to. There was Danson died the other day, and left his money to a hospital."

The hairs of Swithin's white moustache bristled. "My fool of a doctor told me to make my will," he said; "I hate a fellow who tells you to make your will. My appetite's good; I ate a partridge last night. I'm all the better for eating. He told me to leave off champagne! I eat a good breakfast. I'm not eighty. You're the same age, James. You look very shaky."

James Forsyte said: "You ought to have another opinion. Have Blank; he's the first man now. I had him for Emily; cost me two hundred guineas. He sent her to Homburg; that's the first place now. The prince was there—everybody goes there."

Swithin Forsyte answered: "I don't get any sleep at night, now I can't get out; and I've bought a new carriage—gave a pot of money for it. D'you ever have bronchitis? They tell me champagne's dangerous; it's my belief I couldn't take a better thing."

1

James Forsyte rose.

"You ought to have another opinion. Emily sent her love; she would have come in, but she had to go to Niagara. Everybody goes there; it's *the* place now. Rachael goes every morning; she overdoes it—she'll be laid up one of these days. There's a fancy ball there to-night; the Duke gives the prizes."

Swithin Forsyte said angrily: "I can't get things properly cooked here; at the club I get spinach decently done." The bed-clothes jerked at the tremor of his legs.

James Forsyte replied: "You must have done well with Tintos; you must have made a lot of money by them. Your ground-rents must be falling in, too. You must have any amount you don't know what to do with." He mouthed at the words, as if his lips were watering.

Swithin Forsyte glared. "Money!" he said; "my doctor's bill's enormous."

James Forsyte stretched out a cold, damp hand. "Goodbye! You ought to have another opinion. I can't keep the horses waiting: they're a new pair—stood me in three hundred. You ought to take care of yourself. I shall speak to Blank about you. You ought to have him—everybody says he's the first man. Good-bye!"

Swithin Forsyte continued to stare at the ceiling. He thought: 'A poor thing, James! a selfish beggar! Must be worth a couple of hundred thousand!' He wheezed, meditating on life. . . .

He was ill and lonely. For many years he had been lonely, and for two years ill; but as he had smoked his first cigar, so he would live his life—stoutly, to its predestined end. Every day he was driven to the club; sitting forward on the spring cushions of a single brougham, his hands on his knees, swaying a little, strangely solemn. He ascended the steps into that marble hall—the folds of his chin wedged into the aperture of his collar—walking squarely with a stick. Later he would dine, eating majestically, and savouring his food, behind a bottle of champagne set in an ice-pail—his waistcoat defended by a napkin, his eyes rolling a little or glued in a stare on the waiter. Never did he suffer his head or back to droop, for it was not distinguished so to do.

Because he was old and deaf, he spoke to no one; and no one spoke to him. The club gossip, an Irishman, said to each newcomer: "Old Forsyte! Look at 'um! Must ha' had

something in his life to sour 'um!" But Swithin had had
nothing in his life to sour him.

For many days now he had lain in bed in a room exuding
silver, crimson, and electric light, and smelling of opopanax
and of cigars. The curtains were drawn, the firelight gleamed:
on a table by his bed were a jug of barley-water and *The
Times*. He had made an attempt to read, failed, and fell again
to thinking. His face with its square chin looked like a block
of pale leather bedded in the pillow. It was lonely! A woman
in the room would have made all the difference! Why had
he never married? He breathed hard, staring frog-like at the
ceiling ; a memory had come into his mind. It was a long
time ago—forty odd years—but it seemed like yesterday. . . .

It happened when he was thirty-eight, for the first and only
time in his life travelling on the Continent, with his twin-
brother James and a man named Traquair. On the way from
Germany to Venice, he had found himself at the Hôtel Goldene
Alp at Salzburg. It was late August, and weather for the
gods: sunshine on the walls and the shadows of the vine-
leaves, and at night, the moonlight, and again on the walls
the shadows of the vine-leaves. Averse to the suggestions of
other people, Swithin had refused to visit the Citadel ; he had
spent the day alone in the window of his bedroom, smoking a
succession of cigars, and disparaging the appearance of the
passers-by. After dinner he was driven by boredom into the
streets. His chest puffed out like a pigeon's, and with something of a pigeon's cold and inquiring eye, he strutted, annoyed at the frequency of uniforms, which seemed to him both
needless and offensive. His spleen rose at this crowd of foreigners who spoke an unintelligible language, wore hair on
their faces, and smoked bad tobacco. 'A queer lot!' he
thought. The sound of music from a *café* attracted him, he
walked in, vaguely moved by a wish for the distinction of adventure, without the trouble which adventure usually brought
with it ; spurred too, perhaps, by an after-dinner demon. The
café was the *bier-halle* of the 'Fifties, with a door at either end,
and lighted by a large wooden lantern. On a small dais three
musicians were fiddling. Solitary men, or groups, sat at some
dozen tables, and the waiters hurried about replenishing glasses ;
the air was thick with smoke. Swithin sat down. "Wine!"
he said sternly. The astonished waiter brought him wine.

Swithin pointed to a beer-glass on the table. "Here!" he said, with the same ferocity. The waiter poured out the wine. 'Ah!' thought Swithin, 'they can understand if they like.' A group of officers close by were laughing; Swithin stared at them uneasily. A hollow cough sounded almost in his ear. To his left a man sat reading, with his elbows on the corners of a journal, and his gaunt shoulders raised almost to his eyes. He had a thin, long nose, broadening suddenly at the nostrils; a black-brown beard, spread in a savage fan over his chest; what was visible of the face was the colour of old parchment. A strange, wild, haughty-looking creature! Swithin observed his clothes with some displeasure—they were the clothes of a journalist or strolling actor. And yet he was impressed. This was singular. How could he be impressed by a fellow in such clothes! The man reached out a hand, covered with black hairs, and took up a tumbler that contained a dark-coloured fluid: 'Brandy!' thought Swithin. The crash of a falling chair startled him—his neighbour had risen. He was of immense height, and very thin; his great beard seemed to splash away from his mouth; he was glaring at the group of officers, and speaking. Swithin made out two words: "*Hunde! Deutsche Hunde!*" 'Hounds! Dutch hounds!' he thought: 'Rather strong!' One of the officers had jumped up, and now drew his sword. The tall man swung his chair up, and brought it down with a thud. Everybody round started up and closed on him. The tall man cried out: "To me, Magyars!"

Swithin grinned. The tall man fighting such odds excited his unwilling admiration; he had a momentary impulse to go to his assistance. 'Only get a broken nose!' he thought, and looked for a safe corner. But at that moment a thrown lemon struck him on the jaw. He jumped out of his chair and rushed at the officers. The Hungarian, swinging his chair, threw him a look of gratitude—Swithin glowed with momentary admiration of himself. A sword blade grazed his arm : he felt a sudden dislike of the Hungarian. 'This is too much,' he thought, and, catching up a chair, flung it at the wooden lantern. There was a crash—faces and swords vanished. He struck a match, and by the light of it bolted for the door. A second later he was in the street.

II

A voice said in English, "God bless you, brother!"

Swithin looked round, and saw the tall Hungarian holding out his hand. He took it, thinking, 'What a fool I've been!' There was something in the Hungarian's gesture which said, "You are worthy of me!" It was annoying, but rather impressive. The man seemed even taller than before; there was a cut on his cheek, the blood from which was trickling down his beard. "You English!" he said. "I saw you stone Haynau—I saw you cheer Kossuth. The free blood of your people cries out to us." He looked at Swithin. "You are a big man, you have a big soul—and strong, how you flung them down! Ha!" Swithin had an impulse to take to his heels. "My name," said the Hungarian, "is Boleskey. You are my friend." His English was good.

'Bulsh-kai-ee, Burlsh-kai-ee,' thought Swithin; 'what a devil of a name!' "Mine," he said sulkily, "is Forsyte."

The Hungarian repeated it.

"You've had a nasty jab on the cheek," said Swithin; the sight of the matted beard was making him feel sick. The Hungarian put his fingers to his cheek, brought them away wet, stared at them, then with an indifferent air gathered a wisp of his beard and crammed it against the cut.

"Ugh!" said Swithin. "Here! Take my handkerchief!"

The Hungarian bowed. "Thank you!" he said; "I couldn't think of it! Thank you a thousand times!"

"Take it!" growled Swithin; it seemed to him suddenly of the first importance. He thrust the handkerchief into the Hungarian's hand, and felt a pain in his arm. 'There!' he thought, 'I've strained a muscle.'

The Hungarian kept muttering, regardless of passers-by, "Swine! How you threw them over! Two or three cracked heads, anyway—the cowardly swine!"

"Look here!" said Swithin suddenly; "which is my way to the Goldene Alp?"

The Hungarian replied, "But you are coming with me, for a glass of wine?"

Swithin looked at the ground. 'Not if I know it!' he thought.

" Ah ! " said the Hungarian with dignity, " you do not wish
for my friendship ! "

' Touchy beggar ! ' thought Swithin. " Of course," he stammered, " if you put it in that way——"

The Hungarian bowed, murmuring, " Forgive me ! "

They had not gone a dozen steps before a youth, with a beardless face and hollow cheeks, accosted them. " For the love of
Christ, gentlemen," he said, "help me ! "

" Are you a German ? " asked Boleskey.

" Yes," said the youth.

" Then you may rot ! "

" Master, look here ! " Tearing open his coat, the youth displayed his skin, and a leather belt drawn tight round it. Again
Swithin felt that desire to take to his heels. He was filled
with horrid forebodings—a sense of perpending intimacy with
things such as no gentleman had dealings with.

The Hungarian crossed himself. " Brother," he said to the
youth, "come you in ! "

Swithin looked at them askance, and followed. By a dim
light they groped their way up some stairs into a large room,
into which the moon was shining through a window bulging
over the street. A lamp burned low; there was a smell of
spirits and tobacco, with a faint, peculiar scent, as of rose
leaves. In one corner stood a czymbal, in another a great pile
of newspapers. On the wall hung some old-fashioned pistols,
and a rosary of yellow beads. Everything was tidily arranged,
but dusty. Near an open fireplace was a table with the remains
of a meal. The ceiling, floor, and walls were all of dark wood.
In spite of the strange disharmony, the room had a sort of
refinement.

The Hungarian took a bottle out of a cupboard and, filling some glasses, handed one to Swithin. Swithin put it
gingerly to his nose. ' You never know your luck ! Come ! '
he thought, tilting it slowly into his mouth. It was thick, too
sweet, but of a fine flavour.

" Brothers ! " said the Hungarian, refilling, " your healths ! "

The youth tossed off his wine. And Swithin this time did the
same ; he pitied this poor devil of a youth now. " Come round
to-morrow ! " he said, " I'll give you a shirt or two." When the
youth was gone, however, he remembered with relief that he
had not given his address.

' Better so,' he reflected. ' A humbug, no doubt.'

"What was that you said to him?" he asked of the Hungarian.

"I said," answered Boleskey, "'You have eaten and drunk; and now you are my enemy!'"

"Quite right!" said Swithin, "quite right! A beggar is every man's enemy."

"You do not understand," the Hungarian replied politely. "While he was a beggar—I, too, have had to beg" (Swithin thought, 'Good God! this is awful!'), "but now that he is no longer hungry, what is he but a German? No Austrian dog soils my floors!"

His nostrils, as it seemed to Swithin, had distended in an unpleasant fashion; and a wholly unnecessary raucousness invaded his voice. "I am an exile—all of my blood are exiles. Those Godless dogs!" Swithin hurriedly assented.

As he spoke, a face peeped in at the door.

"Rozsi!" said the Hungarian. A young girl came in. She was rather short, with a deliciously round figure and a thick plait of hair. She smiled, and showed her even teeth; her little, bright, wide-set grey eyes glanced from one man to the other. Her face was round, too, high in the cheek-bones, the colour of wild roses, with brows that had a twist-up at the corners. With a gesture of alarm, she put her hand to her cheek, and called, "Margit!" An older girl appeared, taller, with fine shoulders, large eyes, a pretty mouth, and what Swithin described to himself afterwards as a "pudding" nose. Both girls, with little cooing sounds, began attending to their father's face. Swithin turned his back to them. His arm pained him.

'This is what comes of interfering,' he thought sulkily; 'I might have had my neck broken!' Suddenly a soft palm was placed in his, two eyes, half-fascinated, half-shy, looked at him; then a voice called, "Rozsi!" the door was slammed, he was alone again with the Hungarian, harassed by a sense of soft disturbance.

"Your daughter's name is Rosy?" he said; "we have it in England—from rose, a flower."

"Rozsi (Rozgi)," the Hungarian replied; "your English is a hard tongue, harder than French, German, or Czechish, harder than Russian, or Roumanian—I know no more."

"What?" said Swithin, "six languages?" Privately he thought, 'He knows how to lie, anyway.'

"If you lived in a country like mine," muttered the Hungarian, "with all men's hands against you! A free people—dying—but not dead!"

Swithin could not imagine what he was talking of. This man's face, with its linen bandage, gloomy eyes, and great black wisps of beard, his fierce mutterings, and hollow cough, were all most unpleasant. He seemed to be suffering from some kind of mental dog-bite. His emotion indeed appeared so indecent, so uncontrolled and open, that its obvious sincerity produced a sort of awe in Swithin. It was like being forced to look into a furnace. Boleskey stopped roaming up and down. "You think it's over?" he said; "I tell you, in the breast of each one of us Magyars there is a hell. What is sweeter than life? What is more sacred than each breath we draw? Ah! my country!" These words were uttered so slowly, with such intense mournfulness, that Swithin's jaw relaxed; he converted the movement to a yawn.

"Tell me," said Boleskey, "what would you do if the French conquered you?"

Swithin smiled. Then suddenly, as though something had hurt him, he grunted, "The 'Froggies'? Let 'em try!"

"Drink!" said Boleskey—"there is nothing like it"; he filled Swithin's glass. "I will tell you my story."

Swithin rose hurriedly. "It's late," he said. "This is good stuff, though; have you much of it?"

"It is the last bottle."

"What?" said Swithin; "and you gave it to a beggar?"

"My name is Boleskey-Stefan," the Hungarian said, raising his head; "of the Komorn Boleskeys." The simplicity of this phrase—as who shall say: What need of further description? —made an impression on Swithin; he stopped to listen. Boleskey's story went on and on. "There were many abuses," boomed his deep voice, "much wrong done—much cowardice. I could see clouds gathering—rolling over our plains. The Austrian wished to strangle the breath of our mouths—to take from us the shadow of our liberty—the shadow—all we had. Two years ago—the year of '48, when every man and boy answered the great voice—brother, a dog's life!—to use a pen when all of your blood are fighting, but it was decreed for me! My son was killed; my brothers taken—and myself was thrown out like a dog—I had written out my heart, I had written out all the blood that was in my body!" He seemed to tower, a gaunt shadow of a man, with gloomy, flickering eyes staring at the wall.

Swithin rose, and stammered, " Much obliged—very interesting." Boleskey made no effort to detain him, but continued staring at the wall. " Good-night! " said Swithin, and stamped heavily downstairs.

III

When at last Swithin reached the Goldene Alp, he found his brother and friend standing uneasily at the door. Traquair, a prematurely dried-up man, with whiskers and a Scotch accent, remarked, " Ye're airly, man! " Swithin growled something unintelligible, and swung up to bed. He discovered a slight cut on his arm. He was in a savage temper—the elements had conspired to show him things he did not want to see; yet now and then a memory of Rozsi, of her soft palm in his, a sense of having been stroked and flattered, came over him. During breakfast next morning his brother and Traquair announced their intention of moving on. James Forsyte, indeed, remarked that it was no place for a " collector," since all the " old " shops were in the hands of Jews or very grasping persons—he had discovered this at once. Swithin pushed his cup aside. " *You* may do what you like," he said, " *I'm* staying here."

James Forsyte replied, tumbling over his own words : " Why! what do you want to stay here for ? There's nothing for you to do here—there's nothing to see here, unless you go up the Citadel, an' you won't do that."

Swithin growled, " Who says so ? " Having gratified his perversity, he felt in a better temper. He had slung his arm in a silk sash, and accounted for it by saying he had slipped. Later he went out and walked on to the bridge. In the brilliant sunshine spires were glistening against the pearly background of the hills ; the town had a clean, joyous air. Swithin glanced at the Citadel and thought, " Looks a strong place ! Shouldn't wonder if it were impregnable ! " And this for some occult reason gave him pleasure. It occurred to him suddenly to go and look for the Hungarian's house.

About noon, after a hunt of two hours, he was gazing about

him blankly, pale with heat, but more obstinate than ever, when a voice above him called "Mister!" He looked up and saw Rozsi. She was leaning her round chin on her round hand, gazing down at him with her deep-set, clever eyes. When Swithin removed his hat, she clapped her hands. Again he had the sense of being admired, caressed. With a careless air, that sat grotesquely on his tall square person, he walked up to the door; both girls stood in the passage. Swithin felt a confused desire to speak in some foreign tongue. "Maam'selles," he began, "er—*bong jour*—er your father—*père, comment?*"

"We also speak English," said the elder girl; "will you come in, please?"

Swithin swallowed a misgiving and entered. The room had a worn appearance by daylight, as if it had always been the nest of tragic or vivid lives. He sat down, and his eyes said: "I am a stranger, but don't try to get the better of me, please —that is impossible." The girls looked at him in silence. Rozsi wore a rather short skirt of black stuff, a white shirt, and across her shoulders an embroidered yoke; her sister was dressed in dark green, with a coral necklace; both girls had their hair in plaits. After a minute Rozsi touched the sleeve of his hurt arm.

"It's nothing!" muttered Swithin.

"Father fought with a chair, but you had no chair," she said in a wondering voice.

He doubled the fist of his sound arm and struck a blow at space. To his amazement she began to laugh. Nettled at this, he put his hand beneath the heavy table and lifted it. Rozsi clapped her hands. "Ah! now I see—how strong you are!" She made him a curtsey and whisked round to the window. He found the quick intelligence of her eyes confusing; sometimes they seemed to look beyond him at something invisible —this, too, confused him. From Margit he learned that they had been two years in England, where their father had made his living by teaching languages; they had now been a year in Salzburg.

"We wait," suddenly with Rozsi; and Margit, with a solemn face, repeated, "We wait."

Swithin's eyes swelled a little with his desire to see what they were waiting for. How queer they were, with their eyes that gazed beyond him! He looked at their figures. "She would pay for dressing," he thought, and he tried to imagine

Rozsi in a skirt with proper flounces, a thin waist, and hair drawn back over her ears. She would pay for dressing, with that supple figure, fluffy hair, and little hands! And instantly his own hands, face, and clothes disturbed him. He got up, examined the pistols on the wall, and felt resentment at the faded, dusty room. ' Smells like a pot-house!' he thought. He sat down again close to Rozsi.

"Do you love to dance?" she asked: "to dance is to live. First you hear the music—how your feet itch! It is wonderful! You begin slow, quick—quicker; you fly—you know nothing—your feet are in the air. It is wonderful!"

A slow flush had mounted into Swithin's face.

"Ah!" continued Rozsi, her eyes fixed on him, "when I am dancing—out there I see the plains—your feet go one—two—three—quick, quick, quick, quicker—you fly."

She stretched herself, a shiver seemed to pass all down her. "Margit! dance!" and, to Swithin's consternation, the two girls—their hands on each other's shoulders—began shuffling their feet and swaying to and fro. Their heads were thrown back, their eyes half-closed; suddenly the step quickened, they swung to one side, then to the other, and began whirling round in front of him. The sudden fragrance of rose leaves enveloped him. Round they flew again. While they were still dancing, Boleskey came into the room. He caught Swithin by both hands.

"Brother, welcome! Ah! your arm is hurt! I do not forget." His yellow face and deep-set eyes expressed a dignified gratitude. "Let me introduce to you my friend Baron Kasteliz."

Swithin bowed to a man with a small forehead, who had appeared softly, and stood with his gloved hands touching his waist. Swithin conceived a sudden aversion for this cat-like man. About Boleskey there was that which made contempt impossible—the sense of comradeship begotten in the fight; the man's height; something lofty and savage in his face; and an obscure instinct that it would not pay to show distaste; but this Kasteliz, with his neat jaw, low brow, and velvety, volcanic look, excited his proper English animosity. "Your friends are mine," murmured Kasteliz. He spoke with suavity, and hissed his s's. A long, vibrating twang quavered through the room. Swithin turned and saw Rozsi sitting at the czymbal; the notes rang under the little hammers in her hands, inces-

sant, metallic, rising and falling with that strange melody.
Kasteliz had fixed his glowing eyes on her; Boleskey, nodding
his head, was staring at the floor; Margit, with a pale face,
stood like a statue.

'What can they see in it?' thought Swithin; 'it's not a
tune.' He took up his hat. Rozsi saw him and stopped; her
lips had parted with a faintly dismayed expression. His sense
of personal injury diminished; he even felt a little sorry for
her. She jumped up from her seat and twirled round with
a pout. An inspiration seized on Swithin. "Come and dine
with me," he said to Boleskey, "to-morrow—the Goldene Alp
—bring your friend." He felt the eyes of the whole room on
him—the Hungarian's fine eyes; Margit's wide glance; the
narrow, hot gaze of Kasteliz ; and lastly—Rozsi's. A glow of
satisfaction ran down his spine. When he emerged into the
street he thought gloomily, 'Now I've done it!' And not for
some paces did he look round; then, with a forced smile, turned
and removed his hat to the faces at the window.

Notwithstanding this moment of gloom, however, he was in
an exalted state all day, and at dinner kept looking at his
brother and Traquair enigmatically. 'What do they know of
life?' he thought; 'they might be here a year and get no
farther.' He made jokes, and pinned the menu to the waiter's
coat-tails. "I like this place," he said, "I shall spend three
weeks here." James, whose lips were on the point of taking
in a plum, looked at him uneasily.

IV

On the day of the dinner Swithin suffered a good deal. He
reflected gloomily on Boleskey's clothes. He had fixed an early
hour—there would be fewer people to see them. When the
time approached he attired himself with a certain neat splendour, and though his arm was still sore, left off the sling. . . .

Nearly three hours afterwards he left the Goldene Alp between his guests. It was sunset, and along the river-bank the
houses stood out, unsoftened by the dusk; the streets were
full of people hurrying home. Swithin had a hazy vision of
empty bottles, of the ground before his feet, and the accessi-
bility of all the world. Dim recollections of the good things
he had said, of his brother and Traquair seated in the back-

ground eating ordinary meals with inquiring, acid visages, caused perpetual smiles to break out on his face, and he steered himself stubbornly, to prove that he was a better man than either of his guests. He knew, vaguely, that he was going somewhere with an object; Rozsi's face kept dancing before him, like a promise. Once or twice he gave Kasteliz a glassy stare. Towards Boleskey, on the other hand, he felt quite warm, and recalled with admiration the way he had set his glass down empty, time after time. 'I like to see him take his liquor,' he thought ; 'the fellow's a gentleman, after all.'

Boleskey strode on, savagely inattentive to everything ; and Kasteliz had become more like a cat than ever. It was nearly dark when they reached a narrow street close to the cathedral. They stopped at a door held open by an old woman. The change from the fresh air to a heated corridor, the noise of the door closed behind him, the old woman's anxious glances, sobered Swithin.

"I tell her," said Boleskey, "that I reply for you as for my son."

Swithin was angry. What business had this man to reply for him !

They passed into a large room, crowded with men and women; Swithin noticed that they all looked at him. He stared at them in turn—they seemed of all classes, some in black coats or silk dresses, others in the clothes of work-people ; one man, a cobbler, still wore his leather apron, as if he had rushed there straight from his work. Laying his hand on Swithin's arm, Boleskey evidently began explaining who he was ; hands were extended, people beyond reach bowed to him. Swithin acknowledged the greetings with a stiff motion of his head; then seeing other people dropping into seats, he, too, sat down. Some one whispered his name—Margit and Rozsi were just behind him.

"Welcome!" said Margit; but Swithin was looking at Rozsi. Her face was so alive and quivering! 'What's the excitement all about?' he thought. 'How pretty she looks!' She blushed, drew in her hands with a quick tense movement, and gazed again beyond him in the room. 'What is it?' thought Swithin ; he had a longing to lean back and kiss her lips. He tried angrily to see what she was seeing in those faces turned all one way.

Boleskey rose to speak. No one moved; not a sound could

be heard but the tone of his deep voice. On and on he went, fierce and solemn, and with the rise of his voice, all those faces —fair or swarthy—seemed to be glowing with one and the same feeling. Swithin felt the white heat in those faces—it was not decent! In that whole speech he only understood the one word—"Magyar"—which came again and again. He almost dozed off at last. The twang of a czymbal woke him. 'What?' he thought, 'more of that infernal music!' Margit, leaning over him, whispered: "Listen! Racoczy! it is forbidden!" Swithin saw that Rozsi was no longer in her seat; it was she who was striking those forbidden notes. He looked round— everywhere the same unmoving faces, the same entrancement, and fierce stillness. The music sounded muffled, as if it, too, were bursting its heart in silence. Swithin felt within him a touch of panic. Was this a den of tigers? The way these people listened, the ferocity of their stillness, was frightful! . . . He gripped his chair and broke into a perspiration; was there no chance to get away? 'When it stops,' he thought, 'there'll be a rush!' But there was only a greater silence. It flashed across him that any hostile person coming in then would be torn to pieces. A woman sobbed. The whole thing was beyond words unpleasant. He rose, and edged his way furtively towards the doorway. There was a cry of "Police!" The whole crowd came pressing after him. Swithin would soon have been out, but a little behind he caught sight of Rozsi swept off her feet. Her frightened eyes angered him. 'She doesn't deserve it,' he thought sulkily; 'letting all this loose!' and forced his way back to her. She clung to him, and a fever went stealing through his veins; he butted forward at the crowd, holding her tight. When they were outside he let her go.

"I was afraid," she said.

"Afraid!" muttered Swithin; "I should think so." No longer touching her, he felt his grievance revive.

"But you are so strong," she murmured.

"This is no place for you," growled Swithin. "I'm going to see you home."

"Oh!" cried Rozsi; "but papa and—Margit!"

"That's their lookout!" and he hurried her away.

She slid her hand under his arm; the soft curves of her form brushed him gently, each touch only augmented his ill-humour. He burned with a perverse rage, as if all the passions in him were simmering and ready to boil over; it was as if a poison were trying to work its way out of him through the layers of his stolid flesh. He maintained a dogged silence; Rozsi, too, said nothing, but when they reached the door, she drew her hand away.

"You are angry!" she said.

"Angry," muttered Swithin; "no! How d'you make that out?" He had a torturing desire to kiss her.

"Yes, you are angry," she repeated; "I wait here for papa and Margit."

Swithin also waited, wedged against the wall. Once or twice, for his sight was sharp, he saw her steal a look at him, a beseeching look, and hardened his heart with a kind of pleasure. After five minutes Boleskey, Margit, and Kasteliz appeared. Seeing Rozsi they broke into exclamations of relief, and Kasteliz, with a glance at Swithin, put his lips to her hand. Rozsi's look said, "Wouldn't you like to do that?" Swithin turned short on his heel, and walked away.

V

All night he hardly slept, suffering from fever, for the first time in his life. Once he jumped out of bed, lighted a candle, and going to the glass, scrutinised himself long and anxiously. After this he fell asleep, but had frightful dreams. His first thought when he woke was, 'My liver's out of order!' and, thrusting his head into cold water, he dressed hastily and went out. He soon left the house behind. Dew covered everything; blackbirds whistled in the bushes, the air was fresh and sweet. He had not been up so early since he was a boy. Why was he walking through a damp wood at this hour of the morning? Something intolerable and unfamiliar must have sent him out. No fellow in his senses would do such a thing! He came to a dead stop, and began unsteadily to walk back. Regaining the hotel, he went to bed again, and dreamed that in some wild country he was living in a room full of insects, where a house-maid—Rozsi—holding a broom, looked at him with mournful eyes. There seemed an unexplained need for immediate departure; he begged her to forward his things, and shake them out carefully before she put them into the trunk. He understood that the charge for sending would be twenty-two shillings, thought it a great deal, and had the horrors of indecision. "No," he muttered, "pack, and take them myself." The housemaid turned suddenly into a lean creature ; and he awoke with a sore feeling in his heart.

His eye fell on his wet boots. The whole thing was scaring, and jumping up, he began to throw his clothes into his trunks. It was twelve o'clock before he went down, and found his brother and Traquair still at the table arranging an itinerary; he surprised them by saying that he too was coming; and without further explanation set to work to eat. James had heard that there were salt-mines in the neighbourhood—his proposal was to start, and halt an hour or so on the road for their inspection: he said: "Everybody'll ask you if you've seen the salt-mines: I shouldn't like to say I hadn't seen the salt-mines. What's the good, they'd say, of your going there if you haven't seen the salt-mines?" He wondered, too, if they need fee the second waiter—an idle chap!

A discussion followed; but Swithin ate on glumly, conscious that his mind was set on larger affairs. Suddenly on the far side of the street Rozsi and her sister passed, with little baskets on their arms. He started up, and at that moment Rozsi looked round—her face was the incarnation of enticement, the chin tilted, the lower lip thrust a little forward, her round neck curving back over her shoulder. Swithin muttered, "Make your own arrangements—leave me out!" and hurried from the room, leaving James beside himself with interest and alarm.

When he reached the street, however, the girls had disappeared. He hailed a carriage. "Drive!" he called to the man, with a flourish of his stick, and as soon as the wheels had begun to clatter on the stones he leaned back, looking sharply to right and left. He soon had to give up thought of finding them, but made the coachman turn round and round again. All day he drove about, far into the country, and kept urging the driver to use greater speed. He was in a strange state of hurry and elation. Finally, he dined at a little country inn; and this gave the measure of his disturbance—the dinner was atrocious.

Returning late in the evening he found a note written by Traquair. "Are you in your senses, man?" it asked; "we have no more time to waste idling about here. If you want to rejoin us, come on to Danielli's Hotel, Venice." Swithin chuckled when he read it, and feeling frightfully tired, went to bed and slept like a log.

VI

Three weeks later he was still in Salzburg, no longer at the Goldene Alp, but in rooms over a shop near the Boleskeys'. He had spent a small fortune in the purchase of flowers. Margit would croon over them, but Rozsi, with a sober "Many tanks!" as if they were her right, would look long at herself in the glass, and pin one into her hair. Swithin ceased to wonder; he ceased to wonder at anything they did. One evening he found Boleskey deep in conversation with a pale, dishevelled-looking person.

"Our friend Mr. Forsyte — Count D——," said Boleskey.

Swithin experienced a faint, unavoidable emotion; but looking at the Count's trousers, he thought: "Doesn't look much like one!' And with an ironic bow to the silent girls, he turned, and took his hat. But when he had reached the bottom of the dark stairs he heard footsteps. Rozsi came running down, looked out at the door, and put her hands up to her breast as if disappointed : suddenly with a quick glance round she saw him. Swithin caught her arm. She slipped away, and her face seemed to bubble with defiance or laughter; she ran up three steps, looked at him across her shoulder, and fled on up the stairs. Swithin went out bewildered and annoyed.

'What was she going to say to me?' he kept thinking. During these three weeks he had asked himself all sorts of questions: whether he were being made a fool of; whether she were in love with him; what he was doing there, and sometimes at night, with all his candles burning as if he wanted light, the breeze blowing on him through the window, his cigar, half-smoked, in his hand, he sat, an hour or more, staring at the wall. 'Enough of this!' he thought every morning. Twice he packed fully—once he ordered his travelling carriage, but countermanded it the following day. What definitely he hoped, intended, resolved, he could not have said. He was always thinking of Rozsi, he could not read the riddle in her face—she held him in a vice, notwithstanding that everything about her threatened the very fetishes of his existence. And Boleskey! Whenever he looked at him he thought, 'If he were only clean?'

and mechanically fingered his own well-tied cravate. To talk
with the fellow, too, was like being forced to look at things
which had no place in the light of day. Freedom, equality,
self-sacrifice!

'Why can't he settle down at some business,' he thought,
'instead of all this talk?' Boleskey's sudden diffidences, self-
depreciation, fits of despair, irritated him. "Morbid beggar!"
he would mutter; "thank God *I* haven't a thin skin." And
proud too! Extraordinary! An impecunious fellow like that!
One evening, moreover, Boleskey had returned home drunk.
Swithin had hustled him away into his bedroom, helped him
to undress, and stayed until he was asleep. 'Too much of a
good thing!' he thought, 'before his own daughters, too!' It
was after this that he ordered his travelling carriage. The
other occasion on which he packed was one evening, when not
only Boleskey, but Rozsi herself had picked chicken bones with
her fingers.

Often in the mornings he would go to the Mirabell Garden
to smoke his cigar; there, in stolid contemplation of the statues
—rows of half-heroic men carrying off half-distressed females
—he would spend an hour pleasantly, his hat tilted to keep
the sun off his nose. The day after Rozsi had fled from him
on the stairs, he came there as usual. It was a morning of
blue sky and sunlight glowing on the old prim garden, on its
yew-trees, and serio-comic statues, and walls covered with apri-
cots and plums. When Swithin approached his usual seat, who
should be sitting there but Rozsi!

"Good-morning," he stammered; "you knew this was my
seat then?"

Rozsi looked at the ground. "Yes," she answered.

Swithin felt bewildered. "Do you know," he said, "you
treat me very funnily?"

To his surprise Rozsi put her little soft hand down and
touched his; then, without a word, sprang up and rushed
away. It took him a minute to recover. There were people
present; he did not like to run, but overtook her on the bridge,
and slipped her hand beneath his arm.

"You shouldn't have done that," he said; "you shouldn't
have run away from me, you know."

Rozsi laughed. Swithin withdrew his arm; a desire to shake
her seized him. He walked some way before he said, "Will

you have the goodness to tell me what you came to that seat for?"

Rozsi flashed a look at him. "To-morrow is the *fête*," she answered.

Swithin muttered, "Is that all?"

"If you do not take us, we cannot go."

"Suppose I refuse," he said sullenly, "there are plenty of others."

Rozsi bent her head, scurrying along. "No," she murmured, "if *you* do not go—I do not wish."

Swithin drew her hand back within his arm. How round and soft it was! He tried to see her face. When she was nearly home he said good-bye, not wishing, for some dark reason, to be seen with her. He watched till she had disappeared; then slowly retraced his steps to the Mirabell Garden. When he came to where she had been sitting, he slowly lighted his cigar, and for a long time after it was smoked out remained there in the silent presence of the statues.

VII

A crowd of people wandered round the booths, and Swithin found himself obliged to give the girls his arms. 'Like a little Cockney clerk!' he thought. His indignation passed unnoticed; they talked, they laughed, each sight and sound in all the hurly-burly seemed to go straight into their hearts. He eyed them ironically—their eager voices, and little coos of sympathy seemed to him vulgar. In the thick of the crowd he slipped his arm out of Margit's, but, just as he thought that he was free, the unwelcome hand slid up again. He tried again, but again Margit reappeared, serene, and full of pleasant humour; and his failure this time appeared to him in a comic light. But when Rozsi leaned across him, the glow of her round cheek, her curving lip, the inscrutable grey gleam of her eyes, sent a thrill of longing through him. He was obliged to stand by while they parleyed with a gipsy, whose matted locks and skinny hands inspired him with a not unwarranted disgust. "Folly!" he muttered, as Rozsi held out her palm. The old woman mumbled, and shot a malignant look at him. Rozsi drew back her hand, and crossed herself. 'Folly!'

Swithin thought again; and seizing the girls' arms, he hurried them away.

"What did the old hag say?" he asked.

Rozsi shook her head.

"You don't mean that you believe?"

Her eyes were full of tears. "The gipsies are wise," she murmured.

"Come, what did she tell you?"

This time Rozsi looked hurriedly round, and slipped away into the crowd. After a hunt they found her, and Swithin, who was scared, growled: "You shouldn't do such things—it's not respectable."

On higher ground, in the centre of a clear space, a military band was playing. For the privilege of entering this charmed circle Swithin paid three *kronen,* choosing naturally the best seats. He ordered wine, too, watching Rozsi out of the corner of his eye as he poured it out. The protecting tenderness of yesterday was all lost in this medley. It was every man for himself, after all! The colour had deepened again in her cheeks, she laughed, pouting her lips. Suddenly she put her glass aside. "Thank you, very much," she said, "it is enough!"

Margit, whose pretty mouth was all smiles, cried, "*Lieber Gott!* is it not good—life?" It was not a question Swithin could undertake to answer. The band began to play a waltz. "Now they will dance. *Lieber Gott !* and are the lights not wonderful?" Lamps were flickering beneath the trees like a swarm of fireflies. There was a hum as from a gigantic beehive. Passers-by lifted their faces, then vanished into the crowd; Rozsi stood gazing at them spell-bound, as if their very going and coming were a delight.

The space was soon full of whirling couples. Rozsi's head began to beat time. "O Margit!" she whispered.

Swithin's face had assumed a solemn, uneasy expression. A man, raising his hat, offered his arm to Margit. She glanced back across her shoulder to reassure Swithin. "It is a friend," she said.

Swithin looked at Rozsi—her eyes were bright, her lips tremulous. He slipped his hand along the table and touched her fingers. Then she flashed a look at him—appeal, reproach, tenderness, all were expressed in it. Was she expecting him to dance? Did she want to mix with the riff-raff there; wish *him* to make an exhibition of himself in this hurly-burly? A

voice said, "Good-evening!" Before them stood Kasteliz, in
a dark coat tightly buttoned at the waist.

"You are not dancing, *Rozsi Kozsanony?*" (Miss Rozsi).
"Let me, then, have the pleasure." He held out his arm.
Swithin stared in front of him. In the very act of going she
gave him a look that said as plain as words: "Will you not?"
But for answer he turned his eyes away, and when he looked
again she was gone. He paid the score and made his way
into the crowd. But as he went she danced by close to him,
all flushed and panting. She hung back as if to stop him, and
he caught the glistening of tears. Then he lost sight of her
again. To be deserted the first minute he was alone with her,
and for that jackanapes with the small head and volcanic
glances! It was too much! And suddenly it occurred to
him that she was alone with Kasteliz—alone at night, and far
from home. 'Well,' he thought, 'what do I care?' and shoul-
dered his way on through the crowd. It served him right for
mixing with such people here. He left the fair, but the further
he went, the more he nursed his rage, the more heinous seemed
her offence, the sharper grew his jealousy. 'A beggarly baron!'
was his thought.

A figure came alongside—it was Boleskey. One look showed
Swithin his condition. Drunk again! This was the last straw!

Unfortunately Boleskey had recognised him. He seemed
violently excited. "Where—where are my daughters?" he
began.

Swithin brushed past, but Boleskey caught his arm. "Listen
—brother!" he said; "news of my country! After to-morrow——"

"Keep it to yourself!" growled Swithin, wrenching his arm
free. He went straight to his lodgings, and, lying on the hard
sofa of his unlighted sitting-room, gave himself up to bitter
thoughts. But in spite of all his anger, Rozsi's supply-moving
figure, with its pouting lips, and roguish appealing eyes, still
haunted him.

VIII

Next morning there was not a carriage to be had, and Swithin
was compelled to put off his departure till the morrow. The
day was grey and misty; he wandered about with the strained,
inquiring look of a lost dog in his eyes.

Late in the afternoon he went back to his lodgings. In a corner of the sitting-room stood Rozsi. The thrill of triumph, the sense of appeasement, the emotion, that seized on him, crept through to his lips in a faint smile. Rozsi made no sound, her face was hidden by her hands. And this silence of hers weighed on Swithin. She was forcing him to break it. What was behind her hands? His own face was visible! Why didn't she speak? Why was she here? Alone? That was not right surely.

Suddenly Rozsi dropped her hands; her flushed face was quivering—it seemed as though a word, a sign, even, might bring a burst of tears.

He walked over to the window. 'I must give her time!' he thought; then seized by unreasoning terror at this silence, spun round, and caught her by the arms. Rozsi held back from him, swayed forward and buried her face on his breast. . . .

Half an hour later Swithin was pacing up and down his room. The scent of rose leaves had not yet died away. A glove lay on the floor; he picked it up, and for a long time stood weighing it in his hand. All sorts of confused thoughts and feelings haunted him. It was the purest and least selfish moment of his life, this moment after she had yielded. But that pure gratitude at her fiery, simple abnegation did not last; it was followed by a petty sense of triumph, and by uneasiness. He was still weighing the little glove in his hand, when he had another visitor. It was Kasteliz.

"What can I do for you?" Swithin asked ironically.

The Hungarian seemed suffering from excitement. Why had Swithin left his charges the night before? What excuse had he to make? What sort of conduct did he call this?

Swithin, very like a bull-dog at that moment, answered: What business was it of his?

The business of a gentleman! What right had the Englishman to pursue a young girl?

"Pursue?" said Swithin; "you've been spying, then?"

"Spying—I—Kasteliz—Maurus Johann—an insult!"

"Insult!" sneered Swithin; "d'you mean to tell me you weren't in the street just now?"

Kasteliz answered with a hiss, "If you do not leave the city I will make you, with my sword—do you understand?"

" And if you do not leave my room I will throw you out of the window!"

For some minutes Kasteliz spoke in pure Hungarian while Swithin waited, with a forced smile and a fixed look in his eye. He did not understand Hungarian.

" If you are still in the city to-morrow evening," said Kasteliz at last in English, " I will spit you in the street."

Swithin turned to the window and watched his visitor's retiring back with a queer mixture of amusement, stubbornness, and anxiety. 'Well,' he thought, ' I suppose he'll run me through!' The thought was unpleasant; and it kept recurring, but it only served to harden his determination. His head was busy with plans for seeing Rozsi ; his blood on fire with the kisses she had given him.

IX

Swithin was long in deciding to go forth next day. He had made up his mind not to go to Rozsi till five o'clock. ' Mustn't make myself too cheap,' he thought. It was a little past that hour when he at last sallied out, and with a beating heart walked towards Boleskey's. He looked up at the window, more than half expecting to see Rozsi there ; but she was not, and he noticed with faint surprise that the window was not open; the plants, too, outside, looked singularly arid. He knocked. No one came. He beat a fierce tattoo. At last the door was opened by a man with a reddish beard, and one of those sardonic faces only to be seen on shoemakers of Teutonic origin.

" What do you want, making all this noise?" he asked in German.

Swithin pointed up the stairs. The man grinned, and shook his head.

" I want to go up," said Swithin.

The cobbler shrugged his shoulders, and Swithin rushed upstairs. The rooms were empty. The furniture remained, but all signs of life were gone. One of his own bouquets, faded, stood in a glass; the ashes of a fire were barely cold; little scraps of paper strewed the hearth; already the room smelt musty. He went into the bedrooms, and with a feeling of stupefaction stood staring at the girls' beds, side by side against the wall. A bit of ribbon caught his eye; he picked it up and put it in his pocket—it was a piece of evidence that she had once existed. By the mirror some pins were dropped about ; a little powder had been spilled. He looked at his own disquiet face and thought, ' I've been cheated!'

The shoemaker's voice aroused him. *" Tausend Teufel! Eilen Sie, nur! Zeit is Geld! Kann nich' länger warten!"* Slowly he descended.

"Where have they gone?" asked Swithin painfully. "A pound for every English word you speak. A pound!" and he made an O with his fingers.

The corners of the shoemaker's lips curled. *" Geld! Mff! Eilen Sie, nur!"*

But in Swithin a sullen anger had begun to burn. "If you don't tell me," he said, " it'll be the worse for you."

" Sind ein komischer Kerl!" remarked the shoemaker. *" Hier ist meine Frau!"*

A battered-looking woman came hurrying down the passage, calling out in German, "Don't let him go!"

With a snarling sound the shoemaker turned his back, and shambled off.

The woman furtively thrust a letter into Swithin's hand, and furtively waited.

The letter was from Rozsi.

"Forgive me "—it ran—"that I leave you and do not say good-bye. To-day our father had the call from our dear Father-town so long awaited. In two hours we are ready. I pray to the Virgin to keep you ever safe, and that you do not quite forget me.—Your unforgetting good friend,

ROZSI."

When Swithin read it his first sensation was that of a man sinking in a bog; then his obstinacy stiffened. ' I won't be done,' he thought. Taking out a sovereign he tried to make the woman comprehend that she could earn it, by telling him where they had gone. He got her finally to write the words out in his pocket-book, gave her the sovereign, and hurried to the Goldene Alp, where there was a waiter who spoke English.

The translation given him was this:

"At three o'clock they start in a carriage on the road to Linz—they have bad horses—the Herr also rides a white horse."

Swithin at once hailed a carriage and started at full gallop on the road to Linz. Outside the Mirabell Garden he caught sight of Kasteliz and grinned at him. ' I've sold *him* anyway,' he thought; ' for all their talk, they're no good, these foreigners ! '

His spirits rose, but soon fell again. What chance had he of catching them? They had three hours' start ! Still, the roads were heavy from the rain of the last two nights—they had luggage and bad horses ; his own were good, his driver bribed—he might overtake them by ten o'clock ! But did he want to? What a fool he had been not to bring his luggage; he would then have had a respectable position. What a brute he would look without a change of shirt, or anything to shave with ! He saw himself with horror, all bristly, and in soiled linen. People would think him mad. ' I've given myself away,' flashed across him, ' what the devil can I say to them? ' and he stared sullenly at the driver's back. He read Rozsi's letter again; it had a scent of her. And in the growing darkness, jolted by the swinging of the carriage, he suffered tortures from his prudence, tortures from his passion.

It grew colder and dark. He turned the collar of his coat up to his ears. He had visions of Piccadilly. This wild-goose chase appeared suddenly a dangerous, unfathomable business. Lights, fellowship, security ! ' Never again ! ' he brooded; ' why won't they let me alone? ' But it was not clear whether by ' they ' he meant the conventions, the Boleskeys, his passions, or those haunting memories of Rozsi. If he had only had a bag with him ! What was he going to say? What was he going to get by this? He received no answer to these questions. The darkness itself was less obscure than his sensations. From time to time he took out his watch. At each village the driver made inquiries. It was past ten when he stopped the carriage with a jerk. The stars were bright as steel, and by the side of the road a reedy lake showed in the moonlight. Swithin shivered. A man on a horse had halted in the centre of the road. " Drive on ! " called Swithin, with a stolid face. It turned out to be Boleskey, who, on a gaunt white horse, looked like some winged creature. He stood where he could bar the progress of the carriage, holding out a pistol.

' Theatrical beggar !' thought Swithin, with a nervous smile. He made no sign of recognition. Slowly Boleskey brought his lean horse up to the carriage. When he saw who was within he showed astonishment and joy.

" You? " he cried, slapping his hand on his attenuated thigh, and leaning over till his beard touched Swithin. " You have come? You followed us? "

" It seems so," Swithin grunted out.

" You throw in your lot with us. Is it possible? You—you are a knight-errant then! "

" Good God! " said Swithin. Boleskey, flogging his dejected steed, cantered forward in the moonlight. He came back, bringing an old cloak, which he insisted on wrapping round Swithin's shoulders. He handed him, too, a capacious flask.

" How cold you look! " he said. " Wonderful! Wonderful! you English! " His grateful eyes never left Swithin for a moment. They had come up to the heels of the other carriage now, but Swithin, hunched in the cloak, did not try to see what was in front of him. To the bottom of his soul he resented the Hungarian's gratitude. He remarked at last, with wasted irony:

" You're in a hurry, it seems! "

" If we had wings," Boleskey answered, " we would use them."

"Wings! " muttered Swithin thickly; " legs are good enough for me."

X

Arrived at the inn where they were to pass the night, Swithin waited, hoping to get into the house without a " scene," but when at last he alighted the girls were in the doorway, and Margit greeted him with an admiring murmur, in which, however, he seemed to detect irony. Rozsi, pale and tremulous, with a half-scared look, gave him her hand, and, quickly withdrawing it, shrank behind her sister. When they had gone up to their room Swithin sought Boleskey. His spirits had risen remarkably. " Tell the landlord to get us supper," he said; " we'll crack a bottle to our luck." He hurried on the landlord's preparations. The window of the room faced a wood, so near that he could almost touch the trees. The scent from the pines blew in on him. He turned away from that scented darkness, and began to draw the corks of wine-bottles. The sound seemed to conjure up Boleskey. He came in, splashed all over, smelling slightly of stables ; soon after, Margit appeared, fresh and serene, but Rozsi did not come.

" Where is your sister? " Swithin said. Rozsi, it seemed, was tired. " It will do her good to eat," said Swithin. And Boleskey, murmuring, " She must drink to our country," went out to summon her, Margit followed him, while Swithin cut up a chicken. They came back without her. She had " a megrim of the spirit."

Swithin's face fell. " Look here! " he said, " *I'll* go and try. Don't wait for me."

" Yes," answered Boleskey, sinking mournfully into a chair; " try, brother, try—by all means, try."

Swithin walked down the corridor with an odd, sweet, sinking sensation in his chest ; and tapped on Rozsi's door. In a minute, she peeped forth, with her hair loose, and wondering eyes.

" Rozsi," he stammered, " what makes you afraid of me, *now?* "

She stared at him, but did not answer.

" Why won't you come? "

Still she did not speak, but suddenly stretched out to him her bare arm. Swithin pressed his face to it. With a shiver, she whispered above him, " I will come," and gently shut the door.

Swithin stealthily retraced his steps, and paused a minute outside the sitting-room to regain his self-control.

The sight of Boleskey with a bottle in his hand steadied him.

" She is coming," he said. And very soon she did come, her thick hair roughly twisted in a plait.

Swithin sat between the girls; but did not talk, for he was really hungry. Boleskey too was silent, plunged in gloom; Rozsi was dumb; Margit alone chattered.

" You will come to our Father-town? We shall have things to show you. Rozsi, what things we will show him! " Rozsi, with a little appealing movement of her hands, repeated, " What things we will show you! " She seemed suddenly to find her voice, and with glowing cheeks, mouth full, and eyes bright as squirrels, they chattered reminiscences of the " dear Father-town," of " dear friends," of the " dear home."

' A poor place! ' Swithin could not help thinking. This enthusiasm seemed to him common; but he was careful to assume a look of interest, feeding on the glances flashed at him from Rozsi's restless eyes.

As the wine waned Boleskey grew more and more gloomy, but now and then a sort of gleaming flicker passed over his face. He rose to his feet at last.

" Let us not forget," he said, " that we go perhaps to ruin, to death; in the face of all this we go, because our country needs—in this there is no credit, neither to me nor to you, my daughters; but for this noble Englishman, what shall we say? Give thanks to God for a great heart. He comes—not for country, not for fame, not for money, but to help the weak and the oppressed. Let us drink, then, to him ; let us drink again and again to heroic Forsyte!" In the midst of the dead silence, Swithin caught the look of suppliant mockery in Rozsi's eyes. He glanced at the Hungarian. Was he laughing at him? But Boleskey, after drinking up his wine, had sunk again into his seat; and there suddenly, to the surprise of all, he began to snore. Margit rose and, bending over him like a mother, murmured : " He is tired—it is the ride!" She raised him in her strong arms, and leaning on her shoulder Boleskey staggered from the room. Swithin and Rozsi were left alone. He slid his hand towards her hand that lay so close, on the rough tablecloth. It seemed to await his touch. Something gave way in him, and words came welling up; for the moment he forgot himself, forgot everything but that he was near her. Her head dropped on his shoulder, he breathed the perfume of her hair. " Good-night!" she whispered, and the whisper was like a kiss; yet before he could stop her she was gone. Her footsteps died away in the passage, but Swithin sat gazing intently at a single bright drop of spilt wine quivering on the table's edge. In that moment she, in her helplessness and emotion, was all in all to him—his life nothing; all the real things—his conventions, convictions, training, and himself—all seemed remote, behind a mist of passion and strange chivalry. Carefully with a bit of bread he soaked up the bright drop; and suddenly, he thought : ' This is tremendous!' For a long time he stood there in the window, close to the dark pine-trees.

XI

In the early morning he awoke, full of the discomfort of this strange place and the medley of his dreams. Lying, with his nose peeping over the quilt, he was visited by a horrible sus-

picion. When he could bear it no longer, he started up in bed.
What if it were all a plot to get him to marry her? The
thought was treacherous, and inspired in him a faint disgust.
Still, *she* might be ignorant of it! But was she so innocent?
What innocent girl would have come to his room like that?
What innocent girl? Her father, who pretended to be caring
only for his country? It was not probable that any man was
such a fool; it was all part of the game—a scheming rascal!
Kasteliz, too—his threats! They intended him to marry her?
And the horrid idea was strengthened by his reverence for marriage. It was the proper, the respectable condition ; he was
genuinely afraid of this other sort of *liaison*—it was somehow
too primitive! And yet the thought of that marriage made his
blood run cold. Considering that she had already yielded, it
would be all the more monstrous! With the cold, fatal clearness of the morning light he now for the first time saw his position in its full bearings. And, like a fish pulled out of water,
he gasped at what was disclosed. Sullen resentment against
this attempt to force him settled deep into his soul.

He seated himself on the bed, holding his head in his hands,
solemnly thinking out what such marriage meant. In the first
place it meant ridicule, in the next place ridicule, in the last
place ridicule. She would eat chicken bones with her fingers
—those fingers his lips still burned to kiss. She would dance
wildly with other men. She would talk of her "dear Father-
town," and all the time her eyes would look beyond him, somewhere or other into some d——d place he knew nothing of. He
sprang up and paced the room, and for a moment thought he
would go mad.

They meant him to marry her! Even she—she meant him
to marry her! Her tantalising inscrutability; her sudden little tendernesses; her quick laughter; her swift, burning kisses;
even the movements of her hands; her tears—all were evidence against her. Not one of these things that Nature made
her do counted on her side, but how they fanned his longing,
his desire, and distress. He went to the glass and tried to part
his hair with his fingers, but being rather fine, it fell into lank
streaks. There was no comfort to be got from it. He drew
his muddy boots on. Suddenly he thought: 'If I could see
her alone, I could arrive at some arrangement!' Then, with
a sense of stupefaction, he made the discovery that no arrangement could possibly be made that would not be dangerous, even

desperate. He seized his hat, and, like a rabbit that has been
fired at, bolted from the room. He plodded along amongst
the damp woods with his head down, and resentment and dismay in his heart. But, as the sun rose, and the air grew
sweet with pine scent, he slowly regained a sort of equability.
After all, she had already yielded; it was not as if——! And
the tramp of his own footsteps lulled him into feeling that it
would all come right. 'Look at the thing practically,' he
thought. The faster he walked the firmer became his conviction that he could still see it through. He took out his watch
—it was past seven—he began to hasten back. In the yard
of the inn his driver was harnessing the horses; Swithin went
up to him.

" Who told you to put them in? " he asked.

The driver answered, " *Der Herr.*"

Swithin turned away. ' In ten minutes,' he thought, ' I shall
be in that carriage again, with this going on in my head! Driving away from England, from all I'm used to—driving to—
what?' Could he face it? Could he face all that he had been
through that morning; face it day after day, night after night?
Looking up, he saw Rozsi at her open window gazing down at
him; never had she looked sweeter, more roguish. An inexplicable terror seized on him; he ran across the yard and
jumped into his carriage. " To Salzburg! " he cried; " drive
on! " And rattling out of the yard without a look behind, he
flung a sovereign at the hostler. Flying back along the road
faster even than he had come, with pale face, and eyes blank
and staring like a pug-dog's, Swithin spoke no single word;
nor, till he had reached the door of his lodgings, did he suffer
the driver to draw rein.

XII

Towards evening, five days later, Swithin, yellow and travel-
worn, was ferried in a gondola to Danielli's Hotel. His brother,
who was on the steps, looked at him with an apprehensive
curiosity.

" Why, it's you! " he mumbled. " So you've got here safe? "

" Safe? " growled Swithin.

James replied, " I thought you wouldn't leave your friends! "
Then, with a jerk of suspicion, " You haven't brought your
friends? "

" What friends? " growled Swithin.

James changed the subject. " You don't look the thing," he said.

" Really! " muttered Swithin; " what's that to you? "

He appeared at dinner that night, but fell asleep over his coffee. Neither Traquair nor James asked him any further question, nor did they allude to Salzburg; and during the four days which concluded the stay in Venice Swithin went about with his head up, but his eyes half-closed like a dazed man. Only after they had taken ship at Genoa did he show signs of any healthy interest in life, when, finding that a man on board was perpetually strumming, he locked the piano up and pitched the key into the sea.

That winter in London he behaved much as usual, but fits of moroseness would seize on him, during which he was not pleasant to approach.

One evening when he was walking with a friend in Piccadilly, a girl coming from a side-street accosted him in German. Swithin, after staring at her in silence for some seconds, handed her a five-pound note, to the great amazement of his friend; nor could he himself have explained the meaning of this freak of generosity.

Of Rozsi he never heard again. . . .

This, then, was the substance of what he remembered as he lay ill in bed. Stretching out his hand he pressed the bell. His valet appeared, crossing the room like a cat; a Swede, who had been with Swithin many years ; a little man with a dried face and fierce moustache, morbidly sharp nerves, and a queer devotion to his master.

Swithin made a feeble gesture. " Adolf," he said, " I'm very bad."

" Yes, sir! "

" Why do you stand there like a cow?" asked Swithin; " can't you see I'm very bad? "

" Yes, sir! " The valet's face twitched as though it masked the dance of obscure emotions.

" I shall feel better after dinner. What time is it? "

" Five o'clock."

" I thought it was more. The afternoons are very long."

" Yes, sir! "

Swithin sighed, as though he had expected the consolation of denial.

"Very likely I shall have a nap. Bring up hot water at half-past six and shave me before dinner."

The valet moved towards the door. Swithin raised himself.

"What did Mr. James say to you!"

"He said you ought to have another doctor; two doctors, he said, better than one. He said, also, he would look in again on his way 'home.'"

Swithin grunted, "Umph! What else did he say?"

"He said you didn't take care of yourself."

Swithin glared.

"Has anybody else been to see me?"

The valet turned away his eyes. "Mrs. Thomas Forsyte came last Monday fortnight."

"How long have I been ill?"

"Five weeks on Saturday."

"Do you think I'm very bad?"

Adolf's face was covered suddenly with crow's-feet. "You have no business to ask me question like that! I am not paid, sir, to answer question like that."

Swithin said faintly: "You're a peppery fool! Open a bottle of champagne!"

Adolf took a bottle of champagne from a cupboard and held nippers to it. He fixed his eyes on Swithin. "The doctor said——"

"Open the bottle!"

"It is not——"

"Open the bottle—or I give you warning."

Adolf removed the cork. He wiped a glass elaborately, filled it, and bore it scrupulously to the bedside. Suddenly twirling his moustaches, he wrung his hands, and burst out: "It is poison."

Swithin grinned faintly. "You foreign fool!" he said. "Get out!"

The valet vanished.

'He forgot himself!' thought Swithin. Slowly he raised the glass, slowly put it back, and sank gasping on his pillows. Almost at once he fell asleep.

He dreamed that he was at his club, sitting after dinner in the crowded smoking-room, with its bright walls and trefoils of light. It was there that he sat every evening, patient, solemn, lonely, and sometimes fell asleep, his square, pale old face nodding to one side. He dreamed that he was gazing at the picture over the fireplace, of an old statesman with a high collar, supremely finished face, and sceptical eyebrows—the picture, smooth, and reticent as sealing-wax, of one who seemed for ever exhaling the narrow wisdom of final judgments. All round him, his fellow-members were chattering. Only he himself, the old sick member, was silent. If fellows only knew what it was like to sit by yourself and feel ill all the time! What they were saying he had heard a hundred times. They were talking of investments, of cigars, horses, actresses, machinery. What was that? A foreign patent for cleaning boilers? There was no such thing; boilers couldn't be cleaned, any fool knew that! If an Englishman couldn't clean a boiler, no foreigner could clean one. He appealed to the old statesman's eyes. But for once those eyes seemed hesitating, blurred, wanting in finality. They vanished. In their place were Rozsi's little deep-set eyes, with their wide and far-off look; and as he gazed they seemed to grow bright as steel, and to speak to him. Slowly the whole face grew to be there, floating on the dark background of the picture; it was pink, aloof, unfathomable, enticing, with its fluffy hair and quick lips, just as he had last seen it. " Are you looking for something ? " she seemed to say: " I could show you."

" I have everything safe enough," answered Swithin, and in his sleep he groaned.

He felt the touch of fingers on his forehead. ' I'm dreaming,' he thought in his dream.

She had vanished; and far away, from behind the picture, came a sound of footsteps.

Aloud, in his sleep, Swithin muttered: " I've missed it."

Again he heard the rustling of those light footsteps, and close in his ear a sound, like a sob. He awoke; the sob was his own. Great drops of perspiration stood on his forehead. ' What is it ? ' he thought; ' what have I lost ? ' Slowly his mind travelled over his investments; he could not think of any single one that was unsafe. What was it, then, that he had lost? Struggling on his pillows, he clutched the wine-glass. His lips touched the wine. ' This isn't the " Heidseck " ! ' he thought angrily, and before the reality of that displeasure all the dim vision passed away. But as he bent to drink, something snapped, and, with a sigh, Swithin Forsyte died above the bubbles. . . .

When James Forsyte came in again on his way home, the valet, trembling, took his hat and stick.

" How's your master? "

" My master is dead, sir! "

" Dead! He can't be! I left him safe an hour ago! "

On the bed Swithin's body was doubled like a sack; his hand still grasped the glass.

James Forsyte paused. " Swithin! " he said, and with his hand to his ear he waited for an answer; but none came, and slowly in the glass a last bubble rose and burst.

December, 1900.

A STOIC

I

1 §

"Aequam memento rebus in arduis
Servare mentem."—HORACE.

IN the City of Liverpool, on a January day of 1905, the Board-room of " The Island Navigation Company " rested, as it were, after the labours of the afternoon. The long table was still littered with the ink, pens, blotting-paper, and abandoned documents of six persons—a deserted battlefield of the brain. And, lonely, in his chairman's seat at the top end old Sylvanus Heythorp sat, with closed eyes, still and heavy as an image. One puffy, feeble hand, whose fingers quivered, rested on the arm of his chair; the thick white hair on his massive head glistened in the light from a green-shaded lamp. He was not asleep, for every now and then his sanguine cheeks filled, and a sound, half sigh, half grunt, escaped his thick lips between a white moustache and the tiny tuft of white hairs above his cleft chin. Sunk in the chair, that square thick trunk of a body in short black-braided coat seemed divested of all neck.

Young Gilbert Farney, secretary of " The Island Navigation Company," entering his hushed Board-room, stepped briskly to the table, gathered some papers, and stood looking at his chairman. Not more than thirty-five, with the bright hues of the optimist in his hair, beard, cheeks, and eyes, he had a nose and lips which curled ironically. For, in his view, he *was* the Company; and its Board did but exist to chequer his importance. Five days in the week for seven hours a day he wrote, and thought, and wove the threads of its business, and this lot came down once a week for two or three hours, and taught their grandmother to suck eggs. But watching that red-cheeked,

white-haired, somnolent figure, his smile was not so contemptuous as might have been expected. For after all, the chairman
was a wonderful old boy. A man of go and insight could not
but respect him. Eighty! Half paralysed, over head and ears
in debt, having gone the pace all his life—or so they said!—
till at last that mine in Ecuador had done for him—before
the secretary's day, of course, but he had heard of it. The
old chap had bought it up on spec'—" *de l'audace, toujours de
l'audace*," as he was so fond of saying—paid for it half in cash
and half in promises, and then—the thing had turned out
empty, and left him with £20,000 worth of the old shares
unredeemed. The old boy had weathered it out without a bankruptcy so far. Indomitable old buffer; and never fussy like
the rest of them! Young Farney, though a secretary, was
capable of attachment; and his eyes expressed a pitying affection. The Board meeting had been long and " snaggy "—a
final settling of that Pillin business. Rum go the chairman
forcing it on them like this! And with quiet satisfaction the
secretary thought: ' And he never would have got it through if
I hadn't made up my mind that it really is good business! '
For to expand the Company was to expand himself. Still,
to buy four ships with the freight market so depressed was a
bit startling, and there would be opposition at the general meeting. Never mind! He and the chairman could put it through
—put it through. And suddenly he saw the old man looking
at him.

Only from those eyes could one appreciate the strength of
life yet flowing underground in that well-nigh helpless carcase
—deep-coloured little blue wells, tiny, jovial, round windows.

A sigh travelled up through layers of flesh, and he said almost inaudibly:

" Have they come, Mr. Farney? "

" Yes, sir. I've put them in the transfer office; said you'd
be with them in a minute; but I wasn't going to wake you."

" Haven't been asleep. Help me up."

Grasping the edge of the table with his trembling hands, the
old man pulled, and, with Farney heaving him behind, attained his feet. He stood about five feet ten, and weighed fully
fourteen stone; not corpulent, but very thick all through; his
round and massive head alone would have outweighed a baby.
With eyes shut, he seemed to be trying to get the better of his
own weight, then he moved with the slowness of a barnacle

towards the door. The secretary, watching him, thought: ' Marvellous old chap! How he gets about by himself is a miracle! And he can't retire, they say—lives on his fees!'

But the chairman was through the green baize door. At his tortoise gait he traversed the inner office, where the youthful clerks suspended their figuring—to grin behind his back—and entered the transfer office, where eight gentlemen were sitting. Seven rose, and one did not. Old Heythorp raised a saluting hand to the level of his chest and moving to an armchair, lowered himself into it.

" Well, gentlemen? "

One of the eight gentlemen got up again.

" Mr. Heythorp, we've appointed Mr. Brownbee to voice our views. Mr. Brownbee! " And down he sat.

Mr. Brownbee rose—a stoutish man some seventy years of age, with little grey side whiskers, and one of those utterly steady faces only to be seen in England, faces which convey the sense of business from father to son for generations; faces which make wars, and passion, and free thought seem equally incredible; faces which inspire confidence, and awaken in one a desire to get up and leave the room. Mr. Brownbee rose, and said in a suave voice:

" Mr. Heythorp, we here represent about £14,000. When we had the pleasure of meeting you last July, you will recollect that you held out a prospect of some more satisfactory arrangement by Christmas. We are now in January, and I am bound to say we none of us get younger."

From the depths of old Heythorp a preliminary rumble came travelling, reached the surface, and materialised:

" Don't know about you—feel a boy, myself."

The eight gentlemen looked at him. Was he going to try and put them off again? Mr. Brownbee said with unruffled calm:

" I'm sure we're very glad to hear it. But to come to the point. We have felt, Mr. Heythorp, and I'm sure you won't think it unreasonable, that—er—bankruptcy would be the most satisfactory solution. We have waited a long time, and we want to know definitely where we stand; for, to be quite frank, we don't see any prospect of improvement; indeed, we fear the opposite."

" You think I'm going to join the majority."

This plumping out of what was at the back of their minds produced in Mr. Brownbee and his colleagues a sort of chemi-

cal disturbance. They coughed, moved their feet, and turned
away their eyes, till the one who had not risen, a solicitor
named Ventnor, said bluffly:

"Well, put it that way if you like."

Old Heythorp's little deep eyes twinkled.

"My grandfather lived to be a hundred; my father ninety-
six—both of them rips. I'm only eighty, gentlemen; blameless
life compared with theirs."

"Indeed," Mr. Brownbee said, "we hope you have many
years of this life before you."

"More of this than of another." And a silence fell, till old
Heythorp added: "You're getting a thousand a year out of
my fees. Mistake to kill the goose that lays the golden eggs.
I'll make it twelve hundred. If you force me to resign my
directorships by bankruptcy, you won't get a rap, you know."

Mr. Brownbee cleared his throat:

"We think, Mr. Heythorp, you should make it at least fifteen
hundred. In that case we might perhaps consider——"

Old Heythorp shook his head.

"We can hardly accept your assertion that we should get
nothing in the event of bankruptcy. We fancy you greatly
underrate the possibilities. Fifteen hundred a year is the least
you can do for us."

"See you d——d first."

Another silence followed, then Ventnor, the solicitor, said
irascibly:

"We know where we are, then."

Mr. Brownbee added almost nervously:

"Are we to understand that twelve hundred a year is your
—your last word?"

Old Heythorp nodded. "Come again this day month, and
I'll see what I can do for you;" and he shut his eyes.

Round Mr. Brownbee six of the gentlemen gathered, speaking
in low voices; Mr. Ventnor nursed a leg and glowered at old
Heythorp, who sat with his eyes closed. Mr. Brownbee went
over and conferred with Mr. Ventnor, then clearing his throat,
he said:

"Well, sir, we have considered your proposal; we agree to
accept it for the moment. We will come again, as you suggest,
in a month's time. We hope that you will by then have seen
your way to something more substantial, with a view to avoiding

what we should all regret, but which I fear will otherwise become inevitable."

Old Heythorp nodded. The eight gentlemen took their hats,
and went out one by one, Mr. Brownbee courteously bringing
up the rear.

The old man, who could not get up without assistance, stayed
musing in his chair. He had diddled 'em for the moment into
giving him another month, and when that month was up—he
would diddle 'em again! A month ought to make the Pillin
business safe, with all that hung on it. That poor funkey chap
Joe Pillin! A gurgling chuckle escaped his red lips. What
a shadow the fellow had looked, trotting in that evening just
a month ago, behind his valet's announcement: "Mr. Pillin,
sir."

What a parchmenty, precise, threadpaper of a chap, with his
bird's claw of a hand, and his muffled-up throat, and his
quavery:

"How do you do, Sylvanus? I'm afraid you're not——"

"First rate. Sit down. Have some port."

"Port! I never drink it. Poison to me! Poison!"

"Do you good!"

"Oh! I know, that's what you always say. You've a monstrous constitution, Sylvanus. If I drank port and smoked
cigars and sat up till one o'clock, I should be in my grave to-
morrow. I'm not the man I was. The fact is I've come to see
if you can help me. I'm getting old; I'm growing nervous——"

"You always were as chickeny as an old hen, Joe."

"Well, my nature's not like yours. To come to the point, I
want to sell my ships and retire. I need rest. Freights are
very depressed. I've got my family to think of."

"Crack on, and go broke: buck you up like anything!"

"I'm quite serious, Sylvanus."

"Never knew you anything else, Joe."

A quavering cough, and out it had come:

"Now—in a word—won't your 'Island Navigation Company' buy my ships?"

A pause, a twinkle, a puff of smoke. "Make it worth my
while!" He had said it in jest; and then, in a flash, the idea
had come to him. Rosamund and her youngsters! What a
chance to put something between them and destitution when he
had joined the majority! And so he said: "We don't want
your silly ships."

That claw of a hand waved in deprecation. "They're very
good ships—doing quite well. It's only my wretched health.
If I were a strong man I shouldn't dream——"

"What d'you want for 'em?" Good Lord! how he jumped
if you asked him a plain question. The chap was as nervous
as a guinea-fowl!

"Here are the figures—for the last four years. I think you'll
agree that I couldn't ask less than seventy thousand."

Through the smoke of his cigar old Heythorp had digested
those figures slowly, Joe Pillin feeling his teeth and sucking
lozenges the while; then he said:

"Sixty thousand! And out of that you pay me ten per
cent, if I get it through for you. Take it or leave it."

"My dear Sylvanus, that's almost—cynical."

"Too good a price—you'll never get it without me."

"But a—but a commission! You could never disclose it!"

"Arrange that all right. Think it over. Freights'll go
lower yet. Have some port."

"No, no! Thank you. No! So you think freights will go
lower?"

"Sure of it."

"Well, I'll be going. I'm sure I don't know. It's—it's—I
must think."

"Think your hardest."

"Yes, yes. Good-bye. I can't imagine how you still go on
smoking those things and drinking port."

"See you in your grave yet, Joe." What a feeble smile the
poor fellow had! Laugh—he couldn't! And, alone again, he
had browsed, developing the idea which had come to him.

Though, to dwell in the heart of shipping, Sylvanus Heythorp
had lived at Liverpool twenty years, he was from the Eastern
Counties, of a family so old that it professed to despise the
Conquest. Each of its generations occupied nearly twice as
long as those of less tenacious men. Traditionally of Danish
origin, its men folk had as a rule bright reddish-brown hair,
red cheeks, large round heads, excellent teeth and poor morals.
They had done their best for the population of any county in
which they had settled; their offshoots swarmed. Born in the
early twenties of the nineteenth century, Sylvanus Heythorp,
after an education broken by escapades both at school and college, had fetched up in that simple London of the late forties,
where claret, opera, and eight per cent. for your money ruled a

cheery roost. Made partner in his shipping firm well before
he was thirty, he had sailed with a wet sheet and a flowing
tide; dancers, claret, Clicquot, and piquet; a cab with a tiger;
some travel—all that delicious early-Victorian consciousness of
nothing save a golden time. It was all so full and mellow that
he was forty before he had his only love affair of any depth—
with the daughter of one of his own clerks, a *liaison* so awkward
as to necessitate a sedulous concealment. The death of that
girl, after three years, leaving him a natural son, had been the
chief, perhaps the only real, sorrow of his life. Five years
later he married. What for? God only knew! as he was in
the habit of remarking. His wife had been a hard, worldly,
well-connected woman, who presented him with two unnatural
children, a girl and a boy, and grew harder, more worldly,
less handsome, in the process. The migration to Liverpool,
which took place when he was sixty and she forty-two, broke
what she still had of heart, but she lingered on twelve years,
finding solace in bridge, and being haughty towards Liverpool.
Old Heythorp saw her to her rest without regret. He had felt
no love for her whatever, and practically none for her two
children—they were in his view colourless, pragmatical, very
unexpected characters. His son Ernest—in the Admiralty—he
thought a poor, careful stick. His daughter Adela, an excellent manager, delighting in spiritual conversation and the society of tame men, rarely failed to show him that she considered him a hopeless heathen. They saw as little as need be
of each other. She was provided for under that settlement
he had made on her mother fifteen years ago, well before the
not altogether unexpected crisis in his affairs. Very different
was the feeling he had bestowed on that son of his " under the
rose." The boy, who had always gone by his mother's name of
Larne, had on her death been sent to some relations of hers in
Ireland, and there brought up. He had been called to the Dublin bar, and married, young, a girl half Cornish and half Irish;
presently, having cost old Heythorp in all a pretty penny, he
had died impecunious, leaving his fair Rosamund at thirty
with a girl of eight and a boy of five. She had not spent six
months of widowhood before coming over from Dublin to claim
the old man's guardianship. A remarkably pretty woman, like
a full-blown rose, with greenish hazel eyes, she had turned up
one morning at the offices of " The Island Navigation Company," accompanied by her two children—for he had never

divulged to them his private address. And since then they had always been more or less on his hands, occupying a small house in a suburb of Liverpool. He visited them there, but never asked them to the house in Sefton Park, which was in fact his daughter's; so that his proper family and friends were unaware of their existence.

Rosamund Larne was one of those precarious ladies who make uncertain incomes by writing full-bodied storyettes. In the most dismal circumstances she enjoyed a buoyancy bordering on the indecent, which always amused old Heythorp's cynicism. But of his grandchildren Phyllis and Jock (wild as colts) he had become fond. And this chance of getting six thousand pounds settled on them at a stroke had seemed to him nothing but heaven-sent. As things were, if he "went off"—and, of course, he might at any moment—there wouldn't be a penny for them; for he would "cut up" a good fifteen thousand to the bad. He was now giving them some three hundred a year out of his fees; and dead directors unfortunately earned no fees! Six thousand pounds at four and a half per cent., settled so that their mother couldn't "blue it," would give them a certain two hundred and fifty pounds a year—better than beggary. And the more he thought the better he liked it, if only that shaky chap, Joe Pillin, didn't shy off when he'd bitten his nails short over it!

Four evenings later, the "shaky chap" had again appeared at his house in Sefton Park.

"I've thought it over, Sylvanus. I don't like it."

"No; but you'll do it."

"It's a sacrifice. Fifty-four thousand for four ships—it means a considerable reduction in my income."

"It means security, my boy."

"Well, there is that; but you know, I really can't be party to a secret commission. If it came out, think of my name and goodness knows what."

"It won't come out."

"Yes, yes, so you say, but——"

"All you've got to do's to execute a settlement on some third parties that I'll name. I'm not going to take a penny of it myself. Get your own lawyer to draw it up and make him trustee. You can sign it when the purchase has gone through. I'll trust you, Joe. What stock have you got that gives four and a half per cent.?"

" Midland——"

" That'll do. You needn't sell."

" Yes, but who *are* these people? "

" Woman and her children I want to do a good turn to."
What a face the fellow had made! " Afraid of being connected
with a woman, Joe? "

" Yes, you may laugh—I *am* afraid of being connected with
someone else's woman. I don't like it—I don't like it at all.
I've not led your life, Sylvanus."

" Lucky for you; you'd have been dead long ago. Tell your
lawyer it's an old flame of yours—you old dog! "

" Yes, there it is at once, you see. I might be subject to
blackmail."

" Tell him to keep it dark, and just pay over the income,
quarterly."

" I don't like it, Sylvanus—I don't like it."

" Then leave it, and be hanged to you. Have a cigar? "

" You know I never smoke. Is there no other way? "

" Yes. Sell stock in London, bank the proceeds there, and
bring me six thousand pounds in notes. I'll hold 'em till
after the general meeting. If the thing doesn't go through, I'll
hand 'em back to you."

" No; I like that even less."

" Rather I trusted *you,* eh! "

" No, not at all, Sylvanus, not at all. But it's all playing
round the law."

" There's no law to prevent you doing what you like with
your money. What I do's nothing to you. And mind you, I'm
taking nothing from it—not a mag. You assist the widowed
and the fatherless—just your line, Joe! "

" What a fellow you are, Sylvanus; you don't seem capable
of taking anything seriously."

" Care killed the cat! "

Left alone after this second interview he had thought: ' The
beggar'll jump.'

And the beggar *had.* That settlement was drawn and only
awaited signature. The Board to-day had decided on the purchase; and all that remained was to get it ratified at the general meeting. Let him but get that over, and this provision
for his grandchildren made, and he would snap his fingers at
Brownbee and his crew—the canting humbugs! " Hope you
have many years of this life before you! " As if they cared

for anything but his money—*their* money rather! And becoming conscious of the length of his reverie, he grasped the arms of his chair, heaved at his own bulk, in an effort to rise, growing redder and redder in face and neck. It was one of the hundred things his doctor had told him not to do for fear of apoplexy, the humbug! Why didn't Farney or one of those young fellows come and help him up? To call out was undignified. But was he to sit there all night? Three times he failed, and after each failure sat motionless again, crimson and exhausted; the fourth time he succeeded, and slowly made for the office. Passing through, he stopped and said in his extinct voice:

"You young gentlemen had forgotten me."

"Mr. Farney said you didn't wish to be disturbed, sir."

"Very good of him. Give me my hat and coat."

"Yes, sir."

"Thank you. What time is it?"

"Six o'clock, sir."

"Tell Mr. Farney to come and see me to-morrow at noon, about my speech for the general meeting."

"Yes, sir."

"Good-night to you."

"Good-night, sir."

At his tortoise gait he passed between the office stools to the door, opened it feebly, and slowly vanished.

Shutting the door behind him, a clerk said:

"Poor old chairman! He's on his last!"

Another answered;

"Gosh! He's a tough old hulk. He'll go down fightin'."

2 §

Issuing from the offices of "The Island Navigation Company," Sylvanus Heythorp moved towards the corner whence he always took tram to Sefton Park. The crowded street had all that prosperous air of catching or missing something which characterises the town where London and New York and Dublin meet. Old Heythorp had to cross to the far side, and he sallied forth without regard to traffic. That snail-like passage had in it a touch of the sublime; the old man seemed saying: "Knock me down and be d——d to you—I'm not going to hurry." His life was saved perhaps ten times a day by the British character at large, compounded of phlegm and a liking to take something under its protection. The tram conductors on that line were especially used to him, never failing to catch him under the arms and heave him like a sack of coals, while with trembling hands he pulled hard at the rail and strap.

" All right, sir ? "

" Thank you."

He moved into the body of the tram, where somebody would always get up from kindness and the fear that he might sit down on them; and there he stayed motionless, his little eyes tight closed. With his red face, tuft of white hairs above his square cleft block of shaven chin, and his big high-crowned bowler hat, which yet seemed too petty for his head with its thick hair—he looked like some kind of an idol dug up and decked out in gear a size too small.

One of those voices of young men from public schools and exchanges where things are bought and sold, said:

" How de do, Mr. Heythorp? "

Old Heythorp opened his eyes. That sleek cub, Joe Pillin's son! What a young pup—with his round eyes, and his round cheeks, and his little moustache, his fur coat, his spats, his diamond pin!

" How's your father? " he said.

" Thanks, rather below par, worryin' about his ships. Suppose you haven't any news for him, sir? "

Old Heythorp nodded. The young man was one of his pet abominations, embodying all the complacent, little-headed mediocrity of this new generation; natty fellows all turned out of the same mould, sippers and tasters, chaps without drive or capacity, without even vices; and he did not intend to gratify the cub's curiosity.

" Come to my house," he said; " I'll give you a note for him."

" Tha—anks; I'd like to cheer the old man up."

The old man! Cheeky brat! And closing his eyes he relapsed into immobility. The tram wound and ground its upward way, and he mused. When he was that cub's age—twenty-eight or whatever it might be—he had done most things; been up Vesuvius, driven four-in-hand, lost his last penny on the Derby and won it back on the Oaks, known all the dancers and operatic stars of the day, fought a duel with a Yankee at Dieppe and winged him for saying through his confounded nose that

Old England was played out; been a controlling voice already in his shipping firm; drunk five other of the best men in London under the table; broken his neck steeplechasing; shot a burglar in the legs; been nearly drowned, for a bet; killed snipe in Chelsea; been to Court for his sins; stared a ghost out of countenance; and travelled with a lady of Spain. If this young pup had done the last, it would be all he had; and yet, no doubt, he would call himself a "spark."

The conductor touched his arm.

"'Ere you are, sir."

"Thank you."

He lowered himself to the ground, and moved in the bluish darkness towards the gate of his daughter's house. Bob Pillin walked beside him, thinking: 'Poor old josser, he *is* gettin' a back number!' And he said: "I should have thought you ought to drive, sir. My old guv-nor would knock up at once if he went about at night like this."

The answer rumbled out into the misty air:

"Your father's got no chest; never had."

Bob Pillin gave vent to one of those fat cackles which come so readily from a certain type of man; and old Heythorp thought: 'Laughing at his father! Parrot!'

They had reached the porch.

A woman with dark hair and a thin, straight face and figure was arranging some flowers in the hall. She turned and said:

"You really ought not to be so late, Father! It's wicked at this time of year. Who is it—oh! Mr. Pillin, how do you do? Have you had tea? Won't you come to the drawing-room; or do you want to see my father?"

"Tha—anks! I believe your father——" And he thought: 'By Jove! the old chap *is* a caution!' For old Heythorp was crossing the hall without having paid the faintest attention to his daughter. Murmuring again:

"Tha—anks awfully; he wants to give me something," he followed. Miss Heythorp was not his style at all; he had a kind of dread of that thin woman who looked as if she could never be unbuttoned. They said she was a great churchgoer and all that sort of thing.

In his sanctum old Heythorp had moved to his writing-table, and was evidently anxious to sit down.

"Shall I give you a hand, sir?"

Receiving a shake of the head, Bob Pillin stood by the fire

and watched. The old "sport" liked to paddle his own canoe.
Fancy having to lower yourself into a chair like that! When
an old Johnny got to such a state it was really a mercy when
he snuffed out, and made way for younger men. How his
Companies could go on putting up with such a fossil for chairman was a marvel! The fossil rumbled and said in that almost
inaudible voice:

"I suppose you're beginning to look forward to your father's
shoes?"

Bob Pillin's mouth opened. The voice went on:

"Dibs and no responsibility. Tell him from me to drink
port—add five years to his life."

To this unwarranted attack Bob Pillin made no answer save
a laugh; he perceived that a manservant had entered the room.

"A Mrs. Larne, sir. Will you see her?"

At this announcement the old man seemed to try and start;
then he nodded, and held out the note he had written. Bob
Pillin received it together with the impression of a murmur
which sounded like: "Scratch a poll, Poll!" and passing the
fine figure of a woman in a fur coat, who seemed to warm the
air as she went by, he was in the hall again before he perceived
that he had left his hat.

A young and pretty girl was standing on the bearskin before
the fire, looking at him with round-eyed innocence. He thought:
'This is better; I mustn't disturb them for my hat'; and approaching the fire, he said:

"Jolly cold, isn't it?"

The girl smiled: "Yes—jolly."

He noticed that she had a large bunch of violets at her breast,
a lot of fair hair, a short straight nose, and round blue-grey
eyes very frank and open. "Er——" he said, "I've left my hat
in there."

"What larks!" And at her little clear laugh something
moved within Bob Pillin.

"You know this house well?"

She shook her head. "But it's rather scrummy, isn't it?"

Bob Pillin, who had never yet thought so, answered:

"Quite O.K."

The girl threw up her head to laugh again. "O.K.? What's
that?"

Bob Pillin saw her white round throat, and thought: 'She *is*
a ripper!' And he said with a certain desperation:

"My name's Pillin. Yours is Larne, isn't it? Are you a relation here?"

"He's our Guardy. Isn't he a chook?"

That rumbling whisper like "Scratch a poll, Poll!" recurring to Bob Pillin, he said with reservation:

"You know him better than I do."

"Oh! Aren't you his grandson, or something?"

Bob Pillin did not cross himself.

"Lord! No! My dad's an old friend of his; that's all."

"Is your dad like him?"

"Not much."

"What a pity! It would have been lovely if they'd been Tweedles."

Bob Pillin thought: 'This bit is something new. I wonder what her Christian name is.' And he said:

"What did your godfather and godmothers in your baptism—— ? "

The girl laughed; she seemed to laugh at everything.

"Phyllis."

Could he say: "Is my only joy"? Better keep it! But —for what? He wouldn't see her again if he didn't look out! And he said:

"I live at the last house in the park—the red one. D'you know it? Where do you?"

"Oh! a long way—23, Millicent Villas. It's a poky little house. I hate it. We have awful larks, though."

"Who are we?"

"Mother, and myself, and Jock—he's an awful boy. You can't conceive what an awful boy he is. He's got nearly red hair; I think he'll be just like Guardy when he gets old. He's *awful!*"

Bob Pillin murmured:

"I should like to see him."

"Would you? I'll ask mother if you can. You won't want to again; he goes off all the time like a squib." She threw back her head, and again Bob Pillin felt a little giddy. He collected himself, and drawled:

"Are you going in to see your Guardy?"

"No. Mother's got something special to say. We've never been here before, you see. Isn't he fun, though?"

"Fun!"

" I think he's the greatest lark: but he's awfully nice to me.
Jock calls him the last of the Stoic'uns."

A voice called from old Heythorp's den:

" Phyllis! " It had a particular ring, that voice, as if coming from beautifully formed red lips, of which the lower one
must curve the least bit over; it had, too, a caressing vitality,
and a kind of warm falsity.

The girl threw a laughing look back over her shoulder, and
vanished through the door into the room.

Bob Pillin remained with his back to the fire and his puppy
round eyes fixed on the air that her figure had last occupied.
He was experiencing a sensation never felt before. Those
travels with a lady of Spain, charitably conceded him by old
Heythorp, had so far satisfied the emotional side of this young
man; they had stopped short at Brighton and Scarborough,
and been preserved from even the slightest intrusion of love. A
calculated and hygienic career had caused no anxiety either
to himself or his father; and this sudden swoop of something
more than admiration gave him an uncomfortable choky feeling just above his high round collar, and in the temples a sort
of buzzing—those first symptoms of chivalry. A man of the
world does not, however, succumb without a struggle; and if
his hat had not been out of reach, who knows whether he would
not have left the house hurriedly, saying to himself: " No,
no, my boy; Millicent Villas is hardly your form, when your
intentions are honourable " ? For somehow that round and
laughing face, bob of glistening hair, those wide-opened grey
eyes, refused to awaken the beginnings of other intentions—
such is the effect of youth and innocence on even the steadiest
young men. With a kind of moral stammer, he was thinking:
' Can I—dare I offer to see them to their tram? Couldn't I
even nip out and get the car round and send them home in it?
No, I might miss them—better stick it out here! What a
jolly laugh! What a ripping face—strawberries and cream,
hay, and all that! Millicent Villas!' And he wrote it on his
cuff.

The door was opening; he heard that warm vibrating voice:
" Come along, Phyllis! "—the girl's laugh so high and fresh:
" Right-o! Coming! " And with, perhaps, the first real tremor
he had ever known, he crossed to the front door. All the more
chivalrous to escort them to the tram without a hat! And
suddenly he heard: " I've got your hat, young man! " And

her mother's voice, warm, and simulating shock: " Phyllis,
you awful gairl! Did you ever see such an awful gairl, Mr.——"

" Pillin, Mother."

And then—he did not quite know how—insulated from the
January air by laughter and the scent of fur and violets, he
was between them walking to their tram. It was like an experience out of the " Arabian Nights," or something of that sort,
an intoxication which made one say one was going their way,
though one would have to come all the way back in the same
beastly tram. Nothing so warming had ever happened to him
as sitting between them on that drive, so that he forgot the note
in his pocket, and his desire to relieve the anxiety of the " old
man," his father. At the tram's terminus they all got out.
There issued a purr of invitation to come and see them some
time; a clear: " Jock'll love to see you!" A low laugh: " You
awful gairl!" And a flash of cunning zigzagged across his
brain. Taking off his hat, he said:

" Thanks awfully; rather!" and put his foot back on the
step of the tram. Thus did he delicately expose the depths of
his chivalry!

" Oh! you *said* you were going our way! What one-ers you
do tell! Oh!" The words were as music; the sight of those
eyes growing rounder, the most perfect he had ever seen; and
Mrs. Larne's low laugh, so warm yet so preoccupied, and the
tips of the girl's fingers waving back above her head. He
heaved a sigh and knew no more till he was seated at his club
before a bottle of champagne. Home! Not he! He wished
to drink and dream. " The old man " would get his news all
right to-morrow!

3 §

The words: " A Mrs. Larne to see you, sir," had been of a
nature to astonish weaker nerves. What had brought her here?
She knew she mustn't come! Old Heythorp had watched her
entrance with cynical amusement. The way she whiffed herself at that young pup in passing, the way her eyes slid round!
He had a very just appreciation of his son's widow; and a smile
settled deep between his chin tuft and his moustache. She
lifted his hand, kissed it, pressed it to her splendid bust, and
said:

"So here I am at last, you see. Aren't you surprised?"

Old Heythorp shook his head.

"I really had to come and see you, Guardy; we haven't had a sight of you for such an age. And in this awful weather! How are you, dear old Guardy?"

"Never better." And, watching her green-grey eyes, he added: "Haven't a penny for you!"

Her face did not fall; she gave her feather-laugh.

"How dreadful of you to think I came for that! But I *am* in an awful fix, Guardy."

"Never knew you not to be."

"Just let me tell you, dear; it'll be some relief. I'm having the most terrible time."

She sank into a low chair, disengaging an overpowering scent of violets, while melancholy struggled to subdue her face and body.

"The most awful fix. I expect to be sold up any moment. We may be on the streets to-morrow. I daren't tell the children; they're so happy, poor darlings. I shall be obliged to take Jock away from school. And Phyllis will have to stop her piano and dancing; it's an absolute crisis. And all due to those Midland Syndicate people. I've been counting on at least two hundred for my new story, and the wretches have refused it."

With a tiny handkerchief she removed one tear from the corner of one eye. "It *is* hard, Guardy; I worked my brain silly over that story."

From old Heythorp came a mutter which sounded suspiciously like "Rats!"

Heaving a sigh, which conveyed nothing but the generosity of her breathing apparatus, Mrs. Larne went on:

"You couldn't, I suppose, let me have just one hundred?"

"Not a bob."

She sighed again, her eyes slid round the room; then in her warm voice she murmured:

"Guardy, you *were* my dear Philip's father, weren't you? I've never said anything; but *of course* you were. He was so like you, and so is Jock."

Nothing moved in old Heythorp's face. No pagan image consulted with flowers and song and sacrifice could have returned less answer. Her dear Philip! She had led him the devil of a life, or he was a Dutchman! And what the deuce made her suddenly trot out the skeleton like this? But Mrs. Larne's eyes were still wandering.

" What a lovely house! You know, I think you ought to help me, Guardy. Just imagine if your grandchildren were thrown out into the street! "

The old man grinned. He was not going to deny his relationship—it was her look-out, not his. But neither was he going to let her rush him.

" And they will be; you *couldn't* look on and see it. Do come to my rescue this once. You really might do something for them."

With a rumbling sigh he answered:

" Wait. Can't give you a penny now. Poor as a church mouse."

" Oh! Guardy! "

" Fact."

Mrs. Larne heaved one of her most buoyant sighs. She certainly did not believe him.

" Well! " she said; " you'll be sorry when we come round one night and sing for pennies under your window. Wouldn't you like to see Phyllis? I left her in the hall. She's growing such a sweet gairl. Guardy—just fifty! "

" Not a rap."

Mrs. Larne threw up her hands. " Well! You'll repent it. I'm at my last gasp." She sighed profoundly, and the perfume of violets escaped in a cloud. Then, getting up, she went to the door and called: " Phyllis! "

When the girl entered old Heythorp felt the nearest approach to a flutter of the heart for many years. She had put her hair up! She was like a spring day in January; such a relief from that scented humbug, her mother. Pleasant, the touch of her lips on his forehead, the sound of her clear voice, the sight of her slim movements, the feeling that she did him credit—clean-run stock, she and that young scamp Jock—better than the holy woman, his daughter Adela, would produce if anyone were ever fool enough to marry her, or that pragmatical fellow, his son Ernest.

And when they were gone he reflected with added zest on the six thousand pounds he was getting for them out of Joe Pillin and his ships. He would have to pitch it strong in his speech at the general meeting. With freights so low, there was bound to be opposition. No dash nowadays; nothing but

flabby caution! They were a scrim-shanking lot on the Board
—he had had to pull them round one by one—the deuce of a
tug getting this thing through! And yet, the business was
sound enough. Those ships would earn money, properly handled—good money!

His valet, coming in to prepare him for dinner, found him
asleep. He had for the old man as much admiration as may
be felt for one who cannot put his own trousers on. He would
say to the housemaid Molly: "He's a game old blighter—
must have been a rare one in his day. Cocks his hat at you,
even now, I see!" To which the girl, Irish and pretty, would
reply: "Well, an' sure I don't mind, if it gives um a pleasure.
'Tis better annyway than the sad eye I get from herself."

At dinner, old Heythorp always sat at one end of the rosewood table and his daughter at the other. It was the eminent
moment of the day. With napkin tucked high into his waistcoat, he gave himself to the meal with passion. His palate
was undimmed, his digestion unimpaired. He could still eat
as much as two men, and drink more than one. And while he
savoured each mouthful he never spoke if he could help it. The
holy woman had nothing to say that he cared to hear, and he
nothing to say that she cared to listen to. She had a horror,
too, of what she called "the pleasures of the table"—those
lusts of the flesh! She was always longing to dock his grub, he
knew. Would see her further first! What other pleasures were
there at his age? Let her wait till *she* was eighty. But she
never would be; too thin and holy!

This evening, however, with the advent of the partridge she
did speak.

"Who were your visitors, Father?"

Trust her for nosing anything out! Fixing his little blue
eyes on her, he mumbled with a very full mouth: "Ladies."

"So I saw; what ladies?"

He had a longing to say: 'Part of one of my families under
the rose.' As a fact it was the best part of the only one, but
the temptation to multiply exceedingly was almost overpowering. He checked himself, however, and went on eating partridge, his secret irritation crimsoning his cheeks; and he
watched her eyes, those cold precise and round grey eyes, noting
it, and knew she was thinking: 'He eats too much.'

She said: "Sorry I'm not considered fit to be told. You
ought not to be drinking hock."

Old Heythorp took up the long green glass, drained it, and repressing fumes and emotion went on with his partridge. His daughter pursed her lips, took a sip of water, and said:

"I know their name is Larne, but it conveyed nothing to me; perhaps it's just as well."

The old man, mastering a spasm, said with a grin:

"My daughter-in-law and my granddaughter."

"What! Ernest married—Oh! nonsense!"

He chuckled, and shook his head.

"Then do you mean to say, Father, that you were married before you married my mother?"

"No."

The expression on her face was as good as a play!

She said with a sort of disgust: "Not married! I see. I suppose those people are hanging round your neck, then; no wonder you're always in difficulties. Are there any more of them?"

Again the old man suppressed that spasm, and the veins in his neck and forehead swelled alarmingly. If he had spoken he would infallibly have choked. He ceased eating, and putting his hands on the table tried to raise himself. He could not, and subsiding in his chair sat glaring at the stiff, quiet figure of his daughter.

"Don't be silly, Father, and make a scene before Meller. Finish your dinner."

He did not answer. He was not going to sit there to be dragooned and insulted! His helplessness had never so weighed on him before. It was like a revelation. A log—that had to put up with anything! A log! And, waiting for his valet to return, he cunningly took up his fork.

In that saintly voice of hers she said:

"I suppose you don't realise that it's a shock to me. I don't know what Ernest will think——"

"Ernest be d——d."

"I do wish, Father, you wouldn't swear."

Old Heythorp's rage found vent in a sort of rumble. How the devil had he gone on all these years in the same house with that woman, dining with her day after day! But the servant had come back now, and putting down his fork he said:

"Help me up!"

The man paused, thunderstruck, with the *soufflé* balanced. To leave dinner unfinished—it was a portent!

" Help me up ! "

" Mr. Heythorp's not very well, Meller; take his other arm."
The old man shook off her hand.

" I'm very well. Help me up. Dine in my own room in
future."

Raised to his feet, he walked slowly out; but in his sanctum he
did not sit down, obsessed by this first overwhelming realisation
of his helplessness. He stood swaying a little, holding on to
the table, till the servant, having finished serving dinner,
brought in his port.

" Are you waiting to sit down, sir ? "

He shook his head. Hang it, he could do that for himself,
anyway. He must think of something to fortify his position
against that woman. And he said:

" Send me Molly ! "

" Yes, sir." The man put down the port and went.

Old Heythorp filled his glass, drank, and filled again. He
took a cigar from the box and lighted it. The girl came in, a
grey-eyed, dark-haired damsel, and stood with her hands folded,
her head a little to one side, her lips a little parted. The old
man said:

" You're a human being."

" I would hope so, sirr."

" I'm going to ask you something as a human being—not a
servant—see ? "

" No, sirr; but I will be glad to do annything you like."

" Then put your nose in here every now and then, to see if
I want anything. Meller goes out sometimes. Don't say anything; just put your nose in."

" Oh! an' I will; 'tis a pleasure 'twill be to do ut."

He nodded, and when she had gone lowered himself into his
chair with a sense of appeasement. Pretty girl! Comfort to see
a pretty face—not a pale, peeky thing like Adela's. His anger
burned up anew. So she counted on his helplessness, had begun to count on that, had she? She should see that there was
life in the old dog yet! And his sacrifice of the uneaten *soufflé*,
the still less eaten mushrooms, the peppermint sweet with which
he usually concluded dinner, seemed to consecrate that purpose. They all thought he was a hulk, without a shot left in the
locker! He had seen a couple of them at the Board that afternoon shrugging at each other, as though saying: ' Look at
him ! ' And young Farney pitying him. Pity, forsooth! And

56   CARAVAN

that coarse-grained solicitor chap at the creditors' meeting curling his lips as much to say: 'One foot in the grave!' He had seen the clerks dowsing the glim of their grins; and that young pup Bob Pillin screwing up his supercilious mug over his dog-collar. He knew that scented humbug Rosamund was getting scared that he'd drop off before she'd squeezed him dry. And his valet was always looking him up and down queerly. As to that holy woman——! Not quite so fast! Not quite so fast! And filling his glass for the fourth time, he slowly sucked down the dark red fluid, with the "old boots" flavour which his soul loved, and, drawing deep at his cigar, closed his eyes.

II

I §

The room in the hotel where the general meetings of "The Island Navigation Company" were held was nearly full when the secretary came through the door which as yet divided the shareholders from their directors. Having surveyed their empty chairs, their ink and papers, and nodded to a shareholder or two, he stood, watch in hand, contemplating the congregation. A thicker attendance than he had ever seen! Due, no doubt, to the lower dividend, and this Pillin business. And his tongue curled. For if he had a natural contempt for his Board, with the exception of the chairman, he had a still more natural contempt for his shareholders. Amusing spectacle when you come to think of it, a general meeting! Unique! Eighty or a hundred men, and five women, assembled through sheer devotion to their money. Was any other function in the world so single-hearted. Church was nothing to it—so many motives were mingled there with devotion to one's soul. A well-educated young man—reader of Anatole France, and other writers—he enjoyed ironic speculation. What earthly good did they think they got by coming here? Half-past two! He put his watch back into his pocket, and passed into the Board-room.

There, the fumes of lunch and of a short preliminary meeting made cosy the February atmosphere. By the fire four directors were conversing rather restlessly; the fifth was combing his beard; the chairman sat with eyes closed and red lips moving rhythmically in the sucking of a lozenge, the slips of his speech ready in his hand. The secretary said in his cheerful voice: " Time, sir."

Old Heythorp swallowed, lifted his arms, rose with help, and walked through to his place at the centre of the table. The five directors followed. And, standing at the chairman's right, the secretary read the minutes, forming the words precisely with his curling tongue. Then, assisting the chairman to his feet, he watched those rows of faces, and thought: ' Mistake to let them see he can't get up without help. He ought to have let me read his speech—I wrote it.'

The chairman began to speak:

" It is my duty and my pleasure, ladies and gentlemen, for the nineteenth consecutive year to present to you the directors' report and the accounts for the past twelve months. You will all have had special notice of a measure of policy on which your Board has decided, and to which you will be asked to-day to give your adherence—to that I shall come at the end of my remarks. . . ."

" Excuse me, sir; we can't hear a word down here."

' Ah!' thought the secretary, ' I was expecting that.'

The chairman went on, undisturbed. But several shareholders now rose, and the same speaker said testily: " We might as well go home. If the chairman's got no voice, can't somebody read for him? "

The chairman took a sip of water, and resumed. Almost all in the last six rows were now on their feet, and amid a hubbub of murmurs the chairman held out to the secretary the slips of his speech, and fell heavily back into his chair.

The secretary re-read from the beginning; and as each sentence fell from his tongue, he thought: ' How good that is!' ' That's very clear!' ' A neat touch!' ' This is getting them.' It seemed to him a pity they could not know it was all his composition. When at last he came to the Pillin sale he paused for a second.

" I come now to the measure of policy to which I made allusion at the beginning of my speech. Your Board has decided to expand your enterprise by purchasing the entire fleet of Pillin & Co., Ltd. By this transaction we become the owners of the four steamships *Smyrna, Damascus, Tyre,* and *Sidon,* vessels in prime condition with a total freight-carrying capacity of fifteen thousand tons, at the low inclusive price of sixty

thousand pounds. Gentlemen, '*Vestigia nulla retrorsum !*'"
—it was the chairman's phrase, his bit of the speech, and the
secretary did it more than justice. "Times are bad, but your
Board is emphatically of the opinion that they are touching
bottom; and this, in their view, is the psychological moment for
a forward stroke. They confidently recommend your adoption
of their policy and the ratification of this purchase, which they
believe will, in the not far distant future, substantially increase
the profits of the Company." The secretary sat down with reluctance. The speech should have continued with a number of
appealing sentences which he had carefully prepared, but the
chairman had cut them out with the simple comment: "They
ought to be glad of the chance." It was, in his view, an error.

The director who had combed his beard now rose—a man of
presence, who might be trusted to say nothing long and suavely.
While he was speaking the secretary was busy noting whence
opposition was likely to come. The majority were sitting owl-
like—a good sign; but some dozen were studying their copies
of the report, and three at least were making notes—Westgate,
for instance, who wanted to get on the Board, and was sure to
make himself unpleasant—the time-honoured method of vinegar; and Batterson, who also desired to come on, and might be
trusted to support the Board—the time-honoured method of oil;
while, if one knew anything of human nature, the fellow who
had complained that he might as well go home would have
something uncomfortable to say. The director finished his remarks, combed his beard with his fingers, and sat down.

A momentary pause ensued. Then Messieurs Westgate and
Batterson rose together. Seeing the chairman nod towards the
latter, the secretary thought: 'Mistake! He should have
humoured Westgate by giving him precedence.' But that was
the worst of the old man, he had no notion of the *suaviter in
modo!* Mr. Batterson—thus unchained—would like, if he
might be so allowed, to congratulate the Board on having piloted
their ship so smoothly through the troublous waters of the past
year. With their worthy chairman still at the helm, he had no
doubt that in spite of the still low—he would not say falling
—barometer, and the—er—unseasonable climacteric, they might
rely on weathering the—er—he would not say storm. He
would confess that the present dividend of four per cent. was
not one which satisfied every aspiration (Hear, hear!), but
speaking for himself, and he hoped for others—and here Mr.

Batterson looked round—he recognised that in all the circumstances it was as much as they had the right—er—to expect. But following the bold but to *his* mind prudent development which the Board proposed to make, he thought that they might reasonably, if not sanguinely, anticipate a more golden future. (" No, no! ") A shareholder said, " No, no! " That might seem to indicate a certain lack of confidence in the special proposal before the meeting. (" Yes! ") From that lack of confidence he would like at once to dissociate himself. Their chairman, a man of foresight and acumen, and valour proved on many a field and—er—sea, would not have committed himself to this policy without good reason. In his opinion they were in safe hands, and he was glad to register his support of the measure proposed. The chairman had well said in his speech: "*Vestigia nulla retrorsum!*" Shareholders would agree with him that there could be no better motto for Englishmen. Ahem!

Mr. Batterson sat down. And Mr. Westgate rose: He wanted —he said—to know more, much more, about this proposition, which to his mind was of a very dubious wisdom . . . 'Ah!' thought the secretary, 'I told the old boy he must tell them more.' . . . To whom, for instance, had the proposal first been made? To him!—the chairman said. Good! But why were Pillins selling, if freights were to go up, as they were told?

" Matter of opinion."

" Quite so; and in my opinion they are going lower, and Pillins were right to sell. It follows that we are wrong to buy." (" Hear, hear! " " No, no! ") " Pillins are shrewd people. What does the chairman say? Nerves! Does he mean to tell us that this sale was the result of nerves? "

The chairman nodded.

" That appears to me a somewhat fantastic theory; but I will leave that and confine myself to asking the grounds on which the chairman bases his confidence; in fact, what it is which is actuating the Board in pressing on us at such a time what I have no hesitation in stigmatising as a rash proposal. In a word, I want light as well as leading in this matter."

Mr. Westgate sat down.

What would the chairman do now? The situation was distinctly awkward—seeing his helplessness and the luke-warmness of the Board behind him. And the secretary felt more strongly than ever the absurdity of his being an underling, he who in a few well-chosen words could so easily have twisted the meet-

ing round his thumb. Suddenly he heard the long, rumbling
sigh which preluded the chairman's speeches.

"Has any other gentleman anything to say before I move the
adoption of the report?"

Phew! That would put their backs up. Yes, sure enough it
had brought that fellow, who had said he might as well go home,
to his feet! Now for something nasty!

"Mr. Westgate requires answering. I don't like this business.
I don't impute anything to anybody; but it looks to me as if
there were something behind it which the shareholders ought
to be told. Not only that; but, to speak frankly, I'm not satisfied to be ridden over roughshod in this fashion by one who,
whatever he may have been in the past, is obviously not now
in the prime of his faculties."

With a gasp the secretary thought: 'I knew that was a plain-
spoken man!'

He heard again the rumbling beside him. The chairman had
gone crimson, his mouth was pursed, his little eyes were very
blue.

"Help me up," he said.

The secretary helped him, and waited, rather breathless.

The chairman took a sip of water, and his voice, unexpectedly
loud, broke an ominous hush:

"Never been so insulted in my life. My best services have
been at your disposal for nineteen years; you know what measure of success this Company has attained. I am the oldest man
here, and my experience of shipping is, I hope, a little greater
than that of the two gentlemen who spoke last. I have done my
best for you, ladies and gentlemen, and we shall see whether
you are going to endorse an indictment of my judgment and of
my honour, if I am to take the last speaker seriously. This
purchase is for your good. 'There is a tide in the affairs of
men'—and I for one am not content, never have been, to stag-
nate. If that is what you want, however, by all means give
your support to these gentlemen and have done with it. I tell
you freights will go up before the end of the year; the purchase
is a sound one, more than a sound one—I, at any rate, stand or
fall by it. Refuse to ratify it, if you like; if you do, I shall
resign."

He sank back into his seat. The secretary, stealing a glance,
thought with a sort of enthusiasm: 'Bravo! Who'd have
thought he could rally his voice like that? A good touch, too,

about his honour! I believe he's knocked them. It's still dicky, though, if that fellow at the back gets up again; the old chap can't work that stop a second time.' Ah! here was 'old Apple-pie' on his hind legs. That was all right!

"I do not hesitate to say that I am an old friend of the chairman; we are, many of us, old friends of the chairman, and it has been painful to me, and I doubt not to others, to hear an attack made on him. If he is old in body, he is young in mental vigour and courage. I wish we were all as young. We ought to stand by him; I say, we ought to stand by him." ("Hear, hear! Hear, hear!") And the secretary thought: 'That's done it!' And he felt a sudden odd emotion, watching the chairman bobbing his body, like a wooden toy, at old Apple-by; and old Appleby bobbing back. Then, seeing a shareholder close to the door get up, thought: 'Who's that? I know his face—Ah! yes; Ventnor, the solicitor—he's one of the chairman's creditors that are coming again this afternoon. What now?'

"I can't agree that we ought to let sentiment interfere with our judgment in this matter. The question is simply: How are our pockets going to be affected? I came here with some misgivings, but the attitude of the chairman has been such as to remove them; and I shall support the proposition." The secretary thought: 'That's all right—only, he said it rather queerly—rather queerly.'

Then, after a long silence, the chairman, without rising, said:

"I move the adoption of the report and accounts."

"I second that."

"Those in favour signify the same in the usual way. Contrary? Carried." The secretary noted the dissentients, six in number, and that Mr. Westgate did not vote.

A quarter of an hour later he stood in the body of the emptying room supplying names to one of the gentlemen of the Press.

The passionless fellow said: "Haythorp, with an 'a'; oh! an 'e'; he seems an old man. Thank you. I may have the slips? Would you like to see a proof? With an 'a' you said —oh! an 'e' Good afternoon!" And the secretary thought: 'Those fellows, what *does* go on inside them? Fancy not knowing the old chairman by now!' . . .

2 §

Back in the proper office of "The Island Navigation Company" old Heythorp sat smoking a cigar and smiling like a purring cat. He was dreaming a little of his triumph, sifting with his old brain, still subtle, the wheat from the chaff of the demurrers: Westgate—nothing in that—professional discontent till they silenced him with a place on the Board—but not while *he* held the reins! That chap at the back—an ill-conditioned fellow! "Something behind!" Suspicious brute! There *was* something—but—hang it! they might think themselves lucky to get four ships at that price, and all due to him! It was on the last speaker that his mind dwelt with a doubt. That fellow Ventnor, to whom he owed money—there had been something just a little queer about his tone—as much as to say, "I smell a rat." Well! one would see that at the creditors' meeting in half an hour.

"Mr. Pillin, sir."

"Show him in!"

In a fur coat which seemed to extinguish his thin form, Joe Pillin entered. It was snowing, and the cold had nipped and yellowed his meagre face between its slight grey whiskering. He said thinly:

"How are you, Sylvanus? Aren't you perished in this cold?"

"Warm as toast. Sit down. Take off your coat."

"Oh! I should be lost without it. You must have a fire inside you. So—so it's gone through?"

Old Heythorp nodded; and Joe Pillin, wandering like a spirit, scrutinised the shut door. He came back to the table, and said in a low voice:

"It's a great sacrifice."

Old Heythorp smiled.

"Have you signed the deed poll?"

Producing a parchment from his pocket Joe Pillin unfolded it with caution to disclose his signature, and said:

"I don't like it—it's irrevocable."

A chuckle escaped old Heythorp.

"As death."

Joe Pillin's voice passed up into the treble clef.

" I can't bear irrevocable things. I consider you stampeded me, playing on my nerves."

Examining the signatures old Heythorp murmured:

" Tell your lawyer to lock it up. He must think you a sad dog, Joe."

" Ah! Suppose on my death it comes to the knowledge of my wife!"

" She won't be able to make it hotter for you than you'll be already."

Joe Pillin replaced the deed within his coat, emitting a queer thin noise. He simply could not bear joking on such subjects.

" Well," he said, " you've got your way; you always do. Who is this Mrs. Larne? You oughtn't to keep me in the dark. It seems my boy met her at your house. You told me she didn't come there."

Old Heythorp said with relish:

" Her husband was my son by a woman I was fond of before I married; her children are my grandchildren. You've provided for them. Best thing you ever did."

" I don't know—I don't know. I'm sorry you told me. It makes it all the more doubtful. As soon as the transfer's complete, I shall get away abroad. This cold's killing me. I wish you'd give me your recipe for keeping warm."

" Get a new inside."

Joe Pillin regarded his old friend with a sort of yearning. " And yet," he said, " I suppose, with your full-blooded habit, your life hangs by a thread, doesn't it?"

" A stout one, my boy!"

" Well, good-bye, Sylvanus. You're a Job's comforter; I must be getting home." He put on his hat, and, lost in his fur coat, passed out into the corridor. On the stairs he met a man who said:

" How do you do, Mr. Pillin? I know your son. Been seeing the chairman? I see your sale's gone through all right. I hope that'll do us some good, but I suppose you think the other way?"

Peering at him from under his hat, Joe Pillin said:

" Mr. Ventnor, I think? Thank you! It's very cold, isn't it?" And, with that cautious remark, he passed on down.

Alone again, old Heythorp thought: ' By George! What a wavering, quavering, thread-paper of a fellow! What misery

life must be to a chap like that! He walks in fear—he wal-
lows in it. Poor devil!' And a curious feeling swelled his
heart, of elation, of lightness such as he had not known for
years. Those two young things were safe now from penury—
safe! After dealing with those infernal creditors of his he
would go round and have a look at the children. With a hundred and twenty a year the boy could go into the Army—best
place for a young scamp like that. The girl would go off like
hot cakes, of course, but she needn't take the first calf that
came along. As for their mother, she must look after herself;
nothing under two thousand a year would keep *her* out of debt.
But trust her for wheedling and bluffing her way out of any
scrape! Watching his cigar-smoke curl and disperse he was
conscious of the strain he had been under these last six weeks,
aware suddenly of how greatly he had baulked at thought of
to-day's general meeting. Yes! It might have turned out
nasty. He knew well enough the forces on the Board, and off,
who would be only too glad to shelve him. If he were shelved
here his other two Companies would be sure to follow suit, and
bang would go every penny of his income—he would be a pauper
dependent on that holy woman. Well! Safe now for another
year if he could stave off these sharks once more. It might be
a harder job this time, but he was in luck—in luck, and it must
hold. And taking a luxurious pull at his cigar, he rang the
handbell.

"Bring 'em in here, Mr. Farney. And let me have a cup
of China tea as strong as you can make it."

"Yes, sir. Will you see the proof of the press report, or will
you leave it to me?"

"To you."

"Yes, sir. It was a good meeting, wasn't it?"

Old Heythorp nodded.

"Wonderful how your voice came back just at the right
moment. I was afraid things were going to be difficult. The
insult did it, I think. It was a monstrous thing to say. I
could have punched his head."

Again old Heythorp nodded; and, looking into the secretary's
fine blue eyes, he repeated: "Bring 'em in."

The lonely minute before the entrance of his creditors passed
in the thought: 'So that's how it struck him! Short shrift
I should get if it came out.'

The gentlemen, who numbered ten this time, bowed to their

debtor, evidently wondering why the deuce they troubled to be polite to an old man who kept them out of their money. Then, the secretary reappearing with a cup of China tea, they watched while their debtor drank it. The feat was tremulous. Would he get through without spilling it all down his front, or choking? To those unaccustomed to his private life it was slightly miraculous. He put the cup down empty, tremblingly removed some yellow drops from the little white tuft below his lip, relit his cigar, and said:

" No use beating about the bush, gentlemen; I can offer you fourteen hundred a year so long as I live and hold my director-ships, and not a penny more. If you can't accept that, you must make me bankrupt and get about sixpence in the pound. My qualifying shares will fetch a couple of thousand at market price. I own nothing else. The house I live in, and every-thing in it, barring my clothes, my wine, and my cigars, belong to my daughter under a settlement fifteen years old. My solici-tors and bankers will give you every information. That's the position in a nutshell."

In spite of business habits the surprise of the ten gentlemen was only partially concealed. A man who owed them so much would naturally say he owned nothing, but would he refer them to his solicitors and bankers unless he were telling the truth? Then Mr. Ventnor said:

" Will you submit your pass books? "

" No, but I'll authorise my bankers to give you a full state-ment of my receipts for the last five years—longer, if you like."

The strategic stroke of placing the ten gentlemen round the Board table had made it impossible for them to consult freely without being overheard, but the low-voiced transference of thought travelling round was summed up at last by Mr. Brownbee.

" We think, Mr. Heythorp, that your fees and dividends should enable you to set aside for us a larger sum. Sixteen hundred, in fact, is what we think you should give us yearly. Representing, as we do, sixteen thousand pounds, the prospect is not cheering, but we hope you have some good years before you yet. We understand your income to be two thousand pounds."

Old Heythorp shook his head. " Nineteen hundred and thirty pounds in a good year. Must eat and drink; must have a man to look after me—not as active as I was. Can't do on less than five hundred pounds. Fourteen hundred's all I can give you, gentlemen; it's an advance of two hundred pounds. That's my last word."

The silence was broken by Mr. Ventnor.

"And it's my last word that I'm not satisfied. If these other gentlemen accept your proposition I shall be forced to consider what I can do on my own account."

The old man stared at him, and answered:

"Oh! you will, sir; we shall see."

The others had risen and were gathered in a knot at the end of the table; old Heythorp and Mr. Ventnor alone remained seated. The old man's lower lip projected till the white hairs below stood out like bristles. 'You ugly dog,' he was thinking, 'you think you've got something up your sleeve. Well, do your worst!' The "ugly dog" rose abruptly and joined the others. And old Heythorp closed his eyes, sitting perfectly still, with his cigar, which had gone out, sticking up between his teeth. Mr. Brownbee turning to voice the decision come to, cleared his throat.

"Mr. Heythorp," he said, "if your bankers and solicitors bear out your statements, we shall accept your offer *faute de mieux,* in consideration of your——" but meeting the old man's eyes, which said so very plainly: "Blow your consideration!" he ended with a stammer: "Perhaps you will kindly furnish us with the authorisation you spoke of?"

Old Heythorp nodded, and Mr. Brownbee, with a little bow, clasped his hat to his breast and moved towards the door. The nine gentlemen followed. Mr. Ventnor, bringing up the rear, turned and looked back. But the old man's eyes were already closed again.

The moment his creditors were gone, old Heythorp sounded the hand-bell.

"Help me up, Mr. Farney. That Ventnor—what's his holding?"

"Quite small. Only ten shares, I think."

"Ah! What time is it?"

"Quarter to four, sir."

"Get me a taxi."

After visiting his bank and his solicitors he struggled once more into his cab and caused it to be driven towards Millicent Villas. A kind of sleepy triumph permeated his whole being, bumped and shaken by the cab's rapid progress. So! He was

free of those sharks now so long as he could hold on to his
Companies; and he would still have a hundred a year or more
to spare for Rosamund and her youngsters. He could live on
four hundred, or even three-fifty, without losing his independence, for there would be no standing life in that holy woman's
house unless he could pay his own scot! A good day's work!
The best for many a long month!

The cab stopped before the villa.

3 §

There are rooms which refuse to give away their owners, and
rooms which seem to say: 'They really are like this.' Of
such was Rosamund Larne's—a sort of permanent confession,
seeming to remark to anyone who entered: 'Her taste? Well,
you can see—cheerful and exuberant; her habits—yes, she sits
here all the morning in a dressing-gown, smoking cigarettes and
dropping ink; kindly observe my carpet. Notice the piano—it
has a look of coming and going, according to the exchequer.
This very deep-cushioned sofa is permanent, however; the water-
colours on the walls are safe, too—they're by herself. Mark the
scent of mimosa—she likes flowers, and likes them strong. No
clock, of course. Examine the bureau—she is obviously always
ringing for "the drumstick," and saying: "Where's this,
Ellen, and where's that? You naughty gairl, you've been tidy-
ing." Cast an eye on that pile of manuscript—she has evidently a genius for composition; it flows off her pen—like
Shakespeare, she never blots a line. See how she's had the
electric light put in, instead of that horrid gas; but try and
turn either of them on—you can't; last quarter isn't paid, of
course; and she uses an oil lamp, you can tell that by the ceiling.
The dog over there, who will not answer to the name of " Carmen," a Pekinese spaniel like a little Djin, all prominent eyes
rolling their blacks, and no nose between—yes, Carmen looks
as if she didn't know what was coming next; she's right—it's a
pet-and-slap-again life! Consider, too, the fittings of the tea-
tray, rather soiled, though not quite tin, but I say unto you
that no millionaire's in all its glory ever had a liqueur bottle
on it.'

When old Heythorp entered this room, which extended from
back to front of the little house, preceded by the announcement

"Mr. Æsop," it was resonant with a very clatter-bodandigo
of noises, from Phyllis playing the Machiche; from the boy
Jock on the hearthrug, emitting at short intervals the most
piercing notes from an ocarina; from Mrs. Larne on the sofa,
talking with her trailing volubility to Bob Pillin; from Bob
Pillin muttering: "Ye—es! Qui—ite! Ye—es!" and gazing
at Phyllis over his collar. And, on the window-sill, as far as
she could get from all this noise, the little dog Carmen was
rolling her eyes. At sight of their visitor Jock blew one rend-
ing screech, and bolting behind the sofa, placed his chin on its
top, so that nothing but his round pink unmoving face was
visible, and the dog Carmen tried to climb the blind cord.

Encircled from behind by the arms of Phyllis, and preceded
by the gracious perfumed bulk of Mrs. Larne, old Heythorp
was escorted to the sofa. It was low, and when he had plumped
down on to it, the boy Jock emitted a hollow groan. Bob
Pillin was the first to break the silence.

"How are you, sir? I hope it's gone through."

Old Heythorp nodded. His eyes were fixed on the liqueur,
and Mrs. Larne murmured:

"Guardy, you *must* try our new liqueur. Jock, you awful
boy, get up and bring Guardy a glass."

The boy Jock approached the tea-table, took up a glass, put
it to his eye and filled it rapidly.

"You horrible boy, you could see that glass has been used."

In a high round voice rather like an angel's, Jock answered:

"All right, Mother; I'll get rid of it," and rapidly swallowing the yellow liqueur, took up another glass.

Mrs. Larne laughed.

"What *am* I to do with him?"

A loud shriek prevented a response. Phyllis, who had taken
her brother by the ear to lead him to the door, let him go to
clasp her injured self. Bob Pillin went hastening towards her;
and following the young man with her chin, Mrs. Larne said,
smiling:

"Aren't those children awful? He's such a nice fellow. We
like him so much, Guardy."

The old man grinned. So she was making up to that young
pup! Rosamund Larne, watching him, murmured:

"Oh! Guardy, you're as bad as Jock. He takes after you
terribly. Look at the shape of his head. Jock, come here!"

The innocent boy approached: with his girlish complexion, his flowery blue eyes, his perfect mouth, he stood before his mother like a large cherub. And suddenly he blew his ocarina in a dreadful manner. Mrs. Larne launched a box at his ears, and receiving the wind of it he fell prone.

"That's the way he behaves. Be off with you, you awful boy. I want to talk to Guardy."

The boy withdrew on his stomach, and sat against the wall cross-legged, fixing his innocent round eyes on old Heythorp. Mrs. Larne sighed.

"Things are worse and worse, Guardy. I'm at my wits' end to tide over this quarter. You wouldn't advance me a hundred on my new story? I'm sure to get two for it in the end."

The old man shook his head.

"I've done something for you and the children," he said. "You'll get notice of it in a day or two; ask no questions."

"Oh! Guardy! Oh! you dear!" And her gaze rested on Bob Pillin, leaning over the piano, where Phyllis again sat.

Old Heythorp snorted. "What are you cultivating that young gaby for? She mustn't be grabbed up by any fool who comes along."

Mrs. Larne murmured at once:

"Of course, the dear gairl is *much* too young. Phyllis, come and talk to Guardy!"

When the girl was installed beside him on the sofa, and he had felt that little thrill of warmth the proximity of youth can bring, he said:

"Been a good girl?"

She shook her head.

"Can't when Jock's not at school. Mother can't pay for him this term."

Hearing his name, the boy Jock blew his ocarina till Mrs. Larne drove him from the room, and Phyllis went on:

"He's more awful than anything you can think of. Was my dad at all like him, Guardy? Mother's always so mysterious about him. I suppose you knew him well."

Old Heythorp, incapable of confusion, answered stolidly:

"Not very."

"Who was *his* father? I don't believe even mother knows."

"Man about town in my day."

"Oh! your day must have been jolly. Did you wear peg-top trousers, and dundrearies?"

Old Heythorp nodded.

"What larks! And I suppose you had lots of adventures with opera dancers and gambling. The young men are all so good now." Her eyes rested on Bob Pillin. "That young man's a perfect stick of goodness."

Old Heythorp grunted.

"You wouldn't know how good he was," Phyllis went on musingly, "unless you'd sat next him in a tunnel. The other day he had his waist squeezed and he simply sat still and did nothing. And then when the tunnel ended, it was Jock after all, not me. His face was—Oh! ah! ha! ha! Ah! ha!" She threw back her head, displaying all her white, round throat. Then edging near, she whispered:

"He likes to pretend, of course, that he's fearfully lively. He's promised to take mother and me to the theatre and supper afterwards. Won't it be scrummy! Only, I haven't anything to go in."

Old Heythorp said: "What do you want? Irish poplin?"

Her mouth opened wide: "Oh! Guardy! Soft white satin!"

"How many yards'll go round you?"

"I should think about twelve. We could make it ourselves. You *are* a chook!"

A scent of hair, like hay, enveloped him, her lips bobbed against his nose, and there came a feeling in his heart as when he rolled the first sip of a special wine against his palate. This little house was a rumpty-too affair, her mother was a humbug, the boy a cheeky young rascal, but there was a warmth here he never felt in that big house which had been his wife's and was now his holy daughter's. And once more he rejoiced at his day's work, and the success of his breach of trust, which put some little ground beneath these young feet, in a hard and unscrupulous world. Phyllis whispered in his ear:

"Guardy, do look; he *will* stare at me like that. Isn't it awful—like a boiled rabbit?"

Bob Pillin, attentive to Mrs. Larne, was gazing with all his might over her shoulder at the girl. The young man was moonstruck, that was clear! There was something almost touching in the stare of those puppy dog's eyes. And he thought: 'Young beggar—wish I were his age!' The utter injustice of having an old and helpless body, when your desire for enjoyment was as great as ever! They said a man was as old as he felt! Fools! A man was as old as his legs and arms, and not a day younger. He heard the girl beside him utter a discomfortable sound, and saw her face cloud as if tears were not far off; she jumped up, and going to the window, lifted the little dog and buried her face in its brown and white fur. Old Heythorp thought: 'She sees that her humbugging mother is using her as a decoy.' But she had come back, and the little dog, rolling its eyes horribly at the strange figure on the sofa, in a desperate effort to escape succeeded in reaching her shoulder, where it stayed perched like a cat, held by one paw and trying to back away into space. Old Heythorp said abruptly:

"Are you very fond of your mother?"

"Of course I am, Guardy. I adore her."

"H'm! Listen to me. When you come of age or marry, you'll have a hundred and twenty a year of your own that you can't get rid of. Don't ever be persuaded into doing what you don't want. And remember: Your mother's a sieve, no good giving her money; keep what you'll get for yourself—it's only a pittance, and you'll want it all—every penny."

Phyllis's eyes had opened very wide; so that he wondered if she had taken in his words.

"Oh! Isn't money horrible, Guardy?"

"The want of it."

"No, it's beastly altogether. If only we were like birds. Or if one could put out a plate overnight, and have just enough in the morning to use during the day."

Old Heythorp sighed.

"There's only one thing in life that matters—independence. Lose that, and you lose everything. That's the value of money. Help me up."

Phyllis stretched out her hands, and the little dog, running down her back, resumed its perch on the windowsill, close to the blind cord.

Once on his feet, old Heythorp said:

"Give me a kiss. You'll have your satin to-morrow."

Then looking at Bob Pillin, he remarked:

"Going my way? I'll give you a lift."

The young man, giving Phyllis one appealing look, answered dully: "Tha—anks!" and they went out together to the taxi. In that draughtless vehicle they sat, full of who knows what contempt of age for youth, and youth for age; the old man resenting this young pup's aspiration to his granddaughter; the

young man annoyed that this old image had dragged him away
before he wished to go. Old Heythorp said at last:

"Well?"

Thus expected to say something, Bob Pillin muttered:

"Glad your meetin' went off well, sir. You scored a triumph
I should think."

"Why?"

"Oh! I don't know. I thought you had a good bit of
opposition to contend with."

Old Heythorp looked at him.

"Your grandmother!" he said; then, with his habitual instinct of attack, added: "You make the most of your opportunities, I see."

At this rude assault Bob Pillin's red-cheeked face assumed
a certain dignity. "I don't know what you mean, sir. Mrs.
Larne is very kind to me."

"No doubt. But don't try to pick the flowers."

Thoroughly upset, Bob Pillin preserved a dogged silence.
This fortnight, since he had first met Phyllis in old Heythorp's
hall, had been the most singular of his existence up to now. He
would never have believed that a fellow could be so quickly
and completely bowled, could succumb without a kick, without
even wanting to kick. To one with his philosophy of having a
good time and never committing himself too far, it was in the
nature of "a fair knock-out," and yet so pleasurable, except
for the wear and tear about one's chances. If only he knew
how far the old boy really counted in the matter! To say:
"My intentions are strictly honourable" would be old-fashioned;
besides—the old fellow might have no right to hear it. They
called him Guardy, but without knowing more he did not want
to admit the old curmudgeon's right to interfere.

"Are you a relation of theirs, sir?"

Old Heythorp nodded.

Bob Pillin went on with desperation:

"I should like to know what your objection to me is."

The old man turned his head so far as he was able; a grim
smile bristled the hairs about his lips, and twinkled in his eyes.
What did he object to? Why—everything! Object to! That
sleek head, those puppy-dog eyes, fattish red cheeks, high
collars, pearl pin, spats, and drawl—pah! the imbecility, the
smugness of his mug; no go, no devil in any of his sort, in any

of these fish-veined, coddled-up young bloods, nothing but playing for safety! And he wheezed out:

" Milk and water masquerading as port wine."

Bob Pillin frowned.

It was almost too much for the composure even of a man of the world. That this paralytic old fellow should express contempt for his virility was really the last thing in jests. Luckily he could not take it seriously. But suddenly he thought: ' What if he really has the power to stop my going there, and means to turn them against me!' And his heart quailed.

" Awfully sorry, sir," he said, " if you don't think I'm wild enough. Anything I can do for you in that line——"

The old man grunted; and realising that he had been quite witty, Bob Pillin went on:

" I know I'm not in debt, no entanglements, got a decent income, pretty good expectations and all that; but I can soon put that all right if I'm not fit without."

It was perhaps his first attempt at irony, and he could not help thinking how good it was.

But old Heythorp preserved a deadly silence. He looked like a stuffed man, a regular Aunt Sally sitting there, with the fixed red in his cheeks, his stivered hair, square block of a body, and no neck that you could see—only wanting the pipe in his mouth! Could there really be danger from such an old idol? The idol spoke:

" I'll give you a word of advice. Don't hang round there, or you'll burn your fingers. Remember me to your father. Goodnight!"

The taxi had stopped before the house in Sefton Park. An insensate impulse to remain seated and argue the point fought in Bob Pillin with an impulse to leap out, shake his fist in at the window, and walk off. He merely said, however:

" Thanks for the lift. Good-night!" And, getting out deliberately, he walked off.

Old Heythorp, waiting for the driver to help him up, thought: ' Fatter, but no more guts than his father!'

In his sanctum he sank at once into his chair. It was wonderfully still there every day at this hour; just the click of the coals, just the faintest ruffle from the wind in the trees of the park. And it was cosily warm, only the fire lightening the darkness. A drowsy beatitude pervaded the old man. A good day's work! A triumph—that young pup had said. Yes!

Something of a triumph! He had held on, and won. And
dinner to look forward to, yet. A nap—a nap! And soon,
rhythmic, soft, sonorous, his breathing rose, with now and then
that pathetic twitching of the old who dream.

III

I §

When Bob Pillin emerged from the little front garden of 23,
Millicent Villas ten days later, his sentiments were ravelled,
and he could not get hold of an end to pull straight the stuff
of his mind.

He had found Mrs. Larne and Phyllis in the sitting-room,
and Phyllis had been crying; he was sure she had been crying;
and that memory still infected the sentiments evoked by later
happenings. Old Heythorp had said: " You'll burn your
fingers." The process had begun. Having sent her daughter
away on a pretext really a bit too thin, Mrs. Larne had installed
him beside her scented bulk on the sofa, and poured into his
ear such a tale of monetary woe and entanglement, such a mass
of present difficulties and rosy prospects, that his brain still
whirled, and only one thing emerged clearly—that she wanted
fifty pounds, which she would repay him on quarter-day; for
their Guardy had made a settlement by which, until the dear
children came of age, she would have sixty pounds every
quarter. It was only a question of a few weeks; he might ask
Messrs. Scriven and Coles; they would tell him the security
was quite safe. He certainly might ask Messrs. Scriven and
Coles—they happened to be his father's solicitors; but it hardly
seemed to touch the point. Bob Pillin had a certain shrewd caution, and the point was whether he was going to begin to lend
money to a woman who, he could see, might borrow up to seventy
times seven on the strength of his infatuation for her daughter.
That was rather too strong! Yet, if he didn't—she might take a
sudden dislike to him, and where would he be then? Besides,
would not a loan make his position stronger? And then—such
is the effect of love even on the younger generation—that
thought seemed to him unworthy. If he lent at all, it should
be from chivalry—ulterior motives might go hang! And the
memory of the tear-marks on Phyllis's pretty pale-pink cheeks;

and her petulantly mournful: "Oh! young man, isn't money beastly!" scraped his heart, and ravished his judgment. All the same, fifty pounds was fifty pounds, and goodness knew how much more; and what did he know of Mrs. Larne, after all, except that she was a relative of old Heythorp's and wrote stories—told them too, if he was not mistaken? Perhaps it would be better to see Scrivens'. But again that absurd nobility assaulted him. Phyllis! Phyllis! Besides, were not settlements always drawn so that they refused to form security for anything? Thus, hampered and troubled, he hailed a cab. He was dining with the Ventnors on the Cheshire side, and would be late if he didn't get home sharp to dress.

Driving, white-tied and waistcoated, in his father's car, he thought with a certain contumely of the younger Ventnor girl, whom he had been wont to consider pretty before he knew Phyllis. And seated next her at dinner, he quite enjoyed his new sense of superiority to her charms, and the ease with which he could chaff and be agreeable. And all the time he suffered from the suppressed longing which scarcely ever left him now, to think and talk of Phyllis. Ventnor's fizz was good and plentiful, his old Madeira absolutely first chop, and the only other man present a teetotal curate, who withdrew with the ladies to talk his parish shop. Favoured by these circumstances, and the perception that Ventnor was an agreeable fellow, Bob Pillin yielded to his secret itch to get near the subject of his affections.

"Do you happen," he said airily, "to know a Mrs. Larne— relative of old Heythorp's—rather a handsome woman—she writes stories."

Mr. Ventnor shook his head. A closer scrutiny than Bob Pillin's would have seen that he also moved his ears.

"Of old Heythorp's? Didn't know he had any, except his daughter, and that son of his in the Admiralty."

Bob Pillin felt the glow of his secret hobby spreading within him.

"She is, though—lives rather out of town; got a son and daughter. I thought you might know her stories—clever woman."

Mr. Ventnor smiled.

"Ah!" he said enigmatically, "these lady novelists! Does she make any money by them?"

Bob Pillin knew that to make money by writing meant success, but that not to make money by writing was artistic, and implied that you had private means, which perhaps was even more distinguished. And he said:

" Oh! she has private means, I know."

Mr. Ventnor reached for the Madeira.

" So she's a relative of old Heythorp's," he said. " He's a very old friend of your father's. He ought to go bankrupt, you know."

To Bob Pillin, glowing with passion and Madeira, the idea of bankruptcy seemed discreditable in connection with a relative of Phyllis. Besides, the old boy was far from that! Had he not just made this settlement on Mrs. Larne? And he said:

" I think you're mistaken. That's of the past."

Mr. Ventnor smiled.

" Will you bet? " he said.

Bob Pillin also smiled. " I should be bettin' on a certainty."

Mr. Ventnor passed his hand over his whiskered face. " Don't you believe it; he hasn't a mag to his name. Fill your glass."

Bob Pillin said, with a certain resentment:

" Well, I happen to know he's just made a settlement of five or six thousand pounds. Don't know if you call that being bankrupt."

" What! On this Mrs. Larne? "

Confused, uncertain whether he had said something derogatory or indiscreet, or something which added distinction to Phyllis, Bob Pillin hesitated, then gave a nod.

Mr. Ventnor rose and extended his short legs before the fire.

" No, my boy," he said. " No! "

Unaccustomed to flat contradiction, Bob Pillin reddened.

" I'll bet you a tenner. Ask Scrivens'."

Mr. Ventnor ejaculated:

" Scrivens'—but they're not——" then, staring rather hard he added: " I won't bet. You may be right. Scrivens' are your father's solicitors too, aren't they? Always been sorry he didn't come to me. Shall we join the ladies? " And to the drawing-room he preceded a young man more uncertain in his mind than on his feet. . . .

Charles Ventnor was not one to let you see that more was going on within than met the eye. But there was a good deal going on that evening, and after his conversation with young Bob he had occasion more than once to turn away and rub his hands together. When, after that second creditors' meeting,

he had walked down the stairway which led to the offices of
" The Island Navigation Company," he had been deep in
thought. Short, squarely built, rather stout, with moustache and
large mutton-chop whiskers of a red-brown, and a faint floridity
in face and dress, he impressed at first sight only by a certain
truly British vulgarity. One felt that here was a hail-fellow-
well-met man who liked lunch and dinner,went to Scarborough
for his summer holidays, sat on his wife, took his daughters
out in a boat and was never sick. One felt that he went to
church every Sunday morning, looked upwards as he moved
through life, disliked the unsuccessful, and expanded with his
second glass of wine. But then a clear look into his well-
clothed face and red-brown eyes would give the feeling : ' There's
something fulvous here; he might be a bit too foxy.' A third
look brought the thought : ' He's certainly a bully.' He was
not a large creditor of old Heythorp. With interest on the
original, he calculated his claim at three hundred pounds—
unredeemed shares in that old Ecuador mine. But he had
waited for his money eight years, and could never imagine how
it came about that he had been induced to wait so long. There
had been, of course, for one who liked " big pots," a certain
glamour about the personality of old Heythorp, still a bit of a
swell in shipping circles, and a bit of an aristocrat in Liverpool. But during the last year Charles Ventnor had realised
that the old chap's star had definitely set—when that happens,
of course, there is no more glamour, and the time has come to
get your money. Weakness in oneself and others is despicable !
Besides, he had food for thought, and descending the stairs he
chewed it. He smelt a rat—creatures for which both by nature
and profession he had a nose. Through Bob Pillin, on whom he
sometimes dwelt in connection with his younger daughter, he
knew that old Pillin and old Heythorp had been friends for
thirty years and more. That, to an astute mind, suggested
something behind this sale. The thought had already occurred
to him when he read his copy of the report. A commission
would be a breach of trust, of course, but there were ways of
doing things; the old chap was devilish hard pressed, and human nature was human nature ! His lawyerish mind habitually
put two and two together. The old fellow had deliberately appointed to meet his creditors again just after the general meeting which would decide the purchase—had said he might do
something for them then. Had that no significance?

In these circumstances Charles Ventnor had come to the meeting with eyes wide open and mouth tight closed. And he had watched. It was certainly remarkable that such an old and feeble man with no neck at all, who looked indeed as if he might go off with apoplexy any moment, should actually say that he " stood or fell " by this purchase, knowing that if he fell he would be a beggar. Why should the old chap be so keen on getting it through? It would do him personally no good, unless—Exactly! He had left the meeting, therefore, secretly confident that old Heythorp had got something out of this transaction which would enable him to make a substantial proposal to his creditors. So that when the old man had declared that he was going to make none, something had turned sour in his heart, and he had said to himself: " All right, you old rascal! You don't know C. V." The cavalier manner of that beggarly old rip, the defiant look of his deep little eyes, had put a polish on the rancour of one who prided himself on letting no man get the better of him. All that evening, seated on one side of the fire, while Mrs. Ventnor sat on the other, and the younger daughter played Gounod's Serenade on the violin—he cogitated. And now and again he smiled, but not too much. He did not see his way as yet, but had little doubt that before long he would. It would not be hard to knock that chipped old idol off his perch. There was already a healthy feeling among the shareholders that he was past work and should be scrapped. The old chap should find that Charles V. was not to be defied; that when he got his teeth into a thing, he did not let it go. By hook or crook he would have the old man off his Boards, or his debt out of him as the price of leaving him alone. His life or his money—and the old fellow should determine which. With the memory of that defiance fresh within him, he almost hoped it might come to be the first, and turning to Mrs. Ventnor, he said abruptly:

" Have a little dinner Friday week, and ask young Pillin and the curate." He specified the curate, a teetotaller, because he had two daughters, and males and females must be paired, but he intended to pack him off after dinner to the drawing-room to discuss parish matters while he and Bob Pillin sat over their wine. What he expected to get out of the young man he did not as yet know.

On the day of the dinner, before departing for the office, he had gone to his cellar. Would three bottles of Perrier Jouet do the trick, or must he add one of the old Madeira? He decided to be on the safe side. A bottle or so of champagne went very little way with him personally, and young Pillin might be another.

The Madeira having done its work by turning the conversation into such an admirable channel, he had cut it short for fear young Pillin might drink the lot or get wind of the rat. And when his guests were gone, and his family had retired, he stood staring into the fire, putting together the pieces of the puzzle. Five or six thousand pounds—six would be ten per cent. on sixty! Exactly! Scrivens'—young Pillin had said! But Crow & Donkin, not Scriven & Coles, were old Heythorp's solicitors. What could that mean, save that the old man wanted to cover the tracks of a secret commission, and had handled the matter through solicitors who did not know the state of his affairs! But why Pillin's solicitors? With this sale just going through, it must look deuced fishy to them too. Was it all a mare's nest, after all? In such circumstances he himself would have taken the matter to a London firm who knew nothing of anybody. Puzzled, therefore, and rather disheartened, feeling too that touch of liver which was wont to follow his old Madeira, he went up to bed and woke his wife to ask her why the dickens they couldn't always have soup like that!

Next day he continued to brood over his puzzle, and no fresh light came; but having a matter on which his firm and Scrivens' were in touch, he decided to go over in person, and see if he could surprise something out of them. Feeling, from experience, that any really delicate matter would only be entrusted to the most responsible member of the firm, he had asked to see Scriven himself, and just as he had taken his hat to go, he said casually:

"By the way, you do some business for old Mr. Heythorp, don't you?"

Scriven, raising his eyebrows a little, muttered: "Er—no," in exactly the tone Mr. Ventnor himself used when he wished to imply that though he didn't as a fact do business, he probably soon would. He knew therefore that the answer was a true one. And nonplussed, he hazarded:

"Oh! I thought you did, in regard to a Mrs. Larne."

This time he had certainly drawn blood of sorts, for down came Scriven's eyebrows, and he said:

" Mrs. Larne—we know a Mrs. Larne, but not in that connection. Why?"

" Oh! Young Pillin told me——"

" Young Pillin? Why, it's his——!" A little pause, and then: " Old Mr. Heythorp's solicitors are Crow & Donkin, I believe."

Mr. Ventnor held out his hand. " Yes, yes," he said; " goodbye. Glad to have got that matter settled up," and out he went, and down the street, important, smiling. By George! He had got it! " It's his father"—Scriven had been going to say. What a plant! Exactly! Oh! neat! Old Pillin had made the settlement direct; and the solicitors were in the dark; that disposed of his difficulty about *them*. No money had passed between old Pillin and old Heythorp—not a penny. Oh! neat! But not neat enough for Charles Ventnor, who had that nose for rats. Then his smile died, and with a little chill he perceived that it was all based on supposition—not quite good enough to go on! What then? Somehow he must see this Mrs. Larne, or better—old Pillin himself. The point to ascertain was whether she had any connection of her own with Pillin. Clearly young Pillin didn't know of it; for, according to him, old Heythorp had made the settlement. By Jove! That old rascal was deep—all the more satisfaction in proving that he was not as deep as C. V. To unmask the old cheat was already beginning to seem in the nature of a public service. But on what pretext could he visit Pillin? A subscription to the Windeatt almshouses! That would make him talk in self-defence and he would take care to press the request to the actual point of getting a subscription. He caused himself to be driven to the Pillin residence in Sefton Park. Ushered into a room on the ground floor, heated in American fashion, Mr. Ventnor unbuttoned his coat. A man of sanguine constitution, he found this hot-house atmosphere a little trying. And having sympathetically obtained Joe Pillin's reluctant refusal—Quite so! One could not indefinitely extend one's subscriptions even for the best of causes!—he said gently:

" By the way, you know Mrs. Larne, don't you?"

The effect of that simple shot surpassed his highest hopes. Joe Pillin's face, never highly coloured, turned a sort of grey; he opened his thin lips, shut them quickly, as birds do, and something seemed to pass with difficulty down his scraggy throat. The hollows, which nerve exhaustion delves in the

cheeks of men whose cheek-bones are not high, increased alarmingly. For a moment he looked deathly; then, moistening his
lips, he said:

"Larne—Larne? No, I don't seem——"

Mr. Ventnor, who had taken care to be drawing on his
gloves, murmured:

"Oh! I thought—your son knows her; a relation of old Heythorp's," and he looked up.

Joe Pillin had his handkerchief to his mouth; he coughed
feebly, then with more and more vigour:

"I'm in very poor health," he said, at last. "I'm getting
abroad at once. This cold's killing me. What name did you
say?" And he remained with his handkerchief against his
teeth.

Mr. Ventnor repeated:

"Larne. Writes stories."

Joe Pillin muttered into his handkerchief:

"Ah! H'm! No—I—no! My son knows all sorts of people.
I shall have to try Mentone. Are you going? Good-bye!
Good-bye! I'm sorry; ah! ha! My cough—ah! ha h'h'm!
Very distressing. Ye-hes! My cough—ah! ha h'h'm! Most
distressing. Ye-hes!"

Out in the drive Mr. Ventnor took a deep breath of the frosty
air. Not much doubt now! The two names had worked like
charms. This weakly old fellow would make a pretty witness,
would simply crumple under cross-examination. What a con-
trast to that hoary old sinner Heythorp, whose brazenness nothing could affect. The rat was as large as life! And the only
point was how to make the best use of it. Then—for his experience was wide—the possibility dawned on him, that after
all, this Mrs. Larne might only have been old Pillin's mistress—or be his natural daughter, or have some other blackmailing hold on him. Any such connection would account for
his agitation, for his denying her, for his son's ignorance. Only
it wouldn't account for young Pillin's saying that old Heythorp
had made the settlement. He could only have got that from the
woman herself. Still, to make absolutely sure, he had better
try and see her. But how? It would never do to ask Bob Pillin
for an introduction, after this interview with his father. He
would have to go on his own and chance it. Wrote stories did
she? Perhaps a newspaper would know her address; or the
Directory would give it—not a common name! And, hot on

the scent, he drove to a post office. Yes, there it was, right
enough! "Larne, Mrs. R.—23, Millicent Villas." And thinking to himself: 'No time like the present,' he turned in that
direction. The job was delicate. He must be careful not to
do anything which might compromise his power of making public
use of his knowledge. Yes—ticklish! What he did now must
have a proper legal bottom. Still, anyway you looked at it, he
had a *right* to investigate a fraud on himself as a shareholder
of "The Island Navigation Company," and a fraud on himself
as a creditor of old Heythorp. Quite! But suppose this Mrs.
Larne was really entangled with old Pillin, and the settlement
a mere reward of virtue, easy or otherwise. Well! in that
case there'd be no secret commission to make public, and he
needn't go further. So that, in either event, he would be all
right. Only—how to introduce himself? He might pretend
he was a newspaper man wanting a story. No, that wouldn't
do! He must not represent that he was what he was not, in
case he had afterwards to justify his actions publicly, always
a difficult thing, if you were not careful! At that moment
there came into his mind a question Bob Pillin had asked the
other night. "By the way, you can't borrow on a settlement
can you? Isn't there generally some clause against it?" Had
this woman been trying to borrow from him on that settlement?
But at this moment he reached the house, and got out of his
cab still undecided as to how he was going to work the oracle.
Impudence, constitutional and professional, sustained him in
saying to the little maid:

"Mrs. Larne at home? Say Mr. Charles Ventnor, will you?"

His quick brown eyes took in the apparel of the passage which
served for hall—the deep blue paper on the walls, lilac-patterned
curtains over the doors, the well-known print of a nude young
woman looking over her shoulder, and he thought: 'H'm!
Distinctly tasty!' They noted, too, a small brown-and-white
dog cowering in terror at the very end of the passage, and he
murmured affably: "Fluffy! Come here, Fluffy!" till Carmen's teeth chattered in her head.

"Will you come in, sir?"

Mr. Ventnor ran his hand over his whiskers, and, entering a
room, was impressed at once by its air of domesticity. On a
sofa a handsome woman and a pretty young girl were surrounded
by sewing apparatus and some white material. The girl looked
up, but the elder lady rose.

Mr. Ventnor said easily:

"You know my young friend, Mr. Robert Pillin, I think." The lady, whose bulk and bloom struck him to the point of admiration, murmured in a full sweet drawl:

"Oh! Ye—es. Are you from Messrs. Scrivens'?"

With the swift reflection: 'As I thought!' Mr. Ventnor answered:

"Er—not exactly. I *am* a solicitor though; came just to ask about a certain settlement that Mr. Pillin tells me you're entitled under."

"Phyllis dear!"

Seeing the girl about to rise from underneath the white stuff, Mr. Ventnor said quickly:

"Pray don't disturb yourself—just a formality!" It had struck him at once that the lady would have to speak the truth in the presence of this third party, and he went on: "Quite recent, I think. This'll be your first interest—on six thousand pounds? Is that right?" And at the limpid assent of that rich, sweet voice, he thought: 'Fine woman; what eyes!'

"Thank you; that's quite enough. I can go to Scrivens' for any detail. Nice young fellow, Bob Pillin, isn't he?" He saw the girl's chin tilt, and Mrs. Larne's full mouth curling in a smile.

"Delightful young man; we're very fond of him."

And he proceeded:

"I'm quite an old friend of his; have you known him long?"

"Oh! no. How long, Phyllis, since we met him at Guardy's? About a month. But he's so unaffected—quite at home with us. A *nice* fellow."

Mr. Ventnor murmured:

"Very different from his father, isn't he?"

"Is he! We don't know his father; he's a shipowner, I think."

Mr. Ventnor rubbed his hands: "Ye—es," he said, "just giving up—a warm man. Young Pillin's a lucky fellow—only son. So you met him at old Mr. Heythorp's. I know him too—relation of yours, I believe."

"Our dear Guardy—such a wonderful man."

Mr. Ventnor echoed: "Wonderful—regular old Roman."

" Oh! but he's so *kind!* " Mrs. Larne lifted the white stuff:
" Look what he's given this naughty gairl! "

Mr. Ventnor murmured: " Charming! Charming! Bob
Pillin said, I think, that Mr. Heythorp was your settlor."

One of those little clouds which visit the brows of women
who have owed money in their time passed swiftly athwart
Mrs. Larne's eyes. For a moment they seemed saying: ' Don't
you want to know too much? ' Then they slid from under it.

" Won't you sit down? " she said. " You must forgive our
being at work."

Mr. Ventnor, who had need of sorting his impressions, shook
his head.

" Thank you; I must be getting on. Then Messrs. Scriven
can—a mere formality! Good-bye! Good-bye Miss Larne. I'm
sure the dress will be most becoming."

And with memories of a too clear look from the girl's eyes,
of a warm firm pressure from the woman's hand, Mr. Ventnor
backed towards the door and passed away just in time to avoid
hearing in two voices:

" What a nice lawyer! "

" What a horrid man! "

Back in his cab, he continued to rub his hands. No, she
didn't know old Pillin! That was certain; not from her words,
but from her face. She wanted to know him, or about him,
anyway. She was trying to hook young Bob for that sprig of a
girl—it was clear as mud. H'm! it would astonish his young
friend to hear that he had called. Well, let it! And a curious
mixture of emotions beset Mr. Ventnor. He saw the whole
thing now so plainly, and really could not refrain from a certain admiration. The law had been properly diddled! There
was nothing to prevent a man from settling money on a woman
he had never seen; and so old Pillin's settlement could probably
not be upset. But old Heythorp could. It was neat, though,
oh! neat! And that was a fine woman—remarkably! He had
a sort of feeling that if only the settlement had been in danger,
it might have been worth while to have made a bargain—a
woman like that could have made it worth while! And he believed her quite capable of entertaining the proposition! Her
eye! Pity—quite a pity! Mrs. Ventnor was not a wife who
satisfied every aspiration. But alas! the settlement was safe.
This baulking of the sentiment of love, whipped up, if anything,
the longing for justice in Mr. Ventnor. That old chap should

feel his teeth now. As a piece of investigation it was not so bad
—not so bad at all! He had had a bit of luck, of course—no,
not luck—just that knack of doing the right thing at the right
moment which marks a real genius for affairs.

But getting into his train to return to Mrs. Ventnor, he
thought: 'A woman like that would have been——!' And
he sighed.

2 §

With a neatly written cheque for fifty pounds in his pocket
Bob Pillin turned in at 23, Millicent Villas on the afternoon
after Mr. Ventnor's visit. Chivalry had won the day. And
he rang the bell with an elation which astonished him, for he
knew he was doing a soft thing.

" Mrs. Larne is out, sir; Miss Phyllis is at home."

His heart leaped.

" Oh—h! I'm sorry. I wonder if she'd see me?"

The little maid answered:

" I think she's been washin' 'er 'air, sir, but it may be dry
be now. I'll see."

Bob Pillin stood stock still beneath the young woman on the
wall. He could scarcely breathe. If her hair were not dry—
how awful! Suddenly he heard floating down a clear but
smothered: " Oh! Gefoozleme! " and other words which he
could not catch. The little maid came running down.

" Miss Phyllis says, sir, she'll be with you in a jiffy. And
I was to tell you that Master Jock is loose, sir."

Bob Pillin answered " Tha—anks," and passed into the drawing-room. He went to the bureau, took an envelope, enclosed
the cheque, and addressing it: " Mrs. Larne," replaced it in
his pocket. Then he crossed over to the mirror. Never till this
last month had he really doubted his own face; but now he
wanted for it things he had never wanted. It had too much
flesh and colour. It did not reflect his passion. This was a
handicap. With a narrow white piping round his waistcoat
opening, and a button-hole of tuberoses, he had tried to repair
its deficiencies. But do what he would, he was never easy about
himself nowadays, never up to that pitch which could make
him confident in her presence. And until this month to lack
confidence had never been his wont. A clear, high, mocking
voice said:

" Oh—h! Conceited young man! "

And spinning round he saw Phyllis in the doorway. Her light brown hair was fluffed out on her shoulders, so that he felt a kind of fainting-sweet sensation, and murmured inarticulately:

" Oh! I say—how jolly! "

" Lawks! It's awful! Have you come to see mother? "

Balanced between fear and daring, conscious of a scent of hay and verbena and camomile, Bob Pillin stammered:

" Ye—es. I—I'm glad she's not in, though."

Her laugh seemed to him terribly unfeeling.

" Oh! oh! Don't be foolish. Sit down. Isn't washing one's head awful? "

Bob Pillin answered feebly:

" Of course, I haven't much experience."

Her mouth opened.

" Oh! You *are*—aren't you? "

And he thought desperately: ' Dare I—oughtn't I—couldn't I somehow take her hand or put my arm round her, or something? ' Instead, he sat very rigid at his end of the sofa, while she sat lax and lissom at the other, and one of those crises of paralysis which beset would-be lovers fixed him to the soul.

Sometimes during this last month memories of a past existence, when chaff and even kisses came readily to the lips, and girls were fair game, would make him think: ' Is she really such an innocent? Doesn't she really want me to kiss her? ' Alas! such intrusions lasted but a moment before a blast of awe and chivalry withered them, and a strange and tragic delicacy—like nothing he had ever known—resumed its sway. And suddenly he heard her say:

" Why do you know such awful men? "

" What? I don't know any *awful* men."

" Oh yes, you do; one came here yesterday; he had whiskers, and he was awful."

" Whiskers? " His soul revolted in disclaimer. " I believe I only know one man with whiskers—a lawyer."

" Yes—that was him; a perfectly horrid man. Mother didn't mind him, but *I* thought he was a beast."

" Ventnor! Came here? How d'you mean? "

" He did; about some business of yours, too." Her face had

clouded over. Bob Pillin had of late been harassed by the still-born beginning of a poem:

> " I rode upon my way and saw
> A maid who watched me from the door."

It never grew longer, and was prompted by the feeling that her face was like an April day. The cloud which came on it now was like an April cloud, as if a bright shower of rain must follow. Brushing aside the two distressful lines, he said:

" Look here, Miss Larne—Phyllis—look here! "

" All right, I'm looking! "

" What does it mean—how did he come? What did he say? "

She shook her head, and her hair quivered; the scent of camomile, verbena, hay, was wafted; then looking at her lap, she muttered:

" I wish you wouldn't—I wish mother wouldn't—I hate it. Oh! Money! Beastly—beastly! " and a tearful sigh shivered itself into Bob Pillin's reddening ears.

" I say—don't! And do tell me, because——"

" Oh! you *know*."

" I don't—I don't know anything at all. I never——"

Phyllis looked up at him. " Don't tell fibs; you know mother's borrowing money from you, and it's hateful! "

A desire to lie roundly, a sense of the cheque in his pocket, a feeling of injustice, the emotion of pity, and a confused and black astonishment about Ventnor, caused Bob Pillin to stammer:

" Well, I'm d——d! " and to miss the look which Phyllis gave him through her lashes—a look saying:

" Ah! that's better! "

" I *am* d——d! Look here! D'you mean to say that Ventnor came here about my lending money? I never said a word to him——"

" There you see—you *are* lending! "

He clutched his hair.

" We've got to have this out," he added.

" Not by the roots! Oh! you do look funny. I've never seen you with your hair untidy. Oh! oh! "

Bob Pillin rose and paced the room. In the midst of his emotion he could not help seeing himself sidelong in the mirror;

and on pretext of holding his head in both his hands, tried earnestly to restore his hair. Then coming to a halt he said:

"Suppose I *am* lending money to your mother, what does it matter? It's only till quarter-day. Anybody might want money."

Phyllis did not raise her face.

"Why are you lending it?"

"Because—because—why shouldn't I?" and diving suddenly, he seized her hands.

She wrenched them free; and with the emotion of despair, Bob Pillin took out the envelope.

"If you like," he said, "I'll tear this up. I don't want to lend it, if you don't want me to; but I thought—I thought——" It was for her alone he had been going to lend this money!

Phyllis murmured through her hair:

"Yes! You thought that *I*—that's what's so hateful!"

Apprehension pierced his mind.

"Oh? I never—I swear I never——"

"Yes, you did; you thought I wanted you to lend it."

She jumped up, and brushed past him into the window.

So she thought she was being used as a decoy! That was awful—especially since it was true. He knew well enough that Mrs. Larne was working his admiration for her daughter for all that it was worth. And he said with simple fervour:

"What rot!" It produced no effect, and at his wits' end, he almost shouted: "Look, Phyllis! If you don't want me to —here goes!" Phyllis turned. Tearing the envelope across he threw the bits into the fire. "There it is," he said.

Her eyes grew round; she said in an awed voice: "Oh!"

In a sort of agony of honesty he said:

"It was only a cheque. Now you've got your way."

Staring at the fire she answered slowly:

"I expect you'd better go before mother comes."

Bob Pillin's mouth fell ajar; he secretly agreed, but the idea of sacrificing a moment alone with her was intolerable, and he said hardily:

"No, I shall stick it!"

Phyllis sneezed.

"My hair isn't a bit dry," and she sat down on the fender with her back to the fire.

A certain spirituality had come into Bob Pillin's face. If only he could get that wheeze off: "Phyllis is my only joy!"

or even: " Phyllis—do you—won't you—mayn't I?" But nothing came—nothing.

And suddenly she said:

" Oh! don't breathe so loud; it's awful!"

" Breathe? I wasn't!"

" You were; just like Carmen when she's dreaming."

He had walked three steps towards the door, before he
thought: 'What does it matter? I can stand anything from
her'; and walked the three steps back again.

She said softly:

" Poor young man!"

He answered gloomily:

" I suppose you realise that this may be the last time you'll
see me?"

" Why? I thought you were going to take us to the theatre."

" I don't know whether your mother will—after——"

Phyllis gave a little clear laugh.

" You don't know mother. Nothing makes any difference
to her."

And Bob Pillin muttered:

" I see." He did not, but it was of no consequence. Then
the thought of Ventnor again ousted all others. What on earth
—how on earth! He searched his mind for what he could
possibly have said the other night. Surely he had not asked
him to do anything; certainly not given him their address.
There was something very odd about it that had jolly well
got to be cleared up! And he said:

" Are you sure the name of that johnny who came here yesterday was Ventnor?"

Phyllis nodded.

" And he was short, and had whiskers?"

" Yes; red, and red eyes."

He murmured reluctantly:

" It must be him. Jolly good cheek; I simply can't understand. I shall go and see him. How on earth did he know
your address?"

" I expect you gave it him."

" I did not. I won't have you thinking me a squirt."

Phyllis jumped up. " Oh! Lawks! Here's mother!" Mrs.
Larne was coming up the garden. Bob Pillin made for the door.
" Good-bye," he said; " I'm going." But Mrs. Larne was al-

ready in the hall.   Enveloping him in fur and her rich personality, she drew him with her into the drawing-room, where
the back window was open and Phyllis gone.

"I hope," she said, "those naughty children have been making you comfortable.   That nice lawyer of yours came yesterday.   He seemed quite satisfied."

Very red above his collar, Bob Pillin stammered:

"I never told him to; he isn't my lawyer.   I don't know
what it means."

Mrs. Larne smiled.   "My dear boy, it's all right.   You
needn't be so squeamish.   I want it to be quite on a business
footing."

Restraining a fearful inclination to blurt out: "It's not
going to be on any footing!" Bob Pillin mumbled: "I must
go; I'm late."

"And when will you be able——?"

"Oh!   I'll—I'll send—I'll write.   Good-bye!"   And suddenly he found that Mrs. Larne had him by the lapel of his
coat.   The scent of violets and fur was overpowering, and the
thought flashed through him: 'I believe she only wanted to
take money off old Joseph in the Bible.   I can't leave my coat
in her hands!   What shall I do?'

Mrs. Larne was murmuring:

"It would be *so* sweet of you if you could manage it to-day";
and her hand slid over his chest.   "Oh!   You *have* brought
your cheque-book—what a nice boy!"

Bob Pillin took it out in desperation, and, sitting down at
the bureau, wrote a cheque similar to that which he had torn
and burned.   A warm kiss lighted on his eyebrow, his head
was pressed for a moment to a furry bosom; a hand took the
cheque; a voice said: "How delightful!" and a sigh immersed
him in a bath of perfume.   Backing to the door, he gasped:

"Don't mention it; and—and *don't tell Phyllis, please*.
Good-bye!"

Once through the garden gate, he thought: 'By gum! I've
done it now.   That Phyllis should know about it at all!   That
beast Ventnor!'

His face grew almost grim.   He would go and see what that
meant anyway!

3 §

Mr. Ventnor had not left his office when his young friend's
card was brought to him. Tempted for a moment to deny his
own presence, he thought: 'No! What's the good? Bound
to see him sometime!' If he had not exactly courage, he had
that particular blend of self-confidence and insensibility which
must needs distinguish those who follow the law; nor did he
ever forget that he was in the right.

"Show him in!" he said.

He would be quite bland, but young Pillin might whistle for
an explanation; he was still tormented, too, by the memory of
rich curves and moving lips, and the possibilities of better acquaintanceship.

While shaking the young man's hand his quick and fulvous
eye detected at once the discomposure behind that mask of
cheek and collar, and relapsing into one of those swivel chairs
which give one an advantage over men more statically seated, he
said:

"You look pretty bobbish. Anything I can do for you?"

Bob Pillin, in the fixed chair of the consulter, nursed his
bowler on his knee.

"Well, yes, there is. I've just been to see Mrs. Larne."

Mr. Ventnor did not flinch.

"Ah! Nice woman; pretty daughter, too!" And into those
words he put a certain meaning. He never waited to be bullied.
Bob Pillin felt the pressure of his blood increasing.

"Look here, Ventnor," he said, "I want an explanation."

"What of?"

"Why, of your going there, and using my name, and God
knows what."

Mr. Ventnor gave his chair two little twiddles before he
said:

"Well, you won't get it."

Bob Pillin remained for a moment taken aback; then he muttered resolutely:

"It's not the conduct of a gentleman."

Every man has his illusions, and no man likes them disturbed. The gingery tint underlying Mr. Ventnor's colouring
overlaid it; even the whites of his eyes grew red.

" Oh! " he said; " indeed. You mind your own business, will you? "

" It is my business—very much so. You made use of my name, and I don't choose——"

" The devil you don't! Now, I tell you what——" Mr. Ventnor leaned forward—" you'd better hold your tongue, and not exasperate me. I'm a good-tempered man, but I won't stand your impudence."

Clenching his bowler hat, and only kept in his seat by that sense of something behind, Bob Pillin ejaculated:

" Impudence! That's good—after what you did! Look here, why did you? It's so extraordinary! "

Mr. Ventnor answered:

" Oh! is it? You wait a bit, my friend! "

Still more moved by the mystery of this affair, Bob Pillin could only mutter:

" I never gave you their address; we were only talking about old Heythorp."

And at the smile which spread between Mr. Ventnor's whiskers, he jumped up, crying:

" It's not the thing, and you're not going to put me off. I insist on an explanation."

Mr. Ventnor leaned back, crossing his stout legs, joining the tips of his thick fingers. In this attitude he was always self-possessed.

" You do—do you? "

" Yes. You must have had some reason."

Mr. Ventnor gazed up at him.

" I'll give you a piece of advice, young cock, and charge you nothing for it, too: Ask no questions, and you'll be told no lies. And here's another: Go away before you forget yourself again."

The natural stolidity of Bob Pillin's face was only just proof against this speech. He said thickly:

" If you go there again and use my name, I'll——. Well, it's lucky for you you're not my age. Anyway I'll relieve you of my acquaintanceship in future. Good-evening! " and he went to the door. Mr. Ventnor had risen.

" Very well," he said loudly. " Good riddance! You wait and see which boot the leg is on! "

But Bob Pillin was gone, leaving the lawyer with a very red face, a very angry heart, and a vague sense of disorder in his speech. Not only Bob Pillin, but his tender aspirations had all left him; he no longer dallied with the memory of Mrs. Larne, but like a man and a Briton thought only of how to get his own back and punish evildoers. The atrocious words of his young friend, " It's not the conduct of a gentleman," festered in the heart of one who was made gentle not merely by nature but by Act of Parliament, and he registered a solemn vow to wipe the insult out, if not with blood, with verjuice. It was his duty, and they should d——d well see him do it!

IV

I §

Sylvanus Heythorp seldom went to bed before one or rose before eleven. The latter habit alone kept his valet from handing in the resignation which the former habit prompted almost every night.

Propped on his pillows in a crimson dressing-gown, and freshly shaved, he looked more Roman than he ever did, except in his bath. Having disposed of coffee, he was wont to read his letters, and *The Morning Post,* for he had always been a Tory, and could not stomach paying a halfpenny for his news. Not that there were many letters—when a man has reached the age of eighty, who should write to him, except to ask for money?

It was Valentine's Day. Through his bedroom window he could see the trees of the park, where the birds were in song, though he could not hear them. He had never been interested in Nature—full-blooded men with short necks seldom are.

This morning indeed there *were* two letters, and he opened that which smelt of something. Inside was a thing like a Christmas card, save that the naked babe had in his hands a bow and arrow, and words coming out of his mouth: " To be your Valentine." There was also a little pink note with one blue forget-me-not printed at the top. It ran:

" DEAREST GUARDY,—I'm sorry this is such a mangy little valentine; I couldn't go out to get it because I've got a beastly cold, so I asked Jock, and the pig bought this. The satin is simply scrumptious. If you don't come and see me in it some time soon, I shall come and show it to you. I wish I had a moustache, because my top lip feels just like a matchbox, but it's rather ripping having breakfast in bed. Mr. Pillin's taking us to the theatre the day after to-morrow evening. Isn't it nummy! I'm going to have rum and honey for my cold.

" Good-bye,
" Your Phyllis."

So this that quivered in his thick fingers, too insensitive to feel it, was a valentine for *him!* Forty years ago that young thing's grandmother had given him his last. It made him out a very old chap! Forty years ago! Had that been himself living then? And himself, who, as a youth, came on the town in 'forty-five? Not a thought, not a feeling the same! They said you changed your body every seven years. The mind with it, too, perhaps. Well, he had come to the last of his bodies, now! And that holy woman had been urging him to take it to Bath, with her face as long as a tea-tray, and some gammon from that doctor of his. Too full a habit—dock his port—no alcohol—might go off in a coma any night! Knock off—not he! Rather die any day than turn teetotaller! When a man had nothing left in life except his dinner, his bottle, his cigar, and the dreams they gave him—these doctors forsooth must want to cut them off! No, no! *Carpe diem!* while you lived, get something out of it. And now that he had made all the provision he could for those youngsters, his life was no good to anyone but himself; and the sooner he went off the better, if he ceased to enjoy what there was left, or lost the power to say: "I'll do this and that, and you be jiggered!" Keep a stiff lip until you crashed, and then go clean! He sounded the bell beside him twice—for Molly, not his man. And when the girl came in, and stood, pretty in her print frock, her fluffy over-fine dark hair escaping from under her cap, he gazed at her in silence.

" Yes, sirr ? "

" Want to look at you, that's all."

" Oh! an' I'm not tidy, sirr."

" Never mind. Had your valentine ? "

" No, sirr; who would send me one, then ? "

" Haven't you a young man ? "

" Well, I might. But he's over in my country."

" What d'you think of this? "

He held out the little boy.

The girl took the card and scrutinised it reverently; she said in a detached voice:

" Indeed, an' ut's pretty, too."

" Would you like it? "

" Oh; if 'tis not taking ut from you."

Old Heythorp shook his head, and pointed to the dressing-table.

" Over there—you'll find a sovereign. Little present for a good girl."

She uttered a deep sigh. " Oh, sirr, 'tis too much; 'tis kingly."

" Take it."

She took it, and came back, her hands clasping the sovereign and the valentine, in an attitude as of prayer.

The old man's gaze rested on her with satisfaction.

" I like pretty faces—can't bear sour ones. Tell Meller to get my bath ready."

When she had gone he took up the other letter—some lawyer's writing—and opening it with the usual difficulty read:

"February 13*th,* 1905.

" SIR,—Certain facts having come to my knowledge, I deem it my duty to call a special meeting of the shareholders of ' The Island Navigation Coy.,' to consider circumstances in connection with the purchase of Mr. Joseph Pillin's fleet. And I give you notice that at this meeting your conduct will be called in question.

" I am, Sir,

" Yours faithfully,

" CHARLES VENTNOR.

" SYLVANUS HEYTHORP, Esq."

Having read this missive, old Heythorp remained some minutes without stirring. Ventnor! That solicitor chap who had made himself unpleasant at the creditors' meetings!

There are men whom a really bad bit of news at once stampedes out of all power of coherent thought and action, and men who at first simply do not take it in. Old Heythorp took it in fast enough; coming from a lawyer it was about as nasty as it could be. But, at once, with stoic wariness his old brain began casting round. What did this fellow really know? And what exactly could he do? One thing was certain; even if he knew everything, he couldn't upset that settlement. The youngsters were all right. The old man grasped the fact that only his own position was at stake. But this was enough in all conscience; a name which had been before the public fifty odd years—income, independence, more perhaps. It would take little, seeing his age and feebleness, to make his Companies throw him over. But what had the fellow got hold of? How decide whether or not to take notice; to let him do his worst, or to try and get into touch with him? And what was the fellow's motive? He held ten shares! That would never make a man take all this trouble, and over a purchase which was really first-rate business for the Company. Yes! His conscience was quite clean. He had not betrayed his Company—on the contrary, had done it a good turn, got them four sound ships at a low price—against much opposition. That he might have done the Company a better turn, and got the ships at fifty-four thousand, did not trouble him—the six thousand was a deuced sight better employed; and he had not pocketed a penny piece himself! But the fellow's motive? Spite? Looked like it. Spite, because he had been disappointed of his money, and defied into the bargain! H'm! If that were so, he might still be got to blow cold again. His eyes lighted on the pink note with the blue forget-me-not. It marked as it were the high-water mark of what was left to him of life; and this other letter in his hand —by Jove!—low-water mark! And with a deep and rumbling sigh he thought: 'No, I'm not going to be beaten by this fellow.'

"Your bath is ready, sir."

Crumpling the two letters into the pocket of his dressing-gown, he said:

"Help me up; and telephone to Mr. Farney to be good enough to come round." . . .

An hour later, when the secretary entered, his chairman was sitting by the fire perusing the articles of association. And, waiting for him to look up, watching the articles shaking in that thick, feeble hand, the secretary had one of those moments of philosophy not too frequent with his kind. Some said the only happy time of life was when you had no passions, nothing to hope and live for. But did you really ever reach such a stage? The old chairman, for instance, still had his passion for getting his own way, still had his prestige, and set a lot of store by it! And he said:

"Good-morning, sir; I hope you're all right in this east wind. The purchase is completed."

"Best thing the Company ever did. Have you heard from a shareholder called Ventnor. You know the man I mean."

"No, sir. I haven't."

"Well! You may get a letter that'll make you open your eyes. An impudent scoundrel! Just write at my dictation."

"*February* 14*th,* 1905.

"CHARLES VENTNOR, Esq.

"SIR,—I have your letter of yesterday's date, the contents of which I am at a loss to understand. My solicitors will be instructed to take the necessary measures."

'Phew! What's all this about?' the secretary thought.

"Yours truly . . . I'll sign."

And the shaky letters closed the page:

"SYLVANUS HEYTHORP."

"Post that as you go."

"Anything else I can do for you, sir?"

"Nothing, except to let me know if you hear from this fellow."

When the secretary had gone the old man thought: 'So! The ruffian hasn't called the meeting yet. That'll bring him round here fast enough if it's his money he wants—blackmailing scoundrel!'

"Mr. Pillin, sir; and will you wait lunch, or will you have it in the dining-room?"

"In the dining-room."

At the sight of that death's-head of a fellow, old Heythorp felt a sort of pity. He looked bad enough already—and this news would make him look worse. Joe Pillin glanced round at the two closed doors.

"How are you, Sylvanus? I'm very poorly." He came closer, and lowered his voice: "Why did you get me to make that settlement? I must have been mad. I've had a man called Ventnor—I didn't like his manner. He asked me if I knew a Mrs. Larne."

"Ha! What did you say?"

"What could I say? I *don't* know her. But why did he ask?"

" Smells a rat."

Joe Pillin grasped the edge of the table with both hands.

" Oh! " he murmured.   " Oh, don't say that ! "

Old Heythorp held out to him the crumpled letter.

When he had read it Joe Pillin sat down abruptly before the fire.

" Pull yourself together, Joe ; they can't touch you, and they can't upset either the purchase or the settlement.   They can upset me, that's all."

Joe Pillin answered, with trembling lips :

" How you can sit there, and look the same as ever !   Are you sure they can't touch me ? "

Old Heythorp nodded grimly.

" They talk of an Act, but they haven't passed it yet.   They might prove a breach of trust against me.   But I'll diddle them. Keep your pecker up, and get off abroad."

" Yes, yes.   I must.   I'm very bad.   I was going to-morrow. But I don't know, I'm sure, with this hanging over me.   My son knowing her makes it worse.   He knows this man Ventnor, too.   And I daren't say anything to Bob.   What are you thinking of Sylvanus?   You look very funny."

Old Heythorp seemed to rouse himself from a sort of coma.

" I want my lunch," he said.   " Will you stop and have some ? "

Joe Pillin stammered out :

" Lunch !   I don't know when I shall eat again.   What are you going to do, Sylvanus ? "

" Bluff the beggar out of it."

" But suppose you can't ? "

" Buy him off.   He's one of my creditors."

Joe Pillin stared at him afresh.   " You always had such nerve," he said yearningly.   " Do you ever wake up between two and four?   I do—and everything's black."

" Put a good stiff nightcap on, my boy, before going to bed."

" Yes ; I sometimes wish I was less temperate.   But I couldn't stand it.   I'm told your doctor forbids you alcohol."

" He does.   That's why I drink it."

Joe Pillin, brooding over the fire, said :   " This meeting— d'you think they mean to have it?   D'you think this man really knows?   If my name gets into the newspapers——" but encountering his old friend's deep little eyes, he stopped.   " So you advise me to get off to-morrow, then ? "

Old Heythorp nodded.

" Your lunch is served, sir."

Joe Pillin started violently, and rose.

" Well, good-bye, Sylvanus—good-bye! I don't suppose I shall be back till the summer, if I ever come back! " He sank his voice: " I shall rely on you. You won't let them, will you ? "

Old Heythorp lifted his hand, and Joe Pillin put into that swollen shaking paw his pale and spindly fingers. " I wish I had your pluck," he said sadly. " Good-bye, Sylvanus," and turning, he passed out.

Old Heythorp thought: ' Poor shaky chap. All to pieces at the first shot!' And, going to his lunch, ate more heavily than usual.

2 §

Mr. Ventnor, on reaching his office and opening his letters, found, as he had anticipated, one from " that old rascal." Its contents excited in him the need to know his own mind. Fortunately this was not complicated by a sense of dignity—he only had to consider the position with an eye on not being made to *look* a fool. The point was simply whether he set more store by his money than by his desire for—er—justice. If not, he had merely to convene the special meeting, and lay before it the plain fact that Mr. Joseph Pillin, selling his ships for sixty thousand pounds, had just made a settlement of six thousand pounds on a lady whom he did not know, a daughter, ward, or what-not—of the purchasing Company's chairman, who had said, moreover, at the general meeting, that he stood or fell by the transaction ; he had merely to do this, and demand that an explanation be required from the old man of such a startling coincidence. Convinced that no explanation would hold water, he felt sure that his action would be at once followed by the collapse, if nothing more, of that old image, and the infliction of a nasty slur on old Pillin and his hopeful son. On the other hand, three hundred pounds was money; and if old Heythorp were to say to him: " What do you want to make this fuss for?—here's what I owe you!" could a man of business and the world let his sense of justice—however he might itch to have it satisfied—stand in the way of what was after all also his sense of justice?—for this money had been owing to

him for the deuce of a long time. In this dilemma, the words:
" My solicitors will be instructed" were of notable service in
helping him to form a decision, for he had a certain dislike of
other solicitors, and an intimate knowledge of the law of libel
and slander; if by any remote chance there should be a slip
between the cup and the lip, Charles Ventnor might be in the
soup—a position which he deprecated both by nature and profession. High thinking, therefore, decided him at last to answer
thus:

" February 15th, 1905.

" SIR,—I have received your note. I think it may be fair,
before taking further steps in this matter, to ask you for a personal explanation of the circumstances to which I alluded. I
therefore propose with your permission to call on you at your
private residence at five o'clock to-morrow afternoon.

" Yours faithfully,
" CHARLES VENTNOR.

" SYLVANUS HEYTHORP, Esq."

Having sent this missive, and arranged in his mind, the damn-
ing, if circumstantial, evidence he had accumulated, he awaited
the hour with confidence, for his nature was not lacking in the
cock-surety of a Briton. All the same, he dressed himself particularly well that morning, putting on a blue and white striped
waistcoat which, with a cream-coloured tie, set off his fulvous
whiskers and full blue eyes; and he lunched, if anything, more
fully than his wont, eating a stronger cheese and taking a glass
of special Club ale. He took care to be late, too, to show the
old fellow that his coming at all was in the nature of an act of
grace. A strong scent of hyacinths greeted him in the hall;
and Mr. Ventnor, who was an amateur of flowers, stopped to put
his nose into a fine bloom and think uncontrollably of Mrs.
Larne. Pity! The things one had to give up in life—fine
women—one thing and another. Pity! The thought inspired
in him a timely anger; and he followed the servant, intending
to stand no nonsense from this paralytic old rascal.

The room he entered was lighted by a bright fire, and a single
electric lamp with an orange shade on a table covered by a black
satin cloth. There were heavily gleaming oil paintings on the
walls, a heavy old brass chandelier without candles, heavy dark
red curtains, and an indefinable scent of burnt acorns, coffee,

cigars, and old man. He became conscious of a candescent spot on the far side of the hearth, where the light fell on old Heythorp's thick white hair.

"Mr. Ventnor, sir."

The candescent spot moved. A voice said: "Sit down."

Mr. Ventnor sat in an armchair on the opposite side of the fire; and, finding a kind of somnolence creeping over him, pinched himself. He wanted all his wits about him.

The old man was speaking in that extinct voice of his, and Mr. Ventnor said rather pettishly:

"Beg pardon, I don't get you."

Old Heythorp's voice swelled with sudden force:

"Your letters are Greek to me."

"Oh! indeed! I think we can soon make them into plain English!"

"Sooner the better."

Mr. Ventnor passed through a moment of indecision. Should he lay his cards on the table? It was not his habit, and the proceeding was sometimes attended with risk. The knowledge, however, that he could always take them up again, seeing there was no third person here to testify that he had laid them down, decided him, and he said:

"Well, Mr. Heythorp, the long and short of the matter is this: Our friend Mr. Pillin paid you a commission of ten per cent. on the sale of his ships. Oh! yes. He settled the money not on you, but on your relative Mrs. Larne and her children. This, as you know, is a breach of trust on your part."

The old man's voice: "Where did you get hold of that cock-and-bull story?" brought him to his feet before the fire.

"It won't do, Mr. Heythorp. My witnesses are Mr. Pillin, Mrs. Larne, and Mr. Scriven."

"What have you come here for, then—blackmail?"

Mr. Ventnor straightened his waistcoat; a rush of conscious virtue had dyed his face.

"Oh! you take that tone," he said, "do you? You think you can ride roughshod over everything? Well, you're very much mistaken. I advise you to keep a civil tongue and consider your position, or I'll make a beggar of you. I'm not sure this isn't a case for a prosecution!"

"Gammon!"

The choler in Charles Ventnor kept him silent for a moment; then he burst out:

" Neither gammon nor spinach. You owe me three hundred
pounds, you've owed it me for years, and you have the impudence to take this attitude with me, have you? Now, I never
bluster; I say what I mean. You just listen to me. Either
you pay me what you owe me at once, or I call this meeting
and make what I know public. You'll very soon find out where
you are. And a good thing, too, for a more unscrupulous—
unscrupulous——" he paused for breath.

Occupied with his own emotion, he had not observed the
change in old Heythorp's face. The imperial on that lower lip
was bristling, the crimson of those cheeks had spread to the
roots of his white hair. He grasped the arms of his chair, trying to rise; his swollen hands trembled; a little saliva escaped
one corner of his lips. And the words came out as if shaken
by his teeth:

" So—so—you—you bully me!"

Conscious that the interview had suddenly passed from the
phase of negotiation, Mr. Ventnor looked hard at his opponent.
He saw nothing but a decrepit, passionate, crimson-faced old
man at bay, and all the instincts of one with everything on his
side boiled up in him. The miserable old turkey-cock—the
apoplectic image! And he said:

" And you'll do no good for yourself by getting into a passion. At your age, and in your condition, I recommend a little
prudence. Now just take my terms quietly, or you know what'll
happen. I'm not to be intimidated by any of your airs." And
seeing that the old man's rage was such that he simply could
not speak, he took the opportunity of going on: " I don't care
two straws which you do—I'm out to show you who's master.
If you think in your dotage you can domineer any longer—
well, you'll find two can play at that game. Come, now, which
are you going to do?"

The old man had sunk back in his chair, and only his little
deep-blue eyes seemed living. Then he moved one hand, and
Mr. Ventnor saw that he was fumbling to reach the button of an
electric bell at the end of a cord. ' I'll show him,' he thought,
and stepping forward, he put it out of reach.

Thus frustrated, the old man remained motionless, staring
up. The word " blackmail " resumed its buzzing in Mr. Ventnor's ears. The impudence—the consummate impudence of it
from this fraudulent old ruffian with one foot in bankruptcy
and one foot in the grave, if not in the dock.

"Yes," he said, "it's never too late to learn; and for once you've come up against someone a leetle bit too much for you. Haven't you now? You'd better cry ' *Peccavi.*' "

Then, in the deathly silence of the room, the moral force of his position, and the collapse as it seemed of his opponent, awakening a faint compunction, he took a turn over the Turkey carpet to readjust his mind.

"You're an old man, and I don't want to be too hard on you. I'm only showing you that you can't play fast and loose as if you were God Almighty any longer. You've had your own way too many years. And now you can't have it, see!" Then, as the old man again moved forward in his chair, he added: "Now, don't get into a passion again; calm yourself, because I warn you—this is your last chance. I'm a man of my word; and what I say, I do."

By a violent and unsuspected effort the old man jerked himself up and reached the bell. Mr. Ventnor heard it ring, and said sharply:

"Mind you, it's nothing to me which you do. I came for your own good. Please yourself. Well?"

He was answered by the click of the door and the old man's husky voice:

"Show this hound out! And then come back!"

Mr. Ventnor had presence of mind enough not to shake his fist. Muttering: "Very well, Mr. Heythorp! Ah! *Very* well!" he moved with dignity to the door. The careful shepherding of the servant renewed the fire of his anger. Hound! he had been called a hound!

3 §

After seeing Mr. Ventnor off the premises the man Meller returned to his master, whose face looked very odd—"all patchy-like," as he put it in the servants' hall, as though the blood driven to his head had mottled for good the snowy whiteness of the forehead. He received the unexpected order:

"Get me a hot bath ready, and put some pine stuff in it."

When the old man was seated there, the valet asked:

"How long shall I give you, sir?"

"Twenty minutes."

"Very good, sir."

Lying in that steaming brown fragrant liquid, old Heythorp heaved a stertorous sigh. By losing his temper with that ill-conditioned cur he had cooked his goose. It was done to a turn; and he was a ruined man. If only—oh! if only he could have seized the fellow by the neck and pitched him out of the room! To have lived to be so spoken to; to have been unable to lift hand or foot, hardly even his voice—he would sooner have been dead! Yes—sooner have been dead! A dumb and measureless commotion was still at work in the recesses of that thick old body, silver-brown in the dark water, whose steam he drew deep into his wheezing lungs, as though for spiritual relief. To be beaten by a cur like that! To have a common cad of a petti-fogging lawyer drag him down and kick him about; tumble a name which had stood high, in the dust! The fellow had the power to make him a byword and a beggar! It was incredible! But it was a fact. And to-morrow he would begin to do it—perhaps had begun already. His tree had come down with a crash! Eighty years—eighty good years! He regretted none of them—regretted nothing; least of all this breach of trust which had provided for his grandchildren—one of the best things he had ever done. The fellow was a cowardly hound, too! The way he had snatched the bell-pull out of his reach—despicable cur! And a chap like that was to put " paid " to the account of Sylvanus Heythorp, to " scratch " him out of life—so near the end of everything, the very end. His hand raised above the surface fell back on his stomach through the dark water, and a bubble or two rose. Not so fast—not so fast! He had but to slip down a foot, let the water close over his head, and " Good-bye" to Master Ventnor's triumph! Dead men could not be kicked off the Boards of Companies. Dead men could not be beggared, deprived of their independence. He smiled and stirred a little in the bath till the water reached the white hairs on his lower lip. It smelt nice! And he took a long sniff. He had had a good life, a good life! And with the thought that he had it in his power at any moment to put Master Ventnor's nose out of joint—to beat the beggar after all, a sense of assu-agement and well-being crept over him. His blood ran more evenly again. He closed his eyes. They talked about an after-life—people like that holy woman. Gammon! You went to sleep—a long sleep; no dreams. A nap after dinner! Din-ner! His tongue sought his palate! Yes! he could eat a good dinner! That dog hadn't put him off his stroke! The best dinner he had ever eaten was the one he gave to Jack Herring, Chichester, Thornworthy, Nick Treffry and Jolyon Forsyte at Pole's. Good Lord! In 'sixty—yes—'sixty-five? Just before he fell in love with Alice Larne—ten years before he came to Liverpool. That *was* a dinner! Cost twenty-four pounds for the six of them—and Forsyte an absurdly moderate fellow. Only Nick Treffry and himself had been three-bottle men! Dead! Every jack man of them. And suddenly he thought: ' My name's a good one—I was never down before—never beaten! '

A voice above the steam said:

" The twenty minutes is up, sir."

" All right; I'll get out. Evening clothes."

And Meller, taking out dress suit and shirt, thought: ' Now, what does the old bloomer want dressin' up again for; why can't he go to bed and have his dinner there? When a man's like a baby, the cradle's the place for him.' . . .

An hour later, at the scene of his encounter with Mr. Ventnor, where the table was already laid for dinner, old Heythorp stood and gazed. The curtains had been drawn back, the window thrown open to air the room, and he could see out there the shapes of the dark trees and a sky grape-coloured, in the mild, moist night. It smelt good. A sensuous feeling stirred in him, warm from his bath, clothed from head to foot in fresh garments. Deuce of a time since he had dined in full fig! He would have liked a woman dining opposite—but not the holy woman; no, by George!—would have liked to see light falling on a woman's shoulders once again, and a pair of bright eyes! He crossed, snail-like, towards the fire. There that bullying fellow had stood with his back to it—confound his impudence!—as if the place belonged to him. And suddenly he had a vision of his three secretaries' faces—especially young Farney's—as they would look when the pack got him by the throat and pulled him down. His co-directors, too! Old Heythorp! How are the mighty fallen! And that hound jubilant!

His valet passed across the room to shut the window and draw the curtains. This chap too! The day he could no longer pay his wages, and had lost the power to say " Shan't want your services any more "—when he could no longer even pay his doctor for doing his best to kill him off! Power, interest, independence, all—gone! To be dressed and undressed, given pap, like a baby in arms, served as they chose to serve him, and wished out of the way—broken, dishonoured! By money alone an old

man had his being! Meat, drink, movement, breath! When
all his money was gone the holy woman would let him know it
fast enough. They would all let him know it; or if they didn't,
it would be out of pity! He had never been pitied yet—thank
God! And he said:

"Get me up a bottle of Perrier Jouet. What's the menu?"

"Germane soup, sir; filly de sole; sweetbread; cutlet soubees,
rum souffly."

"Tell her to give me a *hors d'œuvre*, and put on a savoury."

"Yes, sir."

When the man had gone, he thought: 'I should have liked an
oyster—too late now!' and going over to his bureau he fum-
blingly pulled out the top drawer. There was little in it—
just a few papers, business papers on his Companies, and a sched-
ule of his debts; not even a copy of his will—he had not made
one, nothing to leave! Letters he had never kept. Half a
dozen bills, a few receipts, and the little pink note with the blue
forget-me-not. That was the lot. An old tree gives up bearing leaves, and its roots dry up, before it comes down in a wind;
an old man's world slowly falls away from him till he stands
alone in the night. Looking at the pink note, he thought:
'Suppose I'd married Alice—a man never had a better mistress!' He fumbled the drawer to; but still he strayed feebly
about the room, with a curious shrinking from sitting down,
legacy from the quarter of an hour he had been compelled to
sit while that hound worried at his throat. He was opposite
one of the pictures now. It gleamed, dark and oily, limning a
Scots Grey who had mounted a wounded Russian on his horse,
and was bringing him back prisoner from the Balaclava charge.
A very old friend—bought in 'fifty-nine. It had hung in his
chambers in the Albany—hung with him ever since. With whom
would it hang when he was gone? For that holy woman would
scrap it, to a certainty, and stick up some Crucifixion or other,
some new-fangled high art thing! She could even do that now
if she liked—for she owned it, owned every mortal stick in the
room, to the very glass he would drink his champagne from;
all made over under the settlement fifteen years ago, before his
last big gamble went wrong. "*De l'audace, toujours de l'audace!*" The gamble which had brought him down till his
throat at last was at the mercy of a bullying hound. The pitcher
and the well! At the mercy——! The sound of a popping cork
dragged him from reverie. He moved to his seat, back to the

window, and sat down to his dinner. By George! They had
got him an oyster! And he said:

"I've forgotten my teeth!"

While the man was gone for them, he swallowed the oysters,
methodically touching them one by one with cayenne, Chili
vinegar, and lemon. Ummm! Not quite what they used to be
at Pimm's in the best days, but not bad—not bad! Then seeing the little blue bowl lying before him, he looked up and
said:

"My compliments to cook on the oysters. Give me the champagne." And he lifted his trembling teeth. Thank God, he
could still put 'em in for himself! The creaming goldenish
fluid from the napkined bottle slowly reached the brim of his
glass, which had a hollow stem; raising it to his lips, very red
between the white hairs above and below, he drank with a
gurgling noise, and put the glass down—empty. Nectar! And
just cold enough!

"I frappé it the least bit, sir."

"Quite right. What's that smell of flowers?"

"It's from those 'yacinths on the sideboard, sir. They come
from Mrs. Larne, this afternoon."

"Put 'em on the table. Where's my daughter?"

"She's had dinner, sir; goin' to a ball, I think."

"A ball!"

"Charity ball, I fancy, sir."

"Ummm! Give me a touch of the old sherry with the soup."

"Yes, sir. I shall have to open a bottle."

"Very well, then, do!"

On his way to the cellar the man confided to Molly, who was
carrying the soup:

"The Gov'nor's going it to-night! What he'll be like to-
morrow I dunno."

The girl answered softly:

"Poor old man, let um have his pleasure." And, in the hall,
with the soup tureen against her bosom, she hummed above the
steam, and thought of the ribbons on her new chemises, bought
out of the sovereign he had given her.

And old Heythorp, digesting his oysters, snuffed the scent of
the hyacinths, and thought of the St. Germain, his favourite
soup. It wouldn't be first-rate, at this time of year—should
be made with little young home-grown peas. Paris was the
place for it. Ah! The French were the fellows for eating, and

—looking things in the face! Not hypocrites—not ashamed of their reason or their senses!

The soup came in. He sipped it, bending forward as far as he could, his napkin tucked in over his shirt-front like a bib. He got the bouquet of that sherry to a T—his sense of smell was very keen to-night; rare old stuff it was—more than a year since he had tasted it—but no one drank sherry nowadays, hadn't the constitution for it! The fish came up, and went down; and with the sweetbread he took his second glass of champagne. Always the best, that second glass—the stomach well warmed, and the palate not yet dulled. Umm! So that fellow thought he had him beaten, did he? And he said suddenly:

"The fur coat in the wardrobe, I've no use for it. You can take it away to-night."

With tempered gratitude the valet answered:

"Thank you, sir; much obliged, I'm sure." So the old buffer had found out there was moth in it!

"Have I worried you much?"

"No, sir; not at all, sir—that is, no more than reason."

"Afraid I have. Very sorry—can't help it. You'll find that, when you get like me."

"Yes, sir; I've always admired your pluck, sir."

"Um! Very good of you to say so."

"Always think of you keepin' the flag flyin', sir."

Old Heythorp bent his body from the waist.

"Much obliged to you."

"Not at all, sir. Cook's done a little spinach in cream with the soubees."

"Ah! Tell her from me it's a capital dinner, so far."

"Thank you, sir."

Alone again, old Heythorp sat unmoving, his brain just narcotically touched. "The flag flyin'—the flag flyin'!" He raised his glass and sucked. He had an appetite now, and finished the three cutlets, and all the sauce and spinach. Pity! he could have managed a snipe—fresh shot! A desire to delay, to lengthen dinner, was strong upon him; there were but the *soufflé* and the savoury to come. He would have enjoyed, too, someone to talk to. He had always been fond of good company —been good company himself, or so they said—not that he had had a chance of late. Even at the Boards they avoided talking to him, he had noticed for a long time. Well! that wouldn't

trouble him again—he had sat through his last Board, no
doubt. They shouldn't kick him off, though; he wouldn't give
them that pleasure—had seen the beggars hankering after his
chairman's shoes too long. The *soufflé* was before him now, and
lifting his glass, he said:

" Fill up."

" These are the special glasses, sir; only four to the bottle."

" Fill up."

The servant filled, screwing up his mouth.

Old Heythorp drank, and put the glass down empty with a
sigh. He had been faithful to his principles, finished the bottle
before touching the sweet—a good bottle—of a good brand!
And now for the *soufflé!* Delicious, flipped down with the old
sherry! So that holy woman was going to a ball, was she?
How deuced funny! Who would dance with a dry stick like
that, all eaten up with a piety which was just sexual disappointment? Ah! yes, lots of women like that—had often noticed
'em—pitied 'em too, until you had to do with them and they
made you as unhappy as themselves, and were tyrants into the
bargain. And he asked:

" What's the savoury? "

" Cheese remmykin, sir."

His favourite.

" I'll have my port with it—the 'sixty-eight."

The man stood gazing with evident stupefaction. He had
not expected this. The old man's face was very flushed, but
that might be the bath. He said feebly:

" Are you sure you ought, sir? "

" No, but I'm going to."

" Would you mind if I spoke to Miss Heythorp, sir? "

" If you do, you can leave my service."

" Well, sir, I don't accept the responsibility."

" Who asked you to? "

" No, sir."

" Well, get it, then; and don't be an ass."

" Yes, sir." If the old man were not humoured he would
have a fit, perhaps!

And the old man sat quietly staring at the hyacinths. He
felt happy, his whole being lined and warmed and drowsed—
and there was more to come! What had the holy folk to give
you compared with the comfort of a good dinner? Could they
make you dream, and see life rosy for a little? No, they could

only give you promissory notes which would never be cashed. A man had nothing but his pluck—they only tried to undermine it, and make him squeal for help. He could see his precious doctor throwing up his hands: "Port after a bottle of champagne—you'll die of it!" And a very good death too —none better. A sound broke the silence of the closed-up room. Music? His daughter playing the piano overhead. Singing too! What a trickle of a voice! Jenny Lind! The Swedish nightingale—he had never missed the nights when she was singing—Jenny Lind!

"It's very hot, sir. Shall I take it out of the case?"

Ah. The ramequin!

"Touch of butter, and the cayenne!"

"Yes, sir."

He ate it slowly, savouring each mouthful; had never tasted a better. With cheese—port! He drank one glass, and said:

"Help me to my chair."

And settled there before the fire with decanter and glass and hand-bell on the little low table by his side, he murmured:

"Bring coffee, and my cigar, in twenty minutes."

To-night he would do justice to his wine, not smoking till he had finished. As old Horace said:

> "Aequam memento rebus in arduis
> Servare mentem."

And, raising his glass, he sipped slowly, spilling a drop or two, shutting his eyes.

The faint silvery squealing of the holy woman in the room above, the scent of hyacinths, the drowse of the fire, on which a cedar log had just been laid, the feeling of the port soaking down into the crannies of his being, made up a momentary Paradise. Then the music stopped; and no sound rose but the tiny groans of the log trying to resist the fire. Dreamily he thought: 'Life wears you out wears you out. Logs on a fire!' And he filled his glass again. That fellow had been careless; there were dregs at the bottom of the decanter and he had got down to them! Then, as the last drop from his tilted glass trickled into the white hairs on his chin, he heard the coffee tray put down, and taking his cigar he put it to his ear, rolling it in his thick fingers. In prime condition! And drawing a first whiff, he said:

"Open that bottle of the old brandy in the sideboard."

" Brandy, sir? I really daren't, sir."

" Are you my servant or not? "

" Yes, sir, but——"

A minute of silence, then the man went hastily to the sideboard, took out the bottle, and drew the cork. The tide of crimson in the old man's face had frightened him.

" Leave it there."

The unfortunate valet placed the bottle on the little table. ' I'll have to tell her,' he thought; ' but if I take away the port decanter and the glass, it won't look so bad.' And, carrying them, he left the room.

Slowly the old man drank his coffee, and the liqueur of brandy. The whole gamut! And watching his cigar-smoke wreathing blue in the orange glow, he smiled. The last night to call his soul his own, the last night of his independence. Send in his resignations to-morrow—not wait to be kicked off! Not give that fellow a chance!

A voice which seemed to come from far off, said:

" Father! You're drinking brandy! How *can* you—you know it's simple poison to you! " A figure in white, scarcely actual, loomed up close. He took the bottle to fill up his liqueur glass, in defiance; but a hand in a long white glove, with another dangling from its wrist, pulled it away, shook it at him, and replaced it in the sideboard. And, just as when Mr. Ventnor stood there accusing him, a swelling and churning in his throat prevented him from speech; his lips moved, but only a little froth came forth.

His daughter had approached again. She stood quite close, in white satin, thin-faced, sallow, with eyebrows raised, and her dark hair frizzed—yes! frizzed—the holy woman! With all his might he tried to say: ' So you bully me, do you—you bully me *to-night!* ' but only the word " so " and a sort of whispering came forth. He heard her speaking. " It's no good your getting angry, Father. After champagne—it's wicked! " Then her form receded in a sort of rustling white mist; she was gone; and he heard the spluttering and growling of her taxi, bearing her to the ball. So! She tyrannised and bullied, even before she had him at her mercy, did she? She should see! Anger had brightened his eyes; the room came clear again. And slowly raising himself he sounded the bell twice, for the girl, not for that fellow Meller, who was in the plot. As soon as her pretty black and white-aproned figure stood before him, he said:

" Help me up ! "

Twice her soft pulling was not enough, and he sank back. The third time he struggled to his feet.

" Thank you; that'll do." Then, waiting till she was gone, he crossed the room, fumbled open the sideboard door, and took out the bottle. Reaching over the polished oak, he grasped a sherry glass; and holding the bottle with both hands, tipped the liquor into it, put it to his lips and sucked. Drop by drop it passed over his palate—mild, very old, old as himself, coloured like sunlight, fragrant. To the last drop he drank it, then hugging the bottle to his shirt-front, he moved snail-like to his chair, and fell back into its depths.

For some minutes he remained there motionless, the bottle clasped to his chest, thinking: ' This is not the attitude of a gentleman. I must put it down on the table—on the table;' but a thick cloud was between him and everything. It was with his hands he would have to put the bottle on the table! But he could not find his hands, could not feel them. His mind see-sawed in strophe and antistrophe: " You can't move ! "— " I will move ! " " You're beaten "—" I'm not beat." " Give up"—" I won't." That struggle to find his hands seemed to last for ever—he *must* find them! After that—go down—all standing—after that! Everything round him was red. Then the red cloud cleared just a little, and he could hear the clock —" tick—tick—tick"; a faint sensation spread from his shoulders down to his wrists, down his palms; and yes—he could feel the bottle! He redoubled his struggle to get forward in his chair; to get forward and put the bottle down. It was not dignified like this ! One arm he could move now; but he could not grip the bottle nearly tight enough to put it down. Working his whole body forward, inch by inch, he shifted himself up in the chair till he could lean sideways, and the bottle, slipping down his chest, dropped slanting to the edge of the low stool-table. Then with all his might he screwed his trunk and arms an inch further, and the bottle stood. He had done it— done it ! His lips twitched into a smile ; his body sagged back to its old position. He had done it ! And he closed his eyes. . . .

At half-past eleven the girl Molly, opening the door, looked at him and said softly: " Sirr ! there's some ladies, and a gentleman ! " But he did not answer. And, still holding the door, she whispered out into the hall:

" He's asleep, miss."

A voice whispered back:

" Oh! Just let me go in, I won't wake him unless he does. But I do want to show him my dress."

The girl moved aside; and on tiptoe Phyllis passed in. She walked to where, between the lamp-glow and the fire-glow, she was lighted up. White satin—her first low-cut dress—the flush of her first supper party—a gardenia at her breast, another in her fingers! Oh! what a pity he was asleep! How red he looked! How funnily old men breathed! And mysteriously, as a child might, she whispered:

" Guardy!"

No answer! And pouting, she stood twiddling the gardenia. Then suddenly she thought: ' I'll put it in his buttonhole! When he wakes up and sees it, how he'll jump!'

And stealing close, she bent and slipped it in. Two faces looked at her from round the door; she heard Bob Pillin's smothered chuckle; her mother's rich and feathery laugh. Oh! How red his forehead was! She touched it with her lips; skipped back, twirled round, danced silently a second, blew a kiss, and like quicksilver was gone.

And the whispering, the chuckling, and one little outpealing laugh rose in the hall.

But the old man slept. Nor until Meller came at his usual hour of half-past twelve, was it known that he would never wake.

1916.

A PORTRAIT

I⊤ is at the age of eighty that I picture him, without the vestige of a stoop, rather above middle height, of very well-proportioned figure, whose flatness of back and easy movements were the admiration of all who saw them. His iron-grey eyes had lost none of their colour, they were set in deep, so that their upper lids were invisible, and had a peculiar questioning directness, apt to change suddenly into twinkles. His head was of fine shape—one did not suspect that it required a specially made hat, being a size larger than almost any other head; it was framed in very silky silvery hair, brushed in an arch across his forehead, and falling in becoming curves over the tips of his ears; and he wore always a full white beard and moustaches, which concealed a jaw and chin of great determination cleft by a dimple. His nose had been broken in his early boyhood; it was the nose of a thinker, broad and of noticeable shape. The colour of his cheeks was a fine dry brown; his brow very capacious, both wide and high, and endowed with a singular serenity. But it was the balance and poise of his head which commanded so much attention. In a theatre, church, concert-hall, there was never any head so fine as his, for the silvery hair and beard lent to its massiveness a curious grace and delicacy.

The owner of that head could not but be endowed with force, sagacity, humour, and the sense of justice. It expressed, indeed, his essential quality—equanimity; for there were two men in him—he of the chin and jaw, a man of action and tenacity, and he of the nose and brow, the man of speculation and impersonality; yet these two were so curiously balanced and blended that there was no harsh ungraceful conflict. And what made this equanimity so memorable was the fact that both his power of action and his power of speculation were of high quality. He was not a commonplace person content with a little of both. He wanted and had wanted throughout life, if one may judge

115

by records, a good deal of both, ever demanding with one half of him strong and continuous action, and with the other half high and clean thought and behaviour. The desire for the best both in material and spiritual things remained with him through life. He felt things deeply; and but for his strange balance, and a yearning for inward peace which never seems to have deserted him, his ship might well have gone down in tragedy.

To those who had watched that journey, his voyage through life seemed favourable, always on the top of the weather. He had worked hard, and he had played hard, but never too hard. And though one might often see him irritated, I think no one ever saw him bored. He perceived a joke quicker than most of us; he was never eccentric, yet fundamentally independent of other people's opinions, and perhaps a little unconscious that there were better men than he. Not that he was conceited, for of this quality, so closely allied to stupidity and humbug, he had about as much as the babe unborn. He was, indeed, a natural foe to anæmia in any of its forms, just as he was instinctively hostile to gross bull-beef men and women. The words, " a bullying chap," were used by him as crushing dispraise. I can recall him now in his chair after dinner, listening to one who, puffing his cigarette, is letting himself go on a stream of robustious, rather swaggering complacencies; with what a comprehending straight look he regards the speaker, not scornful, not sarcastic, but simply, as it were, saying: " No, my young buck, for all your fine full-blooded talk, and all your red face, you are what I see you to be, and you will do what I tell you to do!" Such men had no chance with him when it came to the tug of war; he laid his will on them as if they had been children.

He was that rather rare thing, a pure-blooded Englishman; having no strain of Scotch, Welsh, Irish, or foreign blood in his pedigree for four hundred years at least. He sprang from a long line of farmers intermarrying with their kind in the most southern corner of Devonshire, and it is probable that Norse and British blood were combined in him in a high state of equality. Even in the actual situation of his place of origin, the principle of balance had been maintained, for the old farmhouse from which his grandfather had emerged had been perched close to the cliff. Thus, to the making of him had gone land and sea, the Norseman and the Celt.

Articled to the Law at the age of sixteen by his father, a

Plymouth merchant, whose small ancient ships traded to the Mediterranean in fruits, leather, and wines, he had come to London, and at the earliest possible date (as was the habit with men in those times) had been entered on the rolls as a solicitor. Often has he told me of the dinner he gave in honour of that event. " I was a thread-paper, then," he would say (indeed, he never became fat),—" We began with a barrel of oysters." About that and other festivities of his youth there was all the rich and rollicking flavour of the days of Pickwick. He was practically dependent on his own exertions from the time he began to practise his profession, and it was characteristic of him that he never seems to have been hard pressed for money. The inherent sanity and moderation of his instincts preserved him, one imagines, from the financial ups and downs of most young men, for there was no niggardliness in him, and a certain breadth of conception characterised his money affairs throughout life. It was rather by the laws of gravity, therefore, whereby money judiciously employed attracts money, and the fact that he lived in that moneymaker's Golden Age, the nineteenth century, that he had long been (at the age of eighty) a wealthy man. Money was to him the symbol of a well-spent, well-ordered life, provocative of warmth in his heart because he loved his children, and was careful of them to a fault. He did not marry till he was forty-five, but his feeling for the future of his family manifested itself with the birth of his first child. Selecting a fair and high locality, not too far away from London, he set himself at once to make a country place, where the little things should have fresh air, new milk, and all the fruits of the earth, home-grown round them. Quite wonderful was the forethought he lavished on that house and little estate stretching down the side of a hill, with its walled gardens, pasture, corn-land and coppice. All was solid, and of the best, from the low four-square red brick house with its concrete terrace and French windows, to the cow-houses down by the coppice. From the oak trees, hundreds of years old, on the lawns, to the peach trees just planted along the south sunny walls. But here, too, there was no display for the sake of it, and no extravagance. Everything was at hand, from home-baked bread, to mushrooms wild and tame; from the stables with their squat clock-tower, to pigsties; from roses that won all the local prizes, to bluebells; but nothing redundant or pretentious.

The place was an endless pleasure to him, who to the last preserved his power of taking interest, not only in great, but in little things. Each small triumph over difficulty—the securing of hot water in such a quarter, the better lighting of another, the rescue of the nectarines from wasps, the quality of his Alderney cows, the encouragement of rooks—afforded him as much simple and sincere satisfaction as every little victory he achieved in his profession, or in the life of the Companies which he directed. But with all his shrewd practical sense, and almost naïve pleasure in material advantage, he combined a very real spiritual life of his own. Nor was there anything ascetic in that inner life. It was mellow as the music of Mozart, his most beloved composer; Art and Nature, both had their part in it. He was, for instance, very fond of opera, but only when it could be called "grand"; and it grieved him that opera was no longer what it had been, yet was it secretly a grave satisfaction that he had known those classical glories denied to the present generation. He loved indeed almost all classical music, but (besides Mozart) especially Beethoven, Gluck, and Meyerbeer, whom he insisted (no less than Herbert Spencer) on considering a great composer. Wagner he tried very hard to appreciate and, after visiting Bayreuth, even persuaded himself that he had succeeded, though he never ceased to point out the great difference that existed between this person and Mozart. He loved the Old Masters of painting, having for favourites amongst the Italians: Rafael, Correggio, Titian, Tintoretto; and amongst Englishmen Reynolds and Romney. On the other hand, he regarded Hogarth and Rubens as coarse, but Vandyke he very much admired, because of his beautiful painting of hands, the hall-mark, he would maintain, of an artist's quality. I cannot remember his feeling about Rembrandt, but Turner he certainly distrusted as extravagant. Botticelli and the earlier masters he had not as yet quite learned to relish; and Impressionism, including Whistler, never really made conquest of his taste, though he always resolutely kept his mind open to what was modern—feeling himself young at heart.

Once on a spring day, getting over a stile, I remember him saying:

"Eighty! I can't believe it. Seems very queer. I don't feel it. Eighty!" And, pointing to a blackbird that was singing, he added: "That takes the years off you!" His love of Nature was very intimate, simple, and unconscious. I can see him standing by the pond of a summer evening watching the great flocks of starlings that visited those fields; or, with his head a little to one side, listening rapturously to a skylark. He would contemplate, too, with a sort of serene passion, sunset effects, and every kind of view.

But his greatest joy in life had been his long summer holidays, in Italy or among the Alps, and his memory was a perfect storehouse of peaks, passes, and arrivals at Italian inns. He had been a great walker, and, as an old man, was still very active. I can remember him on horseback at the age of sixty, though he had never been a sportsman—not being in the way of hunting, having insufficient patience for fishing, and preferring to spend such time as he might have had for shooting, in communing with his beloved mountains. His love for all kinds of beauty, indeed, was strangely potent; and perhaps the more natural and deep for its innocence of all tradition and formal culture. He got it, I think, from his mother, of whom he always spoke with reverence as "the most beautiful woman in the Three Towns." Yes, his love of beauty was a sensuous, warm glow pervading the whole of him, secretly separating him from the majority of his associates. A pretty face, a beautiful figure, a mellow tune, the sight of dancing, a blackbird's song, the moon behind a poplar tree, starry nights, sweet scents, and the language of Shakespeare—all these moved him deeply, the more perhaps because he had never learned to express his feelings. His attempts at literature indeed were strangely naïve and stilted; his verse, in the comic vein, rather good; but all, as it were, like his period, ashamed to express any intimate feeling except in classical language. Yet his literary tastes were catholic; Milton was his favourite poet, Byron he also admired; Browning he did not care for; his favourite novelist was George Eliot, and, curiously enough—in later life—Turgenev. I well remember when the translated volumes of that author were coming out, how he would ask for another of those yellow books. He did not know why he liked them, with all those "crack-jaw" Russian names; but assuredly it was because they were written by one who worshipped beauty.

The works of Dickens and Thackeray he read with appreciation, on the whole, finding the first perhaps a little too grotesque, and the second a little too satiric. Scott, Trollope,

Marryat, Blackmore, Hardy, and Mark Twain also pleased him;
but Meredith he thought too " misty."

A great theatre-goer all his life, he was very lukewarm towards modern actors, comparing them adversely with those
constellations of the past, Edmund and Charles Kean, Charlie
Mathews, Farren, Power, " little Robson," and Helen Faucit.
He was, however, a great lover of Kate Vaughan's dancing; an
illustration of the equanimity of one who had formed his taste
on Taglioni.

Irving he would only accept in *Louis XI., The Bells,* and, I
think, *Charles I.,* and for his mannerisms he had a great aversion. There was something of the old grand manner about his
theatre habits. He attended with the very best and thinnest
lavender kid gloves on his hands, which he would hold up rather
high and clap together at the end of an act which pleased him;
even, on memorable occasions adding the word " Bravo." He
never went out before the end of a play, however vehemently
he might call it " poor stuff," which, to be quite honest, he did
about nine times out of ten. And he was ever ready to try
again, having a sort of touching confidence in an art which had
betrayed him so often. His opera hats were notable, usually
of such age as to have lost shape, and surely the largest in
London. Indeed, his dress was less varied than that of any man
I have ever seen; but always neat and well-cut, for he went
habitually to the best shops, and without eccentricity of any
kind. He carried a repeating gold watch and thin round gold
chain which passed, smooth and sinuous as a little snake, through
a small black seal with a bird on it; and he never abandoned
very well made side-spring boots with cork soles, greatly resenting the way other boots dirtied his hands, which were thin
and brown with long polished nails, and blue veins outstanding.
For reading only, he wore tortoise-shelled eyeglasses, which
he would perch low down on the bridge of his nose, so that he
could look over them, for his eyes were very long-sighted. He
was extremely fastidious in his linen, and all personal matters,
yet impatient of being mollycoddled, or in any way over-valeted.
Even on the finest days, he carried an umbrella, the ferrule of
which, from his habit of stumping it on the pavement, had a
worn and harassed look, and was rarely more than half present.

Having been a Conservative Liberal in politics till well past
sixty, it was not until Disraeli's time that he became a Liberal
Conservative. This was curious, for he always spoke doubtfully

of "Dizzy," and even breathed the word "humbug" in connection with him. Probably he was offended by what he termed "the extravagance" in Dizzy's rival. For the Duke of Devonshire and Lord Salisbury he had respect without enthusiasm; and conceived for John Bright a great admiration as soon as he was dead. But on the whole the politician who had most attracted him had been Palmerston, because—if memory serves —he had in such admirable degree the faculty of "astonishing their weak nerves." For, though never a Jingo, and in later days both cautious and sane in his Imperialism, he had all a Briton's essential deep-rooted distrust of the foreigner. He felt that they were not quite safe, not quite sound, and must from time to time be made to feel this. Born two years after the battle of Waterloo, he had inherited a certain high pride of island birth. And yet in one case, where he was for years in close contact with a foreigner he conceived for him so grave a respect, that it was quite amusing to watch the discomfiture of his traditional distrust. It was often a matter of wonder amongst those who knew him that a man of his ability and judgment had never even sought to make his mark in public affairs. Of the several reasons for this, the chief was, undoubtedly, the extraordinary balance of his temperament. To attain pre-eminence in any definite department of life would have warped and stunted too many of his instincts, removed too many of his interests; and so he never specialised in anything. He was quite unambitious, always taking the lead in whatever field he happened to be, by virtue of his great capacity and will-power, but never pushing himself, and apparently without any life-aim, but that of leading a sane, moderate, and harmonious existence.

And it is for this that he remains written on the national page, as the type of a lost and golden time, when life to each man seemed worth living for its own sake, without thought of its meaning as a whole, or much speculation as to its end. There was something classical, measured, and mellow in his march adown the years, as if he had been god-mothered by Harmony. And yet, though he said his prayers and went to church, he could not fairly have been called a religious man; for at the time when he formed his religious habits, "religion" had as yet received no shocks, and reigned triumphant over an unconscious nation whose spirit was sleeping; and when "religion," disturbed to its foundations, began to die, and people all round him

were just becoming religious enough to renounce the beliefs
they no longer held, he was too old to change, and continued to
employ the mechanism of a creed which had never really been
vital to him. He was in essence pagan: All was right with
his world! His love was absorbed by Nature, and his wonder by
the Great Starry Scheme he felt all around. This was God to
him; for it was ever in the presence of the stars that he was
most moved to a sense of divine order. Looking up at those
tremulous cold companions he seemed more reverent, and awed,
than ever he was in the face of creeds or his fellow man.
Whether stirred by the sheer beauty of Night, or by its dark
immensity swarming with those glittering worlds, he would
stand silent, and then, perhaps, say wistfully: "What little
bits of things we are! Poor little wretches!" Yes, it was then
that he really worshipped, adoring the great wonders of Eter-
nity. No one ever heard him talk with conviction of a future
life. He was far too self-reliant to accept what he was told,
save by his own inner voice; and that did not speak to him with
certainty. In fact, as he grew old, to be uncertain of all such
high things was part of his real religion; it seemed to him, I
think, impertinent to pretend to intimate knowledge of what was
so much bigger than himself. But neither his conventional
creed, nor that awed uncertainty which was his real religion were
ever out of hand; they jogged smoothly on in double harness,
driven and guided by a supremer power—his reverence for Life.
He abhorred fanaticism. In this he truly mirrored the spirit
of that great peacefully expanding river, the Victorian Era,
which began when he came of age. And yet, in speaking before
him of deep or abstract things, it was not safe to reckon without
his criticism, which would sometimes make powerfully shrewd
deductions out of the sheer logical insight of a nature neither
fundamentally concerned with other worlds, nor brought up to
the ways of discussion. He was pre-eminently the son of a time
between two ages—a past age of old, unquestioning faith in
authority; a future age of new faith, already born but not yet
grown. Still sheltering in the shade of the old tree which was
severed at the roots and toppling, he never, I think, clearly
saw—though he may have had glimpses—that men, like children whose mother has departed from their home, were slowly
being forced to trust in, and be good to, themselves and to one
another, and so to form out of their necessity, desperately, unconsciously, their new great belief in Humanity. Yes, he was

the son of *a time between two ages*—the product of an era without real faith—an individualist to the core.

His attitude towards the poor, for instance, was essentially that of man to man. Save that he could not tolerate impostors (one of his favourite words), and saw through them with almost startling rapidity, he was compassionate to any who had fallen on evil fortune, and especially to those who had been in any way connected with him. But in these almonary transactions he was always particularly secretive, as if rather doubting their sagacity, and the wisdom of allowing them to become known—himself making up and despatching the parcels of old clothes, and rather surreptitiously producing such coins and writing such cheques as were necessary. But "the poor," in bulk, were always to him the concern of the Poor Law pure and simple, and in no sense of the individual citizen. It was the same with malefactors, he might pity as well as condemn them, but the idea that the society to which he and they belonged was in any way responsible for them, would never have occurred to him. His sense of justice, like that of his period, was fundamentally based on the notion that every man had started with equal, or at all events, with quite sufficient opportunities, and must be judged as if he had. But, indeed, it was not the custom in his day to concern oneself with problems outside one's own class. Within that class, and in all matters domestic, no man was ever born with a nicer sense of justice. It was never overridden by his affections; very seldom, and that with a certain charming *naïveté,* by his interests. This sense of justice, however, in no way prevented him from being loved; for, in spite of a temper apt to take fire, flare up, and quickly die down again, he was one of the most lovable of men. There was not an ounce of dourness or asperity in his composition. His laughter was of a most infectious kind, singularly spontaneous and delightful, resembling the laughter of a child. The change which a joke wrought in the aspect of his large, dignified, and rather noble face, was disconcerting. It became wrinkled, or, as it were, crumpled; and such a twinkling overcame his eyes as was frequently only to be extinguished by moisture. "That's rich!" was his favourite expression to describe what had tickled him; for he had preserved the use of Devonshire expressions, bringing them forth from an intimate pet drawer of memory, and lingering over them with real gusto. He still loved, too, such Devonshire dishes of his boyhood as "junket" and "toad in the hole";

and one of his favourite memories was that of the meals snatched at the old coaching inn at Exeter, while they changed the horses of the Plymouth to London coach. Twenty-four hours at ten miles an hour, without ever a break! Glorious drive! Glorious the joints of beef, the cherry brandy! Glorious the old stage coachman, a "monstrous fat chap" who at that time ruled the road!

In the City, where his office was situated, he was wont, though at all times a very moderate eater, to frequent substantial, old-fashioned hostelries such as Roche's, Pim's, or Birch's in preference to newer and more pretentious places of refreshment. He had a remarkable palate too, and though he drank very little, was, in his prime, considered as fine a judge of wine as any in London. Of tea he was particularly fond, and always consumed the very best Indian, made with extreme care, maintaining that the Chinese variety was only fit for persons of no taste.

He had little liking for his profession, believing it to be beneath him, and that Heaven had intended him for an advocate; in which he was probably right, for his masterful acumen could not have failed to assure him a foremost position at the Bar. And in him, I think, it is certain that a great Judge was lost to the State. Despite this contempt for what he called the "pettifogging" character of his occupation, he always inspired profound respect in his clients; and among the shareholders of his Companies, of which he directed several, his integrity and judgment stood so high that he was enabled to pursue successfully a line of policy often too comprehensive and far-seeing for the temper of the times. The reposeful dignity, and courage, of his head and figure when facing an awkward General Meeting could hardly have been exceeded. He sat, as it were, remote from its gusty temper, quietly determining its course.

Truly memorable were his conflicts with the only other man of his calibre on those Boards, and I cannot remember that he was ever beaten. He was at once the quicker tempered and more cautious. And if he had not the other's stoicism and iron nerve, he saw further into the matter in hand, was more unremitting in his effort, equally tenacious of purpose, and more magnetic. In fact, he had a way with him.

But, after all said, it was in his dealings with children that the best and sweetest side of his personality was manifested. With them he became completely tender, inexhaustibly interested in their interests, absurdly patient, and as careful as a mother. No child ever resisted him, or even dreamed of doing so. From the first moment they loved his white hair and beard, his "feathers" as one little thing called them. They liked the touch of his thin hand, which was never wet or cold; and, holding to it, were always ready to walk with him—wandering with complete unanimity, not knowing quite where or for what reason. How often have I not watched him starting out on that high adventure with his grandson, his face turned gravely down towards a smaller face turned not quite so gravely up; and heard their voices tremendously concerned with all the things they might be going to do together! How often have I not seen them coming back tired as cats, but still concerned about what was next going to happen! And children were always willing to play cricket with him because he bowled to them very slowly, pitching up what he called "three-quarter" balls, and himself always getting "out" almost before he went in. For, though he became in his later years a great connoisseur of cricket, spending many days at Lord's or the Oval, choosing out play of the very highest class, and quite impatient of the Eton and Harrow Match, he still performed in a somewhat rococo fashion, as of a man taught in the late twenties of the last century, and having occasion to revive that knowledge about 1895. He bent his back knee, and played with a perfectly crooked bat, to the end that when he did hit the ball, which was not too often, it invariably climbed the air. There was, too, about his batting, a certain vein of recklessness or bravado, somewhat out of keeping with his general character, so that, as has been said, he was never in too long. And when he got out he would pitch the bat down as if he were annoyed, which would hugely please his grandson, showing of course that he had been trying his very best, as indeed, he generally had. But his bowling was extremely impressive, being effected with very bent knees, and a general air of first putting the ball to the eye, as if he were playing bowls; in this way he would go on and on giving the boy "an innings," and getting much too hot. In fielding he never could remember on the spur of the moment whether it was his knees or his feet that he ought to close; and this, in combination with a habit of bending rather cautiously, because he was liable to lumbago, detracted somewhat from his brilliance; but when the ball was once in his hands, it was most exciting—impossible to tell whether he would throw it at the running batsman, the wicket, or the bowler, according as the game appeared to him at the moment to be double wicket, single wicket, or rounders. He had lived in days when games were not the be-all and end-all of existence, and had never acquired a proper seriousness in such matters. Those who passed from cricket with him to cricket in the cold wide world found a change for which at first they were unable to account. But even more fascinating to children than his way of playing cricket was his perfect indentification with whatever might be the matter in hand. The examination of a shell, the listening to the voice of the sea imprisoned in it, the making of a cocked hat out of *The Times* newspaper, the doing up of little buttons, the feeding of pigeons with crumbs, the holding fast of a tiny leg while walking beside a pony, all these things absorbed him completely, so that no visible trace was left of the man whose judgment on affairs was admirable and profound. Nor, whatever the provocation, could he ever bring himself to point the moral of anything to a child, having that utter toleration of their foibles which only comes from a natural and perfectly unconscious love of being with them. His face, habitually tranquil, wore in their presence a mellow look of almost devil-may-care serenity.

Their sayings, too, he treasured, as though they were pearls. First poems, such as:

> " I sorr a worm,
>   It was half-ly dead;
> I took a great spud,
>   And speared through his head "

were to him of singular fair promise. Their diagnoses of character, moreover, especially after visiting a circus, filled him with pure rapture, and he would frequently repeat this one:

" Father, is Uncle a clever man? "

" H'm! well—yes, certainly."

" I never seen no specimens. He can't balance a pole on his nose, for instance."

To the declining benison of their prayers, from their " darling father and mother," to " all poor people who are in distress," he loved to listen, not so much for the sentiments expressed, as because, in their little night-gowns, they looked so sweet, and were so roundabout in their way of getting to work.

Yes, children were of all living things his chosen friends, and they knew it.

But in his long life he made singularly few fast friendships with grown-up people, and, as far as I know, no enemies. For there was in him, despite his geniality, a very strong vein of fastidiousness, and such essential deep love of domination, that he found, perhaps, few men of his own age and standing to whom he did not feel natively superior. His most real and lifelong friendship was for a certain very big man with a profound hatred of humbug and a streak of "the desperate character" in him. They held each other in the highest esteem, or, as they would probably have put it, swore by one another; the one grumbling at, but reverencing, the other's high and resolute equanimity; the other deploring and admiring the one's deep and generous recklessness. The expressions: "Just like John, the careful fellow!" "Just like Sil, reckless beggar!" were always on their lips; for like all their generation they were sparing of encomium; and great, indeed, must have been their emotion before they would show their feelings. Dear as they were to each other's hearts, they never talked together of spiritual things, they never spoke in generalities, but gravely smoking their cigars, discussed their acquaintances, investments, wine, their nephews and grandchildren, and the affairs of the State—condemning the advertising fashion in which everything was now done. Once in a while they would tell a story—but they knew each other's stories too well; once in a while quote a line of Byron, Shakespeare, or Milton; or whistle to each other, inharmoniously, a bar or two from some song that Grisi, Mario, or Jenny Lind had sung. Once in a while memories of the heyday of their youth, those far-off golden hours, stealing over them, they would sit silent, with their grave steady eyes following the little rings of bluish smoke. . . . Yes, for all their lack of demonstration, they loved each other well.

I seem still to see the subject of this portrait standing at his friend's funeral one bleak November day, the pale autumn sunlight falling on the silver of his uncovered head a little bowed, and on his grave face, for once so sad. I hear the tones of his voice, still full and steady; and from the soul in his eyes, looking as it were, through and through those forms of death to some deep conclusion of his own. I know how big and sane and sweet he was.

His breed is dying now, it has nearly gone. But as I remember him with that great quiet forehead, with his tenderness, and his glance which travelled to the heart of what it rested on, I despair of seeing his like again. For, with him there seems to me to have passed away a principle, a golden rule of life, nay, more, a spirit—the soul of Balance. It has stolen away, as in the early morning the stars steal out of the sky. *He* knew its tranquil secret, and where he is, there must it still be hovering.

1910.

THE GREY ANGEL

HER predilection for things French came from childish recollections of schooldays in Paris and a hasty removal thence by her father during the revolution of '48; of later travels as a little maiden, by diligence, to Pau and the then undiscovered Pyrenees, to Montpellier, and a Nice as yet unspoiled. Unto her seventy-eighth year, her French accent had remained unruffled, her soul in love with French gloves and dresses; and her face had the pale, unwrinkled, slightly aquiline perfection of the French marquise type—it may, perhaps, be doubted whether any French marquise ever looked the part so perfectly.

How it came about that she had settled down in a southern French town, in the summer of 1914, only her roving spirit knew. She had been a widow ten years, which she had passed in the quest of perfection; all her life she had been haunted by that instinct, half-smothered in ministering to her husband, children, and establishments in London and the country. Now, in loneliness, the intrinsic independence of her soul was able to assert itself, and from hotel to hotel she had wandered in England, Wales, Switzerland, France, till she had found what seemingly arrested her. Was it the age of that oldest of Western cities, that little mother of Western civilisation, which captured her fancy? Or did a curious perversity turn her from more obvious abodes; or, again, was she kept there by the charm of a certain church which she would enter every day to steep herself in mellow darkness, the scent of incense, the drone of incantations, and quiet communion with a God higher indeed than she had been brought up to, high-church though she had always been? She had a pretty little apartment, where for very little—the bulk of her small wealth was habitually at the service of others—she could manage with one maid and no " fuss." She had some " nice " French friends there, too. But more probably it was simply the war which kept her, waiting, like so many other people, till it seemed worth while to move and re-establish herself. The immensity and wickedness of this

129

strange event held her suspended, body and spirit, high up on
the hill which had seen the ancient peoples, the Romans, Gauls,
Saracens, and still looked out towards the flat Camargue. Here
in her three rooms, with a little kitchen, the maid Augustine,
a parrot, and the Paris *Daily Mail,* she dwelt marooned by a
world event which stunned her. Not that she worried, exactly.
The defeat of her country and France never entered her head.
She only grieved quietly over the dreadful things that were
being done, and every now and then would glow with admiration at the beautiful way the King and Queen were behaving.
It was no good to " fuss," and one must make the best of things,
as the " dear little Queen" was doing—for each Queen in
turn, and she had seen three reign in her time, was always that
to her. Her ancestors had been uprooted from their lands,
their house burned, her pedigree diverted, in the Stuart wars;
and a reverence for royalty was fastened in her blood.

Quite early in the business she had begun to knit, moving her
slim fingers not too fast, gazing at the grey wool through
glasses, rimless and invisible, perched on the bridge of her firm
well-shaped nose, and now and then speaking to her parrot.
The bird could say, " Scratch a poll, Poll," and " Hullo!"—
those keys to the English language. The maid Augustine, having
completed some small duty, would come and stand, her head
on one side, gazing down with inquiring compassion in her
young, clear-brown eyes. It seemed to her, straight and sturdy
as a young tree, both wonderful and sad that *Madame* should
be seventy-seven, and so frail—*Madame* who had no lines in
her face and such beautiful grey hair; who had so strong a
will-power, too, and knitted such soft comforters *" pour nos
braves chers poilus."* And suddenly she would say: *" Madame
n'est pas fatiguée?"* And *Madame* would answer: " No.
Speak English, Augustine—Polly will pick up your French!"
And, reaching up a pale hand, she would set straight a stray
fluff of the girl's dark-brown hair or improve the set of her
fichu.

Those two got on extremely well, for though *Madame* was—
oh! but very particular, she was always *" très gentille et toujours grande dame."* And that love of form deep in the
French soul promoted the girl's admiration for one whom she
could see would in no circumstances lose her dignity. Besides,
Madame was full of dainty household devices, and could not
bear waste; and these, though exacting, were qualities which

appealed to Augustine. With her French passion for "the family," she used to wonder how in days like these *Madame* could endure to be far away from her son and daughter and the grandchildren, whose photographs hung on the walls; and the long letters her mistress was always writing in a beautiful, fine hand, beginning, "My darling Sybil," "My darling Reggie," and ending always, "Your devoted mother," seemed to a warm and simple heart but meagre substitutes for flesh-and-blood realities. But, as *Madame* would inform her, they were so busy doing things for the dear soldiers, and working for the war; they could not come to her—that would never do. And to go to them would give so much trouble, when the railways were so wanted for the troops; and she had their lovely letters, which she kept—as Augustine observed—in a lavender-scented sachet, and frequently took out to read. Another point of sympathy between those two was their passion for military music and seeing soldiers pass. Augustine's brother and father were at the front, and *Madame's* dead brother had been a soldier in the Crimean War—"long before you were born, Augustine, when the French and English fought the Russians: I was in France then, too, a little girl, and we lived at Nice; the flowers were so lovely, you can't think! And my poor brother was so cold in the siege of Sebastopol." Somehow, that time and that war were more real to her than this.

In December, when the hospitals were already full, her French friends took her to the one which they attended. She went in, her face very calm, with that curious inward composure which never deserted it, carrying in front of her a black silk bag, wherein she had concealed an astonishing collection of treasures for the poor men. A bottle of acidulated drops, packets of cigarettes, two of her own mufflers, a pocket set of draughts, some English riddles translated by herself into French (very curious), some ancient copies of an illustrated paper, boxes of chocolate, a ball of string to make "cats' cradles" (such an amusing game), her own packs of patience cards, some photograph frames, postcards of Arles, and, most singular, a kettle-holder. At the head of each bed she would sit down and rummage in the bag, speaking in her slow but quite good French, to explain the use of the acidulated drops, or to give a lesson in cats' cradles. And the *poilus* would listen with their polite, ironic patience, and be left smiling, curiously fascinated, as if they had been visited by a creature from another world.

She would move on to other beds, quite unconscious of the
effect she had produced on them and of their remarks: "*L'ange
aux cheveux gris*" became her name within those walls. And
the habit of filling that black silk bag and going there to
distribute its contents soon grew to be with her a ruling passion
which neither weather nor her own aches and pains, not inconsiderable, must interfere with. The things she brought became more marvellous every week. But, however much she
carried coals to Newcastle, or tobacco pouches to those who did
not smoke, or homeopathic globules to such as crunched up the
whole bottleful for the sake of the sugar as soon as her back
was turned, no one ever smiled now with anything but real
pleasure at the sight of her calm and truly sweet smile and the
scent of soap on her pale hands. "*Cher fils, je croyais que ceci
vous donnerait un peu de plaisir. Voyez-vous comme c'est
commode, n'est ce pas?*" Each newcomer to the wards was
warned by his comrades that the angel with the grey hair was
to be taken without a smile, exactly as if she were his grandmother.

In the walk to the hospital Augustine would accompany her,
carrying the bag and a large peasant's umbrella to cover them
both, for the winter was hard and snowy, and carriages cost
money, which must now be kept entirely for the almost daily
replenishment of the bag and other calls of war. The girl, to
her chagrin, was always left in a safe place, for it would never
do to take her in and put fancies into her head, or excite the
dear soldiers with anything so taking. The visit over, they
would set forth home, walking very slowly in the high narrow
streets, Augustine pouting a little and shooting swift glances
at anything in uniform, and *Madame* making firm her lips
against a fatigue which sometimes almost overcame her before
she could get home and up the stairs. And the parrot would
greet them indiscreetly with new phrases—" Keep smiling!"
and " Kiss Augustine!" which he sometimes varied with " Kiss
a poll, Poll!" or " Scratch Augustine!" to *Madame's* regret.
Tea would revive her, and then she would knit, for as time
went on and the war seemed to get farther from that end which,
in common with so many, she had expected before now, it
seemed dreadful not to be always doing something to help the
poor dear soldiers; and for dinner, to Augustine's horror, she
now had nothing but soup, or an egg beaten up with milk and
brandy. It saved time and expense—she was sure people ate

too much; and afterward she would read the *Daily Mail,* often putting it down to sigh, and press her lips together, and think, " One must look on the bright side of things," and wonder a little where it was. And Augustine, finishing her work in the tiny kitchen, would sigh too, and think of red trousers and peaked caps, not yet out of date in that southern region, and of her own heart saying " Kiss Augustine ! " and she would peer out between the shutters at the stars sparkling over the Camargue, or look down where the ground fell away beyond an old wall, and nobody walked in the winter night; and muse on her nineteenth birthday coming, and sigh with the thought that she would be old before anyone had loved her; and of how *Madame* was looking " *très fatiguée.*"

Indeed, *Madame* was *très fatiguée* " in these days. The world's vitality and her own were at January ebb. But to think of oneself was impossible; it would be all right presently, and one must not fuss, or mention in one's letters to the dear children that one felt poorly. As for a doctor—that would be sinful waste, and besides, what use were they except to tell you what you knew? And she was terribly vexed when Augustine found her in a faint one morning, and she found Augustine in tears, with her hair all over her face. She rated the girl soundly for making such a fuss over " a little thing like that," and with extremely trembling fingers pushed the brown hair back and told her to wash her face, while the parrot said reflectively, " Scratch a poll—Hullo ! " The girl, who had seen her own grandmother die not long before, and remembered how " *fatiguée* " she had been during her last days, was frightened. Coming back after washing her face, she found her mistress writing on a number of little envelopes the same words : " *En bonne Amitié.*"

" Take this hundred-franc note, Augustine, and get it changed into single francs—the ironmonger will do it if you say it's for me. I am going to take a rest. I shan't buy anything for the bag for a whole week. I shall take francs instead."

" Oh, *Madame!* You must not go out: *vous êtes trop fatiguée.*"

" Nonsense ! How do you suppose our dear little Queen in England would get on with all she has to do, if she were to give in like that? We must none of us give up in these days. Help me to put on my things; I am going to church."

" Oh, *Madame!* Must you go to church? It is not your kind of church. You do not pray there, do you? "

" Of course I pray there. I am very fond of the dear old church. God is in every church, Augustine; you ought to know that at your age."

" But *Madame* has her own religion? "

" Don't be silly. What does that matter? Help me into my cloth coat—not the fur, it's too heavy—and then go and get that money changed."

" But *Madame* should see a doctor. If *Madame* faints again I shall die with fright. *Madame* has no colour—but no colour at all; it must be that there is something wrong."

Madame rose, and taking the girl's ear between thumb and finger pinched it gently.

" You are a very silly girl. What would our soldiers do if all the nurses were like you? "

Reaching the church she sat down gladly, turning her face up toward her favourite picture, a Virgin standing with her Baby in her arms. It was only faintly coloured now; but there were those who said that an Arlésienne must have sat for it. Why it pleased her so she never quite knew, unless by its cool, unrestored devotion, and the faint smiling in the eyes. Religion with her was strange yet very real. She was not clever, and never even began to try and understand what she believed. If she tried to be good she would go to God—wherever God might be; and rarely did she forget to try to be good. Sitting there she thought, or rather prayed: " Let me forget that I have a body, and remember the poor soldiers."

She shivered. It struck cold that morning in the church— the wind bitter from the north-east; some women in black were kneeling, and four candles burned in the gloom of a side aisle— thin, steady little spires of gold. There was no sound at all. A smile came on her lips. She was remembering all those young faces in the wards, the faces, too, of her own children far away, the faces of all she loved; and all the poor souls on land and sea, fighting and working and dying. Her lips moved in prayer: " O God, who makes the birds sing and the stars shine and gives us little children, strengthen my heart so that I may forget my own aches and think of those of other people."

On reaching home again she took gelsemium, her favourite remedy against that shivering, which would keep coming; then, covering herself with her fur coat, she lay down. Augustine, returning with the hundred single francs, placed them noiselessly beside the little pile of envelopes, and, after looking at the motionless face of her mistress, withdrew. Two tears came out of those closed eyes and clung on the pale cheeks below. The seeming sleeper was thinking of her children, away over there in England, her children and their children. Almost unbearably she was longing for a sight of them, recalling each face, voice, different way they had of saying " Mother darling," or " Granny, look what I've got!" and thinking that if only the war would end she would pack at once and go to them—that is, if they would not come to her for a nice long holiday in this beautiful place. She thought of spring and how lovely it would be to see the trees come out again, and almond blossom against a blue sky. The war seemed so long, and winter too. But she must not complain; others had much greater sorrows—the poor widowed women kneeling in the church; the poor boys freezing in the trenches. God in His great mercy would not allow it to last much longer! It would not be like Him! Her eyes rested gloatingly on the piles of francs and envelopes. How could she reduce still further her personal expenditure? It was so dreadful to spend on oneself—an old woman like her. Doctor, indeed! If Augustine fussed any more she would send her away and do for herself! And the parrot, leaving his cage, which he could always do, perched just behind her and said: " Hullo! Kiss me, too!"

That afternoon in the hospital everyone noticed what a beautiful colour she had. *"L'ange aux cheveux gris"* had never been more popular.

She had not meant to give all the francs that day, but she saw how pleased they were, and so the whole ninety-seven had their franc each. The three over would buy Augustine a little brooch to make up to the silly child for her fright in the morning. The buying of this brooch took a long time at the jeweller's, and she had only just fixed on an amethyst before feeling deadly ill with a dreadful pain through her lungs. She went out with her tiny package quickly, not wanting any fuss, and began to mount toward home. She had only three hundred yards to go, and with each step said to herself: " Nonsense! What would the Queen think of you? Remember the poor soldiers with only one leg! You have got both your legs! And the poor men who walk from the battlefield with bullets through the lungs. What is your pain to theirs?" But the pain, like none

she had ever felt—having sharp knife edges—kept passing
through and through her; her legs had no strength at all,
seeming to move simply because her will said: "If you don't,
I'll leave you behind. So there!" She felt as if perspiration
were flowing down, yet her face was dry as a dead leaf when
she put up her hand to it. Her brain stammered, came to a
sudden standstill. Her eyes searched painfully each grey-
shuttered window for her own house, though she knew quite
well that she had not reached it yet. From sheer pain she stood
still, a wry smile on her lips, thinking how Polly would say:
"Keep smiling!" Then she moved on, holding out her hand,
as if to pull on some imaginary rope. So, foot by foot, she
crept to her door. A peculiar floating sensation had come over
her. The pain ceased, and—as if she had passed through no
doors, mounted no stairs—she was up in her room, lying on her
sofa, conscious that she was not in control of her thoughts, and
that Augustine must be thinking her ridiculous. Making a
great effort, she said:

"I forbid you to send for a doctor, Augustine. I shall be
all right in a day or two. And you must put on this little
brooch—I bought it for you. The war will be over to-morrow,
and then we will all go and have tea together in a wood. Granny
will come to you, my darlings."

And when the terrified girl had rushed out she thought:
"There now! I shall get up and do for myself." The doctor
found her half-dressed, trying to feed a perch in the empty
cage with a spoon, while the parrot sat on the mantelpiece, with
his head on one side.

When she had been properly undressed and made to lie down
on the sofa, for she would not go to bed and they dared not
oppose her, the doctor made his diagnosis. It was that of double
pneumonia, which declares for life or death in forty-eight hours.
At her age a desperate case. Her children must be wired to
at once. She had sunk back, seemingly unconscious; and
Augustine slipped out the lavender sachet where the letters
were kept and gave it to the doctor. When he had left the
room to extract addresses and send those telegrams, the girl
sat down by the foot of the couch, staring at that motionless
form, with tears running down her broad cheeks. For many
minutes neither of them stirred, and the only sound was the
restless stropping of the parrot's beak against a wire of his

cage. Then the lips moved, and the girl bent forward. A whispering came forth:

"Mind, Augustine—no one is to tell my children—I can't have them disturbed—over a little thing—like this—and in my purse you'll find another—hundred-franc note. I shall want some more francs for the day after to-morrow. Be a good girl and don't fuss. Give me my gelsemium and my prayer-book. And go to bed just as usual—we must all—keep smiling—like the dear soldiers——" The whispering ceased; then began again in delirious incoherence. The girl sat trembling, covering her ears from those uncanny sounds. She could not follow —with her little English—the swerving, intricate flights of that old spirit mazed by fever—the memories released, the longings disclosed, the half-uttered prayers, the little half-conscious efforts to regain form and dignity. She could only pray to the Virgin. When relieved by the daughter of *Madame's* French friend, who spoke good English, she murmured: *"Oh! Mademoiselle, Madame est très, très fatiguée—la pauvre tête— faut-il enlever les cheveux? Elle fait ça toujours pour elle-même."* To the girl it seemed sacrilege to take off that crown of fine grey hair. Yet, when the old face was covered only by the thin white hair of nature, dignity still surmounted the wandering talk and the moaning from the parched lips, which smiled and pouted, as if remembering the maxims of the parrot. So the night passed. Once her spirit seemed to recover its coherence, and she was heard to whisper: "God has given me this so that I may know what the poor soldiers suffer. Oh! they've forgotten to cover Polly's cage." But high fever soon passes from the very old; and early morning brought a deathlike exhaustion, with utter silence, save for the licking of the flames at the olive-wood logs, and the sound as they slipped or settled down, calcined. The firelight crept fantastically about the walls covered with tapestry of French-grey silk, crept round the screen-head of the couch, and exhibited the pallor of that mask-like face, which covered such tenuous threads of life. Augustine, who had come on guard when the fever died away, sat in the armchair before those flames, trying to watch, but dropping off into the healthy sleep of youth. And out in the clear, hard shivering Southern cold, the old clocks chimed the hours into the winter dark, where the old town brooded above plain and river under the morning stars. The girl dreamed—dreamed of a sweetheart under the acacias by her home, of his pinning their white flowers into her hair; and woke with a little laugh. Light was already coming through the shutter chinks, the fire was but red embers and white ash. She gathered it stealthily together, put on fresh logs, and stole over to the couch. How white! how still! Dead? She jerked her hands up to her full breast, and a cry mounted to her throat. The eyes opened. The lips parted, as if to smile; the voice whispered: "Don't be silly!" The girl's cry changed into a little sob, and bending down she put her lips to the hand outside the quilt. It moved faintly, the lips whispered: "The emerald ring is for you, Augustine. Is it morning? Uncover Polly's cage and open his door."

A telegram had come. Her son and daughter would arrive next morning early. They waited for a moment of consciousness to tell her; but the day went by, and it did not come. She was sinking fast; her only movements were a tiny compression now and then of the lips, a half-opening of the eyes, and once a smile when the parrot spoke. The rally came at eight o'clock. *Mademoiselle* was sitting by the couch when the voice came fairly strong: "Give my love to my dear soldiers, and take them their francs out of my purse, please. Augustine, take care of Polly. I want to see if the emerald ring fits you. Take it off, please. There, you see, it does. That's very nice. Your sweetheart will like that when you have one. What do you say, *Mademoiselle?* My son and daughter are coming? All that way?" The lips smiled, tears forced their way into her eyes. "My darlings! How good of them! Oh! what a cold journey they'll have! Get my room ready, Augustine, with a good fire! What are you crying for? Remember what Polly says: 'Keep smiling!'"

She did not seem anxious as to whether she would live to see her children. Her smile moved *Mademoiselle* to whisper: "*Elle a la sourire divine.*"

"*Ah! Mademoiselle, elle pense toujours aux autres.*" And the girl's tears dropped on the emerald ring.

The long night fell—would she wake again? Both watched, ready at the faintest movement to administer oxygen and brandy. She was still breathing when at six o'clock they heard the express come in and presently the carriage stop before the house. *Mademoiselle* stole down to let them in.

Still in their travelling coats, her son and daughter knelt down beside the couch, watching in the dim candle-light for a sign and cherishing her cold hands. Daylight came; they put the shutters back and blew out the candles. Augustine, huddled in the far corner, cried gently to herself. *Mademoiselle* had withdrawn. The two still knelt, tears running down their cheeks. The least twitching of just-opened lips showed that she breathed. A tiny sigh escaped; her eyelids fluttered. The son, leaning forward, said:

" Sweetheart, we're here."

The eyes opened then; something more than a simple human spirit seemed to look through—the lips parted. They bent to catch the sound.

" My darlings—don't cry; smile!" The eyes closed. A smile, so touching that it rent the heart, flickered and went out. Breath had ceased to pass the lips.

In the silence the French girl's sobbing rose; the parrot stirred in his still-covered cage. And the son and daughter knelt, pressing their faces against the couch.

1917.

QUALITY

I KNEW him from the days of my extreme youth, because he made my father's boots; inhabiting with his elder brother two little shops let into one, in a small by-street—now no more, but then most fashionably placed in the West End.

That tenement had a certain quiet distinction; there was no sign upon its face that he made for any of the Royal Family— merely his own German name of Gessler Brothers; and in the window a few pairs of boots. I remember that it always troubled me to account for those unvarying boots in the window, for he made only what was ordered, reaching nothing down, and it seemed so inconceivable that what he made could ever have failed to fit. Had he bought them to put there? That, too, seemed inconceivable. He would never have tolerated in his house leather on which he had not worked himself. Besides, they were too beautiful—the pair of pumps, so inexpressibly slim, the patent leathers with cloth tops, making water come into one's mouth, the tall brown riding-boots with marvellous sooty glow, as if, though new, they had been worn a hundred years. Those pairs could only have been made by one who saw before him the Soul of Boot—so truly were they prototypes, incarnating the very spirit of all footgear. These thoughts, of course, came to me later, though even when I was promoted to him, at the age of perhaps fourteen, some inkling haunted me of the dignity of himself and brother. For to make boots—such boots as he made—seemed to me then, and still seems to me, mysterious and wonderful.

I remember well my shy remark, one day, while stretching out to him my youthful foot:

" Isn't it awfully hard to do, Mr. Gessler? "

And his answer, given with a sudden smile from out of the sardonic redness of his beard: " Id is an Ardt! "

Himself, he was a little as if made from leather, with his yellow crinkly face, and crinkly reddish hair and beard, and neat folds slanting down his cheeks to the corners of his mouth, and his guttural and one-toned voice; for leather is a sardonic substance, and stiff and slow of purpose. And that was the character of his face, save that his eyes, which were grey-blue had in them the simple gravity of one secretly possessed by the Ideal. His elder brother was so very like him—though watery, paler in every way, with a great industry—that sometimes in early days I was not quite sure of him until the interview was over. Then I knew that it was he, if the words, " I will ask my brudder," had not been spoken; and that, if they had, it was his elder brother.

When one grew old and wild and ran up bills, one somehow never ran them up with Gessler Brothers. It would not have seemed becoming to go in there and stretch out one's foot to that blue iron-spectacled glance, owing him for more than —say—two pairs, just the comfortable reassurance that one was still his client.

For it was not possible to go to him very often—his boots lasted terribly, having something beyond the temporary—some, as it were, essence of boot stitched into them.

One went in, not as into most shops, in the mood of: " Please serve me, and let me go! " but restfully, as one enters a church; and, sitting on the single wooden chair, waited—for there was never anybody there. Soon, over the top edge of that sort of well—rather dark, and smelling soothingly of leather—which formed the shop, there would be seen his face, or that of his elder brother, peering down. A guttural sound, and the tip-tap of bast slippers beating the narrow wooden stairs, and he would stand before one without coat, a little bent, in leather apron, with sleeves turned back, blinking—as if awakened from some dream of boots, or like an owl surprised in daylight and annoyed at this interruption.

And I would say: " How do you do, Mr. Gessler? Could you make me a pair of Russia leather boots? "

Without a word he would leave me, retiring whence he came, or into the other portion of the shop, and I would continue to rest in the wooden chair, inhaling the incense of his trade. Soon he would come back, holding in his thin, veined hand a piece of gold-brown leather. With eyes fixed on it, he would remark: " What a beaudiful biece! " When I, too, had admired it, he would speak again. " When do you wand dem? " And I would answer: " Oh! As soon as you conveniently

can." And he would say: "To-morrow fordnighd?" Or if
he were his elder brother: "I will ask my brudder!"

Then I would murmur: "Thank you! Good-morning Mr.
Gessler." "Goot-morning!" he would reply, still looking at
the leather in his hand. And as I moved to the door, I would
hear the tip-tap of his bast slippers restoring him, up the stairs,
to his dream of boots. But if it were some new kind of footgear that he had not yet made me, then indeed he would observe ceremony—divesting me of my boot and holding it long
in his hand, looking at it with eyes at once critical and loving,
as if recalling the glow with which he had created it, and re-
buking the way in which one had disorganised this masterpiece.
Then, placing my foot on a piece of paper, he would two or
three times tickle the outer edges with a pencil and pass his
nervous fingers over my toes, feeling himself into the heart of
my requirements.

I cannot forget that day on which I had occasion to say to
him: "Mr. Gessler, that last pair of town walking-boots
creaked, you know."

He looked at me for a time without replying, as if expecting
me to withdraw or qualify the statement, then said:

"Id shouldn'd 'ave greaked."

"It did, I'm afraid."

"You goddem wed before dey found demselves?"

"I don't think so."

At that he lowered his eyes, as if hunting for memory of
those boots, and I felt sorry I had mentioned this grave thing.

"Zend dem back!" he said; "I will look at dem."

A feeling of compassion for my creaking boots surged up in
me, so well could I imagine the sorrowful long curiosity of
regard which he would bend on them.

"Zome boods," he said slowly, "are bad from birdt. If
I can do noding wid dem, I dake dem off your bill."

Once (once only) I went absent-mindedly into his shop in
a pair of boots bought in an emergency at some large firm's.
He took my order without showing me any leather, and I could
feel his eyes penetrating the inferior integument of my foot.
At last he said:

"Dose are nod my boods."

The tone was not one of anger, nor of sorrow, not even of
contempt, but there was in it something quiet that froze the
blood. He put his hand down and pressed a finger on the place

where the left boot, endeavouring to be fashionable, was not quite comfortable.

"Id 'urds you dere," he said. "Dose big virms 'ave no self-respect. Drash!" And then, as if something had given way within him, he spoke long and bitterly. It was the only time I ever heard him discuss the conditions and hardships of his trade.

"Dey get id all," he said, "dey get id by adverdisement, nod by work. Dey dake it away from us, who lofe our boods. Id gomes to this—bresently I haf no work. Every year id gets less —you will see." And looking at his lined face I saw things I had never noticed before, bitter things and bitter struggle—and what a lot of grey hairs there seemed suddenly in his red beard!

As best I could, I explained the circumstances of the purchase of those ill-omened boots. But his face and voice made a so deep impression that during the next few minutes I ordered many pairs. Nemesis fell! They lasted more terribly than ever. And I was not able conscientiously to go to him for nearly two years.

When at last I went I was surprised to find that outside one of the two little windows of his shop another name was painted, also that of a bootmaker—making, of course, for the Royal Family. The old familiar boots, no longer in dignified isola-tion, were huddled in the single window. Inside, the now contracted well of the one little shop was more scented and darker than ever. And it was longer than usual, too, before a face peered down, and the tip-tap of the bast slippers began. At last he stood before me, and, gazing through those rusty iron spectacles, said:

"Mr.——, isn'd it?"

"Ah! Mr. Gessler," I stammered, "but your boots are really *too* good, you know! See, these are quite decent still!" And I stretched out to him my foot. He looked at it.

"Yes," he said, "beople do nod wand good boods, id seems."

To get away from his reproachful eyes and voice I hastily remarked: "What have you done to your shop?"

He answered quietly: "Id was too exbensif. Do you wand some boods?"

I ordered three pairs, though I had only wanted two, and quickly left. I had, I know not quite what feeling of being part, in his mind, of a conspiracy against him; or not perhaps so much against him as against his idea of boot. One does not, I suppose, care to feel like that; for it was again many months before my next visit to his shop, paid, I remember, with the feeling: "Oh! well, I can't leave the old boy—so here goes! Perhaps it'll be his elder brother!"

For his elder brother, I knew, had not character enough to reproach me, even dumbly.

And, to my relief, in the shop there did appear to be his elder brother, handling a piece of leather.

"Well, Mr. Gessler," I said, "how are you?"

He came close, and peered at me.

"I am breddy well," he said slowly; "but my elder brudder is dead."

And I saw that it was indeed himself—but how aged and wan! And never before had I heard him mention his brother. Much shocked, I murmured: "Oh! I am sorry!"

"Yes," he answered, "he was a good man, he made a good bood; but he is dead." And he touched the top of his head, where the hair had suddenly gone as thin as it had been on that of his poor brother, to indicate, I suppose, the cause of death. "He could nod ged over losing de oder shop. Do you wand any boods?" And he held up the leather in his hand: "Id's a beaudiful biece."

I ordered several pairs. It was very long before they came —but they were better than ever. One simply could not wear them out. And soon after that I went abroad.

It was over a year before I was again in London. And the first shop I went to was my old friend's. I had left a man of sixty, I came back to one of seventy-five, pinched and worn and tremulous, who genuinely, this time, did not at first know me.

"Oh! Mr. Gessler," I said, sick at heart; "how splendid your boots are! See, I've been wearing this pair nearly all the time I've been abroad; and they're not halfworn out, are they?"

He looked long at my boots—a pair of Russia leather, and his face seemed to regain steadiness. Putting his hand on my instep, he said:

"Do dey vid you here? I 'ad drouble wid dat bair, I remember."

I assured him that they had fitted beautifully.

"Do you wand any boods?" he said. "I can make dem quickly; id is a slack dime."

I answered: "Please, please! I want boots all round—every kind!"

"I will make a vresh model. Your food must be bigger." And with utter slowness, he traced round my foot, and felt my toes, only once looking up to say:

"Did I dell you my brudder was dead?"

To watch him was painful, so feeble had he grown; I was glad to get away.

I had given those boots up, when one evening they came. Opening the parcel, I set the four pairs out in a row. Then one by one I tried them on. There was no doubt about it. In shape and fit, in finish and quality of leather, they were the best he had ever made me. And in the mouth of one of the town walking-boots I found his bill. The amount was the same as usual, but it gave me quite a shock. He had never before sent it in till quarter day. I flew downstairs and wrote a cheque, and posted it at once with my own hand.

A week later, passing the little street, I thought I would go in and tell him how splendidly the new boots fitted. But when I came to where his shop had been, his name was gone. Still there, in the window, were the slim pumps, the patent leathers with cloth tops, the sooty riding-boots.

I went in, very much disturbed. In the two little shops—again made into one—was a young man with an English face.

"Mr. Gessler in?" I said.

He gave me a strange, ingratiating look.

"No, sir," he said, "no. But we can attend to anything with pleasure. We've taken the shop over. You've seen our name, no doubt, next door. We make for some very good people."

"Yes, yes," I said; "but Mr. Gessler?"

"Oh!" he answered; "dead."

"Dead! But I only received these boots from him last Wednesday week."

"Ah!" he said; "a shockin' go. Poor old man starved 'imself."

"Good God!"

"Slow starvation, the doctor called it! You see he went to work in such a way! Would keep the shop on; wouldn't have a soul touch his boots except himself. When he got an order, it took him such a time. People won't wait. He lost everybody. And there he'd sit, goin' on and on—I will say that for him—not a man in London made a better boot! But look at the competition! He never advertised! Would 'ave the best leather, too, and do it all 'imself. Well, there it is. What could you expect with his ideas?"

"But starvation——!"

"That may be a bit flowery, as the sayin' is—but I know myself he was sittin' over his boots day and night, to the very last. You see I used to watch him. Never gave 'imself time to eat; never had a penny in the house. All went in rent and leather. How he lived so long I don't know. He regular let his fire go out. He was a character. But he made good boots."

"Yes," I said, "he made good boots."

1911.

THE MAN WHO KEPT HIS FORM

IN these days every landmark is like Alice's flamingo-croquet-mallet—when you refer to it, the creature curls up into an interrogation mark and looks into your face; and every corner-stone resembles her hedgehog-croquet-ball, which, just before you can use it, gets up and walks away. The old flavours of life are out of fashion, the old scents considered stale; "gentle-man" is a word to sneer at, and "form" a sign of idiocy.

And yet there are families in the British Isles in which gentility has persisted for hundreds of years, and though you may think me old-fashioned and romantic, I am convinced that such gentlefolk often have a certain quality, a kind of inner pluck bred into them, which is not to be despised at all.

This is why I tell you my recollections of Miles Ruding.

My first sight of him—if a new boy may look at a monitor—was on my rather wretched second day at a Public School. The three other pups who occupied an attic with me had gone out, and I was ruefully considering whether I had a right to any wall-space on which to hang two small oleographs depicting very scarlet horsemen on very bay horses, jumping very brown hedges, which my mother had bought me, thinking they might be suitable to the manly taste for which Public Schools are celebrated. I had taken them out of my playbox, together with the photographs of my parents and eldest sister, and spread them all on the window-seat. I was gazing at the little show lugubriously when the door was opened by a boy in "tails."

"Hallo!" he said. "You new?"

"Yes," I answered in a mouselike voice.

"I'm Ruding. Head of the house. You get an allowance of two bob weekly when it's not stopped. You'll see the fagging lists on the board. You don't get any fagging the first fort-night. What's your name?"

"Bartlet."

149

"Oh! Ah!" he examined a piece of paper in his hand.
"You're one of mine. How are you getting on?"

"Pretty well."

"That's all right." He seemed about to withdraw, so I
asked him hastily: "Please, am I allowed to hang these
pictures?"

"Rather—any pictures you like. Let's look at them!" He
came forward. When his eyes fell on the array, he said
abruptly: "Oh! Sorry!" and, taking up the oleos, he turned
his back on the photographs. A new boy is something of a
psychologist out of sheer fright, and when he said "Sorry!"
because his eyes had fallen on the effigies of my people, I felt
somehow that he couldn't be a beast. "You got these at Tompkins'," he said. "I had the same my first term. Not bad. I
should put 'em up here."

While he was holding them to the wall I took a "squint"
at him. He seemed to me of a fabulous height—about five
feet ten, I suppose; thin, and bolt upright. He had a stickup
collar—"barmaids" had not yet come in—but not a very high
one, and his neck was rather long. His hair was peculiar,
dark and crisp, with a reddish tinge; and his dark-grey eyes
were small and deep in, his cheekbones rather high, his cheeks
thin and touched with freckles. His nose, chin, and cheek-
bones all seemed a little large for his face as yet. If I may put
it so, there was a sort of unfinished finish about him. But
he looked straight, and had a nice smile.

"Well, young Bartlet," he said, handing me back the pictures,
"buck up, and you'll be all right."

I put away my photographs, and hung the oleos. Ruding!
The name was familiar. Among the marriages in my family
pedigree, such as "—daughter of Fitzherbert," "daughter of
Tastborough," occurred the entry: "daughter of Ruding"—
some time before the Civil War. Daughter of Ruding! This
demigod might be a far-off kinsman. But I felt I should never
dare to tell him of the coincidence.

Miles Ruding was not brilliant, but pretty good at everything. He was not well dressed—you did not think of dress
in connection with him either one way or the other. He was
not exactly popular—being reserved, far from showy, and not
rich—but he had no "side," and never either patronised or
abused his juniors. He was not indulgent to himself or others,
but he was very just; and, unlike many monitors, seemed to

take no pleasure in " whopping." He never fell off in " trials "
at the end of a term, and was always playing as hard at the
finish of a match as at the start. One would have said he had
an exacting conscience, but he was certainly the last person
to mention such a thing. He never showed his feelings, yet
he never seemed trying to hide them, as I used always to be.
He was greatly respected without seeming to care; an independent, self-dependent bird, who would have cut a greater
dash if he hadn't been so, as it were, uncreative. In all those
two years I only had one at all intimate talk with him, which,
after all, was perhaps above the average number, considering
the difference in our ages. In my fifth term and Ruding's last
but one, there had been some disciplinary rumpus in the house,
which had hurt the dignity of the captain of the football " tor-
pid " eleven—a big Irish boy who played back and was the
mainstay of the side. It happened on the eve of our first house
match, and the sensation may be imagined when this important
person refused to play; physically and spiritually sore, he declared for the part of Achilles and withdrew to his tent. The
house rocked with pro and con. My sympathies, in common
with nearly all below the second fifth, lay with Donelly against
the sixth form. His defection had left me captain of the side,
so that the question whether we could play at all depended on
me. If I declared a sympathetic strike, the rest would follow.
That evening, after long hours of " fronde " with other rebellious spirits, I was alone and still in two minds, when Ruding
came into my room. He leaned against the door, and said:
" Well, Bartlet, you're not going to rat? "

" I—I don't think Donelly ought to have been—been
whopped," I stammered.

" That's as may be," he said, " but the house comes first.
You know that."

Torn between the loyalties, I was silent.

" Look here, young Bartlet," he said suddenly, " it'll be a
disgrace to us all, and it hangs on you."

" All right," I said sulkily, " I'll play."

" Good chap! "

" But I don't think Donelly ought to have been whopped,"
I repeated inanely; " he's—he's too big."

Ruding approached till he looked right down on me in my
old " froust," as we called armchairs. " One of these days,"
he said slowly, " you'll be head of the house yourself. You'll

have to keep up the prestige of the sixth form. If you let great
louts like Donelly cheek little weak six-formers with impunity"
(I remember how impressed I was by the word), "you'll let
the whole show down. My old governor runs a district in Ben-
gal, about as big as Wales, entirely on prestige. He's often
talked to me about it. I hate whopping anybody, but I'd much
rather whop a lout like Donelly than I would a little new chap.
He's a swine, anyway, for turning the house down because his
back is sore."

"It isn't that," I said, "it—it wasn't just."

"If it was unjust," said Ruding, with what seems to me now
extraordinary patience, "then the whole system's wrong, and
that's a pretty big question, young Bartlet. Anyway, it's not for
me to decide. I've got to administer what is. Shake hands, and
do your damnedest to-morrow, won't you?"

I put out my hand with a show of reluctance, though secretly
won over.

We got an awful hiding, but I can still hear Ruding's voice
yelling: "Well played, Bartlet! Well pla-a-ayed!"

I have only one other school recollection of Miles Ruding
which lets any real light in on him. On the day he left for
good I happened to travel up to Town in the same carriage.
He sat looking through the window back at the old Hill, and I
distinctly saw a tear run down his cheek. He must have been
conscious that I had remarked the phenomenon, for he said
suddenly:

"Damn! I've got a grit in my eye," and began to pull the
eyelid down in a manner which did not deceive me in the least.

I then lost sight of him completely for several years. His
people were not well off, and he did not go up to the 'Varsity.
He once said to me: "My family's beastly old, and beastly
poor."

It was during one of my Odysseys in connection with sport
that I saw him again. He was growing fruit on a ranch in
Vancouver Island. Nothing used to strike a young Englishman
travelling in the Colonies more than the difference between
what he saw and what all printed matter led him to expect.
When I ran across Ruding in the Club at Victoria and he in-
vited me to stay with him, I expected rows of fine trees with
large pears and apples hanging on them, a colonial house with
broad verandah, and Ruding in ducks, among rifles and fishing
rods, and spirited horses. What I found was a bare new

wooden house, not yet painted, in a clearing of the heavy forest. His fruit trees had only just been planted, and he would be lucky if he got a crop within three years. He wore, not white ducks, but blue jeans, and worked about twelve hours a day, felling timber and clearing fresh ground. He had one horse to ride and drive, and got off for a day's shooting or fishing about once a month. He had three Chinese boys working under him, and lived nearly as sparingly as they. He had been out of England eight years, and this was his second venture—the first in Southern California had failed after three years of drought. He would be all right for water here, he said; which seemed likely enough in a country whose rainfall is superior to that of England.

"How the devil do you stand the loneliness?" I said.

"Oh! one gets used to it. Besides, this isn't lonely—good Lord, no! You should see some places!"

Living this sort of life, he yet seemed exactly what he used to be—in fact, he had kept his form. He didn't precisely dress for dinner, but he washed. He had English papers sent out to him, and read Victorian poetry, and history natural and unnatural, in the evenings over his pipe. He shaved every day, had his cold tub every morning, and treated his Chinese boys just as he used to treat us new boys at school; so far as I could tell, they seemed to have for him much the feelings we used to have—a respect not amounting to fear, and a liking not quite rising to affection.

"I couldn't live here without a woman," I said one evening.

He sighed. "I don't want to mess myself up with anything short of a wife; and I couldn't ask a girl to marry me till the place is fit for her. This fruit-growing's always a gamble at first."

"You're an idealist," I said.

He seemed to shrink, and it occurred to me suddenly that if there were anything he hated, it would be a generalisation like that. But I was in a teasing mood.

"You're keeping up the prestige of the English gentleman."

His teeth gritted on his pipe-stem. "I'm dashed if I'm keeping up anything except my end; that's quite enough."

"And exactly the same thing," I murmured.

He turned away. I felt he was much annoyed with me for trying to introduce him to self-consciousness. And he was right! It's destructive; and his life held too many destructive elements—silence, solitude, distance from home, and this daily mixing with members of an Eastern race. I used to watch the faces of his Chinese boys—remote as cats, wonderfully carved, and old, and self-sufficient. I appreciate now how much of what was carved and old and self-sufficient Ruding needed in himself to live year in, year out, alone among them, without losing his form. All that week of my visit I looked with diabolical curiosity for some sign of deterioration—of the coarsening or softening which one felt ought naturally to come of such a life. Honestly, I could not find a trace, save that he wouldn't touch whisky, as if he were afraid of it, and shied away at any mention of women.

"Aren't you ever coming home?" I asked when I was taking leave.

"When I've made good here," he said, "I shall come back and marry."

"And then out again?"

"I expect so. I've got no money, you know."

Four years later I happened to see the following in *The Times*: "Ruding—Fuljambe: At St. Thomas's, Market Harborough, Miles Ruding of Bear Ranch, Vancouver Island, to Blanche, daughter of Charles Fuljambe, J. P., Market Harborough." So it seemed he *had* made good! But I wondered what "daughter of Fuljambe" would make of it out there. Well, I came across Ruding and his wife that very summer at Eastbourne, where they were spending the butt end of their long honeymoon. She was pleasant, pretty, vivacious—too vivacious I felt when I thought of Bear Ranch; and Ruding himself, under the stimulus of his new venture, was as nearly creative as I ever saw him. We dined and bathed, played tennis and went riding on the Downs together. Daughter of Fuljambe was quite "a sport"—though, indeed, in 1899 that word had hardly come into use. I confess to wondering why, exactly, she had married my friend, till she gave me the history of it one evening. It seems their families were old neighbours, and when Ruding came back after having been away in the New World for twelve years, he was something of a curiosity, if not of a hero. He had been used to take her out hunting when she was a small child, so that she had an old-time reverence for him. He seemed, in his absence of small-talk and "side," superior to the rattle-pated young men about her—here daughter of Fuljambe gave me a side-long glance—and one day he had

done a thing which toppled her into his arms. She was to go
to a fancy dress ball one evening as a Chinese lady. But in
the morning a cat upset a bottle of ink over her dress and reduced
it to ruin. What was to be done? All the elaborate mask
of make-up and head-dressing, which she had rehearsed to
such perfection, sacrificed for want of a dress to wear it with!
Ruding left that scene of desolation possessed by his one great
creative impulse. It seemed that he had in London a Chinese
lady's dress which he had brought home with him from San
Francisco. No trains from Market Harborough could possibly
get him up to Town and back in time, so he had promptly
commandeered the only neighbouring motor car, driven it up at
a rate which must have approached forty miles an hour—a
really fabulous speed for those days—got the dress, sent daughter
of Fuljambe a wire, motored back at the same furious pace, and
appeared before her door with the dress at eight forty-five.
Daughter of Fuljambe received him in her dressing-gown, with
her hair combed up and her face beautifully painted. Ruding
said quietly: "Here you are; it's the genuine thing," and
disappeared before she had time to thank him. The dress was
superior to the one the cat had spoiled. That night she accepted
him. "Miles didn't properly propose to me," she said; "I saw
he couldn't bear to, because of what he'd done, so I just had
to tell him not to keep his form so awfully. And here we are!
He *is* a dear, isn't he?"

In his dealings with her he certainly was, for she was a self-
centred little person.

They went off to Vancouver Island in September. The following January I heard that he had joined a Yeomanry con-
tingent and gone out to fight the Boers. He left his wife in
England with her people on his way. I met her once or twice
before he was invalided home with enteric. She told me that
she had opposed his going, till she found out it was making him
quite miserable. "And yet, you know," she said, "he's frightfully devoted."

When he recovered they went back to Vancouver Island,
where he found his ranch so let down that he had to begin
nearly all over again. I can imagine what he went through with
his dainty and exacting helpmate. She came home in 1904 to
get over it, and again I met her out hunting.

"Miles is too good for me," she said the second day as we
were jogging home; "he's got such fearful pluck. If only

he'd kick his conscience out of the window sometimes. Oh! Mr. Bartlet, I don't want to go back there—I really don't; it's simply deadly. But he says if he gives this up he'll be thirty-eight without a thing to show for it, and just have to cadge round for a job, and he won't do that; but I don't believe I can stand it much longer."

I wrote to Ruding. His answer was dry and inexpressive, but I could read between the lines: Heaven forbid that he should drag his wife out to him again, but he would have to stick it there another two years; then, perhaps he could sell and buy a farm in England. To clear out now would be ruination. He missed his wife awfully, but—one must hoe one's row, and he would rather she stayed with her people than force herself to rough it out there with him.

Then, of course, came that which a man like Ruding, with his loyalty and his sense of form, is the last to imagine possible. Daughter of Fuljambe met a young man in the Buffs or Greens or Blues, and after, I am sure, a struggle—she was not a bad little sort—went off with him. That happened early in 1906, just as he was beginning to see the end of his struggle with Bear Ranch. I felt very sorry for him, yet inclined to say: "My dear man, where was your imagination; couldn't you see this was bound to happen with 'daughter of Fuljambe' once she got away from you?" And yet, poor devil, what could he have done?

He came home six thousand miles to give her a divorce. A ghoulish curiosity took me into Court. I never had more whole-hearted admiration for Ruding than I had that day, watching him in that pretentiously crooked Court among us tight-lipped, curly-minded lawyers, giving his unemotional evidence. Straight, thin, lined and brown, with grey already in his peculiar-coloured hair, his voice low, his eyes unwavering, in all his lonely figure a sad, quiet protest—it was not I only who was moved by the little speech he made to the Judge: "My Lord, I should like to say that I have no bitter feelings; I think it was my fault for asking a woman to share a rough, lonely life, so far away." It gave me a queer pleasure to see the little bow the Judge made him, as if saying: "Sir, as one gentleman to another." I had meant to get hold of him after the case, but when it came to the point I felt it was the last thing he would want of anyone. He went straight back the six thousand miles and sold his ranch. Cunningham, who used to be in our house, and had a Government post in Esquimault, told me that Ruding made himself quite unpopular over that sale. Some enterprising gentleman, interested in real estate, had reported the discovery of coal seams, which greatly enhanced the value of Bear Ranch and several neighbouring properties. Ruding was offered a big sum. He took it, and had already left the neighbourhood when the report about coal was duly disproved. Ruding at once offered to cancel the price, and take the agricultural value of the property. His offer was naturally accepted, and the disgust of other owners who had sold on the original report may be imagined. More wedded to the rights of property, they upheld the principle " Caveat emptor," and justified themselves by calling Ruding names. With his diminished proceeds he bought another ranch on the mainland.

How he spent the next eight years I only vaguely know. I don't think he came home at all. Cunningham spoke of him as " Still the same steady-going old chap, awfully respected; but no one knows him very well. He looks much as he did, except that he's gone grey."

Then, like a bolt from hell, came the Great War. I can imagine Ruding almost glad. His imagination would not give him the big horror of the thing; he would see it as the inevitable struggle, the long-expected chance to show what he and his country were made of. And I must confess that on the evidence he seems to have been made of even better stuff than his country. He began by dyeing his hair. By dint of this and by slurring the eight of his age so that it sounded like forty odd, he was accepted, and, owing to his Transvaal experience, given a commission in Kitchener's army. But he did not get out to France till early in 1916. He was considered by his Colonel the best officer in the regiment for training recruits, and his hair, of course, had soon gone grey again. They said he chafed terribly at being kept at home. In the spring of 1916 he was mentioned in despatches, and that summer was badly gassed on the Somme. I went to see him in hospital. He had grown a little grey moustache, but otherwise seemed quite unchanged. I grasped at once that he was one of those whose nerve—no matter what happened to him—would see it through. One had the feeling that this would be so as a matter of course, that he himself had not envisaged any other possibility. He was so completely lost in the winning of the war that his own sensations seemed to pass him by. He had become as much of a soldier as the best of those professionally unimaginative stoical creatures, and quite naturally, as if it were in his blood. He dwelt quietly, without visible emotion, in that universal atmosphere of death. All was in the day's work, so long as the country emerged victorious; nor did there seem the least doubt in his mind but that it would so emerge. A part of me went with him all the way, but a part of me stared at him in curiosity, surprise, admiration, and a sort of contempt, as at a creature too single-hearted and uncomplicated. One side of me was bred like him—armorial bearings, daughter of Ruding, and all the rest of it—the other had new blood with all its doubts and ferments.

I saw him several times in that hospital at Teignmouth, where he recovered slowly.

One day I asked him point blank whether one's nerve was not bound to go in time. He looked a little surprised and said rather coldly: "Not if your heart's in the right place."

That was it to a T. His heart was so deeply rooted in exactly the right place that nothing external could get at it. Whatever downed Ruding would have to blow him up bodily— there was no detaching his heart from the rest of him. And that's what I mean by an inbred quality, the inner pluck that you can bet on. I don't say it's not to be found in private soldiers and "new" people, but not in quite the same—shall we say?—matter-of-course way. When those others have it, they're proud of it or conscious of it, or simply primitively virile and thick-skinned; they don't—like such as Ruding— regard not having it as "impossible," a sort of disgrace. If scientists could examine the nerves of men like him, would they discern a faint difference in their colour or texture—the result of generations of nourishment above the average and of a traditional philosophy which for hundreds of years has held fear to be *the* cardinal offence? I wonder.

He went out again in 1917, and was out for the rest of the war. He did nothing very startling or brilliant; but, as at school, he was always on the ball, finishing as hard as when he started. At the Armistice he was a Lieutenant-Colonel, and a Major when he was gazetted out, at the age of fifty-three, with the various weaknesses which gas and a prolonged strain leave in a man of that age, but no pensionable disability. He went back to Vancouver. Anyone at all familiar with fruit-growing knows it for a pursuit demanding the most even and constant attention. When Ruding joined up he had perforce left his ranch in the first hands which came along; and at that time, with almost every rancher in like case, those hands were very poor substitutes for the hands of an owner. He went back to a property practically valueless. He was not in sufficient health to sit down for another long struggle to pull it round, as after the Boer War, so he sold it for a song and came home again, full of confidence that, with his record, he would get a job. He found that his case was that of thousands. They didn't want him back in the Army. They were awfully sorry, but they didn't know what they could do for him. The Governmental education and employment schemes, too, seemed all for younger men. He sat down on the song and the savings from his pay to wait for some ship or other out of his fleet of applications to come home. It did not come; his savings went. How did I know all this? I will tell you.

One night last January I had occasion to take a cab from a restaurant in Soho to my Club in Pall Mall. It was wet, and I got in hastily. I was sitting there comatose from my good dinner when I had a queer feeling that I knew the back of the driver. It had—what shall I call it?—a refined look. The man's hair was grey; and I began trying to recollect the profile I had glimpsed when bolting in. Suddenly with a sort of horror the thought flashed through me: Miles Ruding!

It was!

When I got out and we looked each other in the face, he smiled and my lips quivered. " Old chap," I said, " draw your cab up on that stand and get in with me."

When we were sitting together in his cab we lighted cigarettes, and didn't speak for quite a minute, till I burst out:

" Look here! What does this mean? "

" Bread and butter."

" Good God! And this is what the country——"

" Bartlet," he said, through curiously set lips, with a little fixed smile about the corners, " cut out all that about the country. I prefer this to any more cadging for a job; that's all."

Silent from shame, I broke out at last: " It's the limit! What about the Government schemes? "

" No go! they're all for younger men."

" My dear chap! " was all I could find to say.

"This isn't a bad life in good weather," he went on with that queer smile; "I haven't much of a chest now."

"Do you mean to say you contemplate going on with this?"

"Till something turns up; but I'm no good at asking for things, Bartlet; I simply can't do it."

"What about your people?"

"Dead or broke."

"Come and stay with me till your ship comes home."

He squeezed my arm and shook his head. That's what's so queer about gentility! If only I could have established a blood tie! Ruding would have taken help or support from his kins-folk—would have inherited without a qualm from a second cousin that he'd never seen; but from the rest of the world it would be charity. Sitting in that cab of his, he told me, with-out bitterness, the tale which is that of hundreds since the war. Ruding one could not pity to his face, it would have been im-possible. And, when he had finished, I could only mutter:

"Well, I think it's damnable, considering what the country owes you."

He did not answer. You can say what you like about his limitations, but Miles Ruding was bred to keep his form.

I nearly shook his hand off when I left him, and I could see that he disliked that excessive display of feeling. From my Club doorway I looked round. He had resumed his driver's seat, and, through the rain, I saw him with the cigarette be-tween his lips, and the lamplight shining on his lean profile. Very still he sat—symbol of that lost cause, gentility.

1920.

THE JAPANESE QUINCE

As Mr. Nilson, well known in the City, opened the window of his dressing-room on Campden Hill, he experienced a peculiar sweetish sensation in the back of his throat, and a feeling of emptiness just under his fifth rib. Hooking the window back, he noticed that a little tree in the Square Gardens had come out in blossom, and that the thermometer stood at sixty. ' Perfect morning,' he thought; ' spring at last!'

Resuming some meditations on the price of Tintos, he took up an ivory-backed hand-glass and scrutinised his face. His firm, well-coloured cheeks, with their neat brown moustaches, and his round, well-opened, clear grey eyes, wore a reassuring appearance of good health. Putting on his black frock coat, he went downstairs.

In the dining-room his morning paper was laid out on the sideboard. Mr. Nilson had scarcely taken it in his hand when he again became aware of that queer feeling. Somewhat concerned, he went to the French window and descended the scrolled iron steps into the fresh air. A cuckoo clock struck eight.

' Half an hour to breakfast,' he thought; ' I'll take a turn in the Gardens.'

He had them to himself, and proceeded to pace the circular path with his morning paper clasped behind him. He had scarcely made two revolutions, however, when it was borne in on him that, instead of going away in the fresh air, the feeling had increased. He drew several deep breaths, having heard deep breathing recommended by his wife's doctor; but they augmented rather than diminished the sensation—as if some sweetish liquor in course within him, together with a faint aching just above his heart. Running over what he had eaten the night before, he could recollect no unusual dish, and it occurred to him that it might possibly be some smell affecting him. But he could detect nothing except a faint sweet lemony scent,

161

rather agreeable than otherwise, which evidently emanated from the bushes budding in the sunshine. He was on the point of resuming his promenade, when a blackbird close by burst into song, and, looking up, Mr. Nilson saw at a distance of perhaps five yards a little tree, in the heart of whose branches the bird was perched. He stood staring curiously at this tree, recognising it for that which he had noticed from his window. It was covered with young blossoms, pink and white, and little bright green leaves both round and spiky; and on all this blossom and these leaves the sunlight glistened. Mr. Nilson smiled; the little tree was so alive and pretty! And instead of passing on, he stayed there smiling at the tree.

'Morning like this!' he thought; 'and here I am the only person in the Square who has the—to come out and——!' But he had no sooner conceived this thought than he saw quite near him a man with his hands behind him, who was also staring up and smiling at the little tree. Rather taken aback, Mr. Nilson ceased to smile, and looked furtively at the stranger. It was his next-door neighbour, Mr. Tandram, well known in the City, who had occupied the adjoining house for some five years. Mr. Nilson perceived at once the awkwardness of his position, for, being married, they had not yet had occasion to speak to one another. Doubtful as to his proper conduct, he decided at last to murmur: "Fine morning!" and was passing on, when Mr. Tandram answered: "Beautiful, for the time of year!" Detecting a slight nervousness in his neighbour's voice, Mr. Nilson was emboldened to regard him openly. He was of about Mr. Nilson's own height, with firm, well-coloured cheeks, neat brown moustaches, and round, well-opened, clear grey eyes; and he was wearing a black frock coat. Mr. Nilson noticed that he had his morning paper clasped behind him as he looked up at the little tree. And, visited somehow by the feeling that he had been caught out, he said abruptly:

"Er—can you give me the name of that tree?"

Mr. Tandram answered:

"I was about to ask you that," and stepped towards it. Mr. Nilson also approached the tree.

"Sure to have its name on, I should think," he said.

Mr. Tandram was the first to see the little label, close to where the blackbird had been sitting. He read it out.

"Japanese quince!"

"Ah!" said Mr. Nilson, "thought so. Early flowerers."

" Very," assented Mr. Tandram, and added: " Quite a feelin'
in the air to-day."

Mr. Nilson nodded.

" It was a blackbird singin'," he said.

" Blackbirds," answered Mr. Tandram, " I prefer them to
thrushes myself; more body in the note." And he looked at
Mr. Nilson in an almost friendly way.

" Quite," murmured Mr. Nilson. " These exotics, they don't
bear fruit. Pretty blossom! " and he again glanced up at the
blossom, thinking: ' Nice fellow, this, I rather like him.'

Mr. Tandram also gazed at the blossom. And the little tree,
as if appreciating their attention, quivered and glowed. From
a distance the blackbird gave a loud, clear call. Mr. Nilson
dropped his eyes. It struck him suddenly that Mr. Tandram
looked a little foolish; and, as if he had seen himself, he said:
" I must be going in. Good morning! "

A shade passed over Mr. Tandram's face, as if he, too, had
suddenly noticed something about Mr. Nilson.

" Good morning," he replied, and clasping their journals to
their backs they separated.

Mr. Nilson retraced his steps towards his garden window,
walking slowly so as to avoid arriving at the same time as his
neighbour. Having seen Mr. Tandram mount his scrolled iron
steps, he ascended his own in turn. On the top step he paused.

With the slanting spring sunlight darting and quivering into
it, the Japanese quince seemed more living than a tree. The
blackbird had returned to it, and was chanting out his heart.

Mr. Nilson sighed; again he felt that queer sensation, that
choky feeling in his throat.

The sound of a cough or sigh attracted his attention. There,
in the shadow of his French window, stood Mr. Tandram, also
looking forth across the Gardens at the little quince tree.

Unaccountably upset, Mr. Nilson turned abruptly into the
house, and opened his morning paper.

1910.

THE BROKEN BOOT

THE actor, Gilbert Caister, who had been " out " for six months, emerged from his East-coast seaside lodging about noon in the day, after the opening of " Shooting the Rapids," on tour, in which he was playing Dr. Dominick in the last act. A salary of four pounds a week would not, he was conscious, remake his fortunes, but a certain jauntiness had returned to the gait and manner of one employed again at last.

Fixing his monocle, he stopped before a fishmonger's and, with a faint smile on his face, regarded a lobster. Ages since he had eaten a lobster! One could long for a lobster without paying, but the pleasure was not solid enough to detain him. He moved upstreet and stopped again, before a tailor's window. Together with the actual tweeds, in which he could so easily fancy himself refitted, he could see a reflection of himself, in the faded brown suit wangled out of the production of " Marmaduke Mandeville " the year before the war. The sunlight in this damned town was very strong, very hard on seams and buttonholes, on knees and elbows! Yet he received the ghost of æsthetic pleasure from the reflected elegance of a man long fed only twice a day, of an eyeglass well rimmed out from a soft brown eye, of a velour hat salved from the production of " Educating Simon " in 1912; and in front of the window he removed that hat, for under it was his new phenomenon, not yet quite evaluated, his *mèche blanche*. Was it an asset, or the beginning of the end? It reclined backwards on the right side, conspicuous in his dark hair, above that shadowy face always interesting to Gilbert Caister. They said it came from atrophy of the—something nerve, an effect of the war, or of under-nourished tissue. Rather distinguished, perhaps, but——!

He walked on, and became conscious that he had passed a face he knew. Turning, he saw it also turned on a short and

165

dapper figure—a face rosy, bright, round, with an air of cherubic knowledge, as of a getter-up of amateur theatricals.

Bryce-Green, by George!

"Caister? It is! Haven't seen you since you left the old camp. Remember what sport we had over 'Gotta-Grampus'? By Jove! I am glad to see you. Doing anything with yourself? Come and have lunch with me."

Bryce-Green, the wealthy patron, the moving spirit of entertainment in that south-coast convalescent camp. And, drawling slightly, Caister answered:

"I shall be delighted." But within him something did not drawl: 'By God, you're going to have a feed, my boy!'

And—elegantly threadbare, roundabout and dapper—the two walked side by side.

"Know this place? Let's go in here! Phyllis, cocktails for my friend Mr. Caister and myself, and caviare on biscuits. Mr. Caister is playing here; you must go and see him."

The girl who served the cocktails and the caviare looked up at Caister with interested blue eyes. Precious!—he had been "out" for six months!

"Nothing of a part," he drawled; "took it to fill a gap." And below his waistcoat the gap echoed: 'Yes, and it'll take some filling.'

"Bring your cocktail along, Caister; we'll go into the little further room, there'll be nobody there. What shall we have —a lobstah?"

And Caister murmured: "I love lobstahs."

"Very fine and large here. And how are you, Caister? So awfully glad to see you—only real actor we had."

"Thanks," said Caister, "I'm all right." And he thought: 'He's a damned amateur, but a nice little man.'

"Sit here. Waiter, bring us a good big lobstah and a salad; and then—er—a small fillet of beef with potatoes fried crisp, and a bottle of my special hock. Ah! and a rum omelette— plenty of rum and sugah. Twig?"

And Caister thought: 'Thank God, I do.'

They had sat down opposite each other at one of two small tables in the little recessed room.

"Luck!" said Bryce-Green.

"Luck!" replied Caister; and the cocktail trickling down him echoed: 'Luck!'

"And what do you think of the state of the drama?"

Oh! ho! A question after his own heart. Balancing his monocle by a sweetish smile on the opposite side of his mouth, Caister drawled his answer: " Quite too bally awful! "

" H'm! Yes," said Bryce-Green; "nobody with any genius, is there? "

And Caister thought: ' Nobody with any money.'

" Have you been playing anything great? You were so awfully good in ' Gotta-Grampus ' ! "

" Nothing particular. I've been—er—rather slack." And with their feel around his waist his trousers seemed to echo: ' Slack! '

" Ah! " said Bryce-Green. " Here we are! Do you like claws? "

" Tha-a-nks. Anything! " To eat—until warned by the pressure of his waist against his trousers! What a feast! And what a flow of his own tongue suddenly released—on drama, music, art; mellow and critical, stimulated by the round eyes and interjections of his little provincial host.

" By Jove, Caister! You've got a *mêche blanche*. Never noticed. I'm awfully interested in *mêches blanches*. Don't think me too frightfully rude—but did it come suddenly? "

" No, gradually."

" And how do you account for it? "

' Try starvation,' trembled on Caister's lips.

" I don't," he said.

" I think it's ripping. Have some more omelette? I often wish I'd gone on the regular stage myself. Must be a topping life, if one has talent, like you."

Topping?

" Have a cigar. Waiter! Coffee, and cigars. I shall come and see you to-night. Suppose you'll be here a week? "

Topping! The laughter and applause—" Mr. Caister's rendering left nothing to be desired; its—and its—are in the true spirit of——! "

Silence recalled him from his rings of smoke. Bryce-Green was sitting, with cigar held out and mouth a little open, and bright eyes round as pebbles, fixed—fixed on some object near the floor, past the corner of the tablecloth. Had he burnt his mouth? The eyelids fluttered; he looked at Caister, licked his lips like a dog, nervously, and said:

" I say, old chap, don't think me a beast, but are you at all

—er—er—rocky? I mean—if I can be of any service, don't hesitate! Old acquaintance, don't you know, and all that——"

His eyes rolled out again towards the object, and Caister followed them. Out there above the carpet he saw it—his own boot. It dangled slightly, six inches off the ground—split— right across, twice, between lace and toecap. Quite! He knew it. A boot left him from the rôle of Bertie Carstairs, in "The Dupe," just before the war. Good boots. His only pair, ex- cept the boots of Dr. Dominick, which he was nursing. And from the boot he looked back at Bryce-Green, sleek and con- cerned. A drop, black when it left his heart, suffused his eye behind the monocle; his smile curled bitterly; he said:

"Not at all, thanks! Why?"

"Oh! n-n-nothing. It just occurred to me." His eyes—but Caister had withdrawn the boot. Bryce-Green paid the bill and rose.

"Old chap, if you'll excuse me; engagement at half-past two. So awf'ly glad to have seen you. Good-bye!"

"Good-bye!" said Caister. "Thanks."

He was alone. And, chin on hand, he stared through his monocle into an empty coffee cup. Alone with his heart, his boot, his life to come. . . . 'And what have you been in lately, Mr. Caister?' 'Nothing very much lately. Of course I've played almost everything.' 'Quite so. Perhaps you'll leave your address; can't say anything definite, I'm afraid.' 'I— I should—er—be willing to rehearse on approval; or—if I could read the part?' 'Thank you, afraid we haven't got as far as that.' 'No? Quite! Well, I shall hear from you, per- haps.' And Caister could see his own eyes looking at the manager. God! What a look! . . . A topping life! A dog's life! Cadging—cadging—cadging for work! A life of draughty waiting, of concealed beggary, of terrible depressions, of want of food!

The waiter came skating round as if he desired to clear. Must go! Two young women had come in and were sitting at the other table between him and the door. He saw them look at him, and his sharpened senses caught the whisper:

"Sure—in the last act. Don't you see his *mêche blanche?*"

"Oh! yes—of course! Isn't it—wasn't he——!"

Caister straightened his back; his smile crept out, he fixed his monocle. They had spotted his Dr. Dominick!

"If you've quite finished, sir, may I clear?"

"Certainly. I'm going." He gathered himself and rose. The young women were gazing up. Elegant, with faint smile, he passed them close, so that they could not see, managing—his broken boot.

1922.

THE CHOICE

SOME years ago in Chelsea there used to stand at the crossing of a street leading to the Embankment an old man whose living was derived from the cleanliness of boots. In the intervals of plying his broom he could generally be seen seated on an up-turned wooden box, talking to an Irish terrier, who belonged to a house near by, and had taken a fancy to him. He was a Cornishman by birth, had been a plumber by trade, and was a cheerful, independent old fellow with ruddy cheeks, grey hair and beard, and little, bright, rather watery, grey eyes. But he was a great sufferer from a variety of ailments. He had gout, and some trouble in his side, and feet that were like barometers in their susceptibility to weather. Of all these matters he would speak to us in a very impersonal and un-complaining way, diagnosing himself, as it were, for the bene-fit of his listeners. He was, it seems, alone in the world, not having of course at that time anything to look forward to in the way of a pension, nor, one fancies, very much to look back on except the death of his near relatives and the decline of the plumbing trade. It had declined him for years, but, even before a long illness ousted him in favour of younger men, he had felt very severely the palpable difference in things. In old days plumbing had been a quiet, steady business, in which you were apparently " on your own, and knew where you were "; but latterly " you had just had to do what the builders told you, and of course they weren't going to make allowances; if you couldn't do the job as fast as a young man—out you went, and there you were." This long illness and the death of his wife coming close together (and sweeping away the last of his savings), had determined him therefore to buy a broom and seek for other occupation. To sweep a crossing was not a profession that he himself would have chosen before all others, still it was " better than the 'house—and you were your own master." The climate in those days not being the most suitable for a business which

171

necessitated constant exposure to all elements but that of fire, his ailments were proportionately active; but the one remarkable feature of his perpetual illness was that he was always "better" than he had been. We could not at times help thinking that this continual crescendo of good health should have gradually raised him to a pinnacle of paramount robustness; and it was with a certain disappointment, in the face of his assurances, that we watched him getting, on the contrary, slowly stiffer and feebler, and noted the sure increase of the egglike deposits, which he would proudly have us remark, about his wrists and fingers.

He was so entirely fixed and certain that he was "going in the river" before he went " in the 'house," that one hesitated to suggest that the time was at hand when he should cease to expose himself all day and every day. He had evidently pondered long and with a certain deep philosophy on this particular subject, and fortified himself by hearsay.

"The 'house ain't for a man that respects himself," he would remark. And, since that was his conviction, such as respected themselves could not very well beg him to act against it. At the same time, it became increasingly difficult to pass him without wondering how much longer it would be before he finally sought shelter in the element of water, which was so apt to pour down on him day by day.

It is uncertain whether he discussed this matter of the river *versus* the 'house with the dog, to whom he was always talking; but that they shared a certain fellow-feeling on the subject of exposure and advancing age is more than probable; for, as he would point out: The poor old feller's teeth were going; and the stiffness across his loins was always worse when it was wet. In fact, he was afraid that the old dog was gettin' old! And the dog would sit patiently for an hour at a time looking up at him, trying to find out, perhaps, from his friend's face what a dog should do, when the enemy weighed on him till he could no longer tolerate himself, not knowing, of course, that kindly humans would see to it that he did not suffer more than a dog could bear. On his face with its grizzled muzzle and rheumy eyes, thus turned up, there was never a sign of debate: it was full of confidence that, whatever decision his friend came to, in this momentous question between the river and the 'house, would be all right, perfectly satisfactory in every way to dogs and men.

One very rainy summer our old friend in a burst of confidence disclosed the wish of his heart. It was that he might be suffered to go down once more to Fowey in Cornwall, where he had been born, but had not been for fifty years. By some means or other the money was procured for this enterprise, and he was enabled to set off by excursion train for a fortnight's holiday. He was observed the day before his start talking at great length to the dog, and feeding it out of a paper bag with carraway-seed biscuits. A letter was received from him during his absence, observing certain strange laws of calligraphy, and beginning "Honoured Sir and Lady." It was full of an almost passionate description of a regatta, of a certain "Joe Petherick" who had remembered him, of the "luvly weather" and other sources of his great happiness; and ended "Yours truley obedient." On the fifteenth day he was back at his corner seated on his box in the pouring rain, saying that he was "a different man, ten years younger, and ready to 'go' now, any day"; nor could anything dissuade him from the theory that Heaven had made a special lodgment in our persons on his behalf. But only four days later, the sun being for once in the heavens, he was so long in answering a salutation that we feared he had been visited by some kind of stroke; his old face had lost colour, it seemed stiff, and his eyes had almost disappeared.

Inquiry elicited from him the information that he was better than he had been, but that the dog was dead. They had put it away while he had been gone, and he was afraid that he should miss the "faithful old feller."

"He was very good to me," he said; "always came for a bit of bread or biscuit. And he was company to me; I never knew such a sensible creature." He seemed to think that the dog must have pined during his absence, and that this had accelerated his end by making his owners think he was more decrepit than he really was.

The death of the dog, and the cold damp autumn that year, told heavily on the old man, but it was not till mid-November that he was noted one morning absent from his post. As he did not reappear his lodging was sought out. It was in a humble street, but the house was neat and clean, and the landlady seemed a good, rough woman. She informed us that our old friend was laid up "with pleurisy and the gouty rheumatics"; that by rights, of course, he ought to be in the infirmary, but she didn't like to turn him out, though where she would get her rent from she didn't know, to say nothing of his food, because she couldn't let him starve while there he was cryin' out with the pain, and no one but herself to turn a hand to him, with his door open at the top of the house, where he could holler for her if he wanted. An awful independent old feller, too, or else she wouldn't hesitate, for that was where he ought to be, and no mistake, not having a soul in the world to close his eyes, and that's what it would come to, though she would never be surprised if he got up and went out to-morrow, he was that stubborn!

Leaving her to the avocations which we had interrupted by coming in, we went upstairs.

The door of the back room at the top was, as indeed she had led us to suppose, open; and through it the sound of our friend's voice could be heard travelling forth:

"O Lord God, that took the dog from me, and gave me this here rheumatics, help me to keep a stiff and contrite heart. I am an old man, O Lord God, and I am not one to go into that *place*. So God give me a stiff heart, and I will remember you in my prayers, for that's about all I can do now, O God. I have been a good one in my time, O Lord, and cannot remember doing harm to any man for a long while now, and I have tried to keep upsides with it; so, good Lord, remember and do not forget me, now that I am down, a-lying here all day, and the rent goin' on. For ever and ever, O Lord, Amen."

We allowed a little time to pass before we went in, unwilling that he should think we had overheard that prayer. He was lying in a small dingy bed, with a medicine bottle and glass beside him on an old tin trunk. There was no fire.

He was—it seemed—better than he had been; the doctor's stuff was doing him good.

Certain arrangements were made for his benefit, and in less than three weeks he was back again at his corner.

In the spring of the following year we went abroad and were absent several months. He was no longer at his post when at last we came back, and a policeman informed us that he had not been there for some weeks. We made a second pilgrimage to his lodgings. The house had changed hands. The new landlady was a thin, anxious-looking young woman, who spoke in a thin, anxious voice. Yes, the old man had been taken very ill—double pneumonia and heart disease, she thought. Anyway, she couldn't have the worry and responsibility of him, let alone her rent. She had had the doctor, and had him taken off. Yes, it had upset him a bit; he would never have gone if he'd had his choice; but of course she had her living to get. She had his bits of things locked up all right; he owed her a little rent. In her opinion he'd never come out again. She was very sorry for him, too; he'd given no trouble till he was took ill.

Following up her information we repaired with heavy hearts to the 'house, which he had so often declared he would never enter. Having ascertained the number of his ward we mounted the beautifully clean stairs. In the fifth of a row of beds, our old friend was lying, apparently asleep. But watching him carefully, we saw that his lips, deep sunk between his frosty moustache and beard, were continually moving.

"He's not asleep," said the nurse; "he'll lie like that all the time. He frets."

At the sound of his name he had opened his eyes, which, though paler and smaller and more rheumy, were still almost bright. He fixed them on us with a peculiar stare, as much as to say: "You've taken an advantage of me, finding me here." We could hardly bear that look, and hurriedly asked him how he was. He tried to raise himself and answered huskily that he was better than he had been. We begged him not to exert himself, and told him how it was that we had been away, and so forth. He seemed to pay no attention, but suddenly said: " I'm in here; I don't mean to stay; I'll be goin' out in a day or two." We tried to confirm that theory, but the expression of his eyes seemed to take away our power of comfort, and make us ashamed of looking at him. He beckoned us closer.

"If I'd a had the use of my legs," he whispered, "they'd never have had me. I'd a-gone in the river first. But I don't mean to stay—I'm goin' back home."

The nurse told us, however, that this was out of the question; he was still very ill.

Four days later we went again to see him. He was no longer there. He had gone home. They had buried him that morning.

1910.

ULTIMA THULE

ULTIMA THULE! The words come into my head this winter night. That is why I write down the story, as I know it, of a little old friend.

I used to see him first in Kensington Gardens, where he came in the afternoons, accompanied by a very small girl. One would see them silent before a shrub or flower, or with their heads inclined to heaven before a tree, or leaning above water and the ducks, or stretched on their stomachs watching a beetle, or on their backs watching the sky. Often they would stand holding crumbs out to the birds, who would perch about them, and even drop on their arms little white marks of affection and esteem. They were admittedly a noticeable couple. The child, who was fair-haired and elfinlike, with dark eyes and a pointed chin, wore clothes that seemed somewhat hard put to it. And, if the two were not standing still, she went along pulling at his hand, eager to get there; and, since he was a very little, light old man, he seemed always in advance of his own feet. He was garbed, if I remember, in a daverdy brown overcoat and broad-brimmed soft grey hat, and his trousers, what was visible of them, were tucked into half-length black gaiters which tried to join with very old brown shoes. Indeed, his costume did not indicate any great share of prosperity. But it was his face that riveted attention. Thin, cherry-red, and wind-dried as old wood, it had a special sort of brightness, with its spikes and waves of silvery hair, and blue eyes which seemed to shine. Rather mad, I used to think. Standing by the rails of an enclosure, with his withered lips pursed and his cheeks drawn in till you would think the wind might blow through them, he would emit the most enticing trills and pipings, exactly imitating various birds.

Those who rouse our interest are generally the last people we speak to, for interest seems to set up a kind of special shyness; so it was long before I made his acquaintance. But one

day by the Serpentine, I saw him coming along alone, looking
sad, but still with that queer brightness about him. He sat
down on my bench with his little dried hands on his thin little
knees, and began talking to himself in a sort of whisper. Presently I caught the words: "God cannot be like us." And for
fear that he might go on uttering such precious remarks that
were obviously not intended to be heard, I had either to go
away or else address him. So, on an impulse, I said:

"Why?"

He turned without surprise.

"I've lost my landlady's little girl," he said. "Dead! And
only seven years old."

"That little thing I used to watch you with?"

"Did you? Did you? I'm glad you saw her."

"I used to see you looking at flowers, and trees, and those
ducks."

His face brightened wistfully. "Yes; she was a great companion to an old man like me." And he relapsed into his contemplation of the water. He had a curious, precise way of
speaking, that matched his pipchinesque little old face. At
last he again turned to me those blue youthful eyes which
seemed to shine out of a perfect little nest of crow's-feet.

"We were great friends! But I couldn't expect it. Things
don't last, do they?" I was glad to notice that his voice was
getting cheerful. "When I was in the orchestra at the Harmony Theatre, it never used to occur to me that some day I
shouldn't play there any more. One felt like a bird. That's
the beauty of music, sir. You lose yourself; like that blackbird there." He imitated the note of a blackbird so perfectly
that I could have sworn the bird started.

"Birds and flowers! Wonderful things; wonderful! Why,
even a buttercup——!" He pointed at one of those little
golden flowers with his toe. "Did you ever see such a marvellous thing?" And he turned his face up at me. "And yet,
somebody told me once that they don't agree with cows. Now
can that be? I'm not a countryman—though I was born at
Kingston."

"The cows do well enough on them," I said, "in my part
of the world. In fact, the farmers say they like to see buttercups."

"I'm glad to hear you say that. I was always sorry to think
they disagreed."

When I got up to go, he rose, too.

"I take it as very kind of you," he said, "to have spoken to me."

"The pleasure was mine. I am generally to be found hereabouts in the afternoons any time you like a talk."

"Delighted," he said; "delighted. I make friends of the creatures and flowers as much as possible, but they can't always make us understand." And after we had taken off our respective hats, he reseated himself, with his hands on his knees.

Next time I came across him standing by the rails of an enclosure, and, in his arms, an old and really wretched-looking cat.

"I don't like boys," he said, without preliminary of any sort. "What do you think they were doing to this poor old cat? Dragging it along by a string to drown it; see where it's cut into the fur! I think boys despise the old and weak!" He held it out to me. At the ends of those little sticks of arms the beast looked more dead than alive; I had never seen a more miserable creature.

"I think a cat," he said, "is one of the most marvellous things in the world. Such a depth of life in it."

And, as he spoke, the cat opened its mouth as if protesting at that assertion. It *was* the sorriest-looking beast.

"What are you going to do with it?"

"Take it home; it looks to me as if it might die."

"You don't think that might be more merciful?"

"It depends; it depends. I shall see. I fancy a little kindness might do a great deal for it. It's got plenty of spirit. I can see from its eye."

"May I come along with you a bit?"

"Oh!" he said; "delighted."

We walked on side by side, exciting the derision of nearly everyone we passed—his face looked so like a mother's when she is feeding her baby!

"You'll find this'll be quite a different cat to-morrow," he said. "I shall have to get in, though, without my landlady seeing; a funny woman! I have two or three strays already."

"Can I help in any way?"

"Thank you," he said. "I shall ring the area bell, and as she comes out below I shall go in above. She'll think it's boys. They *are* like that."

"But doesn't she do your rooms, or anything?"

A smile puckered his face. "I've only one; I do it myself. Oh, it'd never do to have her about, even if I could afford it. But," he added, "if you're so kind as to come with me to the door, you might engage her by asking where Mr. Thompson lives. That's me. In the musical world my name was Moronelli; not that I have Italian blood in me, of course."

"And shall I come up?"

"Honoured; but I live very quietly."

We passed out of the gardens at Lancaster Gate, where all the house-fronts seem so successful, and out of it into a little street that was extremely like a grubby child trying to hide under its mother's skirts. Here he took a newspaper from his pocket and wrapped it round the cat.

"She's a funny woman," he repeated; "Scotch descent, you know." Suddenly he pulled an area bell and scuttled up the steps.

When he had opened the door, however, I saw before him in the hall a short, thin woman dressed in black, with a sharp and bumpy face. Her voice sounded brisk and resolute.

"What have you got there, Mr. Thompson?"

"Newspaper, Mrs. March."

"Oh, indeed! Now, you're not going to take that cat upstairs!"

The little old fellow's voice acquired a sudden shrill determination. "Stand aside, please. If you stop me, I'll give you notice. The cat is going up. It's ill, and it is going up."

It was then I said:

"Does Mr. Thompson live here?"

In that second he shot past her, and ascended.

"That's him," she said; "and I wish it wasn't, with his dirty cats. Do you want him?"

"I do."

"He lives at the top." Then, with a grudging apology: "I can't help it; he tries me—he's very trying."

"I am sure he is."

She looked at me. The longing to talk that comes over those who answer bells all day, and the peculiar Scottish desire to justify oneself, rose together in that face which seemed all promontories dried by an east wind.

"Ah!" she said; "he is. I don't deny his heart; but he's got no sense of anything. Goodness knows what he hasn't got up there. I wonder I keep him. An old man like that ought to know better; half-starving himself to feed them." She paused, and her eyes, which had a cold and honest glitter, searched me closely.

"If you're going up," she said, "I hope you'll give him good advice. He never lets me in. I wonder I keep him."

There were three flights of stairs, narrow, clean, and smelling of oilcloth. Selecting one of two doors at random, I knocked. His silvery head and bright, pinched face were cautiously poked out.

"Ah!" he said; "I thought it might be her!"

The room, which was fairly large, had a bare floor with little on it save a camp-bed and chest of drawers with jug and basin. A large bird-cage on the wall hung wide open. The place smelt of soap and a little of beasts and birds. Into the walls, white-washed over a green wall-paper which stared through in places, were driven nails with their heads knocked off, on to which bits of wood had been spiked, so that they stood out as bird-perches high above the ground. Over the open window a piece of wire-netting had been fixed. A little spirit-stove and an old dress-ing-gown hanging on a peg completed the accoutrements of a room which one entered with a certain diffidence. He had not exaggerated. Besides the new cat, there were three other cats and four birds, all—save one, a bullfinch—invalids. The cats kept close to the walls, avoiding me, but wherever my little old friend went they followed him with their eyes. The birds were in the cage, except the bullfinch, which had perched on his shoulder.

"How on earth," I said, "do you manage to keep cats and birds in one room?"

"There is danger," he answered, "but I have not had a disaster yet. Till their legs or wings are mended, they hardly come out of the cage; and after that they keep up on my perches. But they don't stay long, you know, when they're once well. That wire is only put over the window while they're mending; it'll be off to-morrow for this lot."

"And then they'll go?"

"Yes. The sparrow first, and then the two thrushes."

"And this fellow?"

"Ask him," he said. "Would *you* go, bully?" But the bullfinch did not deign to answer.

"And were all those cats, too, in trouble?"

" Yes," he said. " They wouldn't want me if they weren't."

Thereupon he began to warm some blue-looking milk, contemplating the new cat, which he had placed in a round basket close to the little stove, while the bullfinch sat on his head. It seemed time to go.

" Delighted to see you, sir," he said, " any day." And, pointing up at the bullfinch on his head, he added: " Did you ever see anything so wonderful as that bird? The size of its heart! Really marvellous."

To the rapt sound of that word marvellous, and full of the memory of his mysterious brightness while he stood pointing upward to the bird perched on his thick, silvery hair, I went.

The landlady was still at the bottom of the stairs, and began at once. " So you found him! I don't know why I keep him. Of course, he was kind to my little girl." I saw tears gather in her eyes.

" With his cats and his birds, I wonder I keep him! But where would he go? He's no relations, and no friends—not a friend in the world, I think! He's a character. Lives on air —feeding them cats! I've no patience with them, eating him up. He never lets me in. Cats and birds! I wonder I keep him. Losing himself for those rubbishy things! It's my belief he was always like that; and that's why he never got on. He's no sense of anything."

And she gave me a shrewd look, wondering, no doubt, what the deuce I had come about.

I did not come across him again in the gardens for some time, and went at last to pay him a call. At the entrance to a mews just round the corner of his grubby little street, I found a knot of people collected round one of those bears that are sometimes led through the less conspicuous streets of our huge towns. The yellowish beast was sitting up in deference to its master's rod, uttering little grunts, and moving its uplifted snout from side to side, in the way bears have. But it seemed to be extracting more amusement than money from its audience.

" Let your bear down off its hind legs and I'll give you a penny." And suddenly I saw my little old friend under his flopping grey hat, amongst the spectators, all taller than himself. But the bear's master only grinned and prodded the animal in the chest. He evidently knew a good thing when he saw it.

" I'll give you twopence to let him down."

Again the bear-man grinned. "More!" he said, and again prodded the bear's chest. The spectators were laughing now.

"Threepence! And if you don't let him down for that, I'll hit you in the eye."

The bear-man held out his hand. "All a-right," he said, "threepence: I let him down."

I saw the coins pass and the beast dropping on his forefeet; but just then a policeman coming in sight, the man led his bear off, and I was left alone with my little old friend.

"I wish I had that poor bear," he said: "I could teach him to be happy. But, even if I could buy him, what could I do with him up there? She's such a funny woman."

He looked quite dim, but brightened as we went along.

"A bear," he said, "is really an extraordinary animal. What wise little eyes he has! I do think he's a marvellous creation! My cats will have to go without their dinner, though. I was going to buy it with that threepence."

I begged to be allowed the privilege.

"Willingly!" he said. "Shall we go in here? They like cod's head best."

While we stood waiting to be served I saw the usual derisive smile pass over the fishmonger's face. But my little old friend by no means noticed it; he was too busy looking at the fish. "A fish is a marvellous thing, when you come to think of it," he murmured. "Look at its scales. Did you ever see such mechanism?"

We bought five cod's heads, and I left him carrying them in a bag, evidently lost in the anticipation of five cats eating them.

After that I saw him often, going with him sometimes to buy food for his cats, which seemed ever to increase in numbers. His talk was always of his strays, and the marvels of creation, and that time of his life when he played the flute at the Harmony Theatre. He had been out of a job, it seemed, for more than ten years; and, when questioned, only sighed and answered: "Don't talk about it, please!"

His bumpy landlady never failed to favour me with a little conversation. She was one of those women who have terrific consciences, and terrible grudges against them.

"I never get out," she would say.

"Why not?"

"Couldn't leave the house."

"It won't run away!"

But she would look at me as if she thought it might, and repeat:

"Oh! I never get out."

An extremely Scottish temperament.

Considering her descent, however, she was curiously devoid of success, struggling on apparently from week to week, cleaning, and answering the bell, and never getting out, and wondering why she kept my little old friend; just as he struggled on from week to week, getting out and collecting strays, and discovering the marvels of creation, and finding her a funny woman. Their hands were joined, one must suppose, by that dead child.

One July afternoon, however, I found her very much upset. He had been taken dangerously ill three days before.

"There he is," she said; "can't touch a thing. It's my belief he's done for himself, giving his food away all these years to those cats of his. I shooed 'em out to-day, the nasty creatures; they won't get in again."

"Oh!" I said, "you shouldn't have done that. It'll only make him miserable."

She flounced her head up. "Hoh!" she said: "I wonder I've kept him all this time, with his birds and his cats dirtying my house. And there he lies, talking gibberish about them. He made me write to a Mr. Jackson, of some theatre or other—I've no patience with him. And that little bullfinch all the time perching on his pillow, the dirty little thing! I'd have turned it out, too, only it wouldn't let me catch it."

"What does the doctor say?"

"Double pneumonia—caught it getting his feet wet, after some stray, I'll be bound. I'm nursing him. There has to be someone with him all the time."

He was lying very still when I went up, with the sunlight falling across the foot of his bed, and, sure enough, the bullfinch perching on his pillow. In that high fever he looked brighter than ever. He was not exactly delirious, yet not exactly master of his thoughts.

"Mr. Jackson! He'll be here soon. Mr. Jackson! He'll do it for me. I can ask him, if I die. A funny woman. I don't want to eat; I'm not a great eater—I want my breath, that's all."

At sound of his voice the bullfinch fluttered off the pillow and flew round and round the room, as if alarmed at something new in the tones that were coming from its master.

Then he seemed to recognise me. "I think I'm going to die," he said; "I'm very weak. It's lucky there's nobody to mind. If only he'd come soon. I wish"—and he raised himself with feeble excitement—"I wish you'd take that wire off the window; I want my cats. She turned them out. I want him to promise me to take them, and bully-boy, and feed them with my money, when I'm dead."

Seeing that excitement was certainly worse for him than cats, I took the wire off. He fell back, quiet at once; and presently, first one and then another cat came stealing in, till there were four or five seated against the walls. The moment he ceased to speak the bullfinch, too, came back to his pillow. His eyes looked most supernaturally bright, staring out of his little, withered-up old face at the sunlight playing on his bed; he said just audibly: "Did you ever see anything more wonderful than that sunlight? It's really marvellous!" After that he fell into a sort of doze or stupor. And I continued to sit there in the window, relieved, but rather humiliated, that he had not asked me to take care of his cats and bullfinch.

Presently there came the sound of a motor-car in the little street below. And almost at once the landlady appeared. For such an abrupt woman, she entered very softly.

"Here he is," she whispered.

I went out and found a gentleman, perhaps sixty years of age, in a black coat, buff waistcoat, gold watch-chain, light trousers, patent-leather boots, and a wonderfully shining hat. His face was plump and red, with a glossy grey moustache; indeed, he seemed to shine everywhere, save in the eyes, which were of a dull and somewhat liverish hue.

"Mr. Jackson?"

"The same. How is the little old chap?"

Opening the door of the next room, which I knew was always empty, I beckoned Mr. Jackson in.

"He's really very ill; I'd better tell you what he wants to see you about."

He looked at me with that air of "You can't get at me—whoever you may be," which belongs to the very successful.

"Right-o!" he said. "Well?"

I described the situation. "He seems to think," I ended, "that you'll be kind enough to charge yourself with his strays, in case he should die."

Mr. Jackson prodded the unpainted washstand with his gold-headed cane.

" Is he really going to kick it ? "

" I'm afraid so; he's nothing but skin, bone, and spirit, as it is."

" H'm! Stray cats, you say, and a bird! Well, there's no accounting. He was always a cracky little chap. So that's it! When I got the letter I wondered what the deuce! We pay him his five quid a quarter regular to this day. To tell truth, he deserved it. Thirty years he was at our shop; never missed a night. First-rate flute he was. He ought never to have given it up, though I always thought it showed a bit of heart in him. If a man don't look after number one, he's as good as gone; that's what I've always found. Why, I was no more than he was when I started. Shouldn't have been worth a plum if I'd gone on his plan, that's certain." And he gave that profound chuckle which comes from the very stomach of success. " We were having a rocky time at the Harmony; had to cut down everything we could—music, well, that came about first. Little old Moronelli, as we used to call him—old Italian days before English names came in, you know—he was far the best of the flutes; so I went to him and said: ' Look here, Moronelli, which of these other boys had better go ? ' ' Oh! ' he said—I remember his funny little old mug now—' has one of them to go, Mr. Jackson ? Timminsa'—that was the elder— ' he's a wife and family; and Smetoni'—Smith, you know— ' he's only a boy. Times are bad for flutes.' ' I know it's a bit hard,' I said, ' but this theatre's goin' to be run much cheaper; one of 'em's got to get.' ' Oh! ' he said, ' dear me! ' he said, What a funny little old chap it was! Well—what do you think? Next day I had his resignation. Give you my word I did my best to turn him. Why, he was sixty then if he was a day—at sixty a man don't get jobs in a hurry. But not a bit of it! All he'd say was: ' I shall get a place all right! ' But that's it, you know—he never did. Too long in one shop. I heard by accident he was on the rocks; that's how I make him that allowance. But that's the sort of hopeless little old chap he is—no idea of himself. Cats! Why not? I'll take his old cats on; don't you let him worry about that. I'll see to his bird, too. If I can't give 'em a better time than ever they have here, it'll be funny! " And, looking round the little empty room, he again uttered that profound chuckle: " Why, he was with us at the Harmony thirty years—that's time, you know; I made my fortune in it."

" I'm sure," I said, " it'll be a great relief to him."

" Oh! Ah! That's all right. You come down to my place" —he handed me a card: ' Mr. Cyril Porteous Jackson, Ultima Thule, Wimbledon'—" and see how I fix 'em up. But if he's really going to kick it, I'd like to have a look at the little old chap, just for old times' sake."

We went, as quietly as Mr. Jackson's bright boots would permit, into his room, where the landlady was sitting gazing angrily at the cats. She went out without noise, flouncing her head as much as to say: " Well, now you can see what I have to go through, sitting up here. I never get out."

Our little old friend was still in that curious stupor. He seemed unconscious, but his blue eyes were not closed, staring brightly out before them at things we did not see. With his silvery hair and his flushed frailty, he had an unearthly look. After standing perhaps three minutes at the foot of the bed, Mr. Jackson whispered:

" Well, he does look queer. Poor little old chap! You tell him from me I'll look after his cats and bird; he needn't worry. And now, I think I won't keep the car. Makes me feel a bit throaty, you know. Don't move; he might come to."

And, leaning all the weight of his substantial form on those bright and creaking toes, he made his way to the door, flashed at me a diamond ring, whispered hoarsely: "So long! That'll be all right! " and vanished. And soon I heard the whirring of his car and just saw the top of his shiny hat travelling down the little street.

Some time I sat on there, wanting to deliver that message. An uncanny vigil in the failing light, with those five cats—yes, five at least—lying or sitting against the walls, staring like sphinxes at their motionless protector. I could not make out whether it was he in his stupor with his bright eyes that fascinated them, or the bullfinch perched on his pillow, who they knew perhaps might soon be in their power. I was glad when the landlady came up and I could leave the message with her.

When she opened the door to me next day at six o'clock I knew that he was gone. There was about her that sorrowful, unmistakable importance, that peculiar mournful excitement, which hovers over houses where death has entered.

" Yes," she said, " he went this morning. Never came round after you left. Would you like to see him? "

We went up.

He lay, covered with a sheet, in the darkened room. The landlady pulled the window-curtains apart. His face, as white now almost as his silvery head, had in the sunlight a radiance like that of a small, bright angel gone to sleep. No growth of hair, such as comes on most dead faces, showed on those frail cheeks that were now smooth and lineless as porcelain. And on the sheet above his chest the bullfinch sat, looking into his face.

The landlady let the curtains fall, and we went out.

" I've got the cats in here"—she pointed to the room where Mr. Jackson and I had talked—" all ready for that gentleman when he sends. But that little bird, I don't know what to do; he won't let me catch him, and there he sits. It makes me feel all funny."

It had made me feel all funny, too.

" He hasn't left the money for his funeral. Dreadful, the way he never thought about himself. I'm glad I kept him, though." And, not to my astonishment, she suddenly began to cry.

A wire was sent to Mr. Jackson, and on the day of the funeral I went down to " Ultima Thule," Wimbledon, to see if he had carried out his promise.

He had. In the grounds, past the vinery, an outhouse had been cleaned and sanded, with cushions placed at intervals against the wall, and a little trough of milk. Nothing could have been more suitable or luxurious.

" How's that? " he said. " I've done it thoroughly." But I noticed that he looked a little glum.

" The only thing," he said, " is the cats. First night they seemed all right; and the second, there were three of 'em left. But to-day the gardener tells me there's not the ghost of one anywhere. It's not for want of feeding. They've had tripe, and liver, and milk—as much as ever they liked. And cod's heads, you know—they're very fond of them. I must say it's a bit of a disappointment to me."

As he spoke, a sandy cat which I perfectly remembered, for it had only half of its left ear, appeared in the doorway, and stood, crouching, with its green eyes turned on us; then, hearing Mr. Jackson murmur, " Puss, puss ! " it ran for its life, slinking almost into the ground, and vanished among some shrubs.

Mr. Jackson sighed. " Perversity of the brutes!" he said. He led me back to the house through a conservatory full of choice orchids. A gilt bird-cage was hanging there, one of the largest I had ever seen, replete with every luxury the heart of bird could want.

" Is that for the bullfinch?" I asked him.

" Oh!" he said; " didn't you know? The little beggar wouldn't let himself be caught, and the second morning, when they went up, there he lay on the old chap's body, dead. I thought it was very touchin'. But I kept the cage hung up for you to see that I should have given him a good time here. Oh, yes, ' Ultima Thule' would have done him well!"

And from a bright leather case Mr. Jackson offered me a cigar.

The question I had long been wishing to ask him slipped out of me then:

" Do you mind telling me why you called your house ' Ultima Thule?'"

" Why?" he said. " Found it on the gate. Think it's rather distingué, don't you?" and he uttered his profound chuckle.

" First-rate. The whole place is the last word in comfort."

" Very good of you to say so," he said. " I've laid out a goodish bit on it. A man must have a warm corner to end his days in. ' Ultima Thule,' as you say—it isn't bad. There's success about it, somehow."

And with that word in my ears, and in my eyes a vision of the little old fellow in his " Ultima Thule," with the bullfinch lying dead on a heart that had never known success, I travelled back to town.

1914.

COURAGE

At that time (said Ferrand) I was in poverty. Not the kind of poverty that goes without dinner, but the sort that goes without breakfast, lunch, and dinner, and exists as it can on bread and tobacco. I lived in one of those fourpenny lodging-houses, Westminster way. Three, five, seven beds in a room; if you pay regularly, you keep your own bed; if not, they put someone else there who will certainly leave you a memento of himself. It's not the foreigners' quarter; they are nearly all English, and drunkards. Three-quarters of them don't eat—can't; they have no capacity for solid food. They drink and drink. They're not worth wasting your money on—cab-runners, newspaper-boys, sellers of laces, and what you call sandwich-men; three-fourths of them brutalised beyond the power of recovery. What can you expect? They just live to scrape enough together to keep their souls in their bodies; they have no time or strength to think of anything but that. They come back at night and fall asleep—and how dead that sleep is! No, they never eat— just a bit of bread; the rest is drink!

There used to come to that house a little Frenchman, with a yellow, crow's-footed face; not old either, about thirty. But his life had been hard—no one comes to these houses if life is soft, especially no Frenchman; a Frenchman hates to leave his country. He came to shave us—charged a penny; most of us forgot to pay him, so that in all he shaved about three for a penny. He went to others of these houses—this gave him his income— he kept the little shop next door, too, but he never sold anything. How he worked! He also went to one of your Public Institutions; this was not so profitable, for there he was paid a penny for ten shaves. He used to say to me, moving his tired fingers like little yellow sticks: "Pff! I slave! To gain a penny, friend, I'm spending fourpence. What would you have? One must nourish oneself to have the strength to shave ten people for a penny." He was like an ant, running round and round in his little hole, without any chance but just to live; and always in hopes of saving enough to take him back to France, and set him up there. We had a liking for each other. He was the only one, in fact—except a sandwich-man who had been an actor, and was very intelligent, when he wasn't drunk—the only one in all that warren who had ideas. He was fond of pleasure and loved his music-hall—must have gone at least twice a year, and was always talking of it. He had little knowledge of its joys, it's true—hadn't the money for that, but his intentions were good. He used to keep me till the last, and shave me slowly.

"This rests me," he would say. It was amusement for me, too, for I had got into the habit of going for days without opening my lips. It's only a man here and there one can talk with; the rest only laugh; you seem to them a fool, a freak—something that should be put into a cage or tied by the leg.

"Yes," the little man would say, "when I came here first I thought I should soon go back, but now I'm not so sure. I'm losing my illusions. Money has wings, but it's not to *me* it flies. Believe me, friend, I am shaving my soul into these specimens. And how unhappy they are, poor creatures; how they must suffer! Drink! you say. Yes, that saves them—they get a little happiness from that. Unfortunately, I haven't the constitution for it—here." And he would show me where he had no constitution. "You, too, comrade, you don't seem to be in luck; but then, you're young. Ah, well, *faut être philosophe*—but imagine what kind of a game it is in this climate, especially if you come from the South!"

When I went away, which was as soon as I had nothing left to pawn, he gave me money—there's no question of lending in those houses: if a man parts with money he *gives* it; and lucky if he's not robbed into the bargain. There are fellows there who watch for a new pair of shoes, or a good overcoat, profit by their wakefulness as soon as the other is asleep, and promptly disappear. There's no morality in the face of destitution—it needs a man of iron, and these are men of straw. But one thing I will say of the low English—they are not bloodthirsty, like the low French and Italians.

Well, I got a job as fireman on a steamer, made a tour tramping, and six months later I was back again. The first morning I saw the Frenchman. It was shaving-day; he was more like an ant than ever, working away with all his legs and arms; a little yellower, and perhaps more wrinkled.

"Ah!" he called out to me in French, "there you are—back again. I knew you'd come. Wait till I've finished with this specimen—I've a lot to talk about."

We went into the kitchen, a big stone-floored room, with tables for eating—and sat down by the fire. It was January, but, summer or winter, there's always a fire burning in that kitchen.

"So," he said, "you have come back? No luck? Eh! Patience! A few more days won't kill you at your age. What fogs, though! You see, I'm still here, but my comrade, Pigon, is dead. You remember him—the big man with black hair who had the shop down the street. Amiable fellow, good friend to me; and married. Fine woman his wife—a little ripe, seeing she has had children, but of good family. He died suddenly of heart disease. Wait a bit; I'll tell you about that. . . .

"It was not long after you went away, one fine day in October, when I had just finished with these specimens here, and was taking my coffee in the shop, and thinking of that poor Pigon —dead then just three days—when *pom!* comes a knock, and there is Madame Pigon! Very calm—a woman of good family, well brought up, well made—fine woman. But the cheeks pale, and the eyes so red, poor soul.

"'Well, Madame,' I asked her, 'what can I do for you?'

"It seems this poor Pigon died bankrupt; there was not a cent in the shop. He was two days in his grave, and the bailiffs in already.

"'Ah, Monsieur!' she says to me, 'what am I to do?'

"'Wait a bit, Madame!' I get my hat and go back to the shop with her.

"What a scene! Two bailiffs, who would have been the better for a shave, sitting in a shop before the basins; and everywhere, *ma foi,* everywhere, children. Tk! Tk! A little girl of ten, very like her mother; two little boys with little trousers, and one with nothing but a chemise; and others—two, quite small, all rolling on the floor; and what a horrible noise!— all crying, all but the little girl, fit to break themselves in two. The bailiffs seemed perplexed. It was enough to make one weep! Seven! some quite small! That poor Pigon, I had no idea he was so good a rabbit!

"The bailiffs behaved very well.

"'Well,' said the biggest, 'you can have four-and-twenty

hours to find this money; my mate can camp out here in the shop—we don't want to be hard on you!'

"I helped Madame to soothe the children.

"'If I had the money,' I said, 'it should be at your service, Madame—in each well-born heart there should exist humanity; but I have no money. Try and think whether you have no friends to help you.'

"'Monsieur,' she answered, 'I have none. Have I had time to make friends—I, with seven children?'

"'But in France, Madame?'

"'None, Monsieur. I have quarrelled with my family; and reflect—it is now seven years since we came to England, and then only because no one would help us.' That seemed to me bad, but what could I do? I could only say:

"'Hope always, Madame—trust in me!'

"I went away. All day long I thought how calm she was—magnificent! And I kept saying to myself: 'Come, tap your head! tap your head! Something must be done!' But nothing came.

"The next morning it was my day to go to that sacred Institution, and I started off still thinking what on earth could be done for the poor woman; it was as if the little ones had got hold of my legs and were dragging at me. I arrived late, and, to make up time, I shaved them as I have never shaved them; a hot morning—I perspired! Ten for a penny! Ten for a penny! I thought of that, and of the poor woman. At last I finished and sat down. I thought to myself: 'It's too strong! Why do you do it? It's stupid! You are wasting yourself!' And then, my idea came to me! I asked for the manager.

"'Monsieur,' I said, 'it is impossible for me to come here again.'

"'What do you mean?' says he.

"'I have had enough of your—"ten for a penny"—I am going to get married; I can't afford to come here any longer. I lose too much flesh for the money.'

"'What?' he says, 'you're a lucky man if you can afford to throw away your money like this!'

"'Throw away my money! Pardon, Monsieur, but look at me'—I was still very hot—'for every penny I make I lose threepence, not counting the boot leather to and fro. While I was still a bachelor, Monsieur, it was my own affair—I could afford these extravagances; but now—it must finish—I have the honour, Monsieur!'

"I left him, and walked away. I went to the Pigons' shop. The bailiff was still there—Pfui! He must have been smoking all the time.

"'I can't give them much longer,' he said to me.

"'It is of no importance,' I replied; and I knocked, and went into the back room.

"The children were playing in the corner, that little girl, a heart of gold, watching them like a mother; and Madame at the table with a pair of old black gloves on her hands. My friend, I have never seen such a face—calm, but so pale, so frightfully discouraged, so overwhelmed. One would say she was waiting for her death. It was bad, it was bad—with the winter coming on!

"'Good morning, Madame,' I said. 'What news? Have you been able to arrange anything?'

"'No, Monsieur. And you?'

"'No!' And I looked at her again—a fine woman; ah! a fine woman.

"'But,' I said, 'an idea has come to me this morning. Now, what would you say if I asked you to marry me? It might possibly be better than nothing.'

"She regarded me with her black eyes, and answered:

"'But willingly, Monsieur!' and then, comrade, but not till then, she cried."

The little Frenchman stopped, and stared at me hard.

"H'm!" I said at last, "you have courage!"

He looked at me again; his eyes were troubled, as if I had paid him a bad compliment.

"You think so?" he said at last, and I saw that the thought was gnawing at him, as if I had turned the light on some desperate, dark feeling in his heart.

"Yes!" he said, taking his time, while his good yellow face wrinkled and wrinkled, and each wrinkle seemed to darken: "I was afraid of it even when I did it. Seven children!" Once more he looked at me: "And since!—sometimes—sometimes—I could——" He broke off, then burst out again:

"Life is hard! What would you have? I knew her husband. Could I leave her to the streets?"

1904.

THE BRIGHT SIDE

A LITTLE Englishwoman, married to a German, had dwelt with him eighteen years in humble happiness and the district of Putney, where her husband worked in the finer kinds of leather. He was a harmless, busy little man with the gift for turning his hand to anything, which is bred into the peasants of the Black Forest, who on their upland farms make all the necessaries of daily life—their coarse linen from home-grown flax, their leather gear from the hides of their beasts, their clothes from the wool thereof, their furniture from the pine logs of the forest, their bread from home-grown flour milled in simple fashion and baked in the home-made ovens, their cheese from the milk of their own goats. Why he had come to England he probably did not remember—it was so long ago; but he would still know why he had married Dora, the daughter of the Putney carpenter, she being, as it were, salt of the earth: one of those Cockney women, deeply sensitive beneath a well-nigh impermeable mask of humour and philosophy, who quite unself-consciously are always doing things for others. In their little grey Putney house they had dwelt those eighteen years, without perhaps ever having had time to move, though they had often had the intention of doing so for the sake of the children, of whom they had three, a boy and two girls. Mrs. Gerhardt—as I will call her, for her husband had a very German name, and there is more in a name than Shakespeare dreamed of—Mrs. Gerhardt was a little woman with large hazel eyes and dark crinkly hair, in which there were already a few threads of grey when the war broke out. Her boy David, the eldest, was fourteen at that date, and her girls, Minnie and Violet, were eight and five, rather pretty children, especially the little one. Gerhardt, perhaps because he was so handy, had never risen. His firm regarded him as indispensable and paid him fair wages, but he had no " push," having the craftsman's temperament, and employing his spare time in little neat jobs for his house and his neighbours, which

197

brought him no return. They made their way, therefore, without that provision for the future which necessitates the employment of one's time for one's own ends. But they were happy, and had no enemies; and each year saw some mild improvements in their studiously clean house and tiny back garden. Mrs. Gerhardt, who was cook, seamstress, washerwoman, besides being wife and mother, was almost notorious in that street of semi-detached houses for being at the disposal of anyone in sickness or trouble. She was not strong in body, for things had gone wrong when she bore her first, but her spirit had that peculiar power of seeing things as they were, and yet refusing to be dismayed, which so embarrasses Fate. She saw her husband's defects clearly, and his good qualities no less distinctly—they never quarrelled. She gauged her children's characters, too, with an admirable precision, which left, however, loopholes of wonder as to what they would become.

The outbreak of the war found them on the point of going to Margate for Bank Holiday, an almost unparalleled event; so that the importance of the world catastrophe was brought home to them with a vividness which would otherwise have been absent from folk so simple, domestic, and far-removed from that atmosphere in which the egg of war is hatched. Over the origin and merits of the struggle, beyond saying to each other several times that it was a dreadful thing, Mr. and Mrs. Gerhardt held but one little conversation, lying in their iron bed with an immortal brown eiderdown, patterned with red wriggles, over them. They agreed that it was a cruel, wicked thing to invade "that little Belgium," and there left a matter which seemed to them a mysterious and insane perversion of all they had hitherto been accustomed to think of as life. Reading their papers—a daily and a weekly, in which they had as much implicit faith as a million other readers—they were soon duly horrified by the reports therein of "Hun" atrocities; so horrified that they would express their condemnation of the Kaiser and his militarism as freely as if they had been British subjects. It was, therefore, with an uneasy surprise that they began to find these papers talking of "the Huns at large in our midst," of "spies," and the national danger of "nourishing such vipers." They were deeply conscious of not being "vipers," and such sayings began to awaken in both their breasts a humble sense of injustice, as it were. This was more acute in the breast of little Mrs. Gerhardt, because, of course, the shafts were directed not at her,

but at her husband. She knew her husband so well, knew him
incapable of anything but homely kindly busyness, and that he
should be lumped into the category of " Huns " and "spies "
and tarred with the brush of mass hatred amazed and stirred her
indignation, or would have, if her Cockney temperament had
allowed her to take it very seriously. As for Gerhardt, he
became extremely silent, so that it was ever more and more
difficult to tell what he was feeling. The patriotism of the
newspapers took a considerable time to affect the charity of
the citizens of Putney, and so long as no neighbour showed
signs of thinking that little Gerhardt was a monster and a spy,
it was fairly easy for Mrs. Gerhardt to sleep at night, with the
feeling that the remarks in the papers were not really intended
for Gerhardt and herself. But she noticed that her man had
given up reading them and would push them away, if, in the tiny
sitting-room with the heavily-flowered walls, they happened to
rest beside him. He had perhaps a closer sense of impending
Fate than she. The boy, David, went to his first work, and the
girls to their school, and so things dragged on through that
first long war winter and spring. Mrs. Gerhardt, in the intervals of doing everything, knitted socks for " our poor cold boys
in the trenches," but Gerhardt no longer sought out little jobs
to do in the houses of his neighbours. Mrs. Gerhardt thought
that he " fancied " they would not like it. It was early in that
spring that she took a deaf aunt to live with them, the wife
of her mother's brother, no blood-relation, but the poor woman
had nowhere else to go; so David was put to sleep on the horsehair sofa in the sitting-room because she " couldn't refuse the
poor thing." And then, of an April afternoon, while she was
washing the household sheets, her neighbour, Mrs. Clirehugh,
a little spare woman, all eyes, cheekbones, hair and decision,
came in breathless and burst out:
" Oh! Mrs. Gerhardt, 'ave you 'eard? They've sunk the
Loositania! Has I said to Will: Isn't it horful?"
Mrs. Gerhardt, her round arms dripping soapsuds, answered:
" What a dreadful thing! The poor drowning people! Dear!
Oh, dear!"
" Oh! those Huns! I'd shoot the lot, I would!"
" They *are* wicked!" Mrs. Gerhardt echoed: " that was a
dreadful thing to do!"
But it was not till Gerhardt came in at five o'clock, white as
a sheet, that she perceived how this catastrophe affected them.

"I have been called a German," were the first words he uttered; "Dollee, I have been called a German."

"Well, so you are, my dear," said Mrs. Gerhardt.

"You do not see," he answered, with a heat and agitation which surprised her. "I tell you this *Lusitania* will finish our business. They will have me. They will take me away from you all. Already the papers have: 'Intern all the Huns.'" He sat down at the kitchen table and buried his face in hands still grimy from his leather work. Mrs. Gerhardt stood beside him, her eyes unnaturally big.

"But, Max," she said, "what has it to do with you? You couldn't help it, Max!"

Gerhardt looked up; his white face, broad in the brow and tapering to a thin chin, seemed distraught.

"What do they care for that? Is my name Max Gerhardt? What do they care if I hate the war? I am a German. That's enough. You will see."

"Oh!" murmured Mrs. Gerhardt, "they won't be so unjust."

Gerhardt reached up and caught her chin in his hand, and for a moment those two pairs of eyes gazed, straining, into each other. Then he said:

"I don't want to be taken, Dollee. What shall I do away from you and the children? I don't want to be taken, Dollee."

Mrs. Gerhardt, with a feeling of terror and a cheerful smile, answered:

"You mustn't go fancyin' things, Max. I'll make you a nice cup of tea. Cheer up, old man! Look on the bright side!"

But Gerhardt lapsed into the silence which of late she had begun to dread.

That night some shop windows were broken, some German names effaced. The Gerhardts had no shop, no name painted up, and they escaped. In Press and Parliament the cry against "the Huns in our midst" rose with a fresh fury; but, for the Gerhardts, the face of Fate was withdrawn. Gerhardt went to his work as usual, and their laborious and quiet existence remained undisturbed; nor could Mrs. Gerhardt tell whether her "man's" ever-deepening silence was due to his "fancying things" or to the demeanour of his neighbours and fellow-workmen. One would have said that he, like the derelict aunt, was deaf, so difficult to converse with had he become. His length of sojourn in England and his value to his employers, for he had real skill, had saved him for the time being; but, behind the screen, Fate twitched her grinning chaps.

Not till the howl which followed some air raids in 1916 did they take off Gerhardt, with a variety of other elderly men, whose crime it was to have been born in Germany. They did it suddenly, and perhaps it was as well, for a prolonged sight of his silent misery must have upset his family till they would have been unable to look on that bright side of things which Mrs. Gerhardt had, as it were, always up her sleeve. When, in charge of a big and sympathetic constable, he was gone, taking all she could hurriedly get together for him, she hastened to the police station. They were friendly to her there—she must cheer up, 'e'd be all right, she needn't worry. Ah! she could go down to the 'Ome Office, if she liked, and see what could be done. But they 'eld out no 'ope! Mrs. Gerhardt waited till the morrow, having the little Violet in bed with her, and crying quietly into her pillow; then, putting on her Sunday best, she went down to a building in Whitehall, larger than any she had ever entered. Two hours she waited, sitting unobtrusive, with big, anxious eyes, and a line between her brows. At intervals of half an hour she would get up and ask the messenger cheerfully: "I 'ope they haven't forgotten me, sir. Perhaps you'd see to it." And because she was cheerful the messenger took her under his protection, and answered: "All right, Missis. They're very busy, but *I'll* wangle you in some'ow."

When at length she was "wangled" into the presence of a grave gentleman in eye-glasses, realisation of the utter importance of this moment overcame her so that she could not speak. "Oh! dear," she thought, while her heart fluttered like a bird —"he'll never understand; I'll never be able to make him." She saw her husband buried under the dead leaves of despair; she saw her children getting too little food; the deaf aunt, now bedridden, neglected in the new pressure of work which must fall on the only bread-winner left. And choking a little, she said:

"I'm sure I'm very sorry to take up your time, sir; but my 'usband's been taken to the Palace; and we've been married over twenty years, and he's been in England twenty-five; and he's a very good man and a good workman; and I thought perhaps they didn't understand that; and we've got three children and a relation that's bedridden. And of course, we understand that the Germans have been very wicked; Gernardt always said that himself. And it isn't as if he was a spy; so I thought if you could do something for us, sir, I being English myself."

The gentleman, looking past her at the wall, answered wearily: "Gerhardt—I'll look into it. We have to do very hard things, Mrs. Gerhardt."

Little Mrs. Gerhardt, with big eyes almost starting out of her head, for she was no fool, and perceived that this was the end, said eagerly:

"Of course I know that there's a big outcry, and the papers are askin' for it; but the people in our street don't mind 'im, sir. He's always done little things for them; so I thought perhaps you might make an exception in his case."

She noticed that the gentleman's lips tightened at the word outcry, and that he was looking at her now.

"His case was before the Committee, no doubt; but I'll inquire. Good-morning."

Mrs. Gerhardt, accustomed to not being troublesome, rose; a tear rolled down her cheek and was arrested by her smile.

"Thank you sir, I'm sure. Good-morning, sir."

And she went out. Meeting the messenger in the corridor, and hearing his: "Well, Missis?" she answered: "I don't know. I must look on the bright side. Good-bye, and thank you for your trouble." And she turned away feeling as if she had been beaten all over.

The bright side on which she looked did not include the return to her of little Gerhardt, who was duly detained for the safety of the country. Obedient to economy, and with a dim sense that her favourite papers were in some way responsible for this, she ceased to take them in, and took in sewing instead. It had become necessary to do so, for the allowance she received from the Government was about a quarter of Gerhardt's weekly earnings. In spite of its inadequacy it was something, and she felt she must be grateful. But, curiously enough, she could not forget that she was English, and it seemed strange to her that, in addition to the grief caused by separation from her husband, from whom she had never been parted, not even for a night, she should now be compelled to work twice as hard and eat half as much because that husband had paid her country the compliment of preferring it to his own. But, after all, many other people had much worse trouble to grieve over, so she looked on the bright side of all this, especially on those days

once a week when alone, or accompanied by the little Violet,
she visited that Palace where she had read in her favourite
journals to her great comfort that her husband was treated like
a prince. Since he had no money, he was in what they called
" the battalion," and their meetings were held in the bazaar,
where things that " the princes " made were exposed for sale.
Here Mr. and Mrs. Gerhardt would stand in front of some doll,
some blotting-book, calendar, or walking-stick, which had been
fashioned by one of " the princes." There they would hold each
other's hands and try to imagine themselves unsurrounded by
other men and wives, while the little Violet would stray and
return to embrace her father's leg spasmodically. Standing
there, Mrs. Gerhardt would look on the bright side, and explain
to Gerhardt how well everything was going, and he mustn't fret
about them, and how kind the police were, and how auntie
asked after him, and Minnie would get a prize; and how he
oughtn't to mope but eat his food, and look on the bright side.
And Gerhardt would smile the smile which went into her heart
just like a sword, and say:

" All right, Dollee. I'm getting on fine." Then, when the
whistle blew and he had kissed little Violet, they would be
quite silent, looking at each other. And she would say in a
voice so matter-of-fact that it could have deceived no one:

" Well, I must go now. Good-bye, old man."

And he would say:

" Good-bye, Dollee. Kiss me."

They would kiss, and holding little Violet's hand very hard,
she would hurry away in the crowd, taking care not to look
back for fear she might suddenly lose sight of the bright side.
But as the months went on, became a year, eighteen months, two
years, and still she went weekly to see her " prince " in his
Palace, that visit became for her the hardest experience of all
her hard week's doings. For she was a realist, as well as a
heroine, and she could see the lines of despair not only in her
man's heart, but in his face. For a long time he had not said:
" I'm getting on fine, Dollee." His face had a beaten look, his
figure had wasted, he complained of his head.

" It's so noisy," he would say constantly; " oh! it's so noisy,
never a quiet moment—never alone—never—never—never. And
not enough to eat; it's all reduced now, Dollee."

She learned to smuggle food into his hands, but it was very
little, for they had not enough at home either, with the price

of living ever going up and her depleted income ever stationary. They had—her "man" told her—made a fuss in the papers about their being fed like turkey-cocks, while the "Huns" were sinking the ships. Gerhardt, always a spare little man, had lost eighteen pounds. She, naturally well-covered, was getting thin herself, but that she did not notice, too busy all day long, and too occupied in thinking of her "man." To watch him week by week, more hopeless as the months dragged on, was an acute torture, to disguise which was torture even more acute. She had long seen that there *was* no bright side, but if she admitted that, she knew she would go down; so she did not. And she carefully kept from Gerhardt such matters as David's overgrowing his strength because she could not feed him properly; the completely bedridden nature of auntie; and, worse than these, the growing coldness and unkindness of her neighbours. Perhaps they did not mean to be unkind, perhaps they did, for it was not in their nature to withstand the pressure of mass sentiment, the continual personal discomfort of having to stand in queues, the fear of air raids, the cumulative indignation caused by stories of atrocities, true and untrue. In spite of her record of kindliness towards them, she became tarred with the brush at last, for her nerves had given way once or twice, and she had said it was a shame to keep her "man" like that gettin' iller and iller, who had never done a thing. Even her reasonableness—and she was very reasonable—succumbed to the strain of that weekly sight of him, till she could no longer allow for the difficulties which Mrs. Clirehugh assured her the Government had to deal with. Then one day she used the words "fair play," and at once it became current that she had "German sympathies." From that time on she was somewhat doomed. Those who had received kindnesses from her were foremost in showing her coldness, being wounded in their self-esteem. To have received little benefits, such as being nursed when they were sick, from one who had "German sympathies" was too much for the pride which is in every human being, however humble an inhabitant of Putney. Mrs. Gerhardt's Cockney spirit could support this for herself, but she could not bear it for her children. David came home with a black eye and would not say why he had got it. Minnie missed her prize at school, though she had clearly won it. That was just after the last German offensive began; but Mrs. Gerhardt refused to see that this was any reason. Little Violet twice put the heart-rending question to her: "Aren't I English, mummy?"

She was answered: "Yes, my dear, of course."

But the child obviously remained unconvinced in her troubled mind.

And then they took David for the British Army. It was that which so upset the apple-cart in Mrs. Gerhardt that she broke out to her last friend, Mrs. Clirehugh:

"I do think it's hard, Eliza. They take his father and keep him there for a dangerous Hun, year after year like that; and then they take his boy for the army to fight against him. And how I'm to get on without him I don't know."

Little Mrs. Clirehugh, who was Scotch, with a Gloucestershire accent, replied:

"Well, we've got to beat them. They're such a wicked lot. I daresay it's 'ard on you, but we've got to beat them."

"But we never did nothing," cried Mrs. Gerhardt; "it isn't us that's wicked. We never wanted the war; it's nothing but ruin to him. They did ought to let me have my man or my boy, one or the other."

"You should 'ave some feeling for the Government, Dora; they 'ave to do 'ard things."

Mrs. Gerhardt, with a quivering face, had looked at her friend.

"I have," she said at last in a tone which implanted in Mrs. Clirehugh's heart the feeling that Dora was "bitter."

She could not forget it; and she would flaunt her head at any mention of her former friend. It was a blow to Mrs. Gerhardt, who had now no friends, except the deaf and bedridden aunt, to whom all things were the same, war or no war, Germans or no Germans, so long as she was fed.

About then it was that the tide turned, and the Germans began to know defeat. Even Mrs. Gerhardt, who read the papers no longer, learned it daily, and her heart relaxed; that bright side began to reappear a little. She felt they could not feel so hardly toward her "man" now as when they were all in fear; and perhaps the war would be over before her boy went out. But Gerhardt puzzled her. He did not brighten up. The iron seemed to have entered his soul too deeply. And one day, in the bazaar, passing an open doorway, Mrs. Gerhardt had a glimpse of why. There, stretching before her astonished eyes, was a great, as it were, encampment of brown blankets, slung and

looped up anyhow, dividing from each other countless sordid
beds, which were almost touching, and a whiff of huddled
humanity came out to her keen nostrils, and a hum of sound to
her ears. So that was where her "man" had dwelt these
thirty months, in that dirty, crowded, noisy place with dirty-
looking men, such as those she could see lying on the beds, or
crouching by the side of them over their work. He had kept
neat somehow, at least on the days when she came to him—but
that was where he lived! Alone again (for she no longer
brought the little Violet to see her German father), she grieved
all the way home. Whatever happened to him now, even if she
got him back, she knew he would never quite get over it.

And then came the morning when she came out of her door
like the other inhabitants of Putney, at sound of the maroons,
thinking it was an air raid; and, catching the smile on the
toothless mouth of one of her old neighbours, hearing the cheers
of the boys in the school round the corner, knew that it was
Peace. Her heart overflowed then, and, withdrawing hastily,
she sat down in a shiny chair in her empty parlour. Her face
crumpled suddenly, the tears came welling forth, and she cried,
alone in the little cold room. She cried from relief and utter
thankfulness. It was over—over at last! The long waiting—
the long misery—the yearning for her "man"—the grieving
for all those poor boys in the mud and the dreadful shell-holes
and the fighting, the growing terror of anxiety for her own
boy—over, all over! Now they would let Max out, now David
would come back from the army; and people would not be unkind and spiteful to her and the children any more!

For all she was a Cockney, hers was a simple soul, associating
peace with goodwill. Drying her tears, she stood up, and in the
little cheap mirror above the empty grate looked at her face.
It was lined, and she was grey; for more than two years her
"man" had not seen her without her hat. Whatever would
he say? And she rubbed and rubbed her cheeks, trying to
smooth them out. Then her conscience smote her, and she ran
upstairs to the back bed-room, where the deaf aunt lay. Taking
up the amateur ear-trumpet which Gerhardt himself had made
for "auntie," before he was taken away, she bawled into it:

"Peace, Auntie; it's Peace! Think of that. It's Peace!"

"What's that?" answered the deaf woman.

"It's Peace, Auntie, Peace!"

The deaf lady roused herself a little, and some meaning came into the lack-lustre black eyes of her long, leathery face. " You don't say," she said in her wooden voice. " I'm so hungry, Dolly; isn't it time for my dinner? "

" I was just goin' to get it, dearie," replied Mrs. Gerhardt, and hurried back downstairs with her brain teeming, to make the deaf woman's bowl of bread, pepper, salt and onions.

All that day and the next and the next she saw the bright side of things with almost dazzling clearness, waiting to visit her " prince " in his Palace. She found him in a strange and pitiful state of nerves. The news had produced too intense and varied emotions among those crowded thousands of men buried away from normal life so long. She spent all her hour and a half trying desperately to make him see the bright side, but he was too full of fears and doubts, and she went away smiling, but utterly exhausted. Slowly in the weeks which followed she learned that nothing was changed. In the fond hope that Gerhardt might be home now any day, she was taking care that his slippers and some clothes of David's were ready for him, and the hip bath handy for him to have a lovely hot wash. She had even bought a bottle of beer and some of his favourite pickle, saving the price out of her own food, and was taking in the paper again, letting bygones be bygones. But he did not come. And soon the paper informed her that the English prisoners were returning—many in wretched state, poor things, so that her heart bled for them, and made her fiercely angry with the cruel men who had treated them so; but it informed her too that, if the paper had its way, no " Huns " would be tolerated in this country for the future. " Send them all back ! " were the words it used. She did not realise at first that this applied to Gerhardt; but when she did she dropped the journal as if it had been a living coal of fire. Not let him come back to his home, and family, not let him stay, after all they'd done to him, and he never did anything to them ! Not let him stay, but send him out to that dreadful country, which he had almost forgotten in these thirty years; and he with an English wife and children ! In this new terror of utter dislocation the bright side so slipped from her that she was obliged to go out into the back garden in the dark, where a sou'westerly wind was driving the rain. There, lifting her eyes to the evening sky, she uttered her little moan. It couldn't be true; and yet, what they said in her paper had always turned out true, like the taking of Gerhardt away, and the reduction of his food. And the face of the gentleman in the building at Whitehall came before her out of the long past, with his lips tightening, and his words: "We have to do very hard things, Mrs. Gerhardt." Why had they to do them? Her "man" had never done no harm to no one! A flood, bitter as sea water, surged in her, and seemed to choke her very being. Those gentlemen in the papers—why should they go on like that? Had they no hearts, no eyes to see the misery they brought to humble folk? 'I wish them nothing worse than what they've brought to him and me,' she thought wildly, 'nothing worse!'

The rain beat on her face, wetted her grey hair, cooled her eyeballs. 'I mustn't be spiteful,' she thought; and, bending down in the dark, she touched the glass of the tiny conservatory up against the warm kitchen wall, heated by the cunning hot-water pipe that her "man" had put there in his old handy days. Under it were one monthly rose, which still had blossoms, and some straggly small chrysanthemums. She had been keeping them for the feast when he came home; but if he wasn't to come, what should she do? She raised herself. Above the wet roofs, sky-rack was passing wild and dark, but in a cleared space one or two stars shone the brighter for the blackness below. 'I must look on the bright side,' she thought, 'or I can't bear myself.' And she went in to cook the porridge for the evening meal.

The winter passed for her in the most dreadful anxiety. "Repatriate the Huns!" That cry continued to spurt up in her paper like a terrible face seen in some recurrent nightmare; and each week that she went to visit Gerhardt brought solid confirmation to her terror. He was taking it hard, so that sometimes she was afraid that "something" was happening in him. This was the utmost she went towards defining what doctors might have diagnosed as incipient softening of the brain. He seemed to dread the prospect of being sent to his native country.

"I couldn't stick it, Dollee," he would say. "What should I do—whatever should I do? I haven't a friend. I haven't a spot to go to. I should be lost. I'm afraid, Dollee. How could you come out there, you and the children? I couldn't make a living for you. I couldn't make one for myself now."

And she would say: "Cheer up, old man. Look on the bright side. Think of the others." For, though those others were not precisely the bright side, the mental picture of their sufferings, all those poor "princes" and their families, some-how helped her to bear her own. But he shook his head:

"No, I should never see you again."

"I'd follow you," she answered. "Never fear, Max, we'd work in the fields—me and the children. We'd get on somehow. Bear up, my dearie. It'll soon be over now. I'll stick to you, Max, never you fear. But they won't send you, they never will."

And then, like a lump of ice pressed on her breast, came the thought: 'But if they do! Auntie! My boy! My girls! However shall I manage if they do?'

Then long lists began to appear, and in great batches men were shovelled wholesale back to the country whose speech some of them had well-nigh forgotten. Gerhardt's name had not appeared yet. The lists were hung up the day after Mrs. Ger-hardt's weekly visit, but she urged him if his name did appear to appeal against repatriation. It was with the greatest difficulty that she roused in him the energy to promise. "Look on the bright side, Max," she implored him. "You've got a son in the British Army; they'll never send you. They wouldn't be so cruel. Never say die, old man."

His name appeared, but was taken out, and the matter hung again in awful suspense, while the evil face of the recurrent nightmare confronted Mrs. Gerhardt out of her favourite journal. She read that journal again, because so far as in her gentle spirit lay, she hated it. It was slowly killing her "man," and all her chance of future happiness; she hated it, and read it every morning. To the monthly rose and straggly brown-red chrysanthemums in the tiny hothouse there had succeeded spring flowers—a few hardy January snowdrops, and one by one blue scillas, and pale daffodils called "angels' tears."

Peace tarried, but the flowers came up long before their time in their tiny hothouse against the kitchen flue. Then one wonderful day there came to Mrs. Gerhardt a strange letter, announcing that Gerhardt was coming home. He would not be sent to Germany—he was coming home! To-day, that very day—any moment he might be with her. When she received it, who had long received no letters save the weekly letters of her boy still in the army, she was spreading margarine on auntie's bread for breakfast, and, moved beyond all control, she spread it thick, wickedly, wastefully thick, then dropped the knife, sobbed, laughed, clasped her hands on her breast, and without

rhyme or reason began singing, " Hark! the herald angels sing."
The girls had gone to school already, auntie in the room above
could not hear her, no one heard her, nor saw her drop suddenly
into the wooden chair, and, with her bare arms stretched out
one on either side of the plate of bread and margarine, cry her
heart out against the clean white table. Coming home, coming
home, coming home! The bright side! The white stars!

It was a quarter of an hour before she could trust herself to
answer the knocking on the floor, which meant that auntie
was missing her breakfast. Hastily she made the tea and went
up. The woman's dim long face gleamed greedily when she
saw how thick the margarine was spread; but little Mrs. Gerhardt said no word of the reason for that feast. She just
watched her only friend eating it, while moisture still trickled
out from her eyes on to her flushed cheeks, and the words still
hummed in her brain:

> " Peace on earth and mercy mild,
>   Jesus Christ a little child."

Then, still speaking no word, she ran out and put clean
sheets on her and her " man's " bed. She was on wires, she
could not keep still, and all the morning she polished. About
noon she went out into her garden, and from under the glass
plucked every flower that grew there—snowdrops, scillas,
" angels' tears," quite two dozen blossoms. She brought them
into the parlour and opened its window wide. The sun was
shining, and fell on the flowers strewn on the table, ready to be
made into the nosegay of triumphant happiness. While she
stood fingering them, delicately breaking half an inch off their
stalks so that they should last the longer in water, she became
conscious of someone on the pavement outside the window,
and looking up saw Mrs. Clirehugh. The past, the sense of
having been deserted by her friends, left her, and she called out:
" Come in, Eliza; look at my flowers! "

Mrs. Clirehugh came in; she was in black, her cheekbones
higher, her hair looser, her eyes bigger. Mrs. Gerhardt saw
tears starting from those eyes, wetting those high cheekbones,
and cried out:
" Why, what's the matter, dear? "
Mrs. Clirehugh choked. " My baby! "
Mrs. Gerhardt dropped an " angel's tear " and went up to her.
" Whatever's happened? " she cried.

"Dead!" replied Mrs. Clirehugh. "Dead o' the influenza. 'E's to be buried to-day. I can't—I can't——" Wild choking stopped her utterance. Mrs. Gerhardt put an arm round her and drew her head on to her shoulder.

"I can't"—sobbed Mrs. Clirehugh—"find any flowers. It's seein' yours made me cry."

"There, there!" cried Mrs. Gerhardt. "Have them. I'm sure you're welcome, dearie. Have them—I'm so sorry!"

"I don't know," choked Mrs. Clirehugh; "I 'aven't deserved them." Mrs. Gerhardt gathered up the flowers.

"Take them," she said. "I couldn't think of it. Your poor little baby. Take them! There, there, he's spared a lot of trouble. You must look on the bright side, dearie."

Mrs. Clirehugh tossed up her head.

"You're an angel, that's what *you* are!" And grasping the flowers, she hurried out, a black figure passing the window in the sunlight.

Mrs. Gerhardt stood above the emptied table, thinking: "Poor dear—I'm glad she had the flowers. It was a mercy I didn't call out that Max was coming!" And from the floor she picked up the "angel's tear" she had dropped, and set it in a glass of water, where the sunlight fell. She was still gazing at it, pale, slender, lonely in that coarse tumbler, when she heard a knock on the parlour door and went to open it. There stood her "man," with a large brown-paper parcel in his hand. He stood quite still, his head down, the face very grey. She cried out: "Max!" but the thought flashed through her: "He knocked on the door! It's *his* door—he knocked on the door!"

"Dollee?" he said, with a sort of question in his voice.

She threw her arms round him, drew him into the room, and, shutting the door, looked hard into his face. Yes, it was his face, but in the eyes something wandered—lit up, went out, lit up.

"Dollee," he said again, and clutched her hand.

She strained him to her with a sob.

"I'm not well, Dollee," he murmured.

"No, of course not, my dearie man; but you'll soon be all right now—home again with me. Cheer up, cheer up!"

"I'm not well," he said again.

She caught the parcel out of his hand, and, taking the "angel's tear" from the tumbler, fixed it in his coat.

"Here's a spring flower for you, Max; out of your own little

hothouse. You're home again; home again, my dearie. Auntie's
upstairs, and the girls'll be coming soon. And we'll have
dinner."

" I'm not well, Dollee," he said.

Terrified by that reiteration, she drew him down on the little
horsehair sofa, and sat on his knee. " You're home, Max; kiss
me. There's my man!" and she rocked him to and fro against
her, yearning yet fearing to look into his face and see that
"something" wander there—light up, go out, light up. " Look,
dearie," she said, " I've got some beer for you. You'd like a
glass of beer?"

He made a motion of his lips, a sound that was like the
ghost of a smack. It terrified her, so little life was there in it.

He clutched her close, and repeated feebly:

" Yes, all right in a day or two. They let me come—I'm not
well, Dollee." He touched his head.

Straining him to her, rocking him, she murmured over and
over again, like a cat purring to its kitten:

" It's all right, my dearie—soon be well—soon be well! We
must look on the bright side—My man!"

1919.

THE BLACK GODMOTHER

SITTING out on the lawn at tea with our friend and his retriever, we had been discussing those massacres of the helpless which had of late occurred, and wondering that they should have been committed by the soldiery of so civilised a State, when, in a momentary pause of our astonishment, our friend, who had been listening in silence, crumpling the drooping soft ear of his dog, looked up and said, " The cause of atrocities is generally the violence of Fear. Panic's at the back of most crimes and follies."

Knowing that his philosophical statements were always the result of concrete instance, and that he would not tell us what that instance was if we asked him—such being his nature—we were careful not to agree.

He gave us a look out of those eyes of his, so like the eyes of a mild eagle, and said abruptly : " What do you say to this, then? . . . I was out in the dog-days last year with this fellow of mine, looking for Osmunda, and stayed some days in a village—never mind the name. Coming back one evening from my tramp, I saw some boys stoning a mealy-coloured dog. I went up and told the young devils to stop it. They only looked at me in the injured way boys do, and one of them called out, ' It's mad, guv'nor!' I told them to clear off, and they took to their heels. The dog followed me. It was a young, leggy, mild-looking mongrel, cross—I should say—between a brown retriever and an Irish terrier. There was froth about its lips, and its eyes were watery; it looked indeed as if it might be in distemper. I was afraid of infection for this fellow of mine, and whenever it came too close shooed it away, till at last it slunk off altogether. Well, about nine o'clock, when I was settling down to write by the open window of my sitting-room—still daylight, and very quiet and warm—there began that most maddening sound, the barking of an unhappy dog. I could do nothing with that continual ' Yap—yap!' going on, and it was

213

too hot to shut the window; so I went out to see if I could stop it. The men were all at the pub, and the women just finished with their gossip; there was no sound at all but the continual barking of this dog, somewhere away out in the fields. I travelled by ear across three meadows, till I came on a hay-stack by a pool of water. There was the dog sure enough—the same mealy-coloured mongrel, tied to a stake, yapping, and making frantic little runs on a bit of rusty chain; whirling round and round the stake, then standing quite still, and shivering. I went up and spoke to it, but it backed into the hay-stack, and there it stayed shrinking away from me, with its tongue hanging out. It had been heavily struck by something on the head; the cheek was cut, one eye half-closed, and an ear badly swollen. I tried to get hold of it, but the poor thing was beside itself with fear. It snapped and flew round so that I had to give it up and sit down with this fellow here beside me to try and quiet it—a strange dog, you know, will generally form his estimate of you from the way it sees you treat another dog. I had to sit there quite half an hour before it would let me go up to it, pull the stake out, and lead it away. The poor beast, though it was so feeble from the blows it had received, was still half-frantic, and I didn't dare to touch it; and all the time I took good care that this fellow here didn't come too near. Then came the question what was to be done. There was no vet, of course, and I'd no place to put it except my sitting-room, which didn't belong to me. But, looking at its battered head, and its half-mad eyes, I thought: ' No trusting you with these bumpkins; you'll have to come in here for the night!' Well, I got it in, and heaped two or three of those hairy little red rugs landladies are so fond of, up in a corner, and got it on to them, and put down my bread and milk. But it wouldn't eat—its sense of proportion was all gone, fairly destroyed by terror. It lay there moaning, and every now and then it raised its head with a ' yap ' of sheer fright, dreadful to hear, and bit the air, as if its enemies were on it again; and this fellow of mine lay in the opposite corner, with his head on his paw, watching it. I sat up for a long time with that poor beast, sick enough, and wondering how it had come to be stoned and kicked and battered into this state; and next day I made it my business to find out." Our friend paused, scanned us a little angrily, and then went on: " It had made its first appearance, it seems, following a bicyclist. There are men, you know—save the mark—who, when their beasts get ill or too expensive, jump on their bicycles and take them for a quick run, taking care never to look behind them. When they get back home they say: ' Hullo! Where's Fido? Fido is nowhere, and there's an end! Well, this poor puppy gave up just as it got to our village; and, roaming about in search of water, attached itself to a farm labourer. The man—with excellent intentions, as he told me himself—tried to take hold of it, but too abruptly, so that it was startled, and snapped at him. Whereon he kicked it for a dangerous cur, and it went drifting back towards the village, and fell in with the boys coming home from school. It thought, no doubt, that they were going to kick it too, and nipped one of them who took it by the collar. Thereupon they hullabalooed and stoned it down the road to where I found them. Then I put in my little bit of torture, and drove it away, through fear of infection to my own dog. After that it seems to have fallen in with a man who told me: ' Well, you see, he came sneakin' round my house, with the children playin', and snapped at them when they went to stroke him, so that they came running in to their mother, an' she called to me in a fine takin' about a mad dog. I ran out with a shovel and gave 'im one, and drove him out. I'm sorry if he wasn't mad; he looked it right enough. You can't be too careful with strange dogs.' Its next acquaintance was an old stone-breaker, a very decent sort. ' Well! you see,' the old man explained to me, ' the dog came smellin' round my stones, an' it wouldn' come near, an' it wouldn' go away; it was all froth and blood about the jaw, and its eyes glared green at me. I thought to meself, bein' the dog-days—I don't like the look o' you, you look funny! So I took a stone, an' got it here, just on the ear; an' it fell over. And I thought to meself: Well, you've got to finish it, or it'll go bitin' somebody, for sure! But when I come to it with my hammer, the dog it got up—an' you know how it is when there's somethin' you've 'alf killed, and you feel sorry, and yet you feel you must finish it, an' you hit at it blind, you hit at it agen an' agen. The poor thing, it wriggled and snapped, an' I was terrified it'd bite me, an' some'ow it got away.' " Again our friend paused, and this time we dared not look at him.

" The next hospitality it was shown," he went on presently, " was by a farmer, who, seeing it all bloody, drove it off, thinking it had been digging up a lamb that he'd just buried. The

poor homeless beast came sneaking back, so he told his men to
get rid of it. Well, they got hold of it somehow—there was a
hole in its neck that looked as if they'd used a pitchfork—and,
mortally afraid of its biting them, but not liking, as they told
me, to drown it, for fear the owner might come on them, they
got a stake and a chain, and fastened it up, and left it in the
water by the hay-stack where I found it. I had some conversation with that farmer. 'That's right,' he said, 'but who was to
know? I couldn't have my sheep worried. The brute had
blood on his muzzle. These curs do a lot of harm when they've
once been blooded. You can't run risks.'" Our friend cut
viciously at a dandelion with his stick. "Run risks!" he broke
out suddenly. "That was it—from beginning to end of that
poor beast's sufferings, fear! From that fellow on the bicycle,
afraid of the worry and expense, as soon as it showed signs of
distemper, to myself and the man with the pitchfork—not one
of us, I daresay, would have gone out of our way to do it a
harm. But we felt fear, and so—by the law of self-preservation, or whatever you like—it all began, till there the poor thing
was, with a battered head and a hole in its neck, ravenous with
hunger, and too distraught even to lap my bread and milk.
Yes, there's something uncanny about a suffering animal—we
sat watching it, and again we were afraid, looking at its eyes
and the way it bit the air. Fear! It's the black godmother
of all damnable things!"

Our friend bent down, crumpling and crumpling at his dog's
ears. We, too, gazed at the ground, thinking of that poor lost
puppy, and the horrible inevitability of all that happens, seeing
men are what they are; thinking of all the foul doings in the
world, whose black godmother is Fear.

"And what became of the poor dog?" one of us asked at
last.

"When," said our friend slowly, "I'd had my fill of watching, I covered it with a rug, took this fellow away with me, and
went to bed. There was nothing else to do. At dawn I was
awakened by three dreadful cries—not like a dog's at all. I
hurried down. There was the poor beast—wriggled out from
under the rug—stretched on its side, dead. This fellow of
mine had followed me in, and he went and sat down by the
body. When I spoke to him he just looked round, and wagged
his tail along the ground, but would not come away; and there
he sat till it was buried, very interested but not sorry at all."

Our friend was silent, looking angrily at something in the distance.

And we, too, were silent, seeing in spirit that vigil of early morning: The thin, lifeless, sandy-coloured body, stretched on those red mats; and this black creature—now lying at our feet—propped on its haunches like the dog in "The Death of Procris," patient, curious, ungrieved, staring down at it with his bright, interested eyes.

1912.

PHILANTHROPY

MIST enwrapped Restington-on-Sea; not very thick, but exceedingly clammy. It decked the autumn trees in weirdness, cobwebbed the tamarisks, and compelled Henry Ivor to shut his window, excluding the faint hiss and rustle from the beach. He seldom wrote after tea without the accompaniment of fresh air, and was drowsing over his pen when his housekeeper entered.

"A couple to see you, sir; they came once before, when you was away."

Ivor blinked. "Well, show them in."

When the door was again opened a scent of whisky came in first, then a man, a woman, and a dog.

Ivor laid down his pen and rose; he had never seen any of them before, and immediately doubted whether he wanted to see any of them again. Never able, however, to be disagreeable at a moment's notice, he waited defensively. The man, who might have been thirty-five pale, warped, and thin, seemed to extract his face from the grip of nerves.

"Hearing you were down here, sir, and being in the printing trade, if you understand my meaning——"

Ivor nodded; he did not want to nod, but it seemed unavoidable and he looked at the woman. Her face was buttoned, the most expressionless he had ever seen.

"Well?" he said.

The man's lips, thin and down at one corner, writhed again.

"You being a well-known writer," he said, and the scent of whisky deepened.

Ivor thought: "It wants courage to beg; it's damp too. Perhaps he's only primed himself."

"Well" he said again.

"If you understand me," said the man, "I'm in a very delicate position. I expect you know Mr. Gloy—Charles Gloy —editor of Cribbage——"

"No," said Ivor. "But will you sit down?" And he placed two chairs.

The man and the woman sat down on their edges, the dog, too, sat on its edge! Ivor regarded it—a Schipperke—thinking:

"Did they bring their dog to undermine me?" As to that, it was the only kind of dog he did not like, but it looked damp and woeful.

"My brother works for Mr. Gloy," said the man; "so, being at Beachhampton—out of a job, if you understand my meaning —I brought my wife—you being a well-known philanthropist ——"

Ivor nervously took out a cigarette, and nervously put it back.

"I don't know what I can do for you," he murmured.

"I'm one to speak the truth," resumed the man, "if you follow me——" And Ivor did—he followed on and on behind a wandering tale of printing, the war, ill-health. At last he said in despair:

"I really can't recommend people I know nothing about. What exactly do you want me to do?"

The woman's face seemed suddenly to lose a button, as if she were going to cry, but just then the dog whimpered; she took it up on her lap. Ivor thought:

'How much have I got on me?'

"The fact is, Mr. Ivor," said the man, "I'm broke to the world, if you understand my meaning. If once I could get back to London——"

"What do you say, madam?"

The woman's mouth quivered and mumbled; Ivor stopped her with his hand.

"Well," he said, "I can give you enough to get up to London with, and a little over. But that's all, I'm afraid. And, forgive me, I'm very busy." He stood up. The man rose also.

"I don't want to say anything about my wife; you'll forgive my mentioning it, but there's not a lady in England that's her equal at makin' babies' slippers."

"Indeed!" said Ivor. "Well, here you are!" And he held out some pound notes. The man took the notes; one of his trouser-legs was pitiably patched.

"I'm sure I'm more than grateful——" he said; and looking at Ivor as if he expected to be contradicted, added: "I can't say better than that, can I?"

"No," said Ivor, and opened the door.

"I'll be ready to repay you as soon as ever I can—if you understand my meaning."

"Yes," said Ivor. "Good-day! Good-day, Mrs.——! Good-bye, little dog!"

One by one the three passed him and went out into the mist. Ivor saw them trailing down the road, shut the outer door, returned to his chair, sighed profoundly, and took up his pen.

When he had written three pages, and it was getting too dusk to see, his housekeeper came in.

"There's a boy from the Black Cow, sir, come to say they want you down there."

"Want *me*?"

"Yes, sir. That couple—the boy says they don't know what to do with them. They gave your name as being a friend."

"Good Lord!"

"Yes, sir; and the landlord says they don't seem to know where they come from like."

"Heavens!" said Ivor. He got up, however, put on his overcoat, and went out.

In the lighted doorway of the Black Cow stood the landlord.

"Sorry to have troubled you, sir, but really I can't tell how to deal with these friends of yours."

Ivor frowned. "I only saw them for the first time this afternoon. I just gave them money to go up to London with. Are they drunk?"

"Drunk!" said the landlord. "Well, if I'd known the man was half gone when he came in—of course I'd never— As to the woman, she sits and smiles. I can't get them to budge, and it's early closin'——"

"Well," muttered Ivor, "let's look at them!" And he followed the landlord in.

On the window-seat in the bar parlour those two were sitting, with mugs beside them, and the dog asleep on the feet of the woman, whose lips were unbuttoned in a foolish smile. Ivor looked at the man; his face was blank and beatific. Specimens of a damp and doleful world, they now seemed almost blissful.

"Mist' Ivor," he said. "Thought so—I'm not tight——"

"Yes," said Ivor, "but I thought you wanted to go up to London. The station's not half a mile."

"Cert'nly—go up to London."

"Come along, then; I'll show you the way."

"Ve'y good, we can walk, if you understand my meaning." And the man stood up, the dog and the woman also. All three passed unsteadily out.

The man walked first, then the woman, then the dog, wavering into the dusky mist. Ivor followed, praying that they might meet no traffic. The man's voice broke the silence in front.

"Hen'y Ivor!" Ivor closed up nervously.

"Hen'y Ivor! I see 'm sayin' to 'mself: 'What'll they move on for!' I see him, if y' understand my meaning. Wha'sh he good for—Hen'y Ivor—only writer o' books. Is he any better than me—no! Not's good, if you f-follow me. I see 'm thinkin': 'How can I get rid of 'm?'" He stood still suddenly, almost on Ivor's toes. "Where's dog—carry th' dog—get 'is feet wet."

The woman stooped unsteadily, picked up the dog, and they both wavered on again. Ivor walked alongside now, grim and apprehensive. The man seemed to have become aware of him.

"'Mist' Ivor," he said. "Thought so—I'm not tight—can't say better than that, can I?—I'm not writer of books like you —not plutocrat, if you understand my meaning. Want to ask you question: what would you do if you was me?"

There was silence, but for the slip-slippering of the woman's feet behind.

"I don' blame you," said the man, whose speech was getting thicker; "you can't help being a plutothrist. But whash the good of anything for me, except ob-oblivion, if you follow me?"

A faint radiance shone through the mist. The station building loomed suddenly quite close. Ivor steered towards it.

"Goin' up t' London," said the man. "Qui' right!"

He lurched past into the lighted entry, and the woman followed with the dog. Ivor saw them waver through the doorway. And, spinning round, he ran into the mist. 'Perfectly true!' he thought while he was running. Perfectly true! Why had he helped them? What did he care so long as he got rid of man, woman, and dog?

1922.

A MAN OF DEVON

I

MOOR, 20th *July*.

. . . IT is quiet here, sleepy, rather—a farm is never quiet; the sea, too, is only a quarter of a mile away, and when it's windy, the sound of it travels up the combe; for distraction, you must go four miles to Brixham or five to Kingswear, and you won't find much then. The farm lies in a sheltered spot, scooped, so to speak, high up the combe side—behind is a rise of fields, and beyond, a sweep of down. You have the feeling of being able to see quite far, which is misleading, as you soon find out if you walk. It is true Devon country—hills, hollows, hedge-banks, lanes dipping down into the earth or going up like the sides of houses, coppices, cornfields, and little streams wherever there's a place for one; but the downs along the cliff, all gorse and ferns, are wild. The combe ends in a sandy cove with black rock on one side, pinkish cliffs away to the headland on the other, and a coastguard station. Just now, with the harvest coming on, everything looks its richest, the apples ripening, the trees almost too green. It's very hot, still weather; the country and the sea seem to sleep in the sun. In front of the farm are half-a-dozen pines that look as if they had stepped out of another land, but all round the back is orchard as lush, and gnarled, and orthodox as anyone could wish. The house, a long, white building with three levels of roof, and splashes of brown all over it, looks as if it might be growing down into the earth. It was freshly thatched two years ago—and that's all the newness there is about it; they say the front door, oak, with iron knobs, is three hundred years old at least. You can touch the ceilings with your hand. The windows certainly might be larger—a heavenly old place, though, with a flavour of apples, smoke, sweetbriar, bacon, honeysuckle, and age, all over it.

The owner is a man called John Ford, about seventy, and

223

seventeen stone in weight—very big, on long legs, with a grey, stubbly beard, grey watery eyes, short neck and purplish complexion; he is asthmatic, and has a very courteous, autocratic manner. His clothes are made of Harris tweed—except on Sundays, when he puts on black, a seal ring, and a thick gold cable chain. There's nothing mean or small about John Ford; I suspect him of a warm heart, but he doesn't let you know much about him. He's a north-country man by birth, and has been out in New Zealand all his life. This little Devonshire farm is all he has now. He had a large "station" in the North Island, and was much looked up to, kept open house, did everything, as one would guess, in a narrow-minded, large-handed way. He came to grief suddenly; I don't quite know how. I believe his only son lost money on the turf, and then, unable to face his father, shot himself; if you had seen John Ford, you could imagine that. His wife died, too, that year. He paid up to the last penny, and came home, to live on this farm. He told me the other night that he had only one relation in the world, his granddaughter, who lives here with him. Pasiance Voisey—old spelling for Patience, but they pronounce it Pashyence—is sitting out here with me at this moment on a sort of rustic loggia that opens into the orchard. Her sleeves are rolled up, and she's stripping currants, ready for black currant tea. Now and then she rests her elbows on the table, eats a berry, pouts her lips, and begins again. She has a round little face; a long, slender body; cheeks like poppies; a bushy mass of black-brown hair, and dark-brown, almost black eyes; her nose is snub; her lips quick, red, rather full; all her motions quick and soft. She loves bright colours. She's rather like a little cat; sometimes she seems all sympathy, then in a moment as hard as tortoise-shell. She's all impulse; yet she doesn't like to show her feelings; I sometimes wonder whether she has any. She plays the violin.

It's queer to see these two together, queer and rather sad. The old man has a fierce tenderness for her that strikes into the very roots of him. I see him torn between it and his cold north-country horror of his feelings; his life with her is an unconscious torture to him. She's a restless, chafing thing, demure enough one moment, then flashing out into mocking speeches or hard little laughs. Yet she's fond of him in her fashion; I saw her kiss him once when he was asleep. She obeys him generally—in a way as if she couldn't breathe while she was doing it. She's had a queer sort of education—history, geography, elementary mathematics, and nothing else; never been to school; had a few lessons on the violin, but has taught herself most of what she knows. She is well up in the lore of birds, flowers, and insects; has three cats, who follow her about; and is full of pranks. The other day she called out to me, "I've something for you. Hold out your hand and shut your eyes!" It was a large, black slug! She's the child of the old fellow's only daughter, who was sent home for schooling at Torquay, and made a runaway match with one Richard Voisey, a yeoman farmer, whom she met in the hunting-field. John Ford was furious—his ancestors, it appears, used to lead ruffians on the Cumberland side of the Border—he looked on "Squire" Rick Voisey as a cut below him. He was called "Squire," as far as I can make out, because he used to play cards every evening with a parson in the neighbourhood who went by the name of "Devil" Hawkins. Not that the Voisey stock is to be despised. They have had this farm since it was granted to one Richard Voisey by copy dated 8th September, 13 Henry VIII. Mrs. Hopgood, the wife of the bailiff—a dear, quaint, serene old soul with cheeks like a rosy, withered apple, and an unbounded love of Pasiance—showed me the very document.

"I kape it," she said. "Mr. Ford be tu proud—but other folks be proud tu. 'Tis a pra-aper old fam'ly: all the women is Margery, Pasiance, or Mary; all the men's Richards an' Johns an' Rogers; old as they apple-trees."

Rick Voisey was a rackety, hunting fellow, and "dipped" the old farm up to its thatched roof. John Ford took his revenge by buying up the mortgages, foreclosing, and commanding his daughter and Voisey to go on living here rent free; this they dutifully did until they were both killed in a dog-cart accident, eight years ago. Old Ford's financial smash came a year later, and since then he's lived here with Pasiance. I fancy it's the cross in her blood that makes her so restless, and irresponsible: if she had been all a native she'd have been happy enough here, or all a stranger like John Ford himself, but the two strains struggling for mastery seem to give her no rest. You'll think this a far-fetched theory, but I believe it to be the true one. She'll stand with lips pressed together, her arms folded tight across her narrow chest, staring as if she could see beyond the things round her; then something catches her attention, her eyes will grow laughing, soft, or scornful all in a minute! She's eighteen, perfectly fearless in a boat, but you can't get her to mount a horse—a sore subject with her grandfather, who spends most of his day on a lean, half-bred pony, that carries him like a feather, for all his weight.

They put me up here as a favour to Dan Treffry; there's an arrangement of £ s. d. with Mrs. Hopgood in the background. They aren't at all well off; this is the largest farm about, but it doesn't bring them in much. To look at John Ford, it seems incredible he should be short of money—he's too large.

We have family prayers at eight, then breakfast—after that freedom for writing or anything else till supper and evening prayers. At midday one forages for oneself. On Sundays, two miles to church twice, or you get into John Ford's black books. . . . Dan Treffry himself is staying at Kingswear. He says he's made his pile; it suits him down here—like a sleep after years of being too wide-awake; he had a rough time in New Zealand, until that mine made his fortune. You'd hardly remember him; he reminds me of his uncle, old Nicholas Treffry; the same slow way of speaking, with a hesitation, and a trick of repeating your name with everything he says; left-handed too, and the same slow twinkle in his eyes. He has a dark, short beard, and red-brown cheeks; is a little bald on the temples, and a bit grey, but hard as iron. He rides over nearly every day, attended by a black spaniel with a wonderful nose and a horror of petticoats. He has told me lots of good stories of John Ford in the early squatter's times; his feats with horses live to this day; and he was through the Maori wars; as Dan says, " a man after Uncle Nic's own heart."

They are very good friends, and respect each other; Dan has a great admiration for the old man, but the attraction is Pasiance. He talks very little when she's in the room, but looks at her in a sidelong, wistful sort of way. Pasiance's conduct to him would be cruel in any one else, but in her one takes it with a pinch of salt. Dan goes off, but turns up again as quiet and dogged as you please.

Last night, for instance, we were sitting in the loggia after supper. Pasiance was fingering the strings of her violin, and suddenly Dan (a bold thing for him) asked her to play.

" What ! " she said, " before men? No, thank you ! "

" Why not? "

" Because I hate them."

Down came John Ford's hand on the wicker table: "You forget yourself! Go to bed!"

She gave Dan a look, and went; we could hear her playing in her bedroom; it sounded like a dance of spirits; and just when one thought she had finished, out it would break again like a burst of laughter. Presently, John Ford begged our pardons ceremoniously, and stumped off indoors. The violin ceased; we heard his voice growling at her; down he came again. Just as he was settled in his chair there was a soft swish, and something dark came falling through the apple boughs. The violin! You should have seen his face! Dan would have picked the violin up, but the old man stopped him. Later, from my bedroom window, I saw John Ford come out and stand looking at the violin. He raised his foot as if to stamp on it. At last he picked it up, wiped it carefully, and took it in. . . .

My room is next to hers. I kept hearing her laugh, a noise too as if she were dragging things about the room. Then I fell asleep, but woke with a start, and went to the window for a breath of fresh air. Such a black, breathless night! Nothing to be seen but the twisted, blacker branches; not the faintest stir of leaves, no sound but muffled grunting from the cowhouse, and now and then a faint sigh. I had the queerest feeling of unrest and fear, the last thing to expect on such a night. There *is* something here that's disturbing; a sort of suppressed struggle. I've never in my life seen anything so irresponsible as this girl, or so uncompromising as the old man; I keep thinking of the way he wiped that violin. It's just as if a spark would set everything in a blaze. There's a menace of tragedy—or—perhaps it's only the heat, and too much of Mother Hopgood's crame. . . .

II

Tuesday.

. . . I've made a new acquaintance. I was lying in the orchard, and presently, not seeing me, he came along—a man of middle height, with a singularly good balance, and no lumber—rather old blue clothes, a flannel shirt, a dull red necktie, brown shoes, a cap with a leather peak pushed up on the forehead. Face long and narrow, bronzed with a kind of pale burnt-in brownness; a good forehead. A brown moustache, beard rather pointed, blackening about the cheeks; his chin not visible, but from the beard's growth must be big; mouth I should judge sensuous. Nose straight and blunt; eyes grey, with an upward look, not exactly frank, because defiant; two parallel furrows down each cheek, one from the inner corner of the eye, one from the nostril; age perhaps thirty-five. About the face, attitude, movements, something immensely vital, adaptable, daring, and unprincipled.

He stood in front of the loggia, biting his fingers, a kind of nineteenth-century buccaneer, and I wondered what he was doing in this gallery. They say you can tell a man of Kent or a Somersetshire man; certainly you can tell a Yorkshireman, and this fellow could only have been a man of Devon, one of the two main types found in this county. He whistled; and out came Pasiance in a geranium-coloured dress, looking like some tall poppy—you know the slight droop of a poppy's head, and the way the wind sways its stem. . . . She *is* a human poppy, her fuzzy dark hair is like a poppy's lustreless black heart, she has a poppy's tantalising attraction and repulsion, something fatal, or rather fateful. She came walking up to my new friend, then caught sight of me, and stopped dead.

"That," she said to me, "is Zachary Pearse. This," she said to him, "is our *lodger*." She said it with a wonderful soft malice. She wanted to scratch me, and she scratched. Half an hour later I was in the yard, when up came this fellow Pearse.

"Glad to know you," he said, looking thoughtfully at the pigs. "You're a writer, aren't you?"

"A sort of one," I said.

"If by any chance," he said suddenly, "you're looking for a job, I could put something in your way. Walk down to the beach with me, and I'll tell you; my boat's at anchor, smartest little craft in these parts."

It was very hot, and I had no desire whatever to go down to the beach—I went, all the same. We had not gone far when John Ford and Dan Treffry came into the lane. Our friend seemed a little disconcerted, but soon recovered himself. We met in the middle of the lane, where there was hardly room to pass. John Ford, who looked very haughty, put on his *pince-nez* and stared at Pearse.

"Good-day!" said Pearse; "fine weather! I've been up to ask Pasiance to come for a sail. Wednesday we thought, weather permitting; this gentleman's coming. Perhaps you'll come too, Mr. Treffry. You've never seen my place. I'll give you lunch, and show you my father. He's worth a couple of hours' sail any day." It was said in such an odd way that one couldn't resent his impudence. John Ford was seized with a fit of wheezing, and seemed on the eve of an explosion; he glanced at me, and checked himself.

"You're very good," he said icily; "my granddaughter has other things to do. You, gentlemen, will please yourselves"; and, with a very slight bow, he went stumping on to the house. Dan looked at me, and I looked at him.

"You'll come?" said Pearse, rather wistfully. Dan stammered: "Thank you, Mr. Pearse; I'm a better man on a horse than in a boat, but—thank you." Cornered in this way, he's a shy, soft-hearted being. Pearse smiled his thanks. "Wednesday, then, at ten o'clock; you shan't regret it."

"Pertinacious beggar!" I heard Dan mutter in his beard; and found myself marching down the lane again by Pearse's side. I asked him what he was good enough to mean by saying I was coming, without having asked me. He answered, unabashed:

"You see, I'm not friends with the old man; but I knew he'd not be impolite to you, so I took the liberty."

He has certainly a knack of turning one's anger to curiosity. We were down in the combe now; the tide was running out, and the sand all little, wet, shining ridges. About a quarter of a mile out lay a cutter, with her tan sail half down, swinging to the swell. The sunlight was making the pink cliffs glow in the most wonderful way and shifting in bright patches over the sea like moving shoals of goldfish. Pearse perched himself on his dinghy, and looked out under his hand. He seemed lost in admiration.

"If we could only net some of those spangles," he said, "an' make gold of 'em! No more work then."

"It's a big job I've got on," he said presently; "I'll tell you about it on Wednesday. I want a journalist."

"But I don't write for the papers," I said; "I do other sort of work. My game is archæology."

"It doesn't matter," he said, "the more imagination the better. It'd be a thundering good thing for you."

His assurance was amazing, but it was past supper-time, and hunger getting the better of my curiosity, I bade him goodnight. When I looked back, he was still there, on the edge of his boat, gazing at the sea. A queer sort of bird altogether, but attractive somehow.

Nobody mentioned him that evening; but once old Ford, after staring a long time at Pasiance, muttered *à propos* of nothing, "Undutiful children!" She was softer than usual; listening quietly to our talk, and smiling when spoken to. At bedtime she went up to her grandfather, without waiting for the usual command, "Come and kiss me, child."

Dan did not stay to supper, and he has not been here since. This morning I asked Mother Hopgood who Zachary Pearse was. She's a true Devonian; if there's anything she hates, it is to be committed to a definite statement. She ambled round her answer, and at last told me that he was "son of old Cap'en Jan Pearse to Black Mill. 'Tes an old family to Dartymouth an' Plymouth," she went on in a communicative outburst. "They du say Francis Drake tuke five o' they Pearses with 'en to fight the Spaniards. At least that's what I've heard Mr. Zachary zay; but Ha-apgood can tell yu." Poor Hopgood, the amount of information she saddles him with in the course of the day! Having given me thus to understand that she had run dry, she at once went on:

"Cap'en Jan Pearse made a dale of ventures. He's old now— they du say nigh an 'undred. Ha-apgood can tell you."

"But the son, Mrs. Hopgood?"

Her eyes twinkled with sudden shrewdness. She hugged herself placidly.

"An' what would yu take for dinner to-day? There's duck; or yu might like 'toad in the hole,' with an apple tart; or then, there's— Well! we'll see what we can du like." And off she went, without waiting for my answer.

To-morrow is Wednesday. I shan't be sorry to get another look at this fellow Pearse. . . .

III

Friday, 29th July.

. . . Why do you ask me so many questions, and egg me on to write about these people instead of minding my business? If you really want to hear, I'll tell you of Wednesday's doings.

It was a splendid morning; and Dan turned up, to my surprise—though I might have known that when he says a thing, he does it. John Ford came out to shake hands with him, then, remembering why he had come, breathed loudly, said nothing, and went in again. Nothing was to be seen of Pasiance, and we went down to the beach together.

"I don't like this fellow Pearse, George," Dan said to me on the way; "I was fool enough to say I'd go, and so I must, but what's he after? Not the man to do things without a reason, mind you."

I remarked that we should soon know.

"I'm not so sure—queer beggar; I never look at him without thinking of a pirate."

The cutter lay in the cove as if she had never moved. There too was Zachary Pearse seated on the edge of his dinghy.

"A five-knot breeze," he said; "I'll run you down in a couple of hours." He made no inquiry about Pasiance, but put us into his cockleshell and pulled for the cutter. A lantern-jawed fellow, named Prawle, with a spiky, prominent beard, long clean-shaven upper lip, and tanned complexion—a regular hard-weather bird—received us.

The cutter was beautifully clean; built for a Brixham trawler, she still had her number—DH 113—uneffaced. We dived into a sort of cabin, airy, but dark, fitted with two bunks and a small table, on which stood some bottles of stout; there were lockers, too, and pegs for clothes. Prawle, who showed us round, seemed very proud of a steam contrivance for hoisting sails. It was some minutes before we came on deck again; and there, in the dinghy, being pulled towards the cutter, sat Pasiance.

"If I'd known this," stammered Dan, getting red. "I wouldn't have come." She had outwitted us, and there was nothing to be done.

It was a very pleasant sail. The breeze was light from the south-east, the sun warm, the air soft. Presently Pasiance began singing:

"Columbus is dead and laid in his grave,
    Oh! heigh-ho! and laid in his grave;
Over his head the apple-trees wave—
    Oh! heigho! the apple-trees wave. . . .

The apples are ripe and ready to fall,
    Oh! heigho! and ready to fall;
There came an old woman and gathered them all,
    Oh! heigho! and gathered them all. . . .

> The apples are gathered, and laid on the shelf,
>   Oh! heigho! and laid on the shelf;
> If you want any more, you must sing for yourself,
>   Oh! heigho! and sing for yourself."

Her small, high voice came to us in trills and spurts, as
the wind let it, like the singing of a skylark lost in the sky.
Pearse went up to her and whispered something. I caught a
glimpse of her face like a startled wild creature's; shrinking,
tossing her hair, laughing, all in the same breath. She wouldn't
sing again, but crouched in the bows with her chin on her hands,
and the sun falling on one cheek, round, velvety, red as a
peach. . . .

We passed Dartmouth, and half an hour later put into a little
wooded bay. On a low reddish cliff was a house hedged round
by pine-trees. A bit of broken jetty ran out from the bottom
of the cliff. We hooked on to this, and landed. An ancient,
fish-like man came slouching down and took charge of the
cutter. Pearse led us towards the house, Pasiance following
mortally shy all of a sudden.

The house had a dark, overhanging thatch of the rush reeds
that grow in the marshes hereabouts; I remember nothing else
remarkable. It was neither old, nor new; neither beautiful, nor
exactly ugly; neither clean, nor entirely squalid; it perched
there with all its windows over the sea, turning its back contemptuously on the land.

Seated in a kind of porch, beside an immense telescope, was
a very old man in a panama hat, with a rattan cane. His pure-
white beard and moustache, and almost black eyebrows, gave
a very singular, piercing look to his little, restless, dark-grey
eyes; all over his mahogany cheeks and neck was a network
of fine wrinkles. He sat quite upright, in the full sun, hardly
blinking.

"Dad!" said Zachary, "*this* is Pasiance Voisey." The old
man turned his eyes on her and muttered, "How do you do,
ma'am?" then took no further notice. And Pasiance, who
seemed to resent this, soon slipped away and went wandering
about amongst the pines. An old woman brought some plates
and bottles and laid them casually on a table; and we sat round
the figure of old Captain Pearse without a word, as if we were
all under a spell.

Before lunch there was a little scene between Zachary Pearse and Dan, as to which of them should summon Pasiance. It ended in both going, and coming back without her. She did not want any lunch, would stay where she was amongst the pines.

For lunch we had chops, wood-pigeons, mushrooms, and mulberry preserve, and drank wonderful Madeira out of common wine-glasses. I asked the old man where he got it; he gave me a queer look, and answered with a little bow:

" Stood me in tu shillin' the bottle, an' the country got nothing out of it, sir. In the early Thirties; tu' shillin' the bottle; there's no such wine nowaday; and," he added, looking at Zachary, " no such men."

Zachary smiled and said: " You did nothing so big, dad, as what I'm after, now ! "

The old man's eyes had a sort of disdain in them.

" You're going far, then, in the *Pied Witch,* Zack? "

" I am," said Zachary.

" And *where* might yu be goin' in that old trampin' smut factory? "

" Morocco."

" Heu ! " said the old man, " there's nothing there; I know that coast, as I know the back o' my hand." He stretched out a hand covered with veins and hair.

Zachary began suddenly to pour out a flood of words:

" Below Mogador—a fellow there—friend of mine—two years ago now. Concessions—trade—gunpowder—cruisers—feuds—money—chiefs—Gatling guns—Sultan—rifles—rebellion—gold." He detailed a reckless, sordid, bold scheme, which, on the pivot of a trading venture, was intended to spin a whole wheel of political convulsions.

" They'll never let you get there," said old Pearse.

" Won't they? " returned Zachary. " Oh yes, they will, an' when I leave, *there'll be another dynasty, and I'll be a rich man."*

" Yu'll never leave," answered the old man.

Zachary took out a sheet of paper covered with figures. He had worked the whole thing out. So much—equipment, so much—trade, so much—concessions, so much—emergencies. " My last mag ! " he ended, " a thousand short; the ship's ready, and if I'm not there within a month my chance is as good as gone."

This was the pith of his confidences—an appeal for money, and we all looked as men will when that crops up.

" Mad ! " muttered the old man, looking at the sea.

" No," said Zachary. That one word was more eloquent than all the rest of his words put together. This fellow is no visionary. His scheme may be daring, and unprincipled, but —he knows very well what he's about.

" Well ! " said old Pearse, " you shall have five hundred of my money, if it's only to learn what yu're made of. Wheel me in ! " Zachary wheeled him into the house, but soon came back.

" The old man's cheque for five hundred pounds ! " he said, holding it up. " Mr. Treffry, give me another, and you shall have a third of the profits."

I expected Dan to give a point-blank refusal. But he only asked :

" Would that clear you for starting ? "

" With that," said Zachary, " I can get to sea in a fortnight."

" Good ! " Dan said slowly. " Give me a written promise ! To sea in fourteen days and my fair share on the five hundred pounds—no more—no less."

Again I thought Pearse would have jumped at this, but he leaned his chin on his hand, and looked at Dan, and Dan looked at him. While they were staring at each other like this, Pasiance came up with a kitten.

" See ! " she said, " isn't it a darling ? " The kitten crawled and clawed its way up behind her neck. I saw both men's eyes as they looked at Pasiance, and suddenly understood what they were at. The kitten rubbed itself against Pasiance's cheek, overbalanced, and fell, clawing, down her dress. She caught it up and walked away. Some one, I don't know which of us, sighed, and Pearse cried " Done ! "

The bargain had been driven.

" Good-bye, Mr. Pearse," said Dan; " I guess that's all I'm wanted for. I'll find my pony waiting in the village. George, you'll see Pasiance home ? "

We heard the hoofs of his pony galloping down the road; Pearse suddenly excused himself, and disappeared.

This venture of his may sound romantic and absurd, but it's matter-of-fact enough. He's after £ s. d. ! Shades of Drake, Raleigh, Hawkins, Oxenham ! The worm of suspicion gnaws at the rose of romance. What if those fellows, too, were only after £ s. d. ? . . .

I strolled into the pine-wood. The earth there was covered like a bee's body with black and gold stripes; there was the

blue sea below, and white, sleepy clouds, and bumble-bees booming above the heather; it was all softness, a summer's day in
Devon. Suddenly I came on Pearse standing at the edge of
the cliff with Pasiance sitting in a little hollow below, looking
up at him. I heard him say:

"Pasiance—Pasiance!" The sound of his voice, and the
sight of her soft, wondering face made me furious. What business has she with love, at her age? What business have they
with *each* other?

He told me presently that she had started off for home, and
drove me to the ferry, behind on old grey pony. On the way
he came back to his offer of the other day.

"Come with me," he said. "It doesn't do to neglect the
Press; you can see the possibilities. It's one of the few countries left. If I once get this business started you don't know
where it's going to stop. You'd have free passage everywhere,
and whatever you like in reason."

I answered as rudely as I could—but by no means as rudely
as I wanted—that his scheme was mad. As a matter of fact, it's
much too sane for me; for, whatever the body of a scheme, its
soul is the fibre of the schemer.

"Think of it," he urged as if he could see into me. "You
can make what you like of it. Press paragraphs, of course.
But that's mechanical; why, even I could do it, if I had time.
As for the rest, you'll be as free—as free as a man."

There, in five words of one syllable, is the kernel of this fellow
Pearse—"As free as a man!" No rule, no law, not even the
mysterious shackles that bind men to their own self-respects!
"As free as a man!" No ideals; no principles; no fixed star
for his worship; no coil he can't slide out of! But the fellow
has the tenacity of one of the old Devon mastiffs, too. He
wouldn't take "No" for an answer.

"Think of it," he said; "any day will do—I've got a fortnight. . . . Look! there she is!" I thought that he meant
Pasiance; but it was an old steamer, sluggish and black in the
blazing sun of mid-stream, with a yellow-and-white funnel,
and no sign of life on her decks.

"That's her—the *Pied Witch!* Do her twelve knots; you
wouldn't think it! Well! good-evening! You'd better come.
A word to me at any time. I'm going aboard now."

As I was being ferried across I saw him lolling in the stern-sheets of a little boat, the sun crowning his straw hat with glory.

I came on Pasiance, about a mile up the road, sitting in the hedge. We walked on together between the banks—Devonshire banks—as high as houses, thick with ivy and ferns, bramble and hazel boughs, and honeysuckle.

"Do you believe in a God?" she said suddenly. "Grandfather's God is simply awful. When I'm playing the fiddle, I can *feel* God; but grandfather's is such a stuffy God—you know what I mean: the sea, the wind, the trees, colours too—they make one *feel*. But I don't believe that life was meant to be 'good' in. Isn't there anything better than being good? When I'm 'good,' I simply feel wicked." She reached up, caught a flower from the hedge, and slowly tore its petals.

"What would you do," she muttered, "if you wanted a thing, but were afraid of it? But I suppose you're never afraid!" she added, mocking me. I admitted that I was sometimes afraid, and often afraid of being afraid.

"That's nice! I'm not afraid of illness, nor of grandfather, nor of his God; but—I want to be free. If you want a thing badly, you're afraid about it."

I thought of Zachary Pearse's words, "free as a man."

"Why are you looking at me like that?" she said.

I stammered: "What do you mean by freedom?"

"Do you know what I shall do to-night?" she answered. "Get out of my window by the apple-tree, and go to the woods, and play!"

We were going down a steep lane, along the side of a wood, where there's always a smell of sappy leaves, and the breath of the cows that come close to the hedge to get the shade.

There was a cottage in the bottom, and a small boy sat outside playing with a heap of dust.

"Hallo, Johnny!" said Pasiance. "Hold your leg out and show this man your bad place!" The small boy undid a bandage round his bare and dirty little leg, and proudly revealed a sore.

"Isn't it nasty?" cried Pasiance ruefully, tying up the bandage again; "poor little feller! Johnny, see what I've brought you!" She produced from her pocket a stick of chocolate, the semblance of a soldier made of sealing-wax and worsted, and a crooked sixpence.

It was a new glimpse of her. All the way home she was telling me the story of little Johnny's family; when she came to his mother's death, she burst out: " A beastly shame, wasn't it, and they're so poor; it might just as well have been somebody else. I like poor people, but I hate rich ones—stuck-up beasts."

Mrs. Hopgood was looking over the gate, with her cap on one side, and one of Pasiance's cats rubbing itself against her skirts. At the sight of us she hugged herself.

" Where's grandfather? " asked Pasiance. The old lady shook her head.

" Is it a row? " Mrs. Hopgood wriggled, and wriggled, and out came:

" Did you get yure tay, my pretty? No? Well, that's a pity; yu'll be fallin' low-like."

Pasiance tossed her head, snatched up the cat, and ran indoors. I remained staring at Mrs. Hopgood.

" Dear—dear," she chuckled, " poor lamb. So to spake it's ——" and she blurted out suddenly, " chuckin' full of wra-ath, he is. Well, there! "

My courage failed that evening. I spent it at the coast-guard station, where they gave me bread and cheese and some awful cider. I passed the kitchen as I came back. A fire was still burning there, and two figures, misty in the darkness, flitted about with stealthy laughter like spirits afraid of being detected in a carnal meal. They were Pasiance and Mrs. Hopgood; and so charming was the smell of eggs and bacon, and they had such an air of tender enjoyment of this dark revel, that I stifled many pangs, as I crept hungry up to bed.

In the middle of the night I woke and heard what I thought was screaming; then it sounded like wind in trees, then like the distant shaking of a tambourine, with the high singing of a human voice. Suddenly it stopped—two long notes came wailing out like sobs—then utter stillness; and though I listened for an hour or more there was no other sound. . . .

IV

4th August.

. . . For three days after I wrote last, nothing at all happened here. I spent the mornings on the cliff reading, and watching the sun-sparks raining on the sea. It's grand up there with the gorse all round, the gulls basking on the rocks, the partridges calling in the corn, and now and then a young hawk overhead.

The afternoons I spent out in the orchard. The usual routine goes on at the farm all the time—cow-milking, bread-baking, John Ford riding in and out, Pasiance in her garden stripping lavender, talking to the farm hands; and the smell of clover, and cows and hay; the sound of hens and pigs and pigeons, the soft drawl of voices, the dull thud of the farm carts; and day by day the apples getting redder. Then, last Monday, Pasiance was away from sunrise till sunset—nobody saw her go—nobody knew where she had gone. It was a wonderful, strange day, a sky of silver-grey and blue, with a drift of wind-clouds, all the trees sighing a little, the sea heaving in a long, low swell, the animals restless, the birds silent, except the gulls with their old man's laughter and kitten's mewing.

A something wild was in the air; it seemed to sweep across the downs and combe, into the very house, like a passionate tune that comes drifting to your ears when you're sleepy. But who would have thought the absence of that girl for a few hours could have wrought such havoc! We were like uneasy spirits; Mrs. Hopgood's apple cheeks seemed positively to wither before one's eyes. I came across a dairymaid and farm hand discussing stolidly with very downcast faces. Even Hopgood, a hard-bitten fellow with immense shoulders, forgot his imperturbability so far as to harness his horse, and depart on what he assured me was " just a wild-goose chaace." It was long before John Ford gave signs of noticing that anything was wrong, but late in the afternoon I found him sitting with his hands on his knees, staring straight before him. He rose heavily when he saw me, and stalked out. In the evening, as I was starting for the coastguard station to ask for help to search the cliff, Pasiance appeared, walking as if she could hardly drag one leg after the other. Her cheeks were crimson; she was biting her lips to keep tears of sheer fatigue out of her eyes. She passed me in the doorway without a word. The anxiety he had gone through seemed to forbid the old man from speaking. He just came forward, took her face in his hands, gave it a great kiss, and walked away. Pasiance dropped on the floor in the dark passage, and buried her face on her arms. " Leave me alone! " was all she would say. After a bit she dragged herself upstairs. Presently Mrs. Hopgood came to me.

" Not a word out of her—an' not a bite will she ate, an' I had a pie all ready—scrumptious. The good Lord knows the truth —she asked for brandy; have you any brandy, sir? Ha-apgood 'e don't drink it, an' Mister Ford 'e don't allaow for anything but caowslip wine."

I had whiskey.

The good soul seized the flask, and went off hugging it. She returned it to me half empty.

"Lapped it like a kitten laps milk. I misdaoubt it's straong, poor lamb, it lusened 'er tongue pra-aperly. 'I've a-done it,' she says to me, 'Mums—I've a-done it,' an' she laughed like a mad thing; and then, sir, she cried, an' kissed me, an' pushed me thru the door. Gude Lard! What is 't she's a-done?"...

It rained all the next day and the day after. About five o'clock yesterday the rain ceased; I started off to Kingswear on Hopgood's nag to see Dan Treffry. Every tree, bramble, and fern in the lanes was dripping water; and every bird singing from the bottom of his heart. I thought of Pasiance all the time. Her absence that day was still a mystery; one never ceased asking oneself what she had done. There are people who never grow up—they have no right to do things. Actions have consequences—and children have no business with consequences.

Dan was out. I had supper at the hotel, and rode slowly home. In the twilight stretches of the road, where I could touch either bank of the lane with my whip, I thought of nothing but Pasiance and her grandfather; there was something in the half light suited to wonder and uncertainty. It had fallen dark before I rode into the straw-yard. Two young bullocks snuffled at me, a sleepy hen got up and ran off with a tremendous shrieking. I stabled the horse, and walked round to the back. It was pitch black under the apple-trees, and the windows were all darkened. I stood there a little, everything smelled so delicious after the rain; suddenly I had the uncomfortable feeling that I was being watched. Have you ever felt like that on a dark night? I called out at last: "Is any one there?" Not a sound! I walked to the gate—nothing! The trees still dripped with tiny, soft, hissing sounds, but that was all. I slipped round to the front, went in, barricaded the door, and groped up to bed. But I couldn't sleep. I lay awake a long while; dozed at last, and woke with a jump. A stealthy murmur of smothered voices was going on quite close somewhere. It stopped. A minute passed; suddenly came the soft thud as of something falling. I sprang out of bed and rushed to the window. Nothing—but in the distance something that sounded like footsteps. An owl hooted: then clear as crystal, but quite low, I heard Pasiance singing in her room:

> "The apples were ripe and ready to fall,
>   Oh! heigho! and ready to fall."

I ran to her door and knocked.
(Our rooms are like this:—)

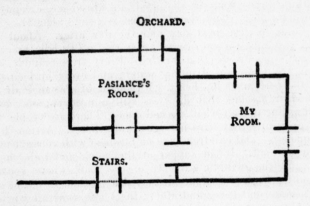

"What is it?" she cried.
"Is anything the matter?"
"Matter?"
"Is anything the matter?"
"Ha—ha—ha—ha! Good-night!" then quite low, I heard her catch her breath, hard, sharply. No other answer, no other sound.

I went to bed and lay awake for hours. . . .

This evening Dan came; during supper he handed Pasiance a roll of music; he had got it in Torquay. The shopman, he said, had told him that it was a " corker."

It was Bach's " Chaconne." You should have seen her eyes shine, her fingers actually tremble while she turned over the pages. Seems odd to think of *her* worshipping at the shrine of Bach—as odd as to think of a wild colt running of its free will into the shafts; but that's just it—with her you can never tell.

"Heavenly!" she kept saying.

John Ford put down his knife and fork.

"Heathenish stuff!" he muttered, and suddenly thundered out, "Pasiance!"

She looked up with a start, threw the music from her, and resumed her place.

During evening prayers, which follow every night immediately on food, her face was a study of mutiny. She went to bed early. It was rather late when we broke up—for once old Ford had been talking of his squatter's life. As we came out, Dan held up his hand. A dog was barking. "It's Lass," he said. "She'll wake Pasiance."

The spaniel yelped furiously. Dan ran out to stop her. He was soon back.

"Somebody's been in the orchard, and gone off down to the cove." He ran on down the path. I, too, ran, horribly uneasy. In front, through the darkness, came the spaniel's bark; the lights of the coastguard station faintly showed. I was first on the beach; the dog came to me at once, her tail almost in her mouth from apology. There was the sound of oars working in rowlocks; nothing visible but the feathery edges of the waves. Dan said behind, "No use! He's gone." His voice sounded hoarse, like that of a man choking with passion.

"George," he stammered, "it's that blackguard. I wish I'd put a bullet in him." Suddenly a light burned up in the darkness on the sea, seemed to swing gently, and vanished. Without another word we went back up the hill. John Ford stood at the gate motionless, indifferent—nothing had dawned on him as yet. I whispered to Dan, "Let it alone!"

"No," he said, "I'm going to show you." He struck a match, and slowly hunted the footsteps in the wet grass of the orchard. "Look—here!"

He stopped under Pasiance's window and swayed the match over the ground. Clear as daylight were the marks of some one who had jumped or fallen. Dan held the match over his head.

"And look there!" he said. The bough of an apple-tree below the window was broken. He blew the match out.

I could see the whites of his eyes, like an angry animal's.

"Drop it, Dan!" I said.

He turned on his heel suddenly, and stammered out, "You're right."

But he had turned into John Ford's arms.

The old man stood there like some great force, darker than the darkness, staring up at the window, as though stupefied. We had not a word to say. He seemed unconscious of our presence. He turned round and left us standing there.

"Follow him!" said Dan. "Follow him—by God! it's not safe."

We followed. Bending, and treading heavily, he went upstairs. He struck a blow on Pasiance's door. "Let me in!" he said. I drew Dan into my bedroom. The key was slowly turned, her door was flung open, and there she stood in her dressing-gown, a candle in her hand, her face crimson, and oh! so young, with its short, crisp hair and round cheeks. The old man—like a giant in front of her—raised his hands, and laid them on her shoulders.

"What's this? You—you've had a man in your room?"

Her eyes did not drop.

"Yes," she said. Dan gave a groan.

"Who?"

"Zachary Pearse," she answered in a voice like a bell.

He gave her one awful shake, dropped his hands, then raised them as though to strike her. She looked him in the eyes; his hands dropped, and he too groaned. As far as I could see, her face never moved.

"I'm married to him," she said; "d'you hear? Married to him. Go out of my room!" She dropped the candle on the floor at his feet, and slammed the door in his face. The old man stood for a minute as though stunned, then groped his way downstairs.

"Dan," I said, "is it true?"

"Ah!" he answered, "it's true; didn't you hear her?"

I was glad I couldn't see his face.

"That ends it," he said at last; "there's the old man to think of."

"What will he do?"

"Go to the fellow this very night." He seemed to have no doubt. Trust one man of action to know another.

I muttered something about being an outsider—wondered if there was anything I could do to help.

"Well," he said slowly, "I don't know that I'm anything but an outsider now; but I'll go along with him, if he'll have me."

He went downstairs. A few minutes later they rode out from

the straw-yard. I watched them past the line of hayricks, into
the blacker shadows of the pines, then the tramp of hoofs began
to fail in the darkness, and at last died away.

I've been sitting here in my bedroom writing to you ever
since, till my candle's almost gone. I keep thinking what the
end of it is to be; and reproaching myself for doing nothing.
And yet, what could I have done? I'm sorry for her—sorrier
than I can say. The night is so quiet—I haven't heard a
sound; is she asleep, awake, crying, triumphant?

It's four o'clock; I've been asleep.

They're back. Dan is lying on my bed. I'll try and tell you
his story as near as I can, in his own words.

"We rode," he said, "round the upper way, keeping out of
the lanes, and got to Kingswear by half-past eleven. The horse-
ferry had stopped running, and we had a job to find any one
to put us over. We hired the fellow to wait for us, and took
a carriage at the 'Castle.' Before we got to Black Mill it was
nearly one, pitch-dark. With the breeze from the south-east,
I made out he should have been in an hour or more. The old
man had never spoken to me once: and before we got there I
had begun to hope we shouldn't find the fellow after all. We
made the driver pull up in the road, and walked round and
round, trying to find the door. Then some one cried, 'Who
are you?'

"'John Ford.'

"'What do you want?' It was old Pearse.

"'To see Zachary Pearse.'

"The long window out of the porch where we sat the other
day was open, and in we went. There was a door at the end
of the room, and a light coming through. John Ford went
towards it; I stayed out in the dark.

"'Who's that with you?'

"'Mr. Treffry.'

"'Let him come in!' I went in. The old fellow was in bed,
quite still on his pillows, a candle by his side; to look at him
you'd think nothing of him but his eyes were alive. It was
queer being there with those two old men."

Dan paused, seemed to listen, then went on doggedly.

"'Sit down, gentlemen,' said old Pearse. 'What may you
want to see my son for?' John Ford begged his pardon, he
had something to say, he said, that wouldn't wait.

"They were very polite to one another," muttered Dan.

"'Will you leave your message with me?' said Pearse.

"'What I have to say to your son is private.'

"'I'm his father.'

"'I'm my girl's grandfather; and her only stand-by.'

"'Ah!' muttered old Pearse, 'Rick Voisey's daughter.'

"'I mean to see your son.'

"Old Pearse smiled. Queer smile he's got, sort of sneering sweet.

"'You can never tell where Zack may be,' he said. 'You think I want to shield him. You're wrong; Zack can take care of himself.'

"'Your son's here!' said John Ford. 'I know.' Old Pearse gave us a very queer look.

"'You come into my house like thieves in the night,' he said, 'and give me the lie, do you?'

"'Your son came to my child's room like a thief in the night; it's for that I want to see him,' and then," said Dan, "there was a long silence. At last Pearse said:

"'I don't understand; has he played the blackguard?'

"John Ford answered, 'He's married her, or, before God, I'd kill him.'

"Old Pearse seemed to think this over, never moving on his pillows. 'You don't know Zack,' he said; 'I'm sorry for you, and I'm sorry for Rick Voisey's daughter; but you don't know Zack.'

"'Sorry!' groaned out John Ford; 'he's stolen my child, and I'll punish him.'

"'Punish!' cried old Pearse, 'we don't take punishment, not in my family.'

"'Captain Jan Pearse, as sure as I stand here, you and your breed will get your punishment of God.' Old Pearse smiled.

"'Mr. John Ford, that's as may be; but sure as I lie here we won't take it of you. You can't punish unless you make to feel, and that you can't du.'"

And that is truth!

Dan went on again:

"'You won't tell me where your son is!' but old Pearse never blinked.

"'I won't,' he said, 'and now you may get out. I lie here an old man alone, with no use to my legs, night on night, an' the house open; any rapscallion could get in; d'ye think I'm afraid of you?'

" We were beat; and walked out without a word. But that old man; I've thought of him a lot—ninety-two, and lying there. Whatever he's been, and they tell you rum things of him, whatever his son may be, he's a *man*. It's not what he said, nor that there was anything to be afraid of just then, but somehow it's the idea of the old chap lying there. I don't ever wish to see a better plucked one."

We sat silent after that; out of doors the light began to stir among the leaves. There were all kinds of rustling sounds, as if the world were turning over in bed.

Suddenly Dan said:

" He's cheated me. I paid him to clear out and leave her alone. D'you think *she's* asleep? " He's made no appeal for sympathy, he'd take pity for an insult; but he feels it badly.

" I'm tired as a cat," he said at last, and went to sleep on my bed.

It's broad daylight now; I too am tired as a cat. . . .

V

Saturday, 6th August.

. . . I take up my tale where I left off yesterday. . . . Dan and I started as soon as we could get Mrs. Hopgood to give us coffee. The old lady was more tentative, more undecided, more pouncing, than I had ever seen her. She was manifestly uneasy: Ha-apgood—who " don't slape "—don't he, if snores are any criterion—had called out in the night, " Hark to th' 'arses' oofs! " Had we heard them? And where might we be going then? 'Twas very earrly to start, an' no breakfast. Ha-apgood had said it was goin' to shaowerr. Miss Pasiance was not tu 'er violin yet, an' Mister Ford 'e kept 'is room. Was it? —would there be——? " Well, an' therr's an 'arvest bug; 'tis some earrly for they! " Wonderful how she pounces on all such creatures, when I can't even see them. She pressed it absently between finger and thumb, and began manœuvring round another way. Long before she had reached her point, we had gulped down our coffee, and departed. But as we rode out she came at a run, holding her skirts high with either hand, raised her old eyes bright and anxious in their setting of fine wrinkles, and said:

" 'Tidden sorrow for *her?* "

A shrug of the shoulders was all the answer she got. We rode by the lanes; through sloping farmyards, all mud and pigs, and dirty straw, and farmers with clean-shaven upper lips and whiskers under the chin; past fields of corn, where larks were singing. Up or down, we didn't draw rein till we came to Dan's hotel.

There was the river gleaming before us under a rainbow mist that hallowed every shape. There seemed affinity between the earth and the sky. I've never seen that particular soft unity out of Devon. And every ship, however black or modern, on those pale waters, had the look of a dream ship. The tall green woods, the red earth, the white houses, were all melted into one opal haze. It was raining, but the sun was shining behind. Gulls swooped by us—ghosts of the old greedy wanderers of the sea.

We had told our two boatmen to pull us out to the *Pied Witch!* They started with great resolution, then rested on their oars.

" The *Pied Witch,* zurr? " asked one politely; " an' which may her be? "

That's the West countryman all over! Never say you " nay," never lose an opportunity, never own he doesn't know, or can't do anything—independence, amiability, and an eye to the main chance. We mentioned Pearse's name.

" Capt'n Zach'ry Pearse! " They exchanged a look half-amused, half-admiring.

" The *Zunflaower,* yu mane. That's her. *Zunflaower,* ahoy! " As we mounted the steamer's black side I heard one say:

" *Pied Witch!* A pra-aper name that—a dandy name for her! " They laughed as they made fast.

The mate of the *Sunflower,* or *Pied Witch,* or whatever she was called, met us—a tall young fellow in his shirt-sleeves, tanned to the roots of his hair, with sinewy, tattooed arms, and grey eyes, charred round the rims from staring at weather.

" The skipper *is* on board," he said. " We're rather busy, as you see. Get on with that, you sea-cooks," he bawled at two fellows who were doing nothing. All over the ship, men were hauling, splicing, and stowing cargo.

" To-day's Friday: we're off on Wednesday with any luck. Will you come this way? " He led us down the companion to a dark hole which he called the saloon. " Names? What! are you Mr. Treffry? Then we're partners!" A schoolboy's glee came on his face.

"Look here!" he said; "I can show *you* something," and he unlocked the door of a cabin. There appeared to be nothing in it but a huge piece of tarpaulin, which depended, bulging, from the topmost bunk. He pulled it up. The lower bunk had been removed, and in its place was the ugly body of a dismounted Gatling gun.

"Got six of them," he whispered, with unholy mystery, through which his native frankness gaped out. "Worth their weight in gold out there just now, the skipper says. Got a heap of rifles, too, and lots of ammunition. He's given me a share. This is better than the P. and O., and playing deck cricket with the passengers. I'd made up my mind already to chuck that, and go in for plantin' sugar, when I ran across the skipper. Wonderful chap, the skipper! I'll go and tell him. He's been out all night; only came aboard at four bells; having a nap now, but he won't mind that for *you*."

Off he went. I wondered what there was in Zachary Pearse to attract a youngster of this sort; one of the customary twelve children of some country parson, no doubt—burning to shoot a few niggers, and for ever frank and youthful.

He came back with his hands full of bottles.

"What'll you drink? The skipper'll be here in a jiffy. Excuse my goin' on deck. We're so busy."

And in five minutes Zachary Pearse did come. He made no attempt to shake hands, for which I respected him. His face looked worn, and more defiant than usual.

"Well, gentlemen?" he said.

"We've come to ask what you're going to do?" said Dan.

"I don't know," answered Pearse, "that that's any of your business."

Dan's little eyes were like the eyes of an angry pig.

"You've got five hundred pounds of mine," he said; "why do you think I gave it you?"

Zachary bit his fingers.

"That's no concern of mine," he said. "I sail on Wednesday. Your money's safe."

"Do you know what I think of you?" said Dan.

"No, and you'd better not tell me!" Then, with one of his peculiar changes, he smiled: "As you like, though."

Dan's face grew very dark. "Give me a plain answer," he said: "What are you going to do about her?"

Zachary looked up at him from under his brows.

"Nothing."

"Are you cur enough to deny that you've married her?"

Zachary looked at him coolly. "Not at all," he said.

"What in God's name did you do it for?"

"You've no monopoly in the post of husband, Mr. Treffry."

"To put a child in that position! Haven't you the heart of a man? What d'ye come sneaking in at night for? By Gad! Don't you know you've done a beastly thing?"

Zachary's face darkened, he clenched his fists. Then he seemed to shut his anger into himself.

"You wanted me to leave her to you," he sneered. "I gave her my promise that I'd take her out there, and we'd have gone off on Wednesday quietly enough, if you hadn't come and nosed the whole thing out with your infernal dog. The fat's in the fire! There's no reason why I should take her now. I'll come back to her a rich man, or not at all."

"And in the meantime?" I slipped in.

He turned to me, in an ingratiating way.

"I would have taken her to save the fuss—I really would —it's not my fault the thing's come out. I'm on a risky job. To have her with me might ruin the whole thing; it would affect my nerve. It isn't safe for her."

"And what's her position to be," I said, "while you're away? Do you think she'd have married you if she'd known you were going to leave her like this? You ought to give up this business. You stole her. Her life's in your hands; she's only a child!"

A quiver passed over his face; it showed that he was suffering.

"Give it up!" I urged.

"My last farthing's in it," he sighed; "the chance of a lifetime."

He looked at me doubtfully, appealingly, as if for the first time in his life he had been given a glimpse of that dilemma of consequences which his nature never recognises. I thought he was going to give in. Suddenly, to my horror, Dan growled, "Play the man!"

Pearse turned his head. "I don't want your advice anyway," he said; "I'll not be dictated to."

"To your last day," said Dan, "you shall answer to me for the way you treat her."

Zachary smiled.

"Do you see that fly?" he said. "Well—I care for you as little as this," and he flicked the fly off his white trousers. "Good-morning!" . . .

The noble mariners who manned our boat pulled lustily for the shore, but we had hardly shoved off when a storm of rain burst over the ship, and she seemed to vanish, leaving a picture on my eyes of the mate waving his cap above the rail, with his tanned young face bent down at us, smiling, keen, and friendly.

. . . We reached the shore drenched, angry with ourselves, and with each other; I started sulkily for home.

As I rode past an orchard, an apple, loosened by the rain-storm, came down with a thud.

> "The apples were ripe and ready to fall,
> Oh! heigho! and ready to fall."

I made up my mind to pack, and go away. But there's a strangeness, a sort of haunting fascination in it all. To you, who don't know the people, it may only seem a piece of rather sordid folly. But it isn't the good, the obvious, the useful that puts a spell on us in life. It's the bizarre, the dimly seen, the mysterious for good or evil.

The sun was out again when I rode up to the farm; its yellow thatch shone through the trees as if sheltering a store of gladness and good news. John Ford himself opened the door to me.

He began with an apology, which made me feel more than ever an intruder; then he said:

"I have not spoken to my granddaughter—I waited to see Dan Treffry."

He was stern and sad-eyed, like a man with a great weight of grief on his shoulders. He looked as if he had not slept; his dress was out of order, he had not taken his clothes off, I think. He isn't a man whom you can pity. I felt I had taken a liberty in knowing of the matter at all. When I told him where we had been, he said:

"It was good of you to take this trouble. That you should have had to! But since such things have come to pass——"
He made a gesture full of horror. He gave one the impression

of a man whose pride was struggling against a mortal hurt.
Presently he asked:

"You saw him, you say? He admitted this marriage? Did
he give an explanation?"

I tried to make Pearse's point of view clear. Before this old
man, with his inflexible will and sense of duty, I felt as if I
held a brief for Zachary, and must try to do him justice.

"Let me understand," he said at last. "He stole her, you
say, to make sure; and deserts her within a fortnight."

"He says he meant to take her——"

"Do you believe that?"

Before I could answer, I saw Pasiance standing at the window. How long she had been there I don't know.

"Is it true that he is going to leave me behind?" she cried
out.

I could only nod.

"Did you hear him your own self?"

"Yes."

She stamped her foot.

"But he promised! He promised!"

John Ford went towards her.

"Don't touch me, grandfather! I hate every one! Let him
do what he likes, I don't care."

John Ford's face turned quite grey.

"Pasiance," he said, "did you want to leave me so much?"

She looked straight at us, and said sharply:

"What's the good of telling stories? I can't help its hurting you."

"What did you think you would find away from here?"

She laughed.

"Find? I don't know—nothing; I wouldn't be stifled anyway. Now I suppose you'll shut me up because I'm a weak
girl, not strong like *men!*"

"Silence!" said John Ford; "I will make him take you."

"You shan't!" she cried; "I won't let you. He's free to
do as he likes. He's free—I tell you all, everybody—free!"

She ran through the window, and vanished.

John Ford made a movement as if the bottom had dropped out
of his world. I left him there.

I went to the kitchen, where Hopgood was sitting at the
table, eating bread and cheese. He got up on seeing me, and
very kindly brought me some cold bacon and a pint of ale.

"I thart I shude be seeing yu, zurr," he said between his bites; "therr's no thart to 'atin' 'bout the 'ouse to-day. The old wumman's puzzivantin' over Miss Pasiance. Young girls are skeery critters"—he brushed his sleeve over his broad, hard jaws, and filled a pipe—"specially when it's in the blood of 'em. Squire Rick Voisey werr a dandy; an' Mistress Voisey— well, she werr a nice lady tu, but"—rolling the stem of his pipe from corner to corner of his mouth—"she werr a pra-aper vixen."

Hopgood's a good fellow, and I believe as soft as he looks hard, but he's not quite the sort with whom one chooses to talk over a matter like this. I went upstairs, and began to pack, but after a bit dropped it for a book, and somehow or other fell asleep.

I woke, and looked at my watch; it was five o'clock. I had been asleep four hours. A single sunbeam was slanting across from one of my windows to the other, and there was the cool sound of milk dropping into pails; then, all at once, a stir as of alarm, and heavy footsteps.

I opened my door. Hopgood and a coastguardman were carrying Pasiance slowly up the stairs. She lay in their arms without moving, her face whiter than her dress, a scratch across the forehead, and two or three drops there of dried blood. Her hands were clasped, and she slowly crooked and stiffened out her fingers. When they turned with her at the stair top, she opened her lips and gasped, "All right, don't put me down. I can bear it." They passed, and, with a half-smile in her eyes, she said something to me that I couldn't catch; the door was shut, and the excited whispering began again below. I waited for the men to come out, and caught hold of Hopgood. He wiped the sweat off his forehead.

"Poor young thing!" he said. "She fell—down the cliffs —'tis her back—coastguard saw her—'twerr they fetched her in. The Lord 'elp her—mebbe she's not broken up much! An' Mister Ford don't know! I'm gwine for the doctor."

There was an hour or more to wait before he came; a young fellow; almost a boy. He looked very grave, when he came out of her room.

"The old woman there—fond of her? nurse her well? . . . Fond as a dog!—good! Don't know—can't tell for certain! Afraid it's the spine, must have another opinion! What a plucky girl! Tell Mr. Ford to have the best man he can get in

Torquay—there's C——. I'll be round the first thing in the morning. Keep her dead quiet. I've left a sleeping draught; she'll have fever to-night."

John Ford came in at last. Poor old man! What it must have cost him not to go to her for fear of the excitement! How many times in the next few hours didn't I hear him come to the bottom of the stairs; his heavy wheezing, and sighing; and the forlorn tread of his feet going back! About eleven, just as I was going to bed, Mrs. Hopgood came to my door.

"Will yu come, sir," she said; "she's asking for yu. Naowt I can zay but what she will see *yu;* zeems crazy, don't it?" A tear trickled down the old lady's cheek. "Du 'ee come; 'twill du err' 'arm mebbe, but I dunno—she'll fret else."

I slipped into the room. Lying back on her pillows, she was breathing quickly with half-closed eyes. There was nothing to show that she had wanted me, or even knew that I was there. The wick of the candles, set by the bedside, had been snuffed too short, and gave but a faint light; both window and door stood open, still there was no draught, and the feeble little flame burned quite still, casting a faint yellow stain on the ceiling like the reflection from a buttercup held beneath a chin. These ceilings are far too low! Across the wide, squat window the apple branches fell in black stripes which never stirred. It was too dark to see things clearly. At the foot of the bed was a chest, and there Mrs. Hopgood had sat down, moving her lips as if in speech. Mingled with the half-musty smell of age, there were other scents, of mignonette, apples, and some sweet-smelling soap. The floor had no carpet, and there was not one single dark object except the violin, hanging from a nail over the bed. A little, round clock ticked solemnly.

"Why won't you give me that stuff, Mums?" Pasiance said in a faint, sharp voice. "I want to sleep."

"Have you much pain?" I asked.

"Of course I have; it's everywhere."

She turned her face towards me.

"You thought I did it on purpose, but you're wrong. If I had, I'd have done it better than this. I wouldn't have this brutal pain." She put her fingers over her eyes. "It's horrible to complain! Only it's so bad! But I won't again—I—promise."

She took the sleeping draught gratefully, making a face, like a child after a powder.

"How long do you think it'll be before I can play again? Oh! I forgot—there are other things to think about." She held out her hand to me. "Look at my ring. Married—isn't it funny? Ha, ha! Nobody will ever understand—that's funny too! Poor Gran! You see, there wasn't any reason—only me. That's the only reason I'm telling you now; Mums is there—but she doesn't count; why don't you count, Mums?"

The fever was fighting against the draught; she had tossed the clothes back from her throat, and now and then raised one thin arm a little, as if it eased her; her eyes had grown large, and innocent like a child's; the candle, too, had flared, and was burning clearly.

"Nobody is to tell *him*—*nobody* at all; promise! . . . If I hadn't slipped, it would have been different. What would have happened then? You can't tell; and *I* can't—that's funny! Do you think I loved him? Nobody marries without love, do they? Not *quite* without love, I mean. But you see I wanted to be free, he said he'd take me; and now he's left me after all! I won't be left, I can't! When I came to the cliff—that bit where the ivy grows right down—there was just the sea there, underneath; so I thought I would throw myself over and it would be all quiet; and I climbed on a ledge, it looked easier from there, but it was so high, I wanted to get back; and then my foot slipped; and now it's all pain. You can't think much, when you're in pain."

From her eyes I saw that she was dropping off.

"Nobody can take you away from—yourself. He's not to be told—not even—I don't—want you—to go away, because ——" But her eyes closed, and she dropped off to sleep.

They don't seem to know this morning whether she is better or worse. . . .

VI

Tuesday, 9th August.

It seems more like three weeks than three days since I wrote. The time passes slowly in a sick house! . . . The doctors were here this morning, they give her forty hours. Not a word of complaint has passed her lips since she knew. To see her you would hardly think her ill; her cheeks have not had time to waste or lose their colour. There is not much pain, but a slow, creeping numbness. . . . It was John Ford's wish that she should be told. She just turned her head to the wall and sighed; then to poor old Mrs. Hopgood, who was crying her heart out: "Don't cry, Mums, I don't care."

When they had gone, she asked for her violin. She made them hold it for her, and drew the bow across the strings; but the notes that came out were so trembling and uncertain that she dropped the bow and broke into a passion of sobbing. Since then, no complaint or moan of any kind. . . .

But to go back. On Sunday, the day after I wrote, as I was coming from a walk, I met a little boy making mournful sounds on a tin whistle.

"Coom ahn!" he said, "the Miss wahnts t' zee yu."

I went to her room. In the morning she had seemed better, but now looked utterly exhausted. She had a letter in her hand.

"It's this," she said. "I don't seem to understand it. He wants me to do something—but I can't think, and my eyes feel funny. Read it to me, please."

The letter was from Zachary. I read it to her in a low voice, for Mrs. Hopgood was in the room, her eyes always fixed on Pasiance above her knitting. When I'd finished, she made me read it again, and yet again. At first she seemed pleased, almost excited, then came a weary, scornful look, and before I'd finished the third time she was asleep. It was a remarkable letter, that seemed to bring the man right before one's eyes. I slipped it under her fingers on the bed-clothes, and went out. Fancy took me to the cliff where she had fallen. I found the point of rock where the cascade of ivy flows down the cliff; the ledge on which she had climbed was a little to my right—a mad place. It showed plainly what wild emotions must have been driving her! Behind was a half-cut cornfield with a fringe of poppies, and swarms of harvest insects creeping and flying; in the uncut corn a landrail kept up a continual charring. The sky was blue to the very horizon, and the sea wonderful, under that back wild cliff stained here and there with red. Over the dips and hollows of the fields great white clouds hung low down above the land. There are no brassy, east-coast skies here; but always sleepy, soft-shaped clouds, full of subtle stir and change. Passages of Zachary Pearse's letter kept rising to my lips. After all he's the man that his native place, and life, and blood have made him. It is useless to expect idealists

where the air is soft and things good to look on (the idealist
grows where he must create beauty or comfort for himself);
useless to expect a man of law and order in one whose fathers
have stared at the sea day and night for a thousand years—the
sea, full of its promises of unknown things, never quite the
same, a slave to its own impulses. Man is an imitative animal. . . .

"Life's hard enough," he wrote, "without tying yourself
down. Don't think too hardly of me! Shall I make you happier by taking you into danger? If I succeed you'll be a rich
woman; but I shall fail if you're with me. To look at you
makes me soft. At sea a man dreams of all the good things on
land, he'll dream of the heather, and honey—you're like that;
and he'll dream of the apple-trees, and the grass of the orchards
—you're like that; sometimes he only lies on his back and wishes
—and you're like that, most of all like that." . . .

When I was reading those words I remember a strange, soft,
half-scornful look came over Pasiance's face; and once she said,
"But that's all nonsense, isn't it?"

Then followed a long passage about what he would gain if
he succeeded, about all that he was risking, the impossibility
of failure, if he kept his wits about him. "It's only a matter
of two months or so," he went on; "stay where you are, dear,
or go to my Dad. He'll be glad to have you. There's my
mother's room. There's no one to say 'No' to your fiddle
there; you can play it by the sea; and on dark nights you'll
have the stars dancing to you over the waters as thick as bees.
I've looked at them often, thinking of you." . . .

Pasiance had whispered to me, "Don't read that bit," and
afterwards I left it out. . . . Then the sensuous side of him
shows up: "When I've brought this off, there's the whole
world before us. There are places I can take you to. There's
one I know, not too warm and not too cold, where you can sit
all day in the shade and watch the creepers, and the cocoa-
palms, still as still; nothing to do or care about; all the fruits
you can think of; no noise but the parrots and the streams, and
a splash when a nigger dives into a water-hole. Pasiance, we'll
go there! With an eighty-ton craft there's no sea we couldn't
know. The world's a fine place for those who go out to take
it; there's lots of unknown stuff in it yet. I'll fill your lap,
my pretty, so full of treasures that you shan't know yourself.
A man wasn't meant to sit at home." . . .

Throughout this letter—for all its real passion—one could feel how the man was holding to his purpose—the rather sordid purpose of this venture. He's unconscious of it; for he *is* in love with her; but he must be furthering his own ends. He is vital—horribly vital! I wonder less now that she should have yielded.

What visions hasn't he dangled before her. There was physical attraction, too—I haven't forgotten the look I saw on her face at Black Mill. But when all's said and done, she married him, because she's Pasiance Voisey, who does things and wants " to get back." And she lies there dying; not he nor any other man will ever take her away. It's pitiful to think of him tingling with passion, writing that letter to this doomed girl in that dark hole of a saloon. " I've wanted money," he wrote, " ever since I was a little chap sitting in the fields among the cows. . . I want it for you now, and I mean to have it. I've studied the thing two years; I know what I know. . . . The moment this is in the post I leave for London. There are a hundred things to look after still; I can't trust myself within reach of you again till the anchor's weighed. When I rechristened her the *Pied Witch,* I thought of you—you witch to me." . . .

There followed a solemn entreaty to her to be on the path leading to the cove at seven o'clock on Wednesday evening (that is, to-morrow) when he would come ashore and bid her good-bye. It was signed, " Your loving husband, Zachary Pearse." . . .

I lay at the edge of that cornfield a long time; it was very peaceful. The church bells had begun to ring. The long shadows came stealing out from the sheaves; wood-pigeons rose one by one, and flapped off to roost; the western sky was streaked with red, and all the downs and combe bathed in the last sunlight. Perfect harvest weather; but oppressively still; the stillness of suspense. . . .

Life at the farm goes on as usual. We have morning and evening prayers. John Ford reads them fiercely, as though he were on the eve of a revolt against his God. Morning and evening he visits her, comes out wheezing heavily, and goes to his own room; I believe, to pray. Since this morning I haven't dared meet him. He is a strong old man—but this will break him up. . . .

VII

Kingswear, *Saturday, 13th August.*

It's over—I leave here to-morrow, and go abroad.

A quiet afternoon—not a breath up in the churchyard! I was there quite half an hour before they came. Some red cows had strayed into the adjoining orchard, and were rubbing their heads against the railing. While I stood there an old woman came and drove them away; afterwards, she stooped and picked up the apples that had fallen before their time.

> "The apples are ripe and ready to fall,
>   Oh! heigh-ho! and ready to fall;
> There came an old woman and gathered them all,
>   Oh! heigho! and gathered them all."

. . . They brought Pasiance very simply—no hideous funeral trappings, thank God—the farm hands carried her, and there was no one there but John Ford, the Hopgoods, myself, and that young doctor. They read the services over her grave. I can hear John Ford's "Amen!" now. When it was over he walked away bareheaded in the sun, without a word. I went up there again this evening, and wandered amongst the tombstones. "Richard Voisey," "John, the son of Richard and Constance Voisey," "Margery Voisey," so many generations of them in that corner; then "Richard Voisey and Agnes his wife," and next to it that new mound on which a sparrow was strutting and the shadows of the apple-trees already hovering.

I will tell you the little left to tell. . . .

On Wednesday afternoon she asked for me again.

"It's only till seven," she whispered. "He's certain to come then. But if I—were to die first—then tell him—I'm sorry for him. They keep saying: 'Don't talk—don't talk!' Isn't it stupid? As if I should have any other chance! There'll be no more talking after to-night! Make everybody come, please —I want to see them all. When you're dying you're freer than any other time—nobody wants you to do things, nobody cares what you say. . . . He promised me I should do what I liked if I married him—I never believed that really—but now I *can* do what I like; and say all the things I want to." She lay

back silent; she could not after all speak the inmost thoughts
that are in each of us, so sacred that they melt away at the
approach of words.

I shall remember her like that—with the gleam of a smile in
her half-closed eyes, her red lips parted—such a quaint look of
mockery, pleasure, regret, on her little round, up-turned face;
the room white, and fresh with flowers, the breeze fluttering the
apple-leaves against the window. In the night they had un-
hooked the violin and taken it away; she had not missed it. . . .
When Dan came, I gave up my place to him. He took her hand
gently in his great paw, without speaking.

"How small my hand looks there," she said, "too small."
Dan put it softly back on the bedclothes and wiped his forehead.
Pasiance cried in a sharp whisper: "Is it so hot in here?
I didn't know." Dan bent down, put his lips to her fingers
and left the room.

The afternoon was long, the longest I've ever spent. Sometimes she seemed to sleep, sometimes whispered to herself about
her mother, her grandfather, the garden, or her cats—all sorts
of inconsequent, trivial, even ludicrous memories seemed to
throng her mind—never once, I think, did she speak of Zachary,
but, now and then, she asked the time. . . . Each hour she
grew visibly weaker. John Ford sat by her without moving,
his heavy breathing was often the only sound; sometimes she
rubbed her fingers on his hand, without speaking. It was a
summary of their lives together. Once he prayed aloud for her
in a hoarse voice; then her pitiful, impatient eyes signed to me.

"Quick," she whispered, "I want *him;* it's all so—cold."

I went out and ran down the path towards the cove.

Leaning on a gate stood Zachary, an hour before his time;
dressed in the same old blue clothes and leather-peaked cap
as on the day when I saw him first. He knew nothing of what
had happened. But at a quarter of the truth, I'm sure he
divined the whole, though he would not admit it to himself.
He kept saying, "It can't be. She'll be well in a few days—
a sprain! D'you think the sea-voyage. . . . Is she strong
enough to be moved now at once?"

It was painful to see his face, so twisted by the struggle between his instinct and his vitality. The sweat poured down his
forehead. He turned round as we walked up the path, and
pointed out to sea. There was his steamer. "I could get
her on board in no time. Impossible! What is it, then? Spine?

Good God! The doctors. . . . Sometimes they'll do wonders!" It was pitiful to see his efforts to blind himself to the reality.

"It *can't* be, she's too young. We're walking very slow." I told him she was dying.

For a second I thought he was going to run away. Then he jerked up his head, and rushed on towards the house. At the foot of the staircase he gripped me by the shoulder.

"It's not true!" he said; "she'll get better now I'm here. I'll *stay*. Let everything go. I'll stay."

"Now's the time," I said, "to show you loved her. Pull yourself together, man!" He shook all over.

"Yes!" was all he answered. We went into her room. It seemed impossible she was going to die; the colour was bright in her cheeks, her lips trembling and pouted as if she had just been kissed, her eyes gleaming, her hair so dark and crisp, her face so young. . . .

Half an hour later I stole to the open door of her room. She was still and white as the sheets of her bed. John Ford stood at the foot; and, bowed to the level of the pillows, his head on his clenched fists, sat Zachary. It was utterly quiet. The fluttering of the leaves had ceased. When things have come to a crisis, how little one feels—no fear, no pity, no sorrow, rather the sense, as when a play is over, of anxiety to get away! Suddenly Zachary rose, brushed past me without seeing, and ran downstairs.

Some hours later I went out on the path leading to the cove. It was pitch-black; the riding light of the *Pied Witch* was still there, looking no bigger than a firefly. Then from in front I heard sobbing—a man's sobs; no sound is quite so dreadful. Zachary Pearse got up out of the bank not ten paces off.

I had no heart to go after him, and sat down in the hedge. There was something subtly akin to her in the fresh darkness of the young night; the soft bank, the scent of honeysuckle, the touch of the ferns and brambles. Death comes to all of us, and when it's over it's over; but this blind business—of those left behind!

A little later the ship whistled twice; her starboard light gleamed faintly—and that was all. . . .

VIII

. . . Do you remember the letters I wrote you from Moor Farm nearly three years ago? To-day I rode over there. I stopped at Brixham on the way for lunch, and walked down to the quay. There had been a shower—but the sun was out again, shining on the sea, the brown-red sails, and the rampart of slate roofs.

A trawler was lying there, which had evidently been in a collision. The spiky-bearded, thin-lipped fellow in torn blue jersey and sea-boots who was superintending the repairs, said to me a little proudly:

" Bane in collision, zurr; like to zee over her? "

Then suddenly screwing up his little blue eyes, he added:

" Why, I remembers yu. Steered yu along o' the young lady in this yer very craft."

It was Prawle, Zachary Pearse's henchman.

" Yes," he went on, " that's the cutter."

" And Captain Pearse? "

He leant his back against the quay, and spat.

" He was a pra-aper man; I never zane none like 'en."

" Did you do any good out there? "

Prawle gave me a sharp glance.

" Gude? No, 'twas arrm we done, vrom ztart to finish—had trouble all the time. What a man cude du, the skipper did. When yu caan't du right, zome calls it ' Providence'! 'Tis all my eye an' Betty Martin! What I zay es, 'tis these times, there's such a dale o' folk, a dale of puzzivantin' fellers; the world's tu small."

With these words there flashed across me a vision of Drake crushed into our modern life by the shrinkage of the world; Drake caught in the meshes of red tape, electric wires, and all the lofty appliances of our civilization. Does a type survive its age; live on into times that have no room for it? The blood is there—and sometimes there's a throw-back. . . . All fancy! Eh?

" So," I said, " you failed! "

Prawle wriggled.

" I wudden' goo for to say that, zurr—'tis an ugly werd. Da-am!" he added, staring at his boots, " 'twas thru me tu. We were along among the haythen, and I mus' nades goo for to break me leg. The capt'n he wudden' lave me. ' One Devon man,' he says to me, ' don' lave anotherr.' We werr six days where he shuld ha' been tu; when we got back to the ship a—— cruiser had got her for gun-runnin'."

" And what has become of Captain Pearse? "

Prawle answered, " Zurr, I belave 'e went to China, 'tis onsartin."

" He's not dead? "

Prawle looked at me with a kind of uneasy anger.

" Yu cudden' kell 'en! 'Tis true, mun 'll die zome day. But therr's not a one that'll show better zport than Capt'n Zach'ry Pearse."

I believe that; he will be hard to kill. The vision of him comes up, with his perfect balance, defiant eyes, and sweetish smile; the way the hair of his beard crisped a little, and got blacker on the cheeks; the sort of desperate feeling he gave, that one would never get the better of him, that he would never get the better of himself.

I took leave of Prawle and half a crown. Before I was off the quay I heard him saying to a lady, " Bane in collision, marm! Like to zee over her? "

After lunch I rode on to Moor. The old place looked much the same; but the apple-trees were stripped of fruit, and their leaves beginning to go yellow and fall. One of Pasiance's cats passed me in the orchard hunting a bird, still with a ribbon round its neck. John Ford showed me all his latest improvements, but never by word or sign alluded to the past. He inquired after Dan, back in New Zealand now, without much interest; his stubbly beard and hair have whitened: he has grown very stout, and I noticed that his legs are not well under control; he often stops to lean on his stick. He was very ill last winter, and sometimes, they say, will go straight off to sleep in the middle of a sentence.

I managed to get a few minutes with the Hopgoods. We talked of Pasiance sitting in the kitchen under a row of plates, with that clinging smell of wood-smoke, bacon, and age bringing up memories, as nothing but scents can. The dear old lady's hair, drawn so nicely down her forehead on each side from the centre of her cap, has a few thin silver lines; and her face is a thought more wrinkled. The tears still come into her eyes when she talks of her " lamb."

Of Zachary I heard nothing, but she told me of old Pearse's death.

" Therr they found 'en, zo to spake, dead—in th' sun; but Ha-apgood can tell yu," and Hopgood, ever rolling his pipe, muttered something, and smiled his wooden smile.

He came to see me off from the straw-yard. " 'Tis like death to the varrm, zurr," he said, putting all the play of his vast shoulders into the buckling of my girths. " Mister Ford— well! And not one of th' old stock to take it when 'e's garn. . . . Ah! it *werr cruel;* my old woman's never been hersel' since. Tell 'ee what 'tis—don't du t' think tu much."

I went out of my way to pass the churchyard. There were flowers, quite fresh, chrysanthemums and asters; above them the white stone, already stained:

" PASIANCE,

WIFE OF ZACHARY PEARSE,

' *The Lord hath given, and the Lord hath taken away.*' "

The red cows were there too; the sky full of great white clouds, some birds whistling a little mournfully, and in the air the scent of fallen leaves. . . .

May, 1900.

THE APPLE-TREE

"The Apple-tree, the singing, and the gold."

MURRAY'S *Hippolytus of Euripides.*

ON their silver-wedding day Ashurst and his wife were motoring along the outskirts of the moor, intending to crown the
festival by stopping the night at Torquay, where they had
first met. This was the idea of Stella Ashurst, whose character
contained a streak of sentiment. If she had long lost the blue-
eyed, flower-like charm, the cool slim purity of face and form,
the apple-blossom colouring, which had so swiftly and so oddly
affected Ashurst twenty-six years ago, she was still at forty-
three a comely and faithful companion, whose cheeks were faintly mottled, and whose grey-blue eyes had acquired a certain
fullness.

It was she who had stopped the car where the common rose
steeply to the left, and a narrow strip of larch and beech, with
here and there a pine, stretched out towards the valley between
the road and the first long high hill of the full moor. She was
looking for a place where they might lunch, for Ashurst never
looked for anything; and this, between the golden furze and
the feathery green larches smelling of lemons in the last sun
of April—this, with a view into the deep valley and up to the
long moor heights, seemed fitting to the decisive nature of one
who sketched in water-colours, and loved romantic spots. Grasping her paint box, she got out.

"Won't this do, Frank?"

Ashurst, rather like a bearded Schiller, grey in the wings,
tall, long-legged, with large remote grey eyes which sometimes
filled with meaning and became almost beautiful, with nose a
little to one side, and bearded lips just open—Ashurst, forty-
eight, and silent, grasped the luncheon basket, and got out too.

"Oh! Look, Frank! A grave!"

By the side of the road, where the track from the top of the
common crossed it at right angles and ran through a gate past

the narrow wood, was a thin mound of turf, six feet by one, with a moorstone to the west, and on it someone had thrown a blackthorn spray and a handful of bluebells. Ashurst looked, and the poet in him moved. At cross-roads—a suicide's grave! Poor mortals with their superstitions! Whoever lay there, though, had the best of it, no clammy sepulchre among other hideous graves carved with futilities—just a rough stone, the wide sky, and wayside blessings! And, without comment, for he had learned not to be a philosopher in the bosom of his family, he strode away up on to the common, dropped the luncheon basket under a wall, spread a rug for his wife to sit on —she would turn up from her sketching when she was hungry —and took from his pocket Murray's translation of the "Hippolytus." He had soon finished reading of "The Cyprian" and her revenge, and looked at the sky instead. And watching the white clouds so bright against the intense blue, Ashurst, on his silver-wedding day, longed for—he knew not what. Maladjusted to life—man's organism! One's mode of life might be high and scrupulous, but there was always an undercurrent of greediness, a hankering, and sense of waste. Did women have it too? Who could tell? And yet, men who gave vent to their appetites for novelty, their riotous longings for new adventures, new risks, new pleasures, these suffered, no doubt, from the reverse side of starvation, from surfeit. No getting out of it—a mal-adjusted animal, civilised man! There could be no garden of his choosing, of "the Apple-tree, the singing, and the gold," in the words of that lovely Greek chorus, no achievable elysium in life, or lasting haven of happiness for any man with a sense of beauty—nothing which could compare with the captured loveliness in a work of art, set down for ever, so that to look on it or read was always to have the same precious sense of exaltation and restful inebriety. Life no doubt had moments with that quality of beauty, of unbidden flying rapture, but the trouble was, they lasted no longer than the span of a cloud's flight over the sun; impossible to keep them with you, as Art caught beauty and held it fast. They were fleeting as one of the glimmering or golden visions one had of the soul in nature, glimpses of its remote and brooding spirit. Here, with the sun hot on his face, a cuckoo calling from a thorn tree, and in the air the honey savour of gorse—here among the little fronds of the young fern, the starry blackthorn, while the bright clouds drifted by high above the hills and dreamy valleys—

here and now was such a glimpse. But in a moment it would pass—as the face of Pan, which looks round the corner of a rock, vanishes at your stare. And suddenly he sat up. Surely there was something familiar about this view, this bit of common, that ribbon of road, the old wall behind him. While they were driving he had not been taking notice—never did; thinking of far things or of nothing—but now he saw! Twenty-six years ago, just at this time of year, from the farmhouse within half a mile of this very spot he had started for that day in Torquay whence it might be said he had never returned. And a sudden ache beset his heart; he had stumbled on just one of those past moments in his life, whose beauty and rapture he had failed to arrest, whose wings had fluttered away into the unknown; he had stumbled on a buried memory, a wild sweet time, swiftly choked and ended. And, turning on his face, he rested his chin on his hands, and stared at the short grass where the little blue milkwort was growing. . . .

And this is what he remembered.

I §

On the first of May, after their last year together at college, Frank Ashurst and his friend Robert Garton were on a tramp. They had walked that day from Brent, intending to make Chagford, but Ashurst's football knee had given out, and according to their map they had still some seven miles to go. They were sitting on a bank beside the road, where a track crossed alongside a wood, resting the knee and talking of the universe, as young men will. Both were over six feet, and thin as rails; Ashurst pale, idealistic, full of absence; Garton queer, round-the-corner, knotted, curly, like some primeval beast. Both had a literary bent; neither wore a hat. Ashurst's hair was smooth, pale, wavy, and had a way of rising on either side of his brow, as if always being flung back; Garton's was a kind of dark unfathomed mop. They had not met a soul for miles.

"My dear fellow," Garton was saying, "pity's only an effect of self-consciousness; it's a disease of the last five thousand years. The world was happier without."

Ashurst, following the clouds with his eyes, answered:

"It's the pearl in the oyster, anyway."

"My dear chap, all our modern unhappiness comes from pity. Look at animals, and Red Indians, limited to felling their own occasional misfortunes; then look at ourselves—never free from feeling the toothaches of others. Let's get back to feeling for nobody, and have a better time."

"You'll never practise that."

Garton pensively stirred the hotch-potch of his hair.

"To attain full growth, one mustn't be squeamish. To starve oneself emotionally's a mistake. All emotion is to the good—enriches life."

"Yes, and when it runs up against chivalry?"

"Ah! That's so English! If you speak of emotion the English always think you want something physical, and are shocked. They're afraid of passion, but not of lust—oh, no!— so long as they can keep it secret."

Ashurst did not answer; he had plucked a blue floweret, and was twiddling it against the sky. A cuckoo began calling from a thorn tree. The sky, the flowers, the songs of birds! Robert was talking through his hat! And he said:

"Well, let's go on, and find some farm where we can put up." In uttering those words, he was conscious of a girl coming down from the common just above them. She was outlined against the sky, carrying a basket, and you could see that sky through the crook of her arm. And Ashurst, who saw beauty without wondering how it could advantage him, thought: 'How pretty!' The wind, blowing her dark frieze skirt against her legs, lifted her battered peacock tam-o'-shanter; her greyish blouse was worn and old, her shoes were split, her little hands rough and red, her neck browned. Her dark hair waved untidy across her broad forehead, her face was short, her upper lip short, showing a glint of teeth, her brows were straight and dark, her lashes long and dark, her nose straight; but her grey eyes were the wonder—dewy as if opened for the first time that day. She looked at Ashurst—perhaps he struck her as strange, limping along without a hat, with his large eyes on her, and his hair flung back. He could not take off what was not on his head, but put up his hand in a salute, and said:

"Can you tell us if there's a farm near here where we could stay the night? I've gone lame."

"There's only our farm near, sir." She spoke without shyness, in a pretty, soft, crisp voice.

"And where is that?"

"Down here, sir."

"Would you put us up?"

" Oh! I think we would."

" Will you show us the way? "

" Yes, sir."

He limped on, silent, and Garton took up the catechism.

" Are you a Devonshire girl? "

" No, sir."

" What then? "

" From Wales."

" Ah! I *thought* you were a Celt; so it's not your farm? "

" My aunt's, sir."

" And your uncle's? "

" He is dead."

" Who farms it, then? "

" My aunt, and my three cousins."

" But your uncle was a Devonshire man? "

" Yes, sir."

" Have you lived here long? "

" Seven years."

" And how d'you like it after Wales? "

" I don't know, sir."

" I suppose you don't remember? "

" Oh, yes! But it is different."

" I believe you! "

Ashurst broke in suddenly:

" How old are you? "

" Seventeen, sir."

" And what's your name? "

" Megan David."

" This is Robert Garton, and I am Frank Ashurst. We wanted to get on to Chagford."

" It is a pity your leg is hurting you."

Ashurst smiled, and when he smiled his face was rather beautiful.

Descending past the narrow wood, they came on the farm suddenly—a long, low, stone-built dwelling with casement windows, in a farmyard where pigs and fowls and an old mare were straying. A short steep-up grass hill behind was crowned with a few Scotch firs, and in front, an old orchard of apple-trees, just breaking into flower, stretched down to a stream and a long wild meadow. A little boy with oblique dark eyes was shepherding a pig, and by the house door stood a woman, who came towards them. The girl said:

" It is Mrs. Narracombe, my aunt."

" Mrs. Narracombe, my aunt," had a quick, dark eye, like a mother wild-duck's, and something of the same snaky turn about her neck.

" We met your niece on the road," said Ashurst; " she thought you might perhaps put us up for the night."

Mrs. Narracombe, taking them in from head to heel, answered:

" Well, I can, if you don't mind one room. Megan, get the spare room ready, and a bowl of cream. You'll be wanting tea, I suppose."

Passing through a sort of porch made by two yew trees and some flowering-currant bushes, the girl disappeared into the house, her peacock tam-o'-shanter bright athwart that rosy-pink and the dark green of the yews.

" Will you come into the parlour and rest your leg? You'll be from college, perhaps?"

" We were, but we've gone down now."

Mrs. Narracombe nodded sagely.

The parlour, brick-floored, with bare table and shiny chairs and sofa stuffed with horsehair, seemed never to have been used, it was so terribly clean. Ashurst sat down at once on the sofa, holding his lame knee between his hands, and Mrs. Narracombe gazed at him. He was the only son of a late professor of chemistry, but people found a certain lordliness in one who was often so sublimely unconscious of them.

" Is there a stream where we could bathe?"

" There's the strame at the bottom of the orchard, but sittin' down you'll not be covered!"

" How deep?"

" Well, 'tis about a foot and a half, maybe."

" Oh! That'll do fine. Which way?"

" Down the lane, through the second gate on the right, an' the pool's by the big apple tree that stands by itself. There's trout there, if you can tickle them."

" They're more likely to tickle us!"

Mrs. Narracombe smiled. " There'll be the tea ready when you come back."

The pool, formed by the damming of a rock, had a sandy bottom; and the big apple tree, lowest in the orchard, grew so close that its boughs almost overhung the water; it was in leaf, and all but in flower—its crimson buds just bursting.

There was not room for more than one at a time in that narrow
bath, and Ashurst waited his turn, rubbing his knee and gazing
at the wild meadow, all rocks and thorn trees and field flowers,
with a grove of beeches beyond, raised up on a flat mound.
Every bough was swinging in the wind, every spring bird calling, and a slanting sunlight dappled the grass. He thought
of Theocritus, and the river Cherwell, of the moon, and the
maiden with the dewy eyes; of so many things that he seemed
to think of nothing; and he felt absurdly happy.

2 §

During a late and sumptuous tea with eggs to it, cream and
jam, and thin, fresh cakes touched with saffron, Garton des-
canted on the Celts. It was about the period of the Celtic
awakening, and the discovery that there was Celtic blood about
this family had excited one who believed that he was a Celt
himself. Sprawling on a horsehair chair, with a hand-made
cigarette dribbling from the corner of his curly lips, he had
been plunging his cold pin-points of eyes into Ashurst's and
praising the refinement of the Welsh. To come out of Wales
into England was like the change from china to earthenware!
Frank, as a d——d Englishman, had not of course perceived
the exquisite refinement and emotional capacity of that Welsh
girl! And, delicately stirring in the dark mat of his still wet
hair, he explained how exactly she illustrated the writings of the
Welsh bard Morgan-ap-Something in the twelfth century.

Ashurst, full length on the horsehair sofa, and jutting far
beyond its end, smoked a deeply-coloured pipe, and did not
listen, thinking of the girl's face when she brought in a relay of
cakes. It had been exactly like looking at a flower, or some
other pretty sight in Nature—till, with a funny little shiver,
she had lowered her glance and gone out, quiet as a mouse.

" Let's go to the kitchen," said Garton, " and see some more
of her."

The kitchen was a white-washed room with rafters, to which
were attached smoked hams; there were flower-pots on the
window-sill, and guns hanging on nails, queer mugs, china and
pewter, and portraits of Queen Victoria. A long, narrow table
of plain wood was set with bowls and spoons, under a string of
high-hung onions; two sheep-dogs and three cats lay here and
there. On one side of the recessed fireplace sat two small boys,

idle, and good as gold; on the other sat a stout, light-eyed, red-faced youth with hair and lashes the colour of the tow he was running through the barrel of a gun; between them Mrs. Narracombe dreamily stirred some savoury-scented stew in a large pot. Two other youths, oblique-eyed, dark-haired, rather sly-faced, like the two little boys, were talking together and lolling against the wall; and a short, elderly, clean-shaven man in corduroys, seated in the window, was conning a battered journal. The girl Megan seemed the only active creature—drawing cider and passing with the jugs from cask to table. Seeing them thus about to eat, Garton said:

"Ah! If you'll let us, we'll come back when supper's over," and without waiting for an answer they withdrew again to the parlour. But the colour in the kitchen, the warmth, the scents, and all those faces, heightened the bleakness of their shiny room, and they resumed their seats moodily.

"Regular gipsy type, those boys. There was only one Saxon —the fellow cleaning the gun. That girl is a very subtle study psychologically."

Ashurst's lips twitched. Garton seemed to him an ass just then. Subtle study! She was a wild flower. A creature it did you good to look at. Study!

Garton went on:

"Emotionally she would be wonderful. She wants awakening."

"Are you going to awaken her?"

Garton looked at him and smiled. 'How coarse and English you are!' that curly smile seemed saying.

And Ashurst puffed his pipe. Awaken her! This fool had the best opinion of himself! He threw up the window and leaned out. Dusk had gathered thick. The farm buildings and the wheel-house were all dim and bluish, the apple trees but a blurred wilderness; the air smelled of wood smoke from the kitchen fire. One bird going to bed later than the others was uttering a half-hearted twitter, as though surprised at the darkness. From the stable came the snuffle and stamp of a feeding horse. And away over there was the loom of the moor, and away and away the shy stars which had not as yet full light, pricking white through the deep blue heavens. A quavering owl hooted. Ashurst drew a deep breath. What a night to wander out in! A padding of unshod hoofs came up the lane, and three dim, dark shapes passed—ponies on an evening march. Their heads, black and fuzzy, showed above the gate. At the tap of his pipe, and a shower of little sparks, they shied round and scampered. A bat went fluttering past, uttering its almost inaudible " chip, chip." Ashurst held out his hand; on the upturned palm he could feel the dew. Suddenly from overhead he heard little burring boys' voices, little thumps of boots thrown down, and another voice, crisp and soft—the girl's putting them to bed, no doubt; and nine clear words: " No, Rick, you can't have the cat in bed "; then came a skirmish of giggles and gurgles, a soft slap, a laugh so low and pretty that it made him shiver a little. A blowing sound, and the glim of the candle which was fingering the dusk above, went out; silence reigned. Ashurst withdrew into the room and sat down; his knee pained him, and his soul felt gloomy.

" You go to the kitchen," he said; " I'm going to bed."

3 §

For Ashurst the wheel of slumber was wont to turn noiseless and slick and swift, but though he seemed sunk in sleep when his companion came up, he was really wide awake; and long after Garton, smothered in the other bed of that low-roofed room, was worshipping darkness with his upturned nose, he heard the owls. Barring the discomfort of his knee, it was not unpleasant—the cares of life did not loom large in night watches for this young man. In fact he had none; just enrolled a barrister, with literary aspirations, the world before him, no father or mother, and four hundred a year of his own. Did it matter where he went, what he did, or when he did it? His bed, too, was hard, and this preserved him from fever. He lay, sniffing the scent of the night which drifted into the low room through the open casement close to his head. Except for a definite irritation with his friend, natural when you have tramped with a man for three days, Ashurst's memories and visions that sleepless night were kindly and wistful and exciting. One vision, specially clear and unreasonable, for he had not even been conscious of noting it, was the face of the youth cleaning the gun; its intent, stolid, yet startled uplook at the kitchen doorway, quickly shifted to the girl carrying the cider jug. This red, blue-eyed, light-lashed, tow-haired face stuck as firmly in his memory as the girl's own face, so dewy and simple. But at last, in the square of darkness through the uncurtained casement, he saw day coming, and heard one hoarse and sleepy caw. Then followed silence, dead as ever, till the song of a blackbird, not properly awake, adventured into the hush. And, from staring at the framed brightening light, Ashurst fell asleep.

Next day his knee was badly swollen; the walking tour was obviously over. Garton, due back in London on the morrow, departed at midday with an ironical smile which left a scar of irritation—healed the moment his loping figure vanished round the corner of the steep lane. All day Ashurst rested his knee, in a green-painted wooden chair on the patch of grass by the yew-tree porch, where the sunlight distilled the scent of stocks and gillyflowers, and a ghost of scent from the flowering-currant bushes. Beatifically he smoked, dreamed, watched.

A farm in spring is all birth—young things coming out of bud and shell, and human beings watching over the process with faint excitement feeding and tending what has been born. So still the young man sat, that a mother-goose, with stately cross-footed waddle, brought her six yellow-necked grey-backed goslings to strop their little beaks against the grass blades at his feet. Now and again Mrs. Narracombe or the girl Megan would come and ask if he wanted anything, and he would smile and say: "Nothing, thanks. It's splendid here." Towards tea-time they came out together, bearing a long poultice of some dark stuff in a bowl, and after a long and solemn scrutiny of his swollen knee, bound it on. When they were gone, he thought of the girl's soft "Oh!"—of her pitying eyes, and the little wrinkle in her brow. And again he felt that unreasoning irritation against his departed friend, who had talked such rot about her. When she brought out his tea, he said:

"How did you like my friend, Megan?"

She forced down her upper lip, as if afraid that to smile was not polite. "He was a funny gentleman; he made us laugh. I think he is very clever."

"What did he say to make you laugh?"

"He said I was a daughter of the bards. What are they?"

"Welsh poets, who lived hundreds of years ago."

"Why am I their daughter, please?"

"He meant that you were the sort of girl they sang about."

She wrinkled her brows. "I think he likes to joke. Am I?"

"Would you believe me, if I told you?"

"Oh, yes."

"Well, I think he was right."

She smiled.

And Ashurst thought: 'You *are* a pretty thing!'

"He said, too, that Joe was a Saxon type. What would that be?"

"Which is Joe? With the blue eyes and red face?"

"Yes. My uncle's nephew."

"Not your cousin, then?"

"No."

"Well, he meant that Joe was like the men who came over to England about fourteen hundred years ago, and conquered it."

"Oh! I know about them; but is he?"

"Garton's crazy about that sort of thing; but I must say Joe does look a bit Early Saxon."

"Yes."

That "Yes" tickled Ashurst. It was so crisp and graceful, so conclusive, and politely acquiescent in what was evidently Greek to her.

"He said that all the other boys were regular gipsies. He should not have said that. My aunt laughed, but she didn't like it, of course, and my cousins were angry. Uncle was a farmer—farmers are not gipsies. It is wrong to hurt people."

Ashurst wanted to take her hand and give it a squeeze, but he only answered:

"Quite right, Megan. By the way, I heard you putting the little ones to bed last night."

She flushed a little. "Please to drink your tea—it is getting cold. Shall I get you some fresh?"

"Do you ever have time to do anything for yourself?"

"Oh, yes."

"I've been watching, but I haven't seen it yet."

She wrinkled her brows in a puzzled frown, and her colour deepened.

When she was gone, Ashurst thought: 'Did she think I was chaffing her? I wouldn't for the world!' He was at that age when to some men "Beauty's a flower," as the poet says, and inspires in them the thoughts of chivalry. Never very conscious of his surroundings, it was some time before he was aware that the youth whom Garton had called "a Saxon type" was standing outside the stable door; and a fine bit of colour he made in his soiled brown velvetcords, muddy gaiters, and blue shirt; red-armed, red-faced, the sun turning his hair from tow to flax; immovably stolid, persistent, unsmiling he stood. Then, seeing Ashurst looking at him, he crossed the yard at that gait of the young countryman always ashamed not to be slow and heavy-dwelling on each leg, and disappeared round the end of the house towards the kitchen entrance. A chill came over Ashurst's mood. Clods! With all the good will in the world, how impossible to get on terms with them! And yet—see that girl! Her shoes were split, her hands rough; but—what was it? Was it really her Celtic blood, as Garton had said?—she was a lady born, a jewel, though probably she could do no more than just read and write!

The elderly, clean-shaven man he had seen last night in the kitchen had come into the yard with a dog, driving the cows to their milking. Ashurst saw that he was lame.

"You've got some good ones there!"

The lame man's face brightened. He had the upward look in his eyes which prolonged suffering often brings.

"Yeas; they'm praaper buties; gude milkers tu."

"I bet they are."

"'Ope as yure leg's better, zurr."

"Thank you, it's getting on."

The lame man touched his own: "I know what 'tes, meself; 'tes a main worritin' thing, the knee. I've a 'ad mine bad this ten year."

Ashurst made the sound of sympathy which comes so readily from those who have an independent income, and the lame man smiled again.

"Mustn't complain, though—they mighty near 'ad it off."

"Ho!"

"Yeas; an' compared with what twas, 'tes almost so gude as nu."

"They've put a bandage of splendid stuff on mine."

"The maid she picks et. She'm a gude maid wi' the flowers. There's folks zeem to know the healin' in things. My mother was a rare one for that. 'Ope as yu'll zune be better, zurr. Goo ahn, therr!"

Ashurst smiled. "Wi' the flowers!" A flower herself.

That evening, after his supper of cold duck, junket, and cider, the girl came in.

"Please, auntie says—will you try a piece of our Mayday cake?"

"If I may come to the kitchen for it."

"Oh, yes! You'll be missing your friend."

"Not I. But are you sure no one minds?"

"Who would mind? We shall be very pleased."

Ashurst rose too suddenly for his stiff knee, staggered, and subsided. The girl gave a little gasp, and held out her hands. Ashurst took them, small, rough, brown; checked his impulse to put them to his lips, and let her pull him up. She came close beside him, offering her shoulder. And leaning on her he walked across the room. That shoulder seemed quite the pleasantest thing he had ever touched. But he had presence of mind enough to catch his stick out of the rack, and withdraw his hand before arriving at the kitchen.

That night he slept like a top, and woke with his knee of almost normal size. He again spent the morning in his chair on the grass patch, scribbling down verses; but in the afternoon he wandered about with the two little boys Nick and Rick. It was Saturday, so they were early home from school; quick, shy, dark little rascals of seven and six, soon talkative, for Ashurst had a way with children. By four o'clock they had shown him all their methods of destroying life, except the tickling of trout; and with breeches tucked up, lay on their stomachs over the trout stream, pretending they had this accomplishment also. They tickled nothing, of course, for their giggling and shouting scared every spotted thing away. Ashurst, on a rock at the edge of the beech clump, watched them, and listened to the cuckoos, till Nick, the elder and less persevering, came up and stood beside him.

"The gipsy bogle zets on that stone," he said.

"What gipsy bogle?"

"Dunno; never zeen 'e. Megan zays 'e zets there; an' old Jim zeed 'e once. 'E was zettin' there naight afore our pony kicked-in father's 'ead. 'E plays the viddle."

"What tune does he play?"

"Dunno."

"What's he like?"

"'E's black. Old Jim zays 'e's all over 'air. 'E's a praaper bogle. 'E don' come only at naight." The little boy's oblique dark eyes slid round. "Dy'u think 'e might want to take me away? Megan's feared of 'e."

" Has she seen him? "

" No. She's not afeared o' yu."

" I should think not. Why should she be? "

" She zays a prayer for yu."

" How do you know that, you little rascal? "

" When I was asleep, she said: ' God bless us all, an' Mr. Ashes.' I yeard 'er whisperin'."

" You're a little ruffian to tell what you hear when you're not meant to hear it! "

The little boy was silent. Then he said aggressively:

" I can skin rabbits. Megan, she can't bear skinnin' 'em. I like blood."

" Oh! you do; you little monster! "

" What's that? "

" A creature that likes hurting others."

The little boy scowled. "They'm only dead rabbits, what us eats."

" Quite right, Nick. I beg your pardon."

" I can skin frogs, tu."

But Ashurst had become absent. " God bless us all, and Mr. Ashes! " And puzzled by that sudden inaccessibility, Nick ran back to the stream where the giggling and shouts again uprose at once.

When Megan brought his tea, he said:

" What's the gipsy bogle, Megan? "

She looked up, startled.

" He brings bad things."

" Surely you don't believe in ghosts? "

" I hope I will never see him."

" Of course you won't. There aren't such things. What old Jim saw was a pony."

" No! There are bogles in the rocks; they are the men who lived long ago."

" They aren't gipsies, anyway; those old men were dead long before gipsies came."

She said simply: " They are all bad."

" Why? If there are any, they're only wild, like the rabbits. The flowers aren't bad for being wild; the thorn trees were never planted—and you don't mind them. I shall go down at night and look for your bogle, and have a talk with him."

" Oh, no! Oh, no! "

" Oh, yes! I shall go and sit on his rock."

She clasped her hands together: "Oh, please!"

"Why! What does it matter if anything happens to me?"

She did not answer; and in a sort of pet he added:

"Well, I daresay I shan't see him, because I suppose I must be off soon."

"Soon?"

"Your aunt won't want to keep me here."

"Oh, yes! We always let lodgings in summer."

Fixing his eyes on her face, he asked:

"Would you like me to stay?"

"Yes."

"I'm going to say a prayer for *you* to-night!"

She flushed crimson, frowned, and went out of the room. He sat cursing himself, till his tea was stewed. It was as if he had hacked with his thick boots at a clump of bluebells. Why had he said such a silly thing? Was he just a towny college ass like Robert Garton, as far from understanding this girl?

4 §

Ashurst spent the next week confirming the restoration of his leg, by exploration of the country within easy reach. Spring was a revelation to him this year. In a kind of intoxication he would watch the pink-white buds of some backward beech tree sprayed up in the sunlight against the deep blue sky, or the trunks and limbs of the few Scotch firs, tawny in violent light, or again on the moor, the gale-bent larches which had such a look of life when the wind streamed in their young green, above the rusty black underboughs. Or he would lie on the banks, gazing at the clusters of dog-violets, or up in the dead bracken, fingering the pink, transparent buds of the dewberry, while the cuckoos called and yaffles laughed, or a lark, from very high, dripped its beads of song. It was certainly different from any spring he had ever known, for spring was within him, not without. In the daytime he hardly saw the family; and when Megan brought in his meals she always seemed too busy in the house or among the young things in the yard to stay talking long. But in the evenings he installed himself in the window seat in the kitchen, smoking and chatting with the lame man Jim, or Mrs. Narracombe, while the girl sewed, or moved about, clearing the supper things away. And sometimes with the sensation a cat must feel when it purrs, he would become conscious that Megan's eyes—those dew-grey eyes—were fixed on him with a sort of lingering soft look which was strangely flattering.

It was on Sunday week in the evening, when he was lying in the orchard listening to a blackbird and composing a love poem, that he heard the gate swing to, and saw the girl come running among the trees, with the red-cheeked, stolid Joe in swift pursuit. About twenty yards away the chase ended, and the two stood fronting each other, not noticing the stranger in the grass—the boy pressing on, the girl fending him off. Ashurst could see her face, angry, disturbed; and the youth's —who would have thought that red-faced yokel could look so distraught! And painfully affected by that sight, he jumped up. They saw him then. Megan dropped her hands, and shrank behind a tree-trunk; the boy gave an angry grunt, rushed at the bank, scrambled over and vanished. Ashurst went slowly up to her. She was standing quite still, biting her lip—very pretty, with her fine, dark hair blown loose about her face, and her eyes cast down.

" I beg your pardon," he said.

She gave him one upward look, from eyes much dilated; then, catching her breath, turned away. Ashurst followed.

" Megan ! "

But she went on; and taking hold of her arm, he turned her gently round to him.

" Stop and speak to me."

" Why do you beg my pardon? It is not to me you should do that."

" Well, then, to Joe."

" How dare he come after me ? "

" In love with you, I suppose."

She stamped her foot.

Ashurst uttered a short laugh. " Would you like me to punch his head ? "

She cried with sudden passion:

" You laugh at me—you laugh at us ! "

He caught hold of her hands, but she shrank back, till her passionate little face and loose dark hair were caught among the pink clusters of the apple blossom. Ashurst raised one of her imprisoned hands and put his lips to it. He felt how chivalrous he was, and superior to that clod Joe—just brushing that small, rough hand with his mouth! Her shrinking ceased suddenly; she seemed to tremble towards him. A sweet warmth overtook Ashurst from top to toe. This slim maiden, so simple and fine and pretty, was pleased, then, at the touch of his lips! And, yielding to a swift impulse, he put his arms round her, pressed her to him, and kissed her forehead. Then he was frightened—she went so pale, closing her eyes, so that the long, dark lashes lay on her pale cheeks; her hands, too, lay inert at her sides. The touch of her breast sent a shiver through him. "Megan!" he sighed out, and let her go. In the utter silence a blackbird shouted. Then the girl seized his hand, put it to her cheek, her heart, her lips, kissed it passionately, and fled away among the mossy trunks of the apple trees, till they hid her from him.

Ashurst sat down on a twisted old tree growing almost along the ground, and, all throbbing and bewildered, gazed vacantly at the blossom which had crowned her hair—those pink buds with one white open apple star. What had he done? How had he let himself be thus stampeded by beauty—or—just the spring! He felt curiously happy, all the same; happy and triumphant, with shivers running through his limbs, and a vague alarm. This was the beginning of—what? The midges bit him, the dancing gnats tried to fly into his mouth, and all the spring around him seemed to grow more lovely and alive; the songs of the cuckoos and the blackbirds, the laughter of the yaffles, the level-slanting sunlight, the apple blossom which had crowned her head—! He got up from the old trunk and strode out of the orchard, wanting space, an open sky, to get on terms with these new sensations. He made for the moor, and from an ash tree in the hedge a magpie flew out to herald him.

Of man—at any age from five years on—who can say he has never been in love? Ashurst had loved his partners at his dancing class; loved his nursery governess; girls in school-holidays; perhaps never been quite out of love, cherishing always some more or less remote admiration. But this was different, not remote at all. Quite a new sensation; terribly delightful, bringing a sense of completed manhood. To be holding in his fingers such a wild flower, to be able to put it to his lips, and feel it tremble with delight against them! What intoxication, and—embarrassment! What to do with it—how meet her next time? His first caress had been cool, pitiful;

but the next could not be, now that, by her burning little kiss on his hand, by her pressure of it to her heart, he knew that she loved him. Some natures are coarsened by love bestowed on them; others, like Ashurst's, are swayed and drawn, warmed and softened, almost exhalted, by what they feel to be a sort of miracle.

And up there among the tors he was racked between the passionate desire to revel in this new sensation of spring fulfilled within him, and a vague but very real uneasiness. At one moment he gave himself up completely to his pride at having captured this pretty, trustful, dewy-eyed thing! At the next he thought with factitious solemnity: 'Yes, my boy! But look out what you're doing! You know what comes of it!'

Dusk dropped down without his noticing—dusk on the carved, Assyrian-looking masses of the rocks. And the voice of Nature said: "This is a new world for you!" As when a man gets up at four o'clock and goes out into a summer morning, and beasts, birds, trees stare at him and he feels as if all had been made new.

He stayed up there for hours, till it grew cold, then groped his way down the stones and heather roots to the road, back into the lane, and came again past the wild meadow to the orchard. There he struck a match and looked at his watch. Nearly twelve! It was black and unstirring in there now, very different from the lingering, bird-befriended brightness of six hours ago! And suddenly he saw this idyll of his with the eyes of the outer world—had mental vision of Mrs. Narracombe's snake-like neck turned, her quick dark glance taking it all in, her shrewd face hardening; saw the gipsy-like cousins coarsely mocking and distrustful; Joe stolid and furious; only the lame man, Jim, with the suffering eyes, seemed tolerable to his mind. And the village pub!—the gossiping matrons he passed on his walks; and then—his own friends—Robert Garton's smile when he went off that morning ten days ago; so ironical and knowing! Disgusting! For a minute he literally hated this earthly, cynical world to which one belonged, willy-nilly. The gate where he was leaning grew grey, a sort of shimmer passed before him and spread into the bluish darkness. The moon! He could just see it over the bank behind; red, nearly round—a strange moon! And turning away, he went up the lane which smelled of the night and cow-dung and young leaves. In the straw-yard he could see the dark shapes of cattle, broken by the pale sickles of their horns, like so many thin moons, fallen ends-up. He unlatched the farm gate stealthily. All was dark in the house. Muffling his footsteps, he gained the porch, and, blotted against one of the yew trees, looked up at Megan's window. It was open. Was she sleeping, or lying awake perhaps disturbed—unhappy at his absence? An owl hooted while he stood there peering up, and the sound seemed to fill the whole night, so quiet was all else, save for the never-ending murmur of the stream running below the orchard. The cuckoos by day, and now the owls—how wonderfully they voiced this troubled ecstasy within him! And suddenly he saw her at her window, looking out. He moved a little from the yew tree, and whispered: "Megan!" She drew back, vanished, reappeared, leaning far down. He stole forward on the grass patch, hit his shin against the green-painted chair, and held his breath at the sound. The pale blur of her stretched-down arm and face did not stir; he moved the chair, and noiselessly mounted it. By stretching up his arm he could just reach. Her hand held the huge key of the front door, and he clasped that burning hand with the cold key in it. He could just see her face, the glint of teeth between her lips, her tumbled hair. She was still dressed—poor child, sitting up for him, no doubt! "Pretty Megan!" Her hot, roughened fingers clung to his; her face had a strange, lost look. To have been able to reach it—even with his hand! The owl hooted, a scent of sweetbriar crept into his nostrils. Then one of the farm dogs barked; her grasp relaxed, she shrank back.

"Good-night, Megan!"

"Good-night, sir!" She was gone! With a sigh he dropped back to earth, and sitting on that chair, took off his boots. Nothing for it but to creep in and go to bed; yet for a long while he sat unmoving, his feet chilly in the dew, drunk on the memory of her lost, half-smiling face, and the clinging grip of her burning fingers, pressing the cold key into his hand.

5 §

He awoke feeling as if he had eaten heavily overnight, instead of having eaten nothing. And far off, unreal, seemed yesterday's romance! Yet it was a golden morning. Full spring had burst at last—in one night the "goldiecups," as the little

boys called them, seemed to have made the field their own, and
from his window he could see apple blossoms covering the
orchard as with a rose and white quilt. He went down almost
dreading to see Megan; and yet, when not she but Mrs. Narracombe brought in his breakfast, he felt vexed and disappointed.
The woman's quick eye and snaky neck seemed to have a new
alacrity this morning. Had she noticed?

"So you an' the moon went walkin' last night, Mr. Ashurst!
Did ye have your supper anywheres?"

Ashurst shook his head.

"We kept it for you, but I suppose you was too busy in your
brain to think o' such a thing as that?"

Was she mocking him, in that voice of hers, which still kept
some Welsh crispness against the invading burr of the West
Country? If she knew! And at that moment he thought:
'No, no; I'll clear out. I won't put myself in such a beastly
false position.'

But, after breakfast, the longing to see Megan began and
increased with every minute, together with fear lest something
should have been said to her which had spoiled everything.
Sinister that she had not appeared, not given him even a glimpse
of her! And the love poem, whose manufacture had been so
important and absorbing yesterday afternoon under the apple
trees, now seemed so paltry that he tore it up and rolled it into
pipe spills. What had he known of love, till she seized his hand
and kissed it! And now—what did he not know? But to write
of it seemed mere insipidity! He went up to his bedroom to
get a book, and his heart began to beat violently, for she was
in there making the bed. He stood in the doorway watching;
and suddenly, with turbulent joy, he saw her stoop and kiss
his pillow, just at the hollow made by his head last night. How
let her know he had seen that pretty act of devotion? And yet
if she heard him stealing away, it would be even worse. She
took the pillow up, holding it as if reluctant to shake out the
impress of his cheek, dropped it, and turned round.

"Megan!"

She put her hands up to her cheeks, but her eyes seemed
to look right into him. He had never before realised the depth
and purity and touching faithfulness in those dew-bright eyes,
and he stammered:

"It was sweet of you to wait up for me last night."

She still said nothing, and he stammered on:

" I was wandering about on the moor; it was such a jolly night. I—I've just come up for a book."

Then, the kiss he had seen her give the pillow afflicted him with sudden headiness, and he went up to her. Touching her eyes with his lips, he thought with queer excitement: ' I've done it! Yesterday all was sudden—anyhow; but now—I've done it!' The girl let her forehead rest against his lips, which moved downwards till they reached hers. That first real lover's kiss—strange, wonderful, still almost innocent—in which heart did it make the most disturbance?

" Come to the big apple tree to-night, after they've gone to bed. Megan—promise!"

She whispered back: " I promise!"

Then, scared at her white face, scared at everything, he let her go, and went downstairs again. Yes! he had done it now! Accepted her love, declared his own! He went out to the green chair as devoid of a book as ever; and there he sat staring vacantly before him, triumphant and remorseful, while under his nose and behind his back the work of the farm went on. How long he had been sitting in that curious state of vacancy he had no notion when he saw Joe standing a little behind him to the right. The youth had evidently come from hard work in the fields, and stood shifting his feet, breathing loudly, his face coloured like a setting sun, and his arms, below the rolled-up sleeves of his blue shirt, showing the hue and furry sheen of ripe peaches. His red lips were open, his blue eyes with their flaxen lashes stared fixedly at Ashurst, who said ironically:

" Well, Joe, anything I can do for you?"

" Yeas."

" What, then?"

" Yu can goo away from yere. Us don' want yu."

Ashurst's face, never too humble, assumed its most lordly look.

" Very good of you, but, do you know, I prefer the others should speak for themselves."

The youth moved a pace or two nearer, and the scent of his honest heat afflicted Ashurst's nostrils.

" What d'yu stay yere for?"

" Because it pleases me."

" Twon't please yu when I've bashed yure head in!"

" Indeed! When would you like to begin that?"

Joe answered only with the loudness of his breathing, but his

eyes looked like those of a young and angry bull. Then a sort
of spasm seemed to convulse his face.

"Megan don' want yu."

A rush of jealousy, of contempt, and anger with this thick,
loud-breathing rustic got the better of Ashurst's self-possession;
he jumped up and pushed back his chair.

"You can go to the devil!"

And as he said those simple words, he saw Megan in the
doorway with a tiny brown spaniel puppy in her arms. She
came up to him quickly:

"Its eyes are blue!" she said.

Joe turned away; the back of his neck was literally crimson.

Ashurst put his finger to the mouth of the little brown bull-
frog of a creature in her arms. How cosy it looked against her!

"It's fond of you already. Ah! Megan, everything is fond
of *you.*"

"What was Joe saying to you, please?"

"Telling me to go away, because you didn't want me here."

She stamped her foot; then looked up at Ashurst. At that
adoring look he felt his nerves quiver, just as if he had seen a
moth scorching its wings.

"To-night!" he said. "Don't forget!"

"No." And smothering her face against the puppy's little
fat, brown body, she slipped back into the house.

Ashurst wandered down the lane. At the gate of the wild
meadow he came on the lame man and his cows.

"Beautiful day, Jim!"

"Ah! 'Tes brave weather for the grass. The ashes be later
than th' oaks this year. 'When th' oak before th' ash——'"

Ashurst said idly: "Where were you standing when you saw
the gipsy bogle, Jim?"

"It might be under that big apple tree, as you might say."

"And you really do think it was there?"

The lame man answered cautiously:

"I shouldn't like to say rightly that 't *was* there. 'Twas in
my mind as 'twas there."

"What do you make of it?"

The lame man lowered his voice.

"They du zay old master, Mist' Narracombe, come o' gipsy
stock. But that's tellin'. They'm a wonderful people, yu know,
for claimin' their own. Maybe they knu 'e was goin', and sent

this feller along for company. That's what I've a-thought about it."

" What was he like? "

" 'E 'ad 'air all over 'is face, an' goin' like this, he was, zame as if 'e 'ad a viddle. They zay there's no such thing as bogles, but I've a-zeen the 'air on this dog standin' up of a dark naight, when I couldn' zee nothin',' meself."

" Was there a moon? "

" Yeas, very near full, but 'twas on'y just risen, gold-like be'ind them trees."

" And you think a ghost means trouble, do you? "

The lame man pushed his hat up; his aspiring eyes looked at Ashurst more earnestly than ever.

" 'Tes not for me to zay that—but 'tes they bein' so unrestin'-like. · There's things us don' understand, that's zartin, for zure. There's people that zee things, tu, an' others that don't never zee nothin'. Now, our Joe—yu might putt anything under 'is eyes an' 'e'd never see it; and them other boys, tu, they'm rattlin' fellers. But yu take an' putt our Megan where there's suthin', she'll zee it, an' more tu, or I'm mistaken."

" She's sensitive, that's why."

" What's that? "

" I mean, she feels everything."

" Ah! She'm very lovin'-'earted."

Ashurst, who felt colour coming into his cheeks, held out his tobacco pouch.

" Have a fill, Jim? "

" Thank 'ee, sir. She'm one in an 'underd, I think."

" I expect so," said Ashurst shortly, and folding up his pouch, walked on.

" Lovin'-'earted! " Yes! And what was he doing? What were his intentions—as they say—towards this loving-hearted girl? The thought dogged him, wandering through fields bright with buttercups, where the little red calves were feeding, and the swallows flying high. Yes, the oaks were before the ashes, brown-gold already; every tree in different stage and hue. The cuckoos and a thousand birds were singing; the little streams were very bright. The ancients believed in a golden age, in the garden of the Hesperides! . . . A queen wasp settled on his sleeve. Each queen wasp killed meant two thousand fewer wasps to thieve the apples which would grow from that blossom in the orchard; but who, with love in his heart, could kill any-

thing on a day like this? He entered a field where a young
red bull was feeding. It seemed to Ashurst that he looked like
Joe. But the young bull took no notice of this visitor, a little
drunk himself, perhaps, on the singing and the glamour of the
golden pasture, under his short legs. Ashurst crossed out un-
challenged to the hillside above the stream. From that slope a
tor mounted to its crown of rocks. The ground there was
covered with a mist of bluebells, and nearly a score of crab-
apple trees were in full bloom. He threw himself down on
the grass. The change from the buttercup glory and oak-
goldened glamour of the fields to this ethereal beauty under the
grey tor filled him with a sort of wonder; nothing the same,
save the sound of running water and the songs of the cuckoos.
He lay there a long time, watching the sunlight wheel till the
crab-trees threw shadows over the bluebells, his only companions
a few wild bees. He was not quite sane, thinking of that
morning's kiss, and of to-night under the apple tree. In such
a spot as this, fauns and dryads surely lived; nymphs, white as
the crab-apple blossom, retired within those trees; fauns, brown
as the dead bracken, with pointed ears, lay in wait for them.
The cuckoos were still calling when he woke, there was the sound
of running water; but the sun had couched behind the tor, the
hillside was cool, and some rabbits had come out. 'To-night!'
he thought. Just as from the earth everything was pushing
up, unfolding under the soft insistent fingers of an unseen
hand, so were his heart and senses being pushed, unfolded.
He got up and broke off a spray from a crab-apple tree. The
buds were like Megan—shell-like, rose-pink, wild, and fresh;
and so, too, the opening flowers, white, and wild, and touching. He put the spray into his coat. And all the rush of
the spring within him escaped in a triumphant sigh. But the
rabbits scurried away.

6 §

It was nearly eleven that night when Ashurst put down the
pocket "Odyssey" which for half an hour he had held in his
hands without reading, and slipped through the yard down to
the orchard. The moon had just risen, very golden, over the
hill, and like a bright, powerful, watching spirit peered through
the bars of an ash tree's half-naked boughs. In among the
apple trees it was still dark, and he stood making sure of his

direction, feeling the rough grass with his feet. A black mass
close behind him stirred with a heavy grunting sound, and three
large pigs settled down again close to each other, under the wall.
He listened. There was no wind, but the stream's burbling
whispering chuckle had gained twice its daytime strength. One
bird, he could not tell what, cried " Pip—pip," " Pip—pip,"
with perfect monotony; he could hear a night-jar spinning very
far off; an owl hooting. Ashurst moved a step or two, and again
halted, aware of a dim living whiteness all round his head.
On the dark unstirring trees innumerable flowers and buds all
soft and blurred were being bewitched to life by the creeping
moonlight. He had the oddest feeling of actual companionship, as if a million white moths or spirits had floated in and
settled between dark sky and darker ground, and were opening
and shutting their wings on a level with his eyes. In the
bewildering, still, scentless beauty of that moment he almost
lost memory of why he had come to the orchard. The flying
glamour which had clothed the earth all day had not gone now
that night had fallen, but only changed into this new form.
He moved on through the thicket of stems and boughs covered
with that live powdering whiteness, till he reached the big apple
tree. No mistaking that, even in the dark, nearly twice the
height and size of any other, and leaning out towards the open
meadows and the stream. Under the thick branches he stood
still again, to listen. The same sounds exactly, and a faint
grunting from the sleepy pigs. He put his hands on the dry,
almost warm tree trunk, whose rough mossy surface gave forth
a peaty scent at his touch. Would she come—would she? And
among these quivering, haunted, moon-witched trees he was
seized with doubts of everything! All was unearthly here, fit
for no earthly lovers; fit only for god and goddess, faun and
nymph—not for him and this little country girl. Would it
not be almost a relief if she did not come? But all the time he
was listening. And still that unknown bird went " Pip—pip,"
" Pip—pip," and there rose the busy chatter of the little trout
stream, whereon the moon was flinging glances through the
bars of her tree-prison. The blossom on a level with his eyes
seemed to grow more living every moment, seemed with its
mysterious white beauty more and more a part of his suspense.
He plucked a fragment and held it close—three blossoms.
Sacrilege to pluck fruit-tree blossom—soft, sacred, young blossom—and throw it away! Then suddenly he heard the gate

close, the pigs stirring again and grunting; and leaning against the trunk, he pressed his hands to its mossy sides behind him, and held his breath. She might have been a spirit threading the trees, for all the noise she made! Then he saw her quite close—her dark form part of a little tree, her white face part of its blossom; so still, and peering towards him. He whispered: "Megan!" and held out his hands. She ran forward, straight to his breast. When he felt her heart beating against him, Ashurst knew to the full the sensations of chivalry and passion. Because she was not of his world, because she was so simple and young and headlong, adoring and defenceless, how could he be other than her protector, in the dark! Because she was all simple Nature and beauty, as much a part of this spring night as was the living blossom, how should he not take all that she would give him—how not fulfil the spring in her heart and his! And torn between these two emotions he clasped her close, and kissed her hair. How long they stood there without speaking he knew not. The stream went on chattering, the owls hooting, the moon kept stealing up and growing whiter; the blossom all round them and above brightened in suspense of living beauty. Their lips had sought each other's, and they did not speak. The moment speech began all would be unreal! Spring has no speech, nothing but rustling and whispering. Spring has so much more than speech in its unfolding flowers and leaves, and the coursing of its streams, and in its sweet restless seeking! And sometimes spring will come alive, and, like a mysterious Presence, stand, encircling lovers with its arms, laying on them the fingers of enchantment, so that, standing lips to lips, they forget everything but just a kiss. While her heart beat against him, and her lips quivered on his, Ashurst felt nothing but simple rapture—Destiny meant her for his arms, Love could not be flouted! But when their lips parted for breath, division began again at once. Only, passion now was so much the stronger, and he sighed:

"Oh! Megan! Why did you come?"

She looked up, hurt, amazed.

"Sir, you asked me to."

"Don't call me 'sir,' my pretty sweet."

"What should I be callin' you?"

"Frank."

"I could not. Oh, no!"

"But you love me—don't you?"

"I could not help lovin' you. I want to be with you—that's all."

"All!"

So faint that he hardly heard, she whispered:

"I shall die if I can't be with you."

Ashurst took a mighty breath.

"Come and be with me, then!"

"Oh!"

Intoxicated by the awe and rapture in that "Oh!" he went on, whispering:

"We'll go to London. I'll show you the world. And I *will* take care of you, I promise, Megan. I'll never be a brute to you!"

"If I can be with you—that is all."

He stroked her hair, and whispered on:

"To-morrow I'll go to Torquay and get some money, and get you some clothes that won't be noticed, and then we'll steal away. And when we get to London, soon perhaps, if you love me well enough, we'll be married."

He could feel her hair shiver with the shake of her head.

"Oh, no! I could not. I only want to be with you!"

Drunk on his own chivalry, Ashurst went on murmuring:

"It's I who am not good enough for you. Oh! Megan, when did you begin to love me?"

"When I saw you in the road, and you looked at me. The first night I loved you; but I never thought you would want me."

She slipped down suddenly to her knees, trying to kiss his feet.

A shiver of horror went through Ashurst; he lifted her up bodily and held her fast—too upset to speak.

She whispered: "Why won't you let me?"

"It's I who will kiss your feet!"

Her smile brought tears into his eyes. The whiteness of her moonlit face so close to his, the faint pink of her opened lips, had the living unearthly beauty of the apple blossom.

And then, suddenly, her eyes widened and stared past him painfully; she writhed out of his arms, and whispered: "Look!"

Ashurst saw nothing but the brightened stream, the furze faintly gilded, the beech trees glistening, and behind them all

the wide loom of the moonlit hill. Behind him came her frozen
whisper: "The gipsy bogle!"

"Where?"

"There—by the stone—under the trees!"

Exasperated, he leapt the stream, and strode towards the
beech clump. Prank of the moonlight! Nothing! In and out
of the boulders and thorn trees, muttering and cursing, yet with
a kind of terror, he rushed and stumbled. Absurd! Silly!
Then he went back to the apple-tree. But she was gone; he
could hear a rustle, the grunting of the pigs, the sound of a
gate closing. Instead of her, only this old apple tree! He
flung his arms round the trunk. What a substitute for her soft
body; the rough moss against his face—what a substitute for
her soft cheek; only the scent, as of the woods, a little the
same! And above him, and around, the blossoms, more living,
more moonlit than ever, seemed to glow and breathe.

7 §

Descending from the train at Torquay station, Ashurst wandered uncertainly along the front, for he did not know this
particular queen of English watering places. Having little
sense of what he had on, he was quite unconscious of being
remarkable among its inhabitants, and strode along in his rough
Norfolk jacket, dusty boots, and battered hat, without observing
that people gazed at him rather blankly. He was seeking a
branch of his London bank, and having found one, found also
the first obstacle to his mood. Did he know anyone in Torquay?
No. In that case, if he would wire to his bank in London,
they would be happy to oblige him on receipt of the reply. That
suspicious breath from the matter-of-fact world somewhat tarnished the brightness of his visions. But he sent the telegram.

Nearly opposite to the post office he saw a shop full of ladies'
garments, and examined the window with strange sensations.
To have to undertake the clothing of his rustic love was more
than a little disturbing. He went in. A young woman came forward; she had blue eyes and a faintly puzzled forehead. Ashurst
stared at her in silence.

"Yes, sir?"

"I want a dress for a young lady."

The young woman smiled. Ashurst frowned—the peculiarity of his request struck him with sudden force.

The young woman added hastily:

"What style would you like—something modish?"

"No. Simple."

"What figure would the young lady be?"

"I don't know; about two inches shorter than you, I should say."

"Could you give me her waist measurement?"

Megan's waist!

"Oh! anything usual!"

"Quite!"

While she was gone he stood disconsolately eyeing the models in the window, and suddenly it seemed to him incredible that Megan—his Megan—could ever be dressed save in the rough tweed skirt, coarse blouse, and tam-o'-shanter cap he was wont to see her in. The young woman had come back with several dresses in her arms, and Ashurst eyed her laying them against her own modish figure. There was one whose colour he liked, a dove-grey, but to imagine Megan clothed in it was beyond him. The young woman went away, and brought some more. But on Ashurst there had now come a feeling of paralysis. How choose? She would want a hat too, and shoes, and gloves; and, suppose, when he had got them all, they commonised her, as Sunday clothes always commonised village folk! Why should she not travel as she was? Ah? But conspicuousness would matter; this was a serious elopement. And, staring at the young woman, he thought: 'I wonder if she guesses, and thinks me a blackguard?'

"Do you mind putting aside that grey one for me?" he said desperately at last. "I can't decide now; I'll come in again this afternoon."

The young woman sighed.

"Oh! certainly. It's a very tasteful costume. I don't think you'll get anything that will suit your purpose better."

"I expect not," Ashurst murmured, and went out.

Freed again from the suspicious matter-of-factness of the world, he took a long breath, and went back to visions. In fancy he saw the trustful, pretty creature who was going to join her life to his; saw himself and her stealing forth at night, walking over the moor under the moon, he with his arm round her, and carrying her new garments, till, in some far-off wood, when dawn was coming, she would slip off her old things and put on these, and an early train at a distant station would bear them away on their honeymoon journey, till London swallowed them up, and the dreams of love came true.

"Frank Ashurst! Haven't seen you since Rugby, old chap!"

Ashurst's frown dissolved; the face, close to his own, was blue-eyed, suffused with sun—one of those faces where sun from within and without join in a sort of lustre. And he answered:

"Phil Halliday, by Jove!"

"What are you doing here?"

"Oh! nothing. Just looking round, and getting some money. I'm staying on the moor."

"Are you lunching anywhere? Come and lunch with us; I'm here with my young sisters. They've had measles."

Hooked in by that friendly arm Ashurst went along, up a hill, down a hill, away out of the town, while the voice of Halliday, redolent of optimism as his face was of sun, explained how "in this mouldy place the only decent things were the bathing and boating," and so on, till presently they came to a crescent of houses a little above and back from the sea, and into the centre one—an hotel—made their way.

"Come up to my room and have a wash. Lunch'll be ready in a jiffy."

Ashurst contemplated his visage in a looking-glass. After his farmhouse bedroom, the comb and one spare shirt *régime* of the last fortnight, this room littered with clothes and brushes was a sort of Capua; and he thought: 'Queer—one doesn't realise——' But what—he did not quite know.

When he followed Halliday into the sitting-room for lunch, three faces, very fair and blue-eyed, were turned suddenly at the words: "This is Frank Ashurst—my young sisters."

Two were indeed young, about eleven and ten. The third was perhaps seventeen, tall and fair-haired too, with pink-and-white cheeks just touched by the sun, and eyebrows, rather darker than the hair, running a little upwards from her nose to their outer points. The voices of all three were like Halliday's, high and cheerful; they stood up straight, shook hands with a quick movement, looked at Ashurst critically, away again at once, and began to talk of what they were going to do in the afternoon. A regular Diana and attendant nymphs! After the farm this crisp, slangy, eager talk, this cool, clean, off-hand refinement, was queer at first, and then so natural that what he had come from became suddenly remote. The names of the two little ones seemed to be Sabina and Freda; of the eldest, Stella.

Presently the one called Sabina turned to him and said:

"I say, will you come shrimping with us?—it's awful fun!"

Surprised by this unexpected friendliness, Ashurst murmured:

"I'm afraid I've got to get back this afternoon."

"Oh!"

"Can't you put it off?"

Ashurst turned to the new speaker, Stella, shook his head, and smiled. She was very pretty! Sabina said regretfully: "You might!" Then the talk switched off to caves and swimming.

"Can you swim far?"

"About two miles."

"Oh!"

"I say!"

"How jolly!"

The three pairs of blue eyes, fixed on him, made him conscious of his new importance. The sensation was agreeable. Halliday said:

"I say, you simply must stop and have a bathe. You'd better stay the night."

"Yes, do!"

But again Ashurst smiled and shook his head. Then suddenly he found himself being catechised about his physical achievements. He had rowed—it seemed—in his college boat, played in his college football team, won his college mile and he rose from table a sort of hero. The two little girls insisted that he must see "their" cave, and they set forth chattering like magpies, Ashurst between them, Stella and her brother a little behind. In the cave, damp and darkish like any other cave, the great feature was a pool with possibility of creatures which might be caught and put into bottles. Sabina and Freda, who wore no stockings on their shapely brown legs, exhorted Ashurst to join them in the middle of it, and help sieve the water. He too was soon bootless and sockless. Time goes fast for one who has a sense of beauty, when there are pretty children in a pool and a young Diana on the edge, to receive with wonder anything you can catch! Ashurst never had much sense of time. It was a shock when, pulling out his watch, he saw it was well past three. No cashing his cheque to-day—the bank would be closed before he could get there. Watching his expression, the little girls cried out at once:

"Hurrah! Now you'll have to stay!"

Ashurst did not answer. He was seeing again Megan's face, when at breakfast he had whispered: "I'm going to Torquay, darling, to get everything; I shall be back this evening. If it's fine we can go to-night. Be ready." He was seeing again how she quivered and hung on his words. What would she think? Then he pulled himself together, conscious suddenly of the calm scrutiny of this other young girl, so tall and fair and Diana-like, at the edge of the pool, of her wondering blue eyes under those brows which slanted up a little. If they knew what was in his mind—if they knew that this very night he had meant——! Well, there would be a little sound of disgust, and he would be alone in the cave. And with a curious mixture of anger, chagrin, and shame, he put his watch back into his pocket and said abruptly:

"Yes; I'm dished for to-day."

"Hurrah! Now you can bathe with us."

It was impossible not to succumb a little to the contentment of these pretty children, to the smile on Stella's lips, to Halliday's "Ripping, old chap! I can lend you things for the night!" But again a spasm of longing and remorse throbbed through Ashurst, and he said moodily:

"I must send a wire!"

The attractions of the pool palling, they went back to the hotel. Ashurst sent his wire, addressing it to Mrs. Narracombe: "Sorry, detained for the night, back to-morrow." Surely Megan would understand that he had too much to do; and his heart grew lighter. It was a lovely afternoon, warm, the sea calm and blue, and swimming his great passion; the favour of these pretty children flattered him, the pleasure of looking at them, at Stella, at Halliday's sunny face; the slight unreality, yet extreme naturalness of it all—as of a last peep at normality before he took this plunge with Megan! He got his borrowed bathing dress, and they all set forth. Halliday and he undressed behind one rock, the three girls behind another. He was first into the sea, and at once swam out with the bravado of justifying his self-given reputation. When he turned he could see Halliday swimming along shore, and the girls flopping and dipping, and riding the little waves, in the way he was accustomed to despise, but now thought pretty and sensible, since it gave him the distinction of the only deep-water fish. But drawing near, he wondered if they would like him, a stranger, to come into their splashing group; he felt shy, approaching that slim nymph. Then Sabina summoned him to teach her to float, and between them the little girls kept him so busy that he had no time even to notice whether Stella was accustomed to his presence, till suddenly he heard a startled sound from her. She was standing submerged to the waist, leaning a little forward, her slim white arms stretched out and pointing, her wet face puckered by the sun and an expression of fear.

" Look at Phil! Is he all right? Oh, look! "

Ashurst saw at once that Phil was not all right. He was splashing and struggling out of his depth, perhaps a hundred yards away; suddenly he gave a cry, threw up his arms, and went down. Ashurst saw the girl launch herself towards him, and crying out: " Go back, Stella! Go back! " he dashed out. He had never swum so fast, and reached Halliday just as he was coming up a second time. It was a case of cramp, but to get him in was not difficult, for he did not struggle. The girl, who had stopped where Ashurst told her to, helped as soon as he was in his depth, and once on the beach they sat down one on each side of him to rub his limbs, while the little ones stood by with scared faces. Halliday was soon smiling. It was—he said—rotten of him, absolutely rotten! If Frank would give him an arm, he could get to his clothes all right now. Ashurst gave him the arm, and as he did so caught sight of Stella's face, wet and flushed and tearful, all broken up out of its calm; and he thought: ' I called her Stella! Wonder if she minded? '

While they were dressing, Halliday said quietly:

" You saved my life, old chap! "

" Rot! "

Clothed, but not quite in their right minds, they went up all together to the hotel and sat down to tea, except Halliday who was lying down in his room. After some slices of bread and jam, Sabina said:

" I say, you know, you *are* a brick! " And Freda chimed in: " Rather! "

Ashurst saw Stella looking down; he got up in confusion, and went to the window. From there he heard Sabina mutter: " I say, let's swear blood bond. Where's your knife, Freda? " and out of the corner of his eye could see each of them solemnly prick herself, squeeze out a drop of blood and dabble on a bit of paper. He turned and made for the door.

" Don't be a stoat! Come back! " His arms were seized; imprisoned between the little girls he was brought back to the table. On it lay a piece of paper with an effigy drawn in blood, and the three names Stella Halliday, Sabina Halliday, Freda Halliday—also in blood, running towards it like the rays of a star. Sabina said:

" That's you. We shall have to kiss you, you know."

And Freda echoed:

" Oh! Blow—Yes! "

Before Ashurst could escape, some wettish hair dangled against his face, something like a bite descended on his nose, he felt his left arm pinched, and other teeth softly searching his cheek. Then he was released, and Freda said:

" Now, Stella."

Ashurst, red and rigid, looked across the table at a red and rigid Stella. Sabina giggled; Freda cried:

" Buck up—it spoils everything! "

A queer, ashamed eagerness shot through Ashurst: then he said quietly:

" Shut up, you little demons! "

Again Sabina giggled.

" Well, then, she can kiss her hand, and you can put it against your nose. It *is* on one side! "

To his amazement the girl did kiss her hand and stretch it out. Solemnly he took that cool, slim hand and laid it to his cheek. The two little girls broke into clapping, and Freda said:

" Now, then, we shall have to save your life at any time; that's settled. Can I have another cup, Stella, not so beastly weak? "

Tea was resumed, and Ashurst, folding up the paper, put it in his pocket. The talk turned on the advantages of measles, tangerine oranges, honey in a spoon, no lessons, and so forth. Ashurst listened, silent, exchanging friendly looks with Stella, whose face was again of its normal sun-touched pink and white. It was soothing to be so taken to the heart of this jolly family, fascinating to watch their faces. And after tea, while the two little girls pressed seaweed, he talked to Stella in the window seat and looked at her water-colour sketches. The whole thing was like a pleasurable dream; time and incident hung up, importance and reality suspended. To-morrow he would go back to Megan, with nothing of all this left save the paper with the blood of these children, in his pocket. Children! Stella was not quite that—as old as Megan! Her talk—quick, rather hard and shy, yet friendly—seemed to flourish on his silences, and about her there was something cool and virginal—a maiden in a bower. At dinner, to which Halliday, who had swallowed too much sea-water, did not come, Sabina said:

"I'm going to call you Frank."

Freda echoed:

"Frank, Frank, Franky."

Ashurst grinned and bowed.

"Every time Stella calls you Mr. Ashurst, she's got to pay a forfeit. It's ridiculous."

Ashurst looked at Stella, who grew slowly red. Sabina giggled; Freda cried:

"She's 'smoking'—'smoking!'—Yah!"

Ashurst reached out to right and left, and grasped some fair hair in each hand.

"Look here," he said, "you two! Leave Stella alone, or I'll tie you together!"

Freda gurgled:

"Ouch! You *are* a beast!"

Sabina murmured cautiously:

"*You* call *her* Stella, you see!"

"Why shouldn't I? It's a jolly name!"

"All right; we give you leave to!"

Ashurst released the hair. Stella! What would she call him—after this? But she called him nothing; till at bedtime he said, deliberately:

"Good-night, Stella!"

"Good-night, Mr. —— Good-night, Frank! It *was* jolly of you, you know!"

"Oh—that! Bosh!"

Her quick, straight handshake tightened suddenly, and as suddenly, became slack.

Ashurst stood motionless in the empty sitting-room. Only last night, under the apple tree and the living blossom, he had held Megan to him, kissing her eyes and lips. And he gasped, swept by that rush of remembrance. To-night it should have begun—his life with her who only wanted to be with him! And now, twenty-four hours and more must pass, because—of not looking at his watch! Why had he made friends with this family of innocents just when he was saying good-bye to innocence, and all the rest of it? 'But I mean to marry her,' he thought; 'I told her so!'

He took a candle, lighted it, and went to his bedroom, which was next to Halliday's. His friend's voice called as he was passing:

"Is that you, old chap? I say, come in."

He was sitting up in bed, smoking a pipe and reading.

"Sit down a bit."

Ashurst sat down by the open window.

"I've been thinking about this afternoon, you know," said Halliday rather suddenly. "They say you go through all your past. I didn't. I suppose I wasn't far enough gone."

"What did you think of?"

Halliday was silent for a little, then said quietly:

"Well, I did think of one thing—rather odd—of a girl at Cambridge that I might have—you know; I was glad I hadn't got her on my mind. Anyhow, old chap, I owe it to you that I'm here; I should have been in the big dark by now. No more bed, or baccy; no more anything. I say, what d'you suppose happens to us?"

Ashurst murmured:

"Go out like flames, I expect."

"Phew!"

"We may flicker, and cling about a bit, perhaps."

"H'm! I think that's rather gloomy. I say, I hope my young sisters have been decent to you?"

"Awfully decent."

Halliday put his pipe down, crossed his hands behind his neck, and turned his face towards the window.

"They're not bad kids!" he said.

Watching his friend, lying there, with that smile, and the candle-light on his face, Ashurst shuddered. Quite true! He might have been lying there with no smile, with all that sunny look gone out for ever! He might not have been lying there at all, but "sanded" at the bottom of the sea, waiting for resurrection on the—ninth day, was it? And that smile of Halliday's seemed to him suddenly something wonderful, as if in it were all the difference between life and death—the little flame—the all! He got up, and said softly:

"Well, you ought to sleep, I expect. Shall I blow out?"
Halliday caught his hand.

"I can't say it, you know; but it must be rotten to be dead.
Good-night, old boy!"

Stirred and moved, Ashurst squeezed the hand, and went
downstairs. The hall door was still open, and he passed out
on to the lawn before the Crescent. The stars were bright in a
very dark blue sky, and by their light some lilacs had that
mysterious colour of flowers by night which no one can describe.
Ashurst pressed his face against a spray; and before his closed
eyes Megan started up, with the tiny brown spaniel pup against
her breast. "I thought of a girl that I might have—you
know. I was glad I hadn't got her on my mind!" He jerked
his head away from the lilac, and began pacing up and down
over the grass, a grey phantom coming to substance for a moment in the light from the lamp at either end. He was with
her again under the living, breathing whiteness of the blossom,
the stream chattering by, the moon glinting steel-blue on the
bathing-pool; back in the rapture of his kisses on her upturned
face of innocence and humble passion, back in the suspense
and beauty of that pagan night. He stood still once more in
the shadow of the lilacs. Here the sea, not the stream, was
Night's voice; the sea with its sigh and rustle; no little bird,
no owl, no nightjar called or spun; but a piano tinkled, and
the white houses cut the sky with solid curve, and the scent
from the lilacs filled the air. A window of the hotel, high up,
was lighted; he saw a shadow move across the blind. And
most queer sensations stirred within him, a sort of churning,
and twining, and turning of a single emotion on itself, as though
spring and love, bewildered and confused, seeking the way,
were baffled. This girl, who had called him Frank, whose hand
had given his that sudden little clutch, this girl so cool and
pure—what would *she* think of such wild, unlawful loving?
He sank down on the grass, sitting there cross-legged, with his
back to the house, motionless as some carved Buddha. Was
he really going to break through innocence, and steal? Sniff
the scent out of a wild flower, and—perhaps—throw it away?
"Of a girl at Cambridge that I might have—you know!"
He put his hands to the grass, one on each side, palms downwards, and pressed; it was just warm still—the grass, barely
moist, soft and firm and friendly. 'What am I going to do?'
he thought. Perhaps Megan was at her window, looking out

at the blossom, thinking of him! Poor little Megan! 'Why
not?' he thought. 'I love her! But do I—really love her? or
do I only want her because she is so pretty, and loves me?
What am I going to do?' The piano tinkled on, the stars
winked; and Ashurst gazed out before him at the dark sea, as
if spell-bound. He got up at last, cramped and rather chilly.
There was no longer light in any window. And he went in to
bed.

8 §

Out of a deep and dreamless sleep he was awakened by the
sound of thumping on the door. A shrill voice called:
"Hi! Breakfast's ready."
He jumped up. Where was he——? Ah!
He found them already eating marmalade, and sat down in
the empty place between Stella and Sabina, who, after watching
him a little, said:
"I say, do buck up; we're going to start at half-past nine."
"We're going to Berry Head, old chap; you *must* come!"
Ashurst thought: 'Come! Impossible. I shall be getting
things and going back.' He looked at Stella. She said quickly:
"Do come!"
Sabina chimed in:
"It'll be no fun without you."
Freda got up and stood behind his chair.
"You've got to come, or else I'll pull your hair!"
Ashurst thought: 'Well—one day more—to think it over!
One day more!' And he said:
"All right! You needn't tweak my mane!"
"Hurrah!"
At the station he wrote a second telegram to the farm, and
then—tore it up; he could not have explained why. From
Brixham they drove in a very little wagonette. There, squeezed
between Sabina and Freda, with his knees touching Stella's,
they played "Up Jenkins"; and the gloom he was feeling gave
way to frolic. In this one day more to think it over, he did not
want to think! They ran races, wrestled, paddled—for to-day
nobody wanted to bathe—they sang catches, played games, and
ate all they had brought. The little girls fell asleep against
him on the way back, and his knees still touched Stella's in the
wagonette. It seemed incredible that thirty hours ago he had

never set eyes on any of those three flaxen heads. In the train he talked to Stella of poetry, discovering her favourites, and telling her his own with a pleasing sense of superiority; till suddenly she said, rather low:

"Phil says you don't believe in a future life, Frank. I think that's dreadful."

Disconcerted, Ashurst muttered:

"I don't either believe or not believe—I simply don't know."

She said quickly:

"I couldn't bear that. What would be the use of living?"

Watching the frown of those pretty oblique brows, Ashurst answered:

"I don't believe in believing things because one wants to."

"But why should one *wish* to live again, if one isn't going to?"

And she looked full at him.

He did not want to hurt her, but an itch to dominate pushed him on to say:

"While one's alive one naturally wants to go on living for ever; that's part of being alive. But it probably isn't anything more."

"Don't you believe in the Bible at all, then?"

Ashurst thought: 'Now I shall really hurt her!'

"I believe in the Sermon on the Mount, because it's beautiful and good for all time."

"But don't you believe Christ was divine?"

He shook his head.

She turned her face quickly to the window, and there sprang into his mind Megan's prayer, repeated by little Nick: "God bless us all, and Mr. Ashes!" Who else would ever say a prayer for him, like her who at this moment must be waiting—waiting to see him come down the lane? And he thought suddenly: 'What a scoundrel I am!'

All that evening this thought kept coming back; but, as is not unusual, each time with less poignancy, till it seemed almost a matter of course to be a scoundrel. And—strange!—he did not know whether he was a scoundrel if he meant to go back to Megan, or if he did not mean to go back to her.

They played cards till the children were sent off to bed; then Stella went to the piano. From over on the window seat, where it was nearly dark, Ashurst watched her between the candles—that fair head on the long, white neck bending to the

movement of her hands. She played fluently, without much
expression; but what a picture she made, the faint golden
radiance, a sort of angelic atmosphere—hovering about her!
Who could have passionate thoughts or wild desires in the
presence of that swaying, white-clothed girl with the seraphic
head? She played a thing of Schumann's called "*Warum?*"
Then Halliday brought out a flute, and the spell was broken.
After this they made Ashurst sing, Stella playing him accom-
paniments from a book of Schumann songs, till, in the middle
of "*Ich grolle nicht*," two small figures clad in blue dressing-
gowns crept in and tried to conceal themselves beneath the
piano. The evening broke up in confusion, and what Sabina
called "a splendid rag."

That night Ashurst hardly slept at all. He was thinking,
tossing and turning. The intense domestic intimacy of these
last two days, the strength of this Halliday atmosphere, seemed
to ring him round, and make the farm and Megan—even Megan
—seem unreal. Had he really made love to her—really promised
to take her away to live with him? He must have been bewitched by the spring, the night, the apple blossom! The
notion that he was going to make her his mistress—that simple
child not yet eighteen—now filled him with a sort of horror,
even while it still stung and whipped his blood. He muttered
to himself: "It's awful, what I've done—awful!" And the
sound of Schumann's music throbbed and mingled with his
fevered thoughts, and he saw again Stella's cool, white, fair-
haired figure and bending neck, the queer, angelic radiance
about her. 'I must have been—I must be—mad!' he thought.
'What came into me? Poor little Megan!' "God bless us
all, and Mr. Ashes!" "I want to be with you—only to be with
you!" And burying his face in his pillow, he smothered down
a fit of sobbing. Not to go back was awful! To go back—
more awful still!

Emotion, when you are young, and give real vent to it, loses
its power of torture. And he fell asleep, thinking: 'What was
it—a few kisses—all forgotten in a month!'

Next morning he got his cheque cashed, but avoided the shop
of the dove-grey dress like the plague; and, instead, bought
himself some necessaries. He spent the whole day in a queer
mood, cherishing a kind of sullenness against himself. Instead
of the hankering of the last two days, he felt nothing but a
blank—all passionate longing gone, as if quenched in that out-

burst of tears. After tea Stella put a book down beside him, and said shyly:

"Have you read that, Frank?"

It was Farrar's *Life of Christ*. Ashurst smiled. Her anxiety about his beliefs seemed to him comic, but touching. Infectious, too, perhaps, for he began to have an itch to justify himself, if not to convert her. And in the evening, when the children and Halliday were mending their shrimping nets, he said:

"At the back of orthodox religion, so far as I can see, there's always the idea of reward—what you can get for being good; a kind of begging for favours. I think it all starts in fear."

She was sitting on the sofa making reefer knots with a bit of string. She looked up quickly:

"I think it's much deeper than that."

Ashurst felt again that wish to dominate.

"You think so," he said; "but wanting the '*quid pro quo*' is about the deepest thing in all of us! It's jolly hard to get to the bottom of it!"

She wrinkled her brows in a puzzled frown.

"I don't think I understand."

He went on obstinately:

"Well, think, and see if the most religious people aren't those who feel that this life doesn't give them all they want. I believe in being good because to be good is good in itself."

"Then you do believe in being good?"

How pretty she looked now—it was easy to be good with her! And he nodded and said:

"I say, show me how to make that knot!"

With her fingers touching his, in manœuvring the bit of string he felt soothed and happy. And when he went to bed he wilfully kept his thoughts on her, wrapping himself in her fair, cool sisterly radiance, as in some garment of protection.

Next day he found they had arranged to go by train to Totnes, and picnic at Berry Pomeroy Castle. Still in that resolute oblivion of the past, he took his place with them in the landau beside Halliday, back to the horses. And, then, along the sea front, nearly at the turning to the railway station, his heart almost leaped into his mouth. Megan—Megan herself!—was walking on the far pathway, in her old skirt and jacket and her tam-o'-shanter, looking up into the faces of the passers-by. Instinctively he threw his hand up for cover, then made a feint

of clearing dust out of his eyes; but between his fingers he
could see her still, moving, not with her free country step, but
wavering, lost-looking, pitiful—like some little dog which has
missed its master and does not know whether to run on, to run
back—where to run. How had she come like this?—what
excuse had she found to get away?—what did she hope for?
But with every turn of the wheels bearing him away from her,
his heart revolted and cried to him to stop them, to get out,
and go to her! When the landau turned the corner to the station he could stand it no more, and opening the carriage door,
muttered: " I've forgotten something! Go on—don't wait for
me! I'll join you at the castle by the next train!" He jumped,
stumbled, spun round, recovered his balance, and walked forward, while the carriage with the astonished Hallidays rolled
on.

From the corner he could only just see Megan, a long way
ahead now. He ran a few steps, checked himself, and dropped
into a walk. With each step nearer to her, further from the
Hallidays, he walked more and more slowly. How did it alter
anything—this sight of her? How make the going to her, and
that which must come of it, less ugly? For there was no hiding
it—since he had met the Hallidays he had become gradually
sure that he would not marry Megan. It would only be a wild
love-time, a troubled, remorseful, difficult time—and then—
well, then he would get tired, just because she gave him everything, was so simple, and so trustful, so dewy. And dew—
wears off! The little spot of faded colour, her tam-o'-shanter
cap, wavered on far in front of him; she was looking up into
every face, and at the house windows. Had any man ever such
a cruel moment to go through? Whatever he did, he felt he
would be a beast. And he uttered a groan which made a nurse-
maid turn and stare. He saw Megan stop and lean against the
sea-wall, looking at the sea; and he too stopped. Quite likely
she had never seen the sea before, and even in her distress could
not resist that sight. ' Yes—she's seen nothing,' he thought;
' everything's before her. And just for a few weeks' passion,
I shall be cutting her life to ribbons. I'd better go and hang
myself rather than do it!' And suddenly he seemed to see
Stella's calm eyes looking into his, the wave of fluffy hair on her
forehead stirred by the wind. Ah! it would be madness, would
mean giving up all that he respected, and his own self-respect.
He turned and walked quickly back towards the station. But

memory of that poor, bewildered little figure, those anxious eyes searching the passers-by, smote him too hard again, and once more he turned towards the sea. The cap was no longer visible; that little spot of colour had vanished in the stream of the noon promenaders. And impelled by the passion of longing, the dearth which comes on one when life seems to be whiling something out of reach, he hurried forward. She was nowhere to be seen; for half an hour he looked for her; then on the beach flung himself face downward in the sand. To find her again he knew he had only to go to the station and wait till she returned from her fruitless quest, to take her train home; or to take train himself and go back to the farm, so that she found him there when she returned. But he lay inert in the sand, among the indifferent groups of children with their spades and buckets. Pity at her little figure wandering, seeking, was well-nigh merged in the spring-running of his blood; for it was all wild feeling now—the chivalrous part, what there had been of it, was gone. He wanted her again, wanted her kisses, her soft, little body, her abandonment, all her quick, warm, pagan emotion; wanted the wonderful feeling of that night under the moon-lit apple boughs; wanted it all with a horrible intensity, as the faun wants the nymph. The quick chatter of the little bright trout-stream, the dazzle of the buttercups, the rocks of the old " wild men"; the calling of the cuckoos and yaffles, the hooting of the owls; and the red moon peeping out of the velvet dark at the living whiteness of the blossom; and her face just out of reach at the window, lost in its love-look; and her heart against his, her lips answering his, under the apple tree—all this besieged him. Yet he lay inert. What was it which struggled against pity and this feverish longing, and kept him there paralysed in the warm sand? Three flaxen heads—a fair face with friendly blue-grey eyes, a slim hand pressing his, a quick voice speaking his name—" So you do believe in being good? " Yes, and a sort of atmosphere as of some old walled-in English garden, with pinks, and corn-flowers, and roses, and scents of lavender and lilac—cool and fair, untouched, almost holy—all that he had been brought up to feel was clean and good. And suddenly he thought: ' She might come along the front again and see me!' and he got up and made his way to the rock at the far end of the beach. There, with the spray biting into his face, he could think more coolly. To go back to the farm and love Megan out in the woods, among the rocks, with everything around wild and fitting—that, he knew, was impossible, utterly. To transplant her to a great town, to keep, in some little flat or rooms, one who belonged so wholly to Nature—the poet in him shrank from it. His passion would be a mere sensuous revel, soon gone; in London, her very simplicity, her lack of all intellectual quality, would make her his secret plaything— nothing else. The longer he sat on the rock, with his feet dangling over a greenish pool from which the sea was ebbing, the more clearly he saw this; but it was as if her arms and all of her were slipping slowly, slowly down from him, into the pool, to be carried away out to sea; and her face looking up, her lost face with beseeching eyes, and dark, wet hair—possessed, haunted, tortured him! He got up at last, scaled the low rock-cliff, and made his way down into a sheltered cove. Perhaps in the sea he could get back his control—lose this fever! And stripping off his clothes, he swam out. He wanted to tire himself so that nothing mattered, and swam recklessly, fast and far; then suddenly, for no reason, felt afraid. Suppose he could not reach shore again—suppose the current set him out—or he got cramp, like Halliday! He turned to swim in. The red cliffs looked a long way off. If he were drowned they would find his clothes. The Hallidays would know; but Megan perhaps never—they took no newspaper at the farm. And Phil Halliday's words came back to him again: "A girl at Cambridge I might have—— Glad I haven't got her on my mind!" And in that moment of unreasoning fear he vowed he would not have her on his mind. Then his fear left him; he swam in easily enough, dried himself in the sun, and put on his clothes. His heart felt sore, but no longer ached; his body cool and refreshed.

When one is as young as Ashurst, pity is not a violent emotion. And, back in the Halliday's sitting-room, eating a ravenous tea, he felt much like a man recovered from fever. Everything seemed new and clear; the tea, the buttered toast and jam tasted absurdly good; tobacco had never smelt so nice. And walking up and down the empty room, he stopped here and there to touch or look. He took up Stella's work-basket, fingered the cotton reels and a gaily-coloured plait of sewing silks, smelt at the little bag filled with woodroffe she kept among them. He sat down at the piano, playing tunes with one finger, thinking: 'To-night she'll play; I shall watch her while she's playing; it does me good to watch her.' He took up the book, which still lay where she had placed it beside him, and tried to read. But Megan's little, sad figure began to come back at once, and he got up and leaned in the window, listening to the thrushes in the Crescent gardens, gazing at the sea, dreamy and blue below the trees. A servant came in and cleared the tea away, and he still stood, inhaling the evening air, trying not to think. Then he saw the Hallidays coming through the gate of the Crescent, Stella a little in front of Phil and the children, with their baskets, and instinctively he drew back. His heart, too sore and discomfited, shrank from this encounter, yet wanted its friendly solace—bore a grudge against this influence, yet craved its cool innocence, and the pleasure of watching Stella's face. From against the wall behind the piano he saw her come in and stand looking a little blank as though disappointed; then she saw him and smiled, a swift, brilliant smile which warmed yet irritated Ashurst.

"You never came after us, Frank."

"No; I found I couldn't."

"Look! We picked such lovely late violets!" She held out a bunch. Ashurst put his nose to them, and there stirred within him vague longings, chilled instantly by a vision of Megan's anxious face lifted to the faces of the passers-by.

He said shortly: "How jolly!" and turned away. He went up to his room, and, avoiding the children, who were coming up the stairs, threw himself on his bed, and lay there with his arms crossed over his face. Now that he felt the die really cast, and Megan given up, he hated himself, and almost hated the Hallidays and their atmosphere of healthy, happy English homes. Why should they have chanced here, to drive away first love—to show him that he was going to be no better than a common seducer? What right had Stella, with her fair, shy beauty, to make him know for certain that he would never marry Megan; and, tarnishing it all, bring him such bitterness of regretful longing and such pity? Megan would be back by now, worn out by her miserable seeking—poor little thing!— expecting, perhaps, to find him there when she reached home. Ashurst bit at his sleeve, to stifle a groan of remorseful longing. He went to dinner glum and silent, and his mood threw a dinge even over the children. It was a melancholy, rather ill-tempered evening, for they were all tired; several times he caught Stella looking at him with a hurt, puzzled expression, and this pleased his evil mood. He slept miserably; got up

quite early, and wandered out. He went down to the beach.
Alone there with the serene, the blue, the sunlit sea, his heart
relaxed a little. Conceited fool—to think that Megan would
take it so hard! In a week or two she would almost have forgotten! And he—well, he would have the reward of virtue!
A good young man! If Stella knew, she would give him her
blessing for resisting that devil she believed in; and he uttered
a hard laugh. But slowly the peace and beauty of sea and sky,
the flight of the lonely seagulls, made him feel ashamed. He
bathed, and turned homewards.

In the Crescent gardens Stella herself was sitting on a camp
stool, sketching. He stole up close behind. How fair and pretty
she was, bent diligently, holding up her brush, measuring,
wrinkling her brows.

He said gently:

" Sorry I was such a beast last night, Stella."

She turned round, startled, flushed very pink, and said in
her quick way:

" It's all right. I knew there was something. Between friends
it doesn't matter, does it ? "

Ashurst answered:

" Between friends—and we are, aren't we ? "

She looked up at him, nodded vehemently, and her upper
teeth gleamed again in that swift, brilliant smile.

Three days later he went back to London, travelling with
the Hallidays. He had not written to the farm. What was
there he could say?

On the last day of April in the following year he and Stella
were married. . . .

Such were Ashurst's memories, sitting against the wall among
the gorse, on his silver-wedding day. At this very spot, where
he had laid out the lunch, Megan must have stood outlined
against the sky when he had first caught sight of her. Of
all queer coincidences! And there moved in him a longing to
go down and see again the farm and the orchard, and the
meadow of the gipsy bogle. It would not take long; Stella
would be an hour yet, perhaps.

How well he remembered it all—the little crowning group
of pine trees, the steep-up grass hill behind! He paused at the
farm gate. The low stone house, the yew-tree porch, the flowering currants—not changed a bit; even the old green chair was

out there on the grass under the window, where he had reached
up to her that night to take the key. Then he turned down
the lane, and stood leaning on the orchard gate—grey skeleton
of a gate, as then. A black pig even was wandering in there
among the trees. Was it true that twenty-six years had passed,
or had he dreamed and awakened to find Megan waiting for
him by the big apple tree? Unconsciously he put up his hand
to his grizzled beard and brought himself back to reality. Opening the gate, he made his way down through the docks and
nettles till he came to the edge, and the old apple tree itself.
Unchanged! A little more of the grey-green lichen, a dead
branch or two, and for the rest it might have been only last
night that he had embraced that mossy trunk after Megan's
flight and inhaled its woody savour, while above his head the
moonlit blossom had seemed to breathe and live. In that early
spring a few buds were showing already; the blackbirds shouting their songs, a cuckoo calling, the sunlight bright and warm.
Incredibly the same—the chattering trout-stream, the narrow
pool he had lain in every morning, splashing the water over his
flanks and chest; and out there in the wild meadow the beech
clump and the stone where the gipsy bogle was supposed to sit.
And an ache for lost youth, a hankering, a sense of wasted love
and sweetness, gripped Ashurst by the throat. Surely, on this
earth of such wild beauty, one was meant to hold rapture to
one's heart, as this earth and sky held it! And yet, one could
not!

He went to the edge of the stream, and looking down at the
little pool, thought: ' Youth and spring! What has become
of them all, I wonder?' And then, in sudden fear of having
this memory jarred by human encounter, he went back to the
lane, and pensively retraced his steps to the cross-roads.

Beside the car an old, grey-bearded labourer was leaning on
a stick, talking to the chauffeur. He broke off at once, as
though guilty of disrespect, and touching his hat, prepared to
limp on down the lane.

Ashurst pointed to the narrow green mound. " Can you tell
me what this is? "

The old fellow stopped; on his face had come a look as
though he were thinking: ' You've come to the right shop,
mister!'

" 'Tes a grave," he said.

" But why out here? "

The old man smiled. "That's a tale, as yu may say. An' not the first time as I've a-told et—there's plenty folks asks 'bout that bit o' turf. 'Maid's Grave' us calls et, 'ereabouts."

Ashurst held out his pouch. "Have a fill?"

The old man touched his hat again, and slowly filled an old clay pipe. His eyes, looking upward out of a mass of wrinkles and hair, were still quite bright.

"If yu don' mind, zurr, I'll zet down—my leg's 'urtin' a bit to-day." And he sat down on the mound of turf.

"There's always a vlower on this grave. An' 'tain't so very lonesome, neither; brave lot o' folks goes by now, in they new motor cars an' things—not as 'twas in th' old days. She've a-got company up 'ere. 'Twas a poor soul killed 'erself."

"I see!" said Ashurst. "Cross-roads burial. I didn't know that custom was kept up."

"Ah! but 'twas a main long time ago. Us 'ad a parson as was very God-fearin' then. Let me see, I've 'ad my pension six year come Michaelmas, an' I were just on fifty when t'appened. There's none livin' knows more about et than what I du. She belonged close 'ere; same farm as where I used to work along o' Mrs. Narracombe—'tes Nick Narracombe's now; I dus a bit for 'im still, odd times."

Ashurst, who was leaning against the gate, lighting his pipe, left his curved hands before his face for long after the flame of the match had gone out.

"Yes?" he said, and to himself his voice sounded hoarse and queer.

"She was one in an 'underd, poor maid! I putts a vlower 'ere every time I passes. Pretty maid an' gude maid she was, though they wouldn't burry 'er up tu th' church, nor where she wanted to be burried neither." The old labourer paused, and put his hairy, twisted hand flat down on the turf beside the bluebells.

"Yes?" said Ashurst.

"In a manner of speakin'," the old man went on, "I think as 'twas a love-story—though there's no one never knu for zartin. Yu can't tell what's in a maid's 'ead—but that's wot I think about it." He drew his hand along the turf. "I was fond o' that maid—don' know as there was anyone as wasn' fond of 'er. But she was tu lovin'-'earted—that's where 'twas, I think." He looked up. And Ashurst, whose lips were trembling in the cover of his beard, murmured again: "Yes?"

" 'Twas in the spring, 'bout now as't might be, or a little later—blossom time—an' we 'ad one o' they young college gentlemen stayin' at the farm—nice feller tu, with 'is 'ead in the air. I liked 'e very well, an' I never see nothin' between 'em, but to my thinkin' e' turned the maid's fancy." The old man took the pipe out of his mouth, spat, and went on:

" Yu see, 'e went away sudden one day, an' never come back. They got 'is knapsack and bits o' things down there still. That's what stuck in my mind—'is never sendin' for 'em. 'Is name was Ashes, or somethin' like that."

" Yes? " said Ashurst once more.

The old man licked his lips.

" 'Er never said nothin', but from that day 'er went kind of dazed lukin'; didn' seem rightly therr at all. I never knu a 'uman creature so changed in me life—never. There was another young feller at the farm—Joe Biddaford 'is name wer', that was praaperly sweet on 'er, tu; I guess 'e used to plague 'er wi' 'is attentions. She got to luke quite wild. I'd zee her sometimes of an avenin' when I was bringin' up the calves; ther' she'd stand in th' orchard, under the big apple tree, lukin' straight before 'er. ' Well,' I used t'think, ' I dunno what 'tes that's the matter wi' yu, but yu'm lukin' pittiful, that yu be ! ' "

The old man relit his pipe, and sucked at it reflectively.

" Yes? " said Ashurst.

" I remembers one day I said to 'er; ' What's the matter, Megan? '—'er name was Megan David, she come from Wales same as 'er aunt, ol' Missis Narracombe. ' Yu'm frettin' about something,' I says. ' No, Jim,' she says, ' I'm not frettin'.' ' Yes, yu be ! ' I says. ' No,' she says, and tu tears cam' rollin' out. ' Yu'm cryin'—what's that, then ? ' I says. She putts 'er 'and over 'er 'eart: ' It 'urts me,' she says; ' but 'twill sune be better,' she says. ' But if anything shude 'appen to me, Jim, I wants to be burried under this 'ere apple tree.' I laughed. ' What's goin' to 'appen to yu ? ' I says: ' don't 'ee be fulish.' ' No,' she says, ' I won't be fulish.' Well, I know what maids are, an' I never thought no more about et, till tu days arter that, 'bout six in the avenin' I was comin' up wi' the calves, when I see somethin' dark lyin' in the strame, close to that big apple tree. I says to meself: ' Is that a pig—funny place for a pig to get to ! ' an' I goes up to et, an' I see what 'twas."

The old man stopped: his eyes, turned upward, had a bright, suffering look.

" 'Twas the maid, in a little narrer pool ther' that's made by the stoppin' of a rock—where I see the young gentleman bathin' once or twice. 'Er was lyin' on 'er face in the watter. There was a plant o' goldie-cups growin' out o' the stone just above 'er 'ead. An' when I come to luke at 'er face, 'twas luvly, buitful, so calm's a baby's—wonderful butiful et was. When the doctor saw 'er, 'e said: ' 'Er culdn' never a-done it in that little bit o' watter ef 'er 'adn't a-been in an extarsy.' Ah! an' judgin' from 'er face, that was just 'ow she was. Et made me cry praaper—butiful et was! 'Twas June then, but she'd a-found a little bit of apple-blossom left over somewheres, and stuck et in 'er 'air. That's why I thinks 'er must a-been in an extarsy, to go to et gay, like that. Why! there wasn't more than a fute and 'arf o' watter. But I tell 'ee one thing—that meadder's 'arnted; I knu et, an' she knu et; an' no one'll per-suade me as 'tesn't. I told 'em what she said to me 'bout bein' burried under th' apple tree. But I think that turned 'em—made et luke tu much 's ef she'd 'ad it in 'er mind deliberate; an' so they burried 'er up 'ere. Parson we 'ad then was very particular, 'e was."

Again the old man drew his hand over the turf.

" 'Tes wonderful, et seems," he added slowly, " what maids 'll du for love. She 'ad a lovin' 'eart; I guess 'twas broken. But us never *knu* nothin'! "

He looked up as if for approval of his story, but Ashurst had walked past him as if he were not there.

Up on the top of the hill, beyond where he had spread the lunch, over, out of sight, he lay down on his face. So had his virtue been rewarded, and "the Cyprian," goddess of love, taken her revenge! And before his eyes, dim with tears, came Megan's face with the sprig of apple blossoms in her dark, wet hair. 'What did I do that was wrong?' he thought. 'What did I do?' But he could not answer. Spring, with its rush of passion, its flowers and song—the spring in his heart and Megan's! Was it just Love seeking a victim! The Greek was right, then—the words of the " Hippolytus " as true to-day!

> " For mad is the heart of Love,
> And gold the gleam of his wing;
> And all to the spell thereof
> Bend when he makes his spring.
> All life that is wild and young

In mountain and wave and stream,
All that of earth is sprung,
Or breathes in the red sunbeam;
Yea, and Mankind. O'er all a royal throne
Cyprian, Cyprian, is thine alone!"

The Greek was right! Megan! Poor little Megan—coming over the hill! Megan under the old apple tree waiting and looking! Megan dead, with beauty printed on her! . . .

A voice said:

"Oh, there you are! Look."

Ashurst rose, took his wife's sketch, and stared at it in silence.

"Is the foreground right, Frank?"

"Yes."

"But there's something wanting, isn't there?"

Ashurst nodded. Wanting? The apple tree, the singing, and the gold!

1916.

THE PRISONER

On a fine day of early summer in a London garden, before the birds had lost their spring song, or the trees dropped their last blossoms, our friend said suddenly:

"Why! there's a goldfinch!" Blackbirds there were, and thrushes, and tits in plenty, an owl at night, and a Christopher Columbus of a cuckoo, who solemnly, once a year, mistook this green island of trees for the main lands of Kent and Surrey, but a goldfinch—never!

"I hear it—over there!" he said again, and, getting up, he walked towards the house.

When he came back, our friend sat down again, and observed:

"I didn't know that you kept a cage-bird!" We admitted that our cook had a canary.

"A mule!" he remarked, very shortly.

Some strong feeling had evidently been aroused in him that neither of us could understand.

Suddenly he burst out:

"I can't bear things in cages; animals, birds, or men. I hate to see or think of them." And looking at us angrily, as though we had taken an advantage in drawing from him this confession, he went on quickly:

"I was staying in a German town some years ago, with a friend who was making inquiries into social matters. He asked me one day to go over a prison with him. I had never seen one, then, and I agreed. It was just such a day as this—a perfectly clear sky, and there was that cool, dancing sparkle on everything that you only see in some parts of Germany. This prison, which stood in the middle of the town, was one of those shaped like a star that have been built over there on the plan of Pentonville. The system, they told us, was the same that you might have seen working here many years ago. The Germans were then, and still, no doubt, are, infatuated with the idea of muring their prisoners up in complete solitude.

315

But it was a new toy to them then, and they were enjoying
it with that sort of fanatical thoroughness which the Germans
give to everything they take up. I don't want to describe this
prison, or what we saw in it; as far as an institution run on
such dreadful lines can be, it was, I daresay, well managed;
the Governor, at all events, impressed me favourably. I'll simply tell you of the one thing which I shall never forget, because it symbolized to me for ever the caging of all creatures,
animal or human, great or small."

Our friend paused; then, with an added irritation in his
voice, as though aware of doing violence to his natural reserve,
he went on:

"We had been all over the grizzly place when the Governor
asked my friend whether he would like to see one or two of the
'life' prisoners.

"'I will show you one,' he said, 'who has been here twenty-
seven years. He is, you will understand'—I remember his very
words—'a little worn by his long confinement.' While we
were going towards this prisoner's cell, they told us his story.
He had been a cabinet-maker's assistant, and when still quite
a boy, joined a gang of burglars to rob his own employer. Surprised during the robbery, he had blindly struck out and killed
his employer on the spot. He was sentenced to death, but, on
the intervention of some Royalty who had been upset by the
sight of corpses, I believe at the Battle of Sadowa, his sentence
was commuted to imprisonment for life.

"When we entered his cell he was standing perfectly still,
gazing at his work. He looked quite sixty, though he could not
have been more than forty-six—a bent, trembling ruin of a
figure, covered by a drab-coloured apron. His face had the
mealy hue and texture of all prisoners' faces. He seemed to
have no features; his cheeks were hollow; his eyes large, but,
looking back, I can't remember their colour—if, indeed, they
had colour in them at all. As we passed in, one by one, through
the iron door, he took off his round cap, drab-coloured too, like
everything about him, showing his dusty, nearly bald head, with
a few short grey hairs on end, and stood in an attitude of 'attention,' humbly staring at us. He was like an owl surprised
by daylight. Have you ever seen a little child ill for the first
time—full of bewilderment at its own suffering? His face was
like that, but so extraordinarily gentle! We had seen many
of the prisoners, and he was the only one that had that awful

gentleness. The sound of his voice, too: '*Ja, Herr Direktor—nein, Herr Direktor!*' soft and despairing—I remember it now—there was not a breath of will-power left. Our friend paused, frowning in his effort to re-create the scene. "He held in his hand," he went on presently, "a sheet of stiff paper, on which he had been transcribing the New Testament in letters from a code of writing for the deaf and dumb. When he passed his thin fingers over the type to show us how easily the deaf and dumb could read it, you could see that his hands were dusty like a miller's. There was nothing in the cell to produce that dust, and in my belief it was not dust on his hands, but some excretion from that human plant running to seed. When he held the sheet of paper up, too, it trembled like the wing of an insect. One of us asked who invented the system he was working at, mentioning some name. '*Nein, nein,*' he said, and he stood shivering with eagerness to recollect the right name. At last he dropped his head, and mumbled out: '*Ah, Herr Direktor, ich kann nicht!*' Then all of a sudden the name came bursting from his lips. At that moment, for the first time, he actually looked like a man. I never before then realised the value of freedom; the real meaning of our relations with other human beings; the necessity for the mind's being burnished from minute to minute by sights and sounds, by the need for remembering and using what we remember. This fellow, you see, had no use for memory in his life; he was like a plant placed where no dew can possibly fall on it. To watch that look pass over his face at the mere remembrance of a name was like catching sight of a tiny scrap of green leaf left in the heart of a withered shrub. Man, I tell you, is wonderful —the most enduring creature that has ever been produced!" Our friend rose and began pacing up and down. "His world was not a large one; about fourteen feet by eight. He'd lived in it for twenty-seven years, without a mouse even for a friend. They do things thoroughly in prisons. Think of the tremendous vital force that must go to the making of the human organism, for a man to live through that. . . . What do you imagine," he went on, turning to us suddenly, "kept even a remnant of his reason alive?—Well, I'll tell you: While we were still looking at his ' deaf and dumb' writing, he suddenly handed us a piece of wood about the size of a large photograph. It was the picture of a young girl, seated in the very centre of a garden, with bright-coloured flowers in her hand;

in the background was a narrow, twisting stream with some
rushes, and a queer bird, rather like a raven, standing on the
bank. And by the side of the girl a tree with large hanging
fruits, strangely symmetrical, unlike any tree that ever grew,
yet with something in it that is in all trees—a look as if they
had spirits, and were the friends of man. The girl was staring
straight at us and with perfectly round, blue eyes, and the flowers
she held in her hand seemed also to stare at us. The whole
picture, it appeared to me, was full of—what shall I say?—a
kind of wonder. It had all the crude colour and drawing of an
early Italian painting, the same look of difficulty conquered by
sheer devotion. One of us asked him if he had learnt to draw
before his imprisonment, but the poor fellow misunderstood the
question. ' Nein, nein,' he said, ' the Herr Direktor knows I
had no model. It is a fancy picture! ' And the smile he gave
us would have made a devil weep! He had put into that picture all that his soul longed for—woman, flowers, birds, trees,
blue sky, running water; and all the wonder of his spirit that
he was cut off from them. He had been at work on it, they
said, for eighteen years, destroying and repeating, until he had
produced this, the hundredth version. It was a masterpiece.
Yes, there he had been for twenty-seven years, condemned for
life to this living death—without scent, sight, hearing, or touch
of any natural object, without even the memory of them, evolv-
ing from his starved soul this vision of a young girl with eyes
full of wonder, and flowers in her hand. It's the greatest triumph of the human spirit, and the greatest testimony to the
power of Art that I have ever seen."

Our friend uttered a short laugh: " So thick-skinned, however, is a man's mind that I didn't even then grasp the agony
of that man's life. But I did later. I happened to see his
eyes as he was trying to answer some question of the Governor's about his health. To my dying day I shall never forget them. They were incarnate tragedy—all those eternities
of solitude and silence he had lived through, all the eternities
he had still to live through before they buried him in the graveyard outside, were staring out of them. They had more sheer
pitiful misery in them than all the eyes put together of all the
free men I've ever seen. I couldn't stand the sight of them,
and hurried out of the cell. I felt then, and ever since, what
they say the Russians feel—for all their lapses into savagery—
the sacredness of suffering. I felt that we ought all of us to

have bowed down before him; that I, though I was free and righteous, was a charlatan and sinner in the face of that living crucifixion. Whatever crime he had committed—I don't care what it was—that poor lost creature had been so sinned against that I was as dirt beneath his feet. When I think of him— there still, for all I know—I feel a sort of frenzy rising in me against my own kind. I feel the miserable aching of all the caged creatures in the world."

Our friend turned his head away, and for quite a minute did not speak. "On our way back, I remember," he said at last, "we drove through the Stadt Park. There it was free and light enough; every kind of tree—limes, copper beeches, oaks, syca- mores, poplars, birches, and apple trees in blossom, were giving out their scent; every branch and leaf was glistening with hap- piness. The place was full of birds, the symbols of freedom, fluttering about, singing their loudest in the sun. Yes, it was all enchanted ground. And I well remember thinking that in the whole range of Nature only men and spiders torture other creatures in that long-drawn-out kind of way; and only men do it in cold blood to their own species. So far as I know that's a fact of natural history; and I can tell you that to see, once for all, as I did, in that man's eyes, its unutterable misery, is never to feel the same towards your own kind again. That night I sat in a *café* window, listening to the music, the talk, the laughter, watching the people pass in the street—shop-folk, soldiers, merchants, officials, priests, beggars, aristocrats, women of pleasure, and the light streaming out from the windows, and the leaves just moving against the most wonderful, dark blue sky. But I saw and heard nothing of it all. I only saw the gentle, mealy-coloured face of that poor fellow, his eyes, and his dusty, trembling hands, and I saw the picture that he had painted there in hell. I've seen it ever since, whenever I see or hear of any sort of solitary caged creature."

Our friend ceased speaking, and very soon after he rose, ex- cused himself, and went away.

1909.

A SIMPLE TALE

TALKING of anti-Semitism one of those mornings, Ferrand said in his good French: "Yes, *monsieur,* plenty of those gentlemen in these days esteem themselves Christian, but I have only once met a Christian who esteemed himself a Jew. *C'était très drôle—je vais vous conter cela.*

"It was one autumn in London, and, the season being over, I was naturally in poverty, inhabiting a palace in Westminster at fourpence the night. In the next bed to me that time there was an old gentleman, so thin that one might truly say he was made of air. English, Scotch, Irish, Welsh—I shall never learn to distinguish those little differences in your race—but I well think he was English. Very feeble, very frail, white as paper, with a long grey beard, and caves in the cheeks, and speaking always softly, as if to a woman. . . . For me it was an experience to see an individual so gentle in a palace like that. His bed and bowl of broth he gained in sweeping out the kennels of all those sorts of types who come to sleep there every night. There he spent all his day long, going out only at ten hours and a half every night, and returning at midnight less one quarter. Since I had not much to do, it was always a pleasure for me to talk with him; for, though he was certainly a little *toqué,*" and Ferrand tapped his temple, "he had great charm of an old man, never thinking of himself no more than a fly that turns in dancing all day beneath a ceiling. If there was something he could do for one of those specimens— to sew on a button, clean a pipe, catch beasts in their clothes, or sit to see they were not stolen, even to give up his place by the fire—he would always do it with his smile so white and gentle; and in his leisure he would read the Holy Book! He inspired in me a sort of affection—there are not too many old men so kind and gentle as that, even when they are 'crackey,' as you call it. Several times I have caught him in washing the feet of one of those sots, or bathing some black eye or other, sure as they often catch—a man of a spiritual refinement really re-

321

markable; in clothes also so refined that one sometimes saw
his skin. Though he had never great thing to say, he heard you
like an angel, and spoke evil of no one; but, seeing that he had
no more vigour than a swallow, it piqued me much how he
would go out like that every night in all the weathers at the
same hour for so long a promenade of the streets. And when
I interrogated him on this, he would only smile his smile of
one not there, and did not seem to know very much of what
I was talking. I said to myself: ' There is something here to
see, if I am not mistaken. One of these good days I shall be
your guardian angel while you fly the night.' For I am a
connoisseur of strange things, *monsieur,* as you know; though,
you may well imagine, being in the streets all day long between two boards of a sacred sandwich does not give you too
strong a desire to *flâner* in the evenings. *Eh, bien!* It was
a night in late October that I at last pursued him. He was
not difficult to follow, seeing he had no more guile than an egg;
passing first at his walk of an old shadow into your St. James's
Park, along where your military types puff out their chests for
the nursemaids to admire. Very slowly he went, leaning on a
staff—*une canne de promenade* such as I have never seen, nearly six feet high, with an end like a shepherd's crook or the handle
of a sword, a thing truly to make the *gamins* laugh—even me
it made to smile, though I am not too well accustomed to mock
at age and poverty, to watch him march in leaning on that cane.
I remember that night—very beautiful, the sky of a clear dark,
the stars as bright as they can ever be in these towns of our
high civilisation, and the leaf-shadows of the plane-trees, colour
of grapes on the pavement, so that one had not the heart to put
foot on them. One of those evenings when the spirit is light,
and policemen a little dreamy and well-wishing. Well, as I
tell you, my Old marched, never looking behind him, like a man
who walks in sleep. By that big church—which, like all those
places, had its air of coldness, far and ungrateful among us
others, little human creatures who have built it—he passed,
into the great Eaton Square, whose houses ought well to be inhabited by people very rich. There he crossed to lean against
the railings of the garden in the centre, very tranquil, his long
white beard falling over hands joined on his staff, in awaiting
what—I could not figure to myself at all. It was the hour
when your high *bourgeoisie* return from the theatre in their
carriages, whose manikins sit, the arms crossed, above horses

fat as snails. And one would see through the window some
lady *bercée doucement,* with the face of one who has eaten too
much and loved too little. And gentlemen passed me, marching for a mouthful of fresh air, *très comme il faut,* their concertina hats pushed up, and nothing at all in their eyes. I
remarked my Old, who, making no movement, watched them all
as they went by, till presently a carriage stopped at a house
nearly opposite. At once, then, he began to cross the road
quickly, carrying his great stick. I observed the lackey pulling
the bell and opening the carriage door, and three people coming
forth—a man, a woman, a young man. Very high *bourgeoisie,*
some judge, knight, mayor—what do I know?—with his wife
and son, mounting under the porch. My Old had come to the
bottom of the steps, and spoke, in bending himself forward, as
if supplicating. At once those three turned their faces, very
astonished. Although I was very intrigued, I could not hear
what he was saying, for, if I came nearer, I feared he would
see me spying on him. Only the sound of his voice I heard,
gentle as always; and his hand I saw wiping his forehead, as
though he had carried something heavy from very far. Then
the lady spoke to her husband, and went into the house, and
the young son followed in lighting a cigarette. There rested
only that good father of the family, with his grey whiskers
and nose a little bent, carrying an expression as if my Old were
making him ridiculous. He made a quick gesture, as though
he said, ' Go! ' then he too fled softly. The door was shut. At
once the lackey mounted, the carriage drove away, and all was
as if it had never been, except that my Old was standing there,
quite still. But soon he came returning, carrying his staff as if
it burdened him. And recoiling in a porch to see him pass I
saw his visage full of dolour, of one overwhelmed with fatigue
and grief; so that I felt my heart squeeze me. I must well
confess, *monsieur,* I was a little shocked to see this old sainted
father asking, as it seemed, for alms. That is a thing I myself have never done, not even in the greatest poverty—one is
not like your ' gentlemen '—one does always some little thing
for the money he receives, if it is only to show a drunken man
where he lives. And I returned in meditating deeply over this
problem, which well seemed to me fit for the angels to examine;
and knowing what time my Old was always re-entering, I took
care to be in my bed before him. He came in as ever, treading
softly so as not to wake us others, and his face had again its

serenity, a little ' crackey.' As you may well have remarked,
monsieur, I am not one of those individuals who let everything
grow under the nose without pulling them up to see how they
are made. For me the greatest pleasure is to lift the skirts of
life, to unveil what there is under the surface of things which
are not always what they seem, as says your good little poet.
For that one must have philosophy, and a certain industry,
lacking to all those gentlemen who think they alone are in-
dustrious because they sit in chairs and blow into the telephone
all day, in filling their pockets with money. Myself, I coin
knowledge of the heart—it is the only gold they cannot take
from you. So that night I lay awake. I was not content with
what I had seen; for I could not imagine why this old man,
so unselfish, so like a saint in thinking ever of others, should
go thus every night to beg, when he had always in this palace
his bed, and that with which to keep his soul within his rags.
Certainly we all have our vices, and gentlemen the most revered
do, in secret, things they would cough to see others doing; but
that business of begging seemed scarcely in his character of
an old altruist—for in my experience, *monsieur*, beggars are
not less egoist than millionaires. As I say, it piqued me much,
and I resolved to follow him again. The second night was of
the most different. There was a great wind, and white clouds
flying in the moonlight. He commenced his pilgrimage in passing by your House of Commons, as if toward the river. I like
much that great river of yours. There is in its career something
of very grand; it ought to know many things, although it is so
silent, and gives to no one the secrets which are confided to it.
He had for objective, it seemed, that long row of houses very
respectable, which gives on the Embankment, before you arrive
at Chelsea. It was painful to see the poor Old, bending almost
double against that great wind coming from the west. Not too
many carriages down here, and few people—a true wilderness,
lighted by tall lamps which threw no shadows, so clear was the
moon. He took his part soon, as of the other night, standing
on the far side of the road, watching for the return of some
lion to his den. And presently I saw one coming, accompanied
by three lionesses, all taller than himself. This one was bearded,
and carried spectacles—a real head of learning; walking, too,
with the step of a man who knows his world. Some professor
—I said to myself—with his harem. They gained their house
at fifty paces from my Old; and, while this learned one was open-

ing the door, the three ladies lifted their noses in looking at
the moon. A little of æsthetic, a little of science—as always
with that type there! At once I had perceived my Old coming
across, blown by the wind like a grey stalk of thistle; and his
face, with its expression of infinite pain as if carrying the
sufferings of the world. At the moment they see him those
three ladies drop their noses and fly within the house as if he
were the pestilence, in crying, 'Henry!' And out comes my
monsieur again, in his beard and spectacles. For me, I would
freely have given my ears to hear, but I saw that this good
Henry had his eye on me, and I did not budge, for fear to
seem in conspiracy. I heard him only say: 'Impossible! Impossible! Go to the proper place!' and he shut the door. My
Old remained, with his long staff resting on a shoulder bent as
if that stick were of lead. And presently he commenced to
march again whence he had come, curved and trembling, the
very shadow of a man, passing me, too, as if I were the air.
That time also I regained my bed before him, in meditating
very deeply, still more uncertain of the psychology of this affair, and resolved once again to follow him, saying to myself:
'This time I shall run all risks to hear.' There are two kinds
of men in this world, *monsieur*—one who will not rest content till he has become master of all the toys that make a fat
existence—in never looking to see of what they are made; and
the other, for whom life is tobacco and a crust of bread, and
liberty to take all to pieces, so that his spirit may feel good
within him. Frankly, I am of that kind. I rest never till I
have found out why this is that; for me mystery is the salt of
life, and I must well eat of it. I put myself again, then, to
following him the next night. This time he traversed those
little dirty streets of your great Westminster where all is mixed
in a true pudding of lords and poor wretches at two sous the
dozen; of cats and policemen; kerosene flames, abbeys, and the
odour of fried fish. Ah! truly it is frightful to see your low
streets in London; that gives me a conviction of hopelessness
such as I have never caught elsewhere; piquant, too, to find
them so near to that great House which sets example of good
government to all the world. There is an irony so ferocious
there, *monsieur,* that one can well hear the good God of your
bourgeois laugh in every wheel that rolls, and the cry of each
cabbage that is sold; and see him smile in the smoky light of
every flare, and in the candles of your cathedral, in saying to

himself: 'I have well made this world. Is there not variety here?—*en voilà une bonne soupe!*' This time, however, I attended my Old like his very shadow, and could hear him sighing as he marched, as if he also found the atmosphere of those streets too strong. But all of a sudden he turned a corner, and we were in the most quiet, most beautiful little street I have seen in all your London. It was of small, old houses, very regular, which made as if they inclined themselves in their two rows before a great church at the end, grey in the moonlight, like a mother. There was no one in the street, and no more cover than hair on the head of a pope. But I had some confidence now that my Old would not remark me standing there so close, since in these pilgrimages he seemed to remark nothing. Leaning on his staff, I tell you he had the air of an old bird in a desert, reposing on one leg by a dry pool, his soul looking for water. It gave me that notion one has sometimes in watching the rare spectacles of life—that sentiment which, according to me, pricks artists to their work. We had not stayed there too long before I saw a couple marching from the end of the street, and thought: 'Here they come to their nest.' Vigorous and gay they were, young married ones, eager to get home; one could see the white neck of the young wife, the white shirt of the young man, gleaming under their cloaks. I know them well, those young couples in great cities, without a care, taking all things, the world before them, *très amoureux,* without, as yet, children; jolly and pathetic, having life still to learn—which, believe me, *monsieur,* is a sad enough affair for nine rabbits out of ten. They stopped at the house next to where I stood; and, since my Old was coming fast as always to the feast, I put myself at once to the appearance of ringing the bell of the house before me. This time I had well the chance of hearing. I could see, too, the faces of all three, because I have by now the habit of seeing out of the back hair. The pigeons were so anxious to get to their nest that my Old had only time to speak, as they were in train to vanish. ' Sir, let me rest in your doorway!' *Monsieur,* I have never seen a face so hopeless, so cribbled with fatigue, yet so full of a gentle dignity as that of my Old while he spoke those words. It was as if something looked from his visage surpassing what belongs to us others, so mortal and so cynic as human life must well render all who dwell in this earthly paradise. He held his long staff upon one shoulder, and I had the idea, sinister enough, that it was crush-

ing his body of a spectre down into the pavement. I know not
how the impression came, but it seemed to me that this devil
of a stick had the nature of a heavy cross reposing on his shoulder; I had pain to prevent myself turning, to find if in truth
'I had them,' as your drunkards say. Then the young man
called out: 'Here's a shilling for you, my friend!' But my
Old did not budge, answering always: 'Sir, let me rest in
your doorway!' As you may well imagine, *monsieur,* we were
all in the silence of astonishment, I pulling away at my bell
next door, which was not ringing, seeing I took care it did
not; and those two young people regarding my Old with eyes
round as moons, out of their pigeon-house, which I could well
see was prettily feathered. Their hearts were making seesaw,
I could tell; for at that age one is still impressionable. Then
the girl put herself to whispering, and her husband said those
two words of your young 'gentlemen,' 'Awfully sorry!' and
put out his hand, which held now a coin large as a saucer.
But again my Old only said: 'Sir, let me rest in your doorway!' And the young man drew back his hand quickly as if he
were ashamed, and saying again, 'Sorry!' he shut the door. I
have heard many sighs in my time—they are the good little ac-
companiments to the song we sing, we others who are in poverty;
but the sigh my Old pushed then—how can I tell you?—had
an accent as if it came from Her, the faithful companion, who
marches in holding the hands of men and women so that they
may never make the grand mistake to imagine themselves for
a moment the good God. Yes, *monsieur,* it was as if pushed by
Suffering herself, that bird of the night, never tired of flying
in this world where they talk always of cutting her wings. Then
I took my resolution, and, coming gently from behind, said:
'My Old—what is it? Can I do anything for you?' Without looking at me, he spoke as to himself: 'I shall never find
one who will let me rest in his doorway. For my sin I shall
wander for ever!' At this moment, *monsieur,* there came to me
an inspiration so clear that I marvelled I had not already had
it a long time before. He thought himself the Wandering Jew!
I had well found it. This was certainly his fixed idea, of a
cracked old man! And I said: 'My Jew, do you know this?
In doing what you do, you have become as Christ, in a world
of wandering Jews!' But he did not seem to hear me, and only
just as we arrived at our palace became again that old gentle
being, thinking never of himself."

Behind the smoke of his cigarette a smile curled Ferrand's red lips under his long nose a little on one side.

"And, if you think of it, *monsieur,* it is well like that. Provided there exists always that good man of a Wandering Jew, he will certainly have become as Christ, in all these centuries of being refused from door to door. Yes, yes, he must well have acquired charity the most profound that this world has ever seen, in watching the crushing virtue of others. All those gentry, of whom he asks night by night to let him rest in their doorways, they tell him where to go, how to *ménager* his life, even offer him money, as I had seen; but, to let him rest, to trust him in their houses—this strange old man—as a fellow, a brother voyager—that they will not; it is hardly in the character of good citizens in a Christian country. And, as I have indicated to you, this Old of mine, cracked as he was, thinking himself that Jew who refused rest to the good Christ, had become, in being refused for ever, the most Christ-like man I have ever encountered on this earth, which, according to me, is composed almost entirely of those who have themselves the character of the Wandering Jew."

Puffing out a sigh of smoke, Ferrand added: "I do not know whether he continued to pursue his idea, for I myself took the road next morning, and I have never seen him since."

1914.

THE CONSUMMATION

ABOUT 1889 there lived in London a man named Harrison, of an amiable and perverse disposition. One morning, at Charing Cross Station, a lady in whom he was interested said to him:

"But Mr. Harrison, why don't you *write?* You are just the person!"

Harrison saw that he was, and at the end of two years had produced eleven short stories, with two of which he was not particularly pleased, but as he naturally did not like to waste them, he put them with the others and sent them all to a publisher. In the course of time he received from the publisher a letter saying that for a certain consideration or commission he would be prepared to undertake the risk of publishing these stories upon Harrison's incurring all the expenses. This pleased Harrison, who, feeling that no time should be wasted in making his "work" public, wrote desiring the publisher to put the matter in hand. The publisher replied to this with an estimate and an agreement, to which Harrison responded with a cheque. The publisher answered at once with a polite letter, suggesting that for Harrison's advantage a certain additional sum should be spent on advertisements. Harrison saw the point of this directly, and replied with another cheque—knowing that between gentlemen there could be no question of money.

In due time the book appeared. It was called "In the Track of the Stars," by Cuthbert Harrison; and within a fortnight Harrison began to receive reviews. He read them with an extraordinary pleasure, for they were full of discriminating flattery. One asked if he were a "Lancelot in disguise." Two Liberal papers described the stories as masterpieces; one compared them to the best things in Poe and de Maupassant; and another called him a second Rudyard Kipling. He was greatly encouraged, but, being by nature modest, he merely wrote to the publisher inquiring what he thought of a second edition. His publisher replied with an estimate, mentioning casually that he had already sold about four hundred copies. Harrison

referred to his cheque-book and saw that the first edition had
been a thousand copies. He replied, therefore, that he would
wait. He waited, and at the end of six months wrote again.
The publisher replied that he had now sold four hundred and
three copies, but that, as Mr. Harrison had at present an unknown name, he did not advise a second edition: there was no
market for short stories. These had, however, been so well received that he recommended Mr. Harrison to write a long story.
The book was without doubt a success, so far as a book of short
stories could ever be a success. . . . He sent Harrison a small
cheque, and a large number of reviews which Harrison had
already received.

Harrison decided not to have a second edition, but to rest
upon his *succés d'estime*. All his relations were extremely
pleased, and almost immediately he started writing his long
story. Now it happened that among Harrison's friends was
a man of genius, who sent Harrison a letter.

"I had no idea," he said, "that you could write like this;
of course, my dear fellow, the stories are not 'done'; there
is no doubt about it, they are *not* 'done.' But you have plenty
of time; you are young, and I see that you can do things. Come
down here and let us have a talk about what you are at now."

On receiving this Harrison wasted no time, but went down.
The man of genius, over a jug of claret-cup, on a summer's
afternoon, pointed out how the stories were not "done."

"They show a feeling for outside drama," said he, "but there
is none of the real drama of psychology."

Harrison showed him his reviews. He left the man of genius
on the following day with a certain sensation of soreness. In
the course of a few weeks, however, the soreness wore off, and
the words of the man of genius began to bear fruit, and at
the end of two months Harrison wrote:

"You are quite right—the stories were not 'done.' I think,
however, that I am now on the right path."

At the end of another year, after submitting it once or twice
to the man of genius, he finished his second book, and called
it "John Endacott." About this time he left off alluding to
his "work" and began to call his writings "stuff."

He sent it to the publisher with the request that he would
consider its publication on a royalty. In rather more than
the ordinary course of time the publisher replied, that in his
opinion (a lay one) "John Endacott" didn't quite fulfil the

remarkable promise of Mr. Harrison's first book; and, to show
Harrison his perfect honesty, he enclosed an extract from the
" reader's " opinion, which stated that Mr. Harrison had " fallen
between the stools of art and the British public." Much against
the publisher's personal feelings, therefore, the publisher considered that he could only undertake the risk in the then bad
condition of trade—if Mr. Harrison would guarantee the expenses.

Harrison hardened his heart, and replied that he was not prepared to guarantee the expenses. Upon which the publisher returned his manuscript, saying that in his opinion (a lay one)
Mr. Harrison was taking the wrong turning, which he (the
publisher) greatly regretted, for he had much appreciated the
pleasant relations which had always existed between them.

Harrison sent the book to a younger publisher, who accepted
it on a postponed royalty. It appeared.

At the end of three weeks Harrison began to receive reviews.
They were mixed. One complained that there was not enough
plot; another, fortunately by the same post, that there was too
much plot. The general tendency was to regret that the author
of " In the Track of the Stars " had not fulfilled the hopes
raised by his first book, in which he had shown such promise
of completely hitting the public taste. This might have depressed Harrison had he not received a letter from the man
of genius couched in these terms:

" My dear fellow, I am more pleased than I can say. I am
now more than ever convinced that you can do things."

Harrison at once began a third book.

Owing to the unfortunate postponement of his royalty he
did not receive anything from his second book. The publisher
sold three hundred copies. During the period (eighteen months)
that he was writing his third book the man of genius introduced
Harrison to a critic, with the words: " You may rely on his
judgment; the beggar is infallible."

While to the critic he said: " I tell you, this fellow can do
things."

The critic was good to Harrison, who, as before said, was
of an amiable disposition.

When he had finished his third book he dedicated it to the
man of genius and called it " Summer."

" My dear fellow," wrote the man of genius, when he received

his copy, "It is *good!* There is no more to be said about it;
it *is* good! I read it with indescribable pleasure."

On the same day Harrison received a letter from the critic
which contained the following: "Yes, it's undoubtedly an advance. It's not quite Art, but it's a great advance!"

Harrison was considerably encouraged. The same publisher
brought out the book, and sold quite two hundred copies; but
he wrote rather dolefully to Harrison, saying that the public
demand seemed "almost exhausted." Recognising the fact
that comparisons are odious, Harrison refrained from comparing the sale of the book with that of "In the Track of the
Stars," in which he had shown such promise of "completely
hitting the public taste." Indeed, about this time he began to
have dreams of abandoning the sources of his private income
and living the true literary life. He had not many reviews,
and began his fourth book.

He was two years writing this "work," which he called "A
Lost Man," and dedicated to the critic. He sent a presentation
copy to the man of genius, from whom he received an almost
immediate reply:

"My dear fellow, it is amazing, really amazing how you
progress! Who would ever imagine you were the same man
that wrote 'In the Track of the Stars'! Yet I pique myself
on the fact that even in your first book I spotted that you could
do things. Oh!—I wish I could write like you! 'A Lost Man'
is wonderfully good."

The man of genius was quite sincere in these remarks, which
he wrote after perusing the first six chapters. He never, indeed, actually finished reading the book—he felt so tired, as if
Harrison had exhausted him—but he always alluded to it as
"wonderfully good," just as if he really had finished it.

Harrison sent another copy to the critic, who wrote a genuinely warm letter, saying that he, Harrison, had "achieved" it
at last. "This," he said, "is *art*. I doubt if you will ever do
anything better than this. . . . I crown you."

Harrison at once commenced his fifth book.

He was more than three years upon this new "work," and
called it "A Pilgrimage." There was a good deal of difficulty
in getting it published. Two days after it appeared, however,
the critic wrote to Harrison: "I cannot tell you," he said,
"how very good I think your new book. It is perhaps stronger
than 'A Lost Man,' perhaps more original. If anything it is

too—I have not finished it yet, but I've written off at once to let you know."

As a matter of fact, he never finished the book. He could not—it was too——! "It's wonderfully good," he said, however, to his wife, and he made *her* read it.

Meanwhile, the man of genius wired saying: "Am going to write to you about your book. Positively am, but have lumbago and cannot hold pen."

Harrison never received any letter, but the critic received one saying: "Can you read it? I *can't*. Altogether over ' done.'

Harrison was elated. His new publisher was not. He wrote in a peevish strain, saying there was *absolutely no sale*. Mr. Harrison must take care what he was doing or he would exhaust his public, and enclosing a solitary review, which said amongst other things: "This book may be very fine art, too fine altogether. *We* found it dull."

Harrison went abroad, and began his sixth book. He named it "The Consummation," and worked at it in hermit-like solitude; in it, for the first time, he satisfied himself. He wrote, as it were, with his heart's blood, with an almost bitter delight. And he often smiled to himself as he thought how with his first book he had so nearly hit the public taste; and how of his fourth the critic had said: "This is *art*. I doubt if you will ever do anything better than this." How far away they seemed! Ah! *this* book was indeed the "consummation" devoutly to be wished.

In the course of time he returned to England and took a cottage at Hampstead, and there he finished the book. The day after it was finished he took the manuscript and, going to a secluded spot on the top of the Heath, lay down on the grass to read it quietly through. He read three chapters, and, putting the remainder down, sat with his head buried in his hands.

"Yes," he thought, "I *have* done it at last. *It is good,* wonderfully good!" and for two hours he sat like that, with his head in his hands. He had indeed exhausted his public. It was *too* good—*he could not read it himself!*

Returning to his cottage, he placed the manuscript in a drawer. He never wrote another word.

1904.

ACME

IN these days no man of genius need starve. The following story of my friend Bruce may be taken as proof of this assertion. Nearly sixty when I first knew him, he must have written already some fifteen books, which had earned him the reputation of "a genius" with the few who know. He used to live in York Street, Adelphi, where he had two rooms up the very shaky staircase of a house chiefly remarkable for the fact that its front door seemed always open. I suppose there never was a writer more indifferent to what people thought of him. He profoundly neglected the Press—not with one of those neglects which grow on writers from reading reviews of their own works —he seemed never to read criticism, but with the basic neglect of "an original," a nomadic spirit, a stranger in modern civilisation, who would leave his attics for long months of wandering, and come back there to hibernate and write a book. He was a tall, thin man, with a face rather like Mark Twain's, black eyebrows which bristled and shot up, a bitten drooping grey moustache, and fuzzy grey hair; but his eyes were like owl's eyes, piercing, melancholy, dark brown, and gave to his rugged face an extraordinary expression of a spirit remote from the flesh which had captured it. He was a bachelor, who seemed to avoid women; perhaps they had "learned" him that; for he must have been very attractive to them.

The year of which I write had been to my friend Bruce the devil, monetarily speaking. With his passion for writing that for which his Age had no taste—what could he expect? His last book had been a complete frost. He had undergone, too, an operation which had cost him much money and left him very weak. When I went to see him that October, I found him stretched out on two chairs, smoking the Brazilian cigarettes which he affected—and which always affected me, so black and strong they were, in their yellow maize-leaf coverings. He had a writing-pad on his knee, and sheets of paper scattered all

around. The room had a very meagre look. I had not seen
him for a year and more, but he looked up at me as if I'd been
in yesterday.

"Hallo!" he said; "I went into a thing they call a cinema
last night. Have you ever been?"

"Ever been? Do you know how long the cinema has been
going? Since about 1900."

"Well! What a *thing!* I'm writing a skit on it!"

"How—a skit?"

"Parody—wildest yarn you ever read."

He took up a sheet of paper and began chuckling to himself.

"My heroine," he said, "is an Octoroon. Her eyes swim,
and her lovely bosom heaves. Everybody wants her, and she's
more virtuous than words can say. The situations she doesn't
succumb to would freeze your blood; they'd roast your marrow.
She has a perfect devil of a brother, with whom she was brought
up, and who knows her deep dark secret and wants to trade
her off to a millionaire who also has a deep dark secret. Altogether there are four deep dark secrets in my yarn. It's a
corker."

"What a waste of your time!" I said.

"My time!" he answered fiercely. "What's the use of my
time? Nobody buys my books."

"Who's attending you?"

"Doctors! They take your money, that's all. I've got no
money. Don't talk about me!" Again he took up a sheet of
manuscript and chuckled.

"Last night—at that place—they had—good God!—a race
between a train and a motor-car. Well, I've got one between a
train, a motor-car, a flying machine, and a horse."

I sat up.

"May I have a look at your skit," I said, "when you've
finished it?"

"It *is* finished. Wrote it straight off. D'you think I could
stop and then go on again with a thing like that?" He gathered
the sheets and held them out to me. "Take the thing—it's
amused me to do it. The heroine's secret is that she isn't an
Octoroon at all; she's a De La Casse—purest Creole blood of the
South; and her villainous brother isn't her brother; and the
bad millionaire isn't a millionaire; and her penniless lover is.
It's rich, I tell you!"

"Thanks," I said drily, and took the sheets.

I went away concerned about my friend, his illness, and his poverty, especially his poverty, for I saw no end to it.

After dinner that evening I began languidly to read his skit. I had not read two pages of the thirty-five before I started up, sat down again, and feverishly read on. Skit! By George! He had written a perfect scenario—or, rather, that which wanted the merest professional touching-up to be perfect. I was excited. It was a little gold-mine if properly handled. Any good film company, I felt convinced, would catch at it. Yes! But how to handle it? Bruce was such an unaccountable creature, such a wild old bird! Imagine his having only just realised the cinema! If I told him his skit was a serious film, he would say: " Good God! " and put it in the fire, priceless though it was. And yet, how could I market it without *carte blanche,* and how get *carte blanche* without giving my discovery away? I was deathly keen on getting some money for him; and this thing, properly worked, might almost make him independent. I felt as if I had a priceless museum piece which a single stumble might shatter to fragments. The tone of his voice when he spoke of the cinema—" What a *thing!* " kept coming back to me. He was prickly proud, too—very difficult about money. Could I work it without telling him anything? I knew he never looked at a newspaper. But should I be justified in taking advantage of that—in getting the thing accepted and produced without his knowing? I revolved the question for hours, and went to see him again next day.

He was reading.

" Hallo! You again? What do you think of this theory— that the Egyptians derive from a Saharan civilisation? "

" I don't think," I said.

" It's nonsense. This fellow—— "

I interrupted him.

" Do you want that skit back, or can I keep it? "

" Skit? What skit? "

" The thing you gave me yesterday."

" That! Light your fire with it. This fellow—— "

" Yes," I said; " I'll light a fire with it. I see you're busy."

" Oh, no! I'm not," he said. " I've nothing to do. What's the good of my writing? I earn less and less with every book that comes out. I'm dying of poverty."

" That's because you won't consider the public."

"*How* can I consider the public when I don't know what they want?"

"Because you won't take the trouble to find out. If I suggested a way to you of pleasing the public and making money, you'd kick me out of the room."

And the words: "For instance, I've got a little gold-mine of yours in my pocket," were on the tip of my tongue, but I choked them back. 'Daren't risk it!' I thought. 'He's given you the thing. *Carte blanche—cartes serrés!*'

I took the gold-mine away and promptly rough-shaped it for the film. It was perfectly easy, without any alteration of the story. Then I was faced with the temptation to put his name to it. The point was this: If I took it to a film company as an authorless scenario, I should only get authorless terms; whereas, if I put his name to it, with a little talking I could double the terms at least. The film public didn't know his name, of course, but the inner literary public did, and it's wonderful how you can impress the market with the word "genius" judiciously used. It was too dangerous, however; and at last I hit on a middle course. I would take it to them with no name attached, but tell them it was by "a genius," and suggest that they could make capital out of the incognito. I knew they would feel it *was* by a genius.

I took it to an excellent company next day, with a covering note saying: "The author, a man of recognised literary genius, for certain reasons prefers to remain unknown." They took a fortnight in which to rise, but they rose. They had to. The thing was too good in itself. For a week I played them over terms. Twice I delivered an ultimatum—twice they surrendered; they knew too well what they had got. I could have made a contract with £2,000 down which would have brought at least another £2,000 before the contract term closed; but I compounded for one that gave me £3,000 down, as likely to lead to less difficulty with Bruce. The terms were not a whit too good for what was really the "acme" of scenarios. If I could have been quite open, I could certainly have done better. Finally, however, I signed the contract, delivered the manuscript, and received a cheque for the price. I was elated, and at the same time knew that my troubles were just beginning. With Bruce's feeling about the film, how the deuce should I get him to take the money? Could I go to his publishers, and conspire with them to trickle it out to him gradually, as if it came from his books? That meant letting them into the secret; besides, he was too used to receiving practically nothing from his books; it would lead him to make enquiry, and the secret was bound to come out. Could I get a lawyer to spring an inheritance on him? That would mean no end of lying and elaboration, even if a lawyer would consent. Should I send him the money in Bank of England notes, with the words: " From a lifelong admirer of your genius"? I was afraid he would suspect a trick, or stolen notes, and go to the police to trace them. Or should I just go, put the cheque on the table, and tell him the truth?

The question worried me terribly, for I didn't feel entitled to consult others who knew him. It was the sort of thing that, if talked over, would certainly leak out. It was not desirable, however, to delay cashing a big cheque like that. Besides, they had started on the production. It happened to be a slack time, with a dearth of good films, so that they were rushing it on. And in the meantime there was Bruce—starved of everything he wanted, unable to get away for want of money, depressed about his health and his future. And yet so completely had he always seemed to me different, strange, superior to this civilisation of ours, that the idea of going to him and saying simply: " This is yours, for the film you wrote," scared me. I could hear his: " I? Write for the cinema? What do you mean? "

When I came to think of it, I had surely taken an extravagant liberty in marketing the thing without consulting him. I felt he would never forgive that, and my feeling towards him was so affectionate, even reverential, that I simply hated the idea of being cast out of his affections. At last I hit on a way that by introducing my own interest might break my fall. I cashed the cheque, lodged the money at my bank, drew my own cheque on it for the full amount, and armed with that and the contract, went to see him.

He was lying on two chairs, smoking his Brazilians, and playing with a stray cat which had attached itself to him. He seemed rather less prickly than usual, and after beating about the bushes of his health and other matters, I began:

" I've got a confession to make, Bruce."

" Confession! " he said. " What confession? "

" You remember that skit on the film you wrote, and gave me, about six weeks ago? "

" No."

" Yes, you do—about an Octoroon."

He chuckled. "Oh! Ah! That!"

I took a deep breath, and went on:

"Well, I sold it; and the price of course belongs to you."

"What? Who'd print a thing like that?"

"It isn't printed. It's been made into a film—superfilm, they call it."

His hand came to a pause on the cat's back, and he glared at me. I hastened on:

"I ought to have told you what I was doing, but you're so prickly, and you've got such confounded superior notions. I thought if I did, you'd be biting off your nose to spite your own face. The fact is, it made a marvellous scenario. Here's the contract, and here's a cheque on my bank for the price—£3,000. If you like to treat me as your agent, you owe me £300. I don't expect it, but I'm not proud, like you, and I shan't sneeze."

"Good God!" he said.

"Yes, I know. But it's all nonsense, Bruce. You can carry scruples to altogether too great length. Tainted source! Everything's tainted, if you come to that. The film's a quite justified expression of modern civilisation—a natural outcome of the Age. It gives amusement; it affords pleasure. It may be vulgar, it may be cheap, but we *are* vulgar, and we *are* cheap, and it's no use pretending we're not—not you, of course, Bruce, but people at large. A vulgar Age wants vulgar amusement, and if we can give it that amusement, we ought to; life's not too cheery, anyway."

The glare in his eyes was almost paralysing me, but I managed to stammer on:

"You live out of the world—you don't realise what humdrum people want; something to balance the greyness, the—the banality of their lives. They want blood, thrill, sensation of all sorts. You didn't mean to give it them, but you have, you've done them a benefit, whether you wish to or not, and the money's yours and you've got to take it."

The cat suddenly jumped down. I waited for the storm to burst.

"I know," I dashed on, "that you hate and despise the film——"

Suddenly his voice boomed out:

"Bosh! What are you talking about? Film! I go there every other night."

It was my turn to say: "Good God!" And, ramming contract and cheque into his empty hand, I bolted, closely followed by the cat.

1923.

DEFEAT

She had been standing there on the pavement a quarter of an hour or so after her shilling's worth of concert. Women of her profession are not supposed to have redeeming points, especially when—like May Belinski, as she now preferred to dub herself—they are German; but this woman certainly had music in her soul. She often gave herself these "music baths" when the Promenade Concerts were on, and had just spent half her total wealth in listening to some Mozart and a Beethoven symphony.

She was feeling almost elated, full of divine sound, and of the summer moonlight that was filling the whole dark town. Women "of a certain type" have, at all events, emotions— and what a comfort that is, even to themselves! To stand just there had become rather a habit of hers. One could seem to be waiting for somebody coming out of the concert, not yet over—which, of course, was precisely what she *was* doing. One need not for ever be stealthily glancing and perpetually moving on in that peculiar way, which, while it satisfied the police and Mrs. Grundy, must not quite deceive others as to her business in life. She had only "been at it" long enough to have acquired a nervous dread of almost everything—not long enough to have passed through that dread to callousness. Some women take so much longer than others. And even for a woman "of a certain type" her position was exceptionally nerve-racking in war-time, going as she did by a false name. Indeed, in all England there could hardly be a greater pariah than was this German woman of the night.

She idled outside a book-shop humming a little, pretending to read the titles of the books by moonlight, taking off and putting on one of her stained yellow gloves. Now and again she would move up as far as the posters outside the hall, scrutinising them as if interested in the future, then stroll back again. In her worn and discreet dark dress, and her small hat, she had

343

nothing about her to rouse suspicion, unless it were the trail of violet powder she left on the moonlight.

For the moonlight this evening was almost solid, seeming with its cool still vibration to replace the very air; in it the war-time precautions against light seemed fantastic, like shading candles in a room still full of daylight. What lights there were had the effect of strokes and stipples of dim colour laid by a painter's brush on a background of ghostly whitish-blue. The dreamlike quality of the town was perhaps enhanced for her eyes by the veil she was wearing—in daytime no longer white. As the music died out of her, elation also ebbed. Somebody had passed her, speaking German, and she was overwhelmed by a rush of nostalgia. On this moonlit night by the banks of the Rhine—whence she came—the orchards would be heavy with apples; there would be murmurs and sweet scents; the old castle would stand out clear, high over the woods and the chalky-white river. There would be singing far away, and the churning of a distant steamer's screw; and perhaps on the water a log raft still drifting down in the blue light. There would be German voices talking. And suddenly tears oozed up in her eyes, and crept down through the powder on her cheeks. She raised her veil and dabbed at her face with a little, not-too-clean handkerchief, screwed up in her yellow-gloved hand. But the more she dabbed the more those treacherous tears ran. Then she became aware that a tall young man in khaki was also standing before the shop-window, not looking at the titles of the books, but eyeing her askance. His face was fresh and open, with a sort of kindly eagerness in his blue eyes. Mechanically she drooped her wet lashes, raised them obliquely, drooped them again, and uttered a little sob. . . .

This young man, captain in a certain regiment, and discharged from hospital at six o'clock that evening, had entered Queen's Hall at half-past-seven. Still rather brittle and sore from his wound, he had treated himself to a seat in the grand circle, and there had sat, very still and dreamy, the whole concert through. It had been like eating after a long fast—something of the sensation Polar explorers must experience when they return to their first full meal. For he was of the New Army, and before the war had actually believed in music, art, and all that sort of thing. With a month's leave before him, he could afford to feel that life was extraordinarily joyful, his own experiences particularly wonderful; and, coming out into

the moonlight, he had taken what can only be described as a
great gulp of it, for he was a young man with a sense of beauty.
When one has been long in the trenches, lain out wounded in a
shell-hole twenty-four hours, and spent three months in hospital, beauty has such an edge of novelty, such a sharp sweetness, that it almost gives pain. And London at night is very
beautiful. He strolled slowly towards the Circus, still drawing
the moonlight deep into his lungs, his cap tilted up a little
on his forehead in that moment of unmilitary abandonment;
and whether he stopped before the book-shop window because
the girl's figure was in some sort a part of beauty, or because
he saw that she was crying, he could not have made clear to
anyone.

Then something—perhaps the scent of powder, perhaps the
yellow glove, or the oblique flutter of the eyelids—told him
that he was making what he would have called "a blooming
error," unless he wished for company, which had not been in
his thoughts. But her sob affected him, and he said:

" What's the matter? "

Again her eyelids fluttered sideways, and she stammered:

" Not'ing. The beautiful evening—that's why! "

That a woman of what he now clearly saw to be " a certain
type " should perceive what he himself had just been perceiving,
struck him forcibly, and he said:

" Cheer up."

She looked up again swiftly. " All right! But you are not
lonelee like me."

For one of that sort she looked somehow honest; her tear-
streaked face was rather pretty, and he murmured:

" Well, let's walk a bit and talk it over."

They turned the corner and walked east, along streets empty
and beautiful, with their dulled orange-glowing lamps, and
here and there the glint of some blue or violet light. He found
it queer and rather exciting—for an adventure of just this
kind he had never had. And he said doubtfully:

" How did you get into this? Isn't it an awfully hopeless
life? "

" Ye-es, it ees——" her voice had a queer soft emphasis.
" You are limping—haf you been wounded? "

" Just out of hospital."

" The horrible war—all the misery is because of the war.
When will it end? "

He looked at her, and said:

" I say—what nationality are you?"

" Rooshian."

" Really! I never met a Russian girl."

He was conscious that she looked at him, then very quickly
down. And he said suddenly:

" Is it as bad as they make out?"

She slipped her yellow-gloved hand through his arm.

" Not when I haf anyone as nice as you; I never haf yet,
though;" she smiled—and her smile was like her speech, slow,
confiding. " You stopped because I was sad; others stop because I am gay. I am not fond of men at all. When you
know, you are not fond of them."

" Well! You hardly know them at their best, do you? You
should see them at the front. By George! they're simply splendid—officers and men, every blessed soul. There's never been
anything like it—just one long bit of jolly fine self-sacrifice;
it's perfectly amazing."

Turning her blue-grey eyes on him, she answered:

" I expect you are not the last at that. You see in them
what you haf in yourself, I think."

" Oh! not a bit—you're quite out. I assure you when we
made the attack where I got wounded there wasn't a single
man in my regiment who wasn't an absolute hero. The way
they went in—never thinking of themselves—it was simply
superb!"

Her teeth came down on her lower lip, and she answered
in a queer voice: " It is the same too, perhaps, with—the
enemy."

" Oh, yes, I know that."

" Ah! You are not a mean man. How I hate mean men!"

" Oh! they're not mean really—they simply don't understand."

" Oh! you are a baby—a good baby, aren't you?"

He did not quite like being called a baby, and frowned; but
was at once touched by the disconcertion in her powdered face.
How quickly she was scared!

She said clingingly:

" But I li-ike you for it. It is so good to find a ni-ice man."

This was worse, and he said abruptly:

" About being lonely? Haven't you any Russian friends?"

" Rooshian! No! The town is so beeg! Haf you been in the concert? "

" Yes."

" I, too—I love music."

" I suppose all Russians do."

She looked up at his face again, and seemed to struggle to keep silent; then she said quietly:

" I go there always when I haf the money."

" What! Are you so on the rocks? "

" Well, I haf just one shilling now." And she laughed.

The sound of that little laugh upset him—she had a way of making him feel sorry for her every time she spoke.

They had come by now to a narrow square, east of Gower Street.

" This is where I lif," she said. " Come in! "

He had one long moment of violent hesitation, then yielded to the soft tugging of her hand, and followed. The passage-hall was dimly lighted, and they went upstairs into a front room, where the curtains were drawn, and the gas turned very low. Opposite the window were other curtains dividing off the rest of the apartment. As soon as the door was shut she put up her face and kissed him—evidently formula. What a room! Its green and beetroot colouring and the prevalence of cheap plush disagreeably affected him. Everything in it had that callous look of rooms which seem to be saying to their occupants: " You're here to-day and you'll be gone to-mor-row." Everything except one little plant, in a common pot, of maidenhair fern, fresh and green, looking as if it had been watered within the hour; in this room it had just the same un-expected touchingness that peeped out of the girl's matter-of-fact cynicism.

Taking off her hat, she went towards the gas, but he said quickly:

" No, don't turn it up; let's have the window open and the moonlight in." He had a sudden dread of seeing anything plainly—it was stuffy, too, and, pulling the curtains apart, he threw up the window. The girl had come obediently from the hearth, and sat down opposite him, leaning her arm on the window-sill and her chin on her hand. The moonlight caught her cheek where she had just renewed the powder, and her fair crinkly hair; it caught the plush of the furniture, and his own khaki, giving them all a touch of unreality.

"What's your name?" he said.

"May. Well, I call myself that. It's no good askin' yours."

"You're a distrustful little soul, aren't you?"

"I haf reason to be, don't you think?"

"Yes, I suppose you're bound to think us all brutes?"

"Well, I haf a lot of reasons to be afraid all my time. I am dreadfully nervous now; I am not trusting anybody. I suppose you haf been killing lots of Germans?"

He laughed.

"We never know, unless it happens to be hand to hand. I haven't come in for that yet."

"But you would be very glad if you had killed some?"

"Glad? I don't think so. We're all in the same boat so far as that's concerned. We're not glad to kill each other. We do our job—that's all."

"Oh! it is frightful. I expect I haf my broders killed."

"Don't you get any news ever?"

"News! No indeed, no news of anybody in my country. I might not haf a country; all that I ever knew is gone—fader, moder, sisters, broders, all—never any more I shall see them, I suppose, now. The war it breaks and breaks—it breaks hearts." Her little teeth fastened again on her lower lip in that sort of pretty snarl. "Do you know what I was thinkin' when you came up? I was thinkin' of my native town and the river there in the moonlight. If I could see it again I would be glad. Were you ever homeseek?"

"Yes, I have been—in the trenches; but one's ashamed, with all the others."

"Ah! ye-es!" It came from her with a hiss. "Ye-es! You are all comrades there. What is it like for me here, do you think, where everybody hates and despises me, and would catch me, and put me in prison, perhaps?"

He could see her breast heaving with a quick breathing painful to listen to. He leaned forward, patting her knee, and murmuring: "So sorry."

She said in a smothered voice:

"You are the first who has been kind to me for so long! I will tell you the truth—I am not Rooshian at all—I am German."

Hearing that half-choked confession, his thought was: "Does she really think we fight against women?" And he said:

"My dear girl, who cares?"

Her eyes seemed to search right into him. She said slowly:
"Another man said that to me. But he was thinkin' of
other things. You are a veree ni-ice boy. I am so glad I met
you. You see the good in people, don't you? That is the first
thing in the world—because there is really not much good in
people, you know."

He said, smiling:

"You're a dreadful little cynic!" Then thought: 'Well
—of course!'

"Cyneec? How long do you think I would live if I was
not a cyneec? I should drown myself to-morrow. Perhaps
there are good people, but, you see, I don't know them."

"I know lots."

She leaned forward eagerly.

"Well now—see, ni-ice boy—you haf never been in a hole,
haf you?"

"I suppose not a real hole."

"No, I should think not, with your face. Well, suppose I
am still a good girl, as I was once, you know, and you took
me to some of your good people, and said: 'Here is a little
German girl that has no work, and no money, and no friends.'
Your good people they will say: 'Oh! how sad! A German
girl!' and they will go and wash their hands."

Silence fell on him. He saw his mother, his sister, others
—good people, he would swear! And yet——! He heard their
voices, frank and clear; and they seemed to be talking of the
Germans. If only she were not German as well!

"You see!" he heard her say, and could only mutter:

"I'm sure there *are* people."

"No. They would not take a German, even if she was good.
Besides, I don't want to be good any more—I am not a humbug—I have learned to be bad. Aren't you going to kees me,
ni-ice boy?"

She put her face close to his. Her eyes troubled him, but
he drew back. He thought she would be offended or persistent,
but she was neither; just looked at him fixedly with a curious
inquiring stare; and he leaned against the window, deeply disturbed. It was as if all clear and simple enthusiasm had been
suddenly knocked endways; as if a certain splendour of life
that he had felt and seen of late had been dipped in cloud.
Out there at the front, over here in hospital, life had been
seeming so—as it were—heroic; and yet it held such mean

and murky depths as well! The voices of his men, whom he
had come to love like brothers, crude burring voices, cheery in
trouble, making nothing of it; the voices of doctors and nurses,
patient, quiet, reassuring voices; even his own voice, infected
by it all, kept sounding in his ears. All wonderful somehow,
and simple; and nothing mean about it anywhere! And now
so suddenly to have lighted upon this, and all that was behind it—this scared girl, this base, dark, thoughtless use of
her! And the thought came to him: ' I suppose my fellows
wouldn't think twice about taking her on! Why, I'm not even
certain of myself, if she insists!' And he turned his face and
stared out at the moonlight. He heard her voice:

"Eesn't it light? No air-raid to-night. When the Zepps
burned—what a horrible death! And all the people cheered
—it is natural. Do you hate us veree much?"

He turned round and said sharply:

"Hate? I don't know."

"I don't hate even the English—I despise them. I despise
my people too—perhaps more, because they began this war.
Oh, yes! I know that. I despise all the peoples. Why haf
they made the world so miserable—why haf they killed all our
lives—hundreds and thousands and millions of lives—all for
not'ing? They haf made a bad world—everybody hating, and
looking for the worst everywhere. They haf made me bad, I
know. I believe no more in anything. What is there to believe in? Is there a God? No! Once I was teaching little
English children their prayers—isn't that funnee? I was reading to them about Christ and love. I believed all those things.
Now I believe not'ing at all—no one who is not a fool or a liar
can believe. I would like to work in a hospital; I would like to
go and help poor boys like you. Because I am a German they
would throw me out a hundred times, even if I was good. It
is the same in Germany and France and Russia—everywhere.
But do you think I will believe in love and Christ and a God
and all that—not I! I think we are animals—that's all. Oh!
yes—you fancy it is because my life has spoiled me. It is not
that at all—that's not the worst thing in life. These men are
not ni-ice, like you, but it's their nature, and," she laughed,
"they help me to live, which is something for me, anyway.
No, it is the men who think themselves great and good, and
make the war with their talk and their hate, killing us all—
killing all the boys like you, and keeping poor people in prison,

and telling us to go on hating; and all those dreadful cold-blooded creatures who write in the papers—the same in my country, just the same; it is because of all them that I think we are only animals."

He got up, acutely miserable. He could see her following him with her eyes, and knew she was afraid she had driven him away. She said coaxingly: "Don't mind me talking, ni-ice boy. I don't know anyone to talk to. If you don't like it, I can be quiet as a mouse."

He muttered:

"Oh! go on, talk away. I'm not obliged to believe you, and I don't."

She was on her feet now, leaning against the wall, her dark dress and white face just touched by the slanting moonlight; and her voice came again, slow and soft and bitter:

"Well, look here, ni-ice boy, what sort of a world is it, where millions are being tortured—horribly tortured, for no fault of theirs at all? A beautiful world, isn't it? 'Umbug! silly rot, as you boys call it. You say it is all 'Comrade!' and brave-ness out there at the front, and people don't think of them-selves. Well, I don't think of myself veree much. What does it matter?—I am lost now, anyway; but I think of my people at home, how they suffer and grieve. I think of all the poor people there and here who lose those they love, and all the poor prisoners. Am I not to think of them? And if I do, how am I to believe it a beautiful world, ni-ice boy?"

He stood very still, biting his lips.

"Look here! We haf one life each, and soon it is over. Well, I think that is lucky."

He said resentfully:

"No! there's more than that."

"Ah!" she went on softly, "you think the war is fought for the future; you are giving your lives for a better world, aren't you?"

"We must fight till we win," he said between his teeth.

"Till you win. My people think that, too. All the peoples think that if they win the world will be better. But it will not, you know; it will be much worse, anyway."

He turned away from her and caught up his cap; but her voice followed him.

"I don't care which wins, I despise them all—animals—animals! Ah! Don't go, ni-ice boy—I will be quiet now."

He took some notes from his tunic pocket, put them on the table, and went up to her.

"Good-night."

She said plaintively:

"Are you really going? Don't you like me enough?"

"Yes, I like you."

"It is because I am German, then?"

"No."

"Then why won't you stay?"

He wanted to answer: "Because you upset me so;" but he just shrugged his shoulders.

"Won't you kees me once?"

He bent, and put his lips to her forehead; but as he took them away she threw her head back, pressed her mouth to his and clung to him.

He sat down suddenly, and said:

"Don't! I don't want to feel a brute."

She laughed. "You are a funny boy, but you are veree good. Talk to me a little, then. No one talks to me. I would much rather talk, anyway. Tell me, haf you seen many German prisoners?"

He sighed—from relief, or was it from regret?

"A good many."

"Any from the Rhine?"

"Yes, I think so."

"Were they very sad?"

"Some were—some were quite glad to be taken."

"Did you ever see the Rhine? Isn't it beautiful? It will be wonderful to-night. The moonlight will be the same here as there; in Rooshia too, and France, everywhere; and the trees will look the same as here, and people will meet under them and make love just as here. Oh! isn't it stupid, the war?—as if it was not good to be alive."

He wanted to say: "You can't tell how good it is to be alive till you're facing death, because you don't live till then. And when a whole lot of you feel like that—and are ready to give their lives for each other, it's worth all the rest of life put together." But he couldn't get it out to this girl who believed in nothing.

"How were you wounded, ni-ice boy?"

"Attacking across open ground—four machine-gun bullets got me at one go off."

" Weren't you veree frightened when they ordered you to attack?" No, he had not been frightened just then! And he shook his head and laughed.

" It was great. We did laugh that morning. They got me much too soon, though—a swindle!"

She stared at him.

" You laughed?"

" Yes, and what do you think was the first thing I was conscious of next morning—my old colonel bending over me and giving me a squeeze of lemon. If you knew my colonel, you'd still believe in things. There *is* something, you know, behind all this evil. After all, you can only die once, and if it's for your country all the better."

Her face, with intent eyes just touched with dark, had in the moonlight a most strange, other-world look. Her lips moved:

" No, I believe in nothing. My heart is dead."

" You think so, but it isn't, you know, or you wouldn't have been crying when I met you."

" If it were not dead, do you think I could live my life—walking the streets every night, pretending to like strange men —never hearing a kind word—never talking, for fear I will be known for a German. Soon I shall take to drinking, then I shall be '*kaput*' very quick. You see, I am practical; I see things clear. To-night I am a little emotional; the moon is funny, you know. But I live for myself only now. I don't care for anything or anybody."

" All the same, just now you were pitying your people, and prisoners, and that."

" Yes, because they suffer. Those who suffer are like me— I pity myself, that's all; I am different from your English-women. I see what I am doing; I do not let my mind become a turnip just because I am no longer moral."

" Nor your heart either."

" Ni-ice boy, you are veree obstinate. But all that about love is 'umbug. We love ourselves, nothing more."

Again, at that intense soft bitterness in her voice, he felt stifled and got up, leaning on the window sill. The air out there was free from the smell of dust and stale perfume. He felt her fingers slip between his own, and stay unmoving. If she was so hard and cynical, why should he pity her? Yet he did. The touch of that hand within his own roused his protective instinct. She had poured out her heart to him—a per-

fect stranger! He pressed it a little, and felt her fingers crisp
in answer. Poor little devil! This was a friendlier moment
than she had known for years! And after all, fellow-feeling
was bigger than principalities and powers! Fellow-feeling was
all-pervading as this moonlight, which she had said would be
the same in Germany—as this white ghostly glamour wrapping
the trees, making the orange lamps so quaint and decoratively
useless out in the narrow square, where emptiness and silence
reigned. He looked round into her face—in spite of kohl and
powder, and the red salve on her lips, it had a queer, unholy,
touching beauty. And he had suddenly the strangest feeling,
as if they stood there—the two of them—proving that kindness
and human fellowship were stronger than lust, stronger than
hate; proving it against meanness and brutality, and the sudden shouting of newspaper boys in some neighbouring streets,
whose cries, passionately vehement, clashed into each other,
and obscured the words—what was it they were calling? His
head went up to listen; he felt her hand rigid within his arm
—she too was listening. The cries came nearer, hoarser, more
shrill and clamorous; the empty moonlight seemed of a sudden
crowded with figures, footsteps, voices, and a fierce distant cheering. "Great victory—great victory! Official! British! Severe
defeat of the 'Uns! Many thousand prisoners!" So it sped
by, intoxicating, filling him with a fearful joy; and leaning
far out, he waved his cap and cheered like a madman; and
the whole night seemed to him to flutter and vibrate and answer.
Then he turned to rush down into the street, struck against
something soft, and recoiled. The girl! She stood with hands
clenched, her face convulsed, panting, and even in the madness of his joy he felt for her. To hear this—in the midst
of enemies! All confused with the desire to do something,
he stooped to take her hand; and the dusty reek of the tablecloth clung to his nostrils. She snatched away her fingers,
swept up the notes he had put down, and held them out to him.
"Take them—I will not haf your English money—take
them." And suddenly she tore them across twice, three times,
let the bits flutter to the floor, and turned her back to him.
He stood looking at her leaning against the plush-covered table
which smelled of dust, her head down, a dark figure in a dark
room with the moonlight sharpening her outline—hardly a moment he stayed, then made for the door. . . .
When he was gone, she still stood there, her chin on her breast

—she who cared for nothing, believed in nothing—with the sound in her ears of cheering, of hurrying feet, and voices; stood in the centre of a pattern made by fragments of the torn-up notes, staring out into the moonlight, seeing, not this hated room and the hated square outside, but a German orchard, and herself, a little girl, plucking apples, a big dog beside her; a hundred other pictures, too, such as the drowning see. Her heart swelled; she sank down on the floor, laid her forehead on the dusty carpet, and pressed her body to it.

She who did not care—who despised all peoples, even her own—began, mechanically, to sweep together the scattered fragments of the notes, assembling them with the dust into a little pile, as of fallen leaves, and dabbling in it with her fingers, while the tears ran down her cheeks. For her country she had torn them, her country in defeat! She, who had just one shilling in this great town of enemies, who wrung her stealthy living out of the embraces of her foes! And suddenly in the moonlight she sat up and began to sing with all her might—"*Die Wacht am Rhein.*"

1916.

VIRTUE

HAROLD MELLESH, minor clerk in an Accident Assurance Society, having occasion to be present at a certain Police Court to give evidence in the matter of a smashed car, stood riveted by manifestations of the law entirely new to him. His eyes, blue and rather like those of a baby, were opened very widely, his ingenuous forehead wrinkled, his curly hair was moving on his scalp, his fists involuntarily clenching his straw hat. He had seen four ladies of the town dealt with—three " jugged," and one fined—before his sensations reached their climax. Perhaps she was prettier than the others, certainly younger, and she was crying.

" First time you've been here—two pounds, and ten shillings costs."

" But I haven't any money, sir."

" Very well—fourteen days."

Tears streaking the remains of powder—a queer little sound, and the sensations within young Mellesh simmered like a kettle coming to the boil. He touched a blue sleeve in front of him.

" Here," he said, " I'll pay her fine."

He felt the glance of the policeman running over him like a chilly insect.

" Friend of yours? "

" No."

" I shouldn't, then. She'll be here again within the month."

The girl was passing, he saw the swallowing movement of her throat and said with desperation:

" I don't care. I'll pay it."

The policeman's glance crept about him clammily.

" Come with me, then."

Young Mellesh followed him out.

" Here," said his policeman to the one in charge of the girl, " this gentleman'll pay the fine."

Conscious of a confusion of glances, of his own cheeks reddening furiously, young Mellesh brought out his money—just two pounds fifteen; and, handing over the two pounds ten, he thought: 'My hat! What would Alice say?'

He heard the girl's gasped out: "Ow! Thank you!" his policeman's muttered: "Waste o' money! Still, it was a kind action," and passed out into the street. Now that his feelings had given off that two pound ten's worth of steam he felt chilly and dazed, as if virtue had gone out of him. A voice behind him said:

"Thank you ever so much—it *was* kind of you."

Raising his straw hat he stood uncomfortably to let her pass. She pushed a card into his hand. "Any time you're passing, I'll be glad to see you; I'm very grateful."

"Not at all!" With a smile, confused like her own, he turned off towards his office.

All day, among his accidents, he felt uncertain. Had he been a fool; had he been a hero? Sometimes he thought: 'What brutes they are to those girls!' and sometimes: 'Don't know; suppose they must do something about it.' And he avoided considering how to explain the absence of two pounds ten shillings on which Alice had been reckoning. His soul was simple like the expression on his face.

He reached home at the usual hour—six-thirty. His home was grey and small and had a little bit of green up Chalk Farm way, where the Tube made all things possible.

His wife, who had just put their baby daughter to bed, was sitting in the parlour darning his socks. She looked up—surely her forehead was rather like a knee!

"You wear your socks properly, Harold," she said; "it's all I can do to mend this pair." Her eyes were china-blue, round like saucers; her voice had the monotony of one brought up to minimise emotion. A farmer's daughter, young Mellesh had become engaged to her during a holiday in Somerset. Pale himself, from office and the heat, he thought how pale she looked.

"The heat's dreadful, isn't it?" she said. "Sometimes I wish we'd never had baby. It does tie you in the evenings. I *am* looking forward to Whitsuntide, that I am."

Young Mellesh, tall and straggly, bent over and kissed her forehead. How on earth to let her know that he had "blewed" their holiday? He was realising that he had done an awful thing. Perhaps—oh! surely she would understand how he couldn't sit and see that girl "jugged" before his eyes for want of it! But not until the end of their small supper did he say abruptly:

"I got quite upset this morning, Alice. Had to go down to the Police Court about that car smash I told you of, and afterwards I saw them run in a lot of those Piccadilly girls. It fair sickened me to see the way they treat them."

His wife looked up; her face was childlike.

"Why, what do they do to them?"

"Quod them for speakin' to men in the street."

"I s'pose they're up to no good."

Irritated by the matter-of-factness in her voice, he went on:
"They speak to 'em as if they were dirt."

"Well, aren't they?"

"They may be a loose lot, but so are men."

"Men wouldn't be so loose if they weren't there."

"I suppose it's what you call a vicious circle;" and, pleased with his play on words, he added: "One or two of them were pretty."

His wife smiled; her smile had a natural teasing quality.

"They treat *them* better, I suppose?"

That was jolly cynical! and he blurted out:

"One, quite young, never there before, they gave her a fortnight just because she hadn't any money—I couldn't stick it; I paid her fine."

There was sweat on his forehead. His wife's face had gone quite pink.

"You paid? How much?"

He was on the point of saying: "Ten shillings." But something in his soul revolted. "Regular pill—two pound ten;" and he thought glumly: 'Oh! what a fool I've been!'

He did wish Alice wouldn't open her mouth like that, when nothing was coming out—made her look so silly! Her face puckered suddenly, then became quite blank; he was moved as if he had hit or pinched her.

"Awfully sorry, Alice," he muttered. "Never meant to—she—she cried."

"Course she cried! You fool, Harold!"

He got up, very much disturbed.

"Well, and what would *you* have done?"

"Me? Let her stew in her own juice, of course. It wasn't your affair."

She too had risen. He thrust his fingers through his hair. The girl's face, tear-streaked, confusedly pretty, had come up before him, her soft common grateful voice tickled his ears again. His wife turned her back. So! he was in for a fit of sulks. Well! No doubt he had deserved it.

"I dare say I *was* a fool," he muttered, "but I did think you'd understand how I felt when I saw her cry. Suppose it had been you!" From the toss of her head, he knew he had said something pretty fatal.

"Oh! So that's what you think of me!"

He grasped her shoulder.

"Of course I don't, Alice, don't be so silly!"

She shook off his hand.

"Whose money was it? Now baby and me'll get no holiday. And all because you see a slut crying."

Before he could answer she was gone. He had an awful sense of having outraged justice. Given away her holiday—given his wife's holiday to a girl of the streets! Still, it was his own holiday, too; besides, he earned the money! He'd never wanted to give it to the girl; hadn't got anything for it! Suppose he'd put it into the offertory bag, would Alice have been in such a temper even if it was their holiday? He didn't see much difference. He sat down with knees apart, and elbows planted on them, staring at the peonies on the Brussels carpet paid for on the hire system. And all those feelings that rise in people who live together, when they don't agree, swirled in his curly head, and troubled his eyes, candid like a baby's. If they *would* treat the wretched girls like dirt! If only she hadn't cried! She hadn't meant to cry; he could tell that by the sound of it. And who was the magistrate—he didn't look too like a saint; who was any man to treat her like that? Alice oughtn't—— No! But suddenly he saw Alice again bending over his socks—pale and tired with the heat—doing things for him or baby—and he had given away her holiday! No denying that! Compunction flooded him. He must go up and find her and try and make his peace—he would pawn his bicycle—she should have her holiday—oh! yes!

He opened the door and listened. The little house was ominously quiet—only the outside evening sounds from buses passing in the main road, from children playing on the doorsteps of the side street, from a man with a barrow of bananas. She must be up in the bedroom with baby! He mounted the

steep whitewashed stairway. It wanted a carpet, and fresh
paint; ah! and a lot of other things Alice wanted—you couldn't
have everything at once on four pound ten a week—with the
price of living what it was. But she ought to have remembered
there were things he wanted too—yes, precious bad, and never
thought of getting. The door of their bedroom was locked;
he rattled the handle. She opened suddenly, and stood facing
him on the little landing.

"I don't want you up here."

"Look here, Alice—this is rotten."

She closed the door behind her.

"It is! You go down again, I don't want you. Think I
believe that about crying! I'd be ashamed, if I were you!"

Ashamed! He might have been too soft, but why ashamed?

"Think I don't know what men are like? You can just go
to your rotten girl, if she's so pretty!" She stood hard and
stiff against the door, with red spots in her cheeks. She almost
made him feel a villain—such conviction in her body.

"Alice! Good Lord! You must be crazy! I've done
nothing!"

"But you'd like to. Go along! I don't want you!"

The stabbing stare of her blue eyes, the muffled energy of
her voice, the bitterness about her mouth all made a fellow
feel—well, that he knew nothing about anything—coming from
one's wife like that! He leaned back against the wall.

"Well, I'm damned!" was all he could get out.

"D'you mean to say she didn't ask you?"

The insides of his hands grew wet. The girl's card in his
pocket!

"Well, if you like to be a cat I can't help it. What d'you take
me for?"

"Giving your own child's money to a dirty slut! You owed
it—that's the truth—or will. Go on with you; don't stand
there!"

He had a nasty longing to smite her on the mouth—it looked
so bitter. "Well," he said slowly, "now I understand."

What was it that he understood? That she was all of a piece
with something, with that Police Court, with the tone of the
men's voices, with something unsparing, hard and righteous,
which came down sharp on people?

"I thought—I think you might——" he stammered.

"Ugh!" The sound exasperated him so, that he turned to go downstairs.

"You whited sepulchre!"

The door clicked before he could answer the odd insult; he heard the key turned. Idiotic! The little landing seemed too small to hold his feelings. Would he ever have said a word to Alice, if he *had* done it? Why! He had never even thought of doing anything!

Giddy from chagrin he ran downstairs, and, clawing his straw hat from the rack, went out. The streets were malodorous from London fog, fried fish, petrol, hot dirty people; he strode along troubled, his eyes very rueful. So this was what he was really married to—this—this! It was like being married to that Police Court! It wasn't human—no, it wasn't—to be so suspicious and virtuous as all that! What was the use of being decent and straight, if this was all you got for it? Someone touched him on the shoulder.

"Mister, you're all white behind; let me brush you."

He stood still confusedly, while a stout fair man smote his back up and down with a large flat hand. Whited sepulchre! A bubble of rage rose to his lips. All right! She should see! He felt for the girl's card, and was suddenly amazed to find that he had no need to look at it—he remembered the address. Not far off, on the other side of the Euston Road! That was funny—had he been looking at it without realising? They said you had a subconscious mind. Well, what about it? No, it was his conscious mind that was going to serve Alice out! He had reached the Euston Road. Crossing it, he began to feel a queer pleasurable weakness in the legs. By this he knew that he was going to do wrong. He was not going to visit the girl just to serve his wife out, but because the prospect was——! That was bad—bad: it would put Alice in the right! He stood still at the corner of a narrow square, with a strip of garden, and railings round it. He leaned against those railings, his eyes searching the trees. He had always been quite straight with his wife—it was she who had put the idea into his head. And yet his legs being pleasurably weak seemed in an odd way to excuse her. It was like his doubt whether they hadn't to do something about it at the Police Court. Barring Alice—barring the Police Court—where would he—would any man be? Without virtue, entirely without virtue. A pigeon in the garden cooed. "Any time you're passing, I'll be glad to see you."

It had sounded genuine—really grateful. And the girl had
looked—not worse than anybody else! If Alice had been sympathetic about it he would never have thought of the girl
again; that is—well——! The doubt set his legs in motion.
He was a married man, and that was all about it. But he
looked across at the numbers on the houses. Twenty-seven!
Yes, there it was! A bloom of lilac brushed his face. The
scent jerked him suddenly back to the farm in Somerset, and
he and Alice courting. Alice—not the Alice on the landing!
He scrutinised the shabby house, and suddenly went hot all
over. Suppose he went in there—what would that girl think?
That he had paid her fine because——! But that wasn't it at
all—oh! no—he wasn't a squirt like that! He turned his face
away, and walked on fast and far.

The signs were lit above the theatres; traffic was scanty, the
streets a long dawdle of what vehicles and humans were about.
He came to Leicester Square and sat down on a bench. The
lights all round him brightened slowly under the dusk—theatre
lights, street lamps. And the pity of things smote him, sitting
there. So much of everything; and one got so little of anything! Adding figures up all day, going home to Alice—that
was life! Well; it wasn't so bad when Alice was nice to him.
But—Crikey!—what one missed! That book about the South
Sea Islands—places, peoples, sights, sounds, scents, all over
the world! Four pound ten a week, a wife, a baby! Well, you
couldn't have things both ways—but had he got them either
way? Not with the Alice on the landing!

Ah! Well! Poor Alice; jolly hard on her to miss her holiday! But she might have given him the chance to tell her
that he would pawn his bicycle. Or was it all a bad dream?
Had he ever really been in that Police Court, seen them herd-
ing those girls to prison—girls who did what they did because
—well, like himself, they had missed too much. They'd catch
a fresh lot to-night. What a fool he'd been to pay that fine!

'Glad I didn't go into that girl's house, anyway,' he thought.
'I would have felt a scum!' The only decent thing about it
all had been her look when she said: "Ow! thank you!" That
gave him a little feeling of warmth even now; and then—it, too,
chilled away. Nothing for it! When he had done sitting there,
he must go home! If Alice had thought him a wrong-un before, what would she think when he returned? Well, there it

was! The milk was spilt! But he did wish she hadn't got such a virtue on her.

The sky deepened and darkened, the lights stared white; the Square Garden with its flower-beds seemed all cut out and stiff, like scenery on a stage. Must go back and "stick" it! No good to worry!

He got up from the bench and gave himself a shake. His eyes, turned towards the lights of the Alhambra, were round, candid, decent, like the eyes of a baby.

1922.

THE NEIGHBOURS

In the remote country, Nature, at first sight so serene, so simple, will soon intrude on her observer a strange discomfort; a feeling that some familiar spirit haunts the old lanes, rocks, wasteland, and trees, and has the power to twist all living things around into some special shape befitting its genius.

When moonlight floods the patch of moorland about the centre of the triangle between the little towns of Hartland, Torrington, and Holsworthy, a pagan spirit steals forth through the wan gorse; gliding round the stems of the lonely, gibbet-like fir trees, peeping out amongst the reeds of the white marsh. That spirit has the eyes of a borderer, who perceives in every man a possible foe. And, in fact, this high corner of the land has remained border to this day, where the masterful, acquisitive invader from the North dwells side by side with the unstable, proud, quick-blooded Celt-Iberian.

In two cottages crowning some fallow land two families used to live side by side. That long white dwelling seemed all one, till the eye, peering through the sweet-brier which smothered the right-hand half, perceived the rude, weather-beaten presentment of a Running Horse, denoting the presence of intoxicating liquors; and in a window of the left-hand half, that strange conglomeration of edibles and shoe-leather which proclaims the one shop of a primitive hamlet.

These married couples were by name Sandford at the eastern and Leman at the western end; and he who saw them for the first time thought: "What splendid-looking people!"

They were all four above the average height, and all four as straight as darts. The innkeeper, Sandford, was a massive man, stolid, grave, light-eyed, with big fair moustaches, who might have stepped straight out of some Norseman's galley. Leman was lean and lathy, a regular Celt, with an amiable, shadowy, humorous face. The two women were as different as the men. Mrs. Sandford's fair, almost transparent cheeks

coloured easily, her eyes were grey, her hair pale brown; Mrs.
Leman's hair was of a lustreless jet-black, her eyes the colour
of a peaty stream, and her cheeks had the close creamy texture
of old ivory.

Those accustomed to their appearance soon noted the qualifi-
cations of their splendour. In Sandford, whom neither sun
nor wind ever tanned, there was a look as if nothing would
ever turn him from acquisition of what he had set his heart on;
his eyes had the idealism of the worshipper of property, ever
marching towards a heaven of great possessions. Followed by
his cowering spaniel, he walked to his fields (for he farmed
as well as kept the inn) with a tread that seemed to shake the
lanes, disengaging an air of such heavy and complete insulation
that even the birds were still. He rarely spoke. He was not
popular. He was feared—no one quite knew why.

On Mrs. Sandford, for all her pink and white, sometimes
girlish look, he had set the mark of his slow, heavy domination. Her voice was seldom heard. Once in a while, however,
her reserve would yield to garrulity, as of water flowing through
a broken dam. In these outbursts she usually spoke of her
neighbours the Lemans, deploring the state of their marital
relations. "A woman," she would say, "must give way to a
man sometimes; I've had to give way to Sandford myself, I
have." Her lips, from long compression, had become thin as
the edge of a teacup; all her character seemed to have been
driven down below the surface of her long, china-white face.
She had not broken, but she had chipped; her edges had become jagged, sharp. The consciousness that she herself had
been beaten to the earth seemed to inspire in her that waspish
feeling towards Mrs. Leman—"a woman with a proud temper,"
as she would say in her almost lady-like voice; "a woman who's
never bowed down to a man—that's what she'll tell you herself.
'Tisn't the drink that makes Leman behave so mad, 'tis because she won't give way to him. We're glad to sell drink to
anyone we can, of course; but 'tisn't that what's makin' Leman
so queer. 'Tis her."

Leman, whose long figure was often to be seen seated on the
wooden bench of his neighbour's stone-flagged little inn, had,
indeed, begun to have the soaked look and scent of a man never
quite drunk, and hardly ever sober. He spoke slowly, his
tongue seemed thickening; he no longer worked; his humorous, amiable face had grown hangdog and clouded. All the

village knew of his passionate outbreaks and bursts of desperate weeping; and of two occasions when Sandford had been compelled to wrest a razor from him. People took a morbid interest in this rapid deterioration, speaking of it with misgiving and relish, unanimous in their opinion that—summat'd'appen about that; the drink wer duin' for George Leman, *that* it wer, praaperly!

But Sandford—that blond, ashy-looking Teuton—was not easy of approach, and no one cared to remonstrate with him; his taciturnity was too impressive, too impenetrable. Mrs. Leman, too, never complained. To see this black-haired woman, with her stoical, alluring face, come out for a breath of air, and stand in the sunlight, her baby in her arms, was to have looked on a very woman of the Britons. In conquering races the men, they say, are superior to the women; in conquered races, the women to the men. She was certainly superior to Leman. That woman might be bent and mangled, she could not be broken; her pride was too simple, too much a physical part of her. No one ever saw a word pass between her and Sandford. It was almost as if the old racial feelings of this borderland were pursuing in these two their unending conflict. For there they lived, side by side under the long, thatched roof, this great primitive, invading male, and that black-haired, lithe-limbed woman of older race, avoiding each other, never speaking—as much too much for their own mates as they were, perhaps, worthy of each other.

In this lonely parish, houses stood far apart, yet news travelled down the May-scented lanes and over the whin-covered moor with a strange speed; blown perhaps by the west wind, whispered by the pagan genius of the place in his wanderings, or conveyed by small boys on large farm horses.

On Whit-Monday it was known that Leman had been drinking all Sunday; for he had been heard on Sunday night shouting out that his wife had robbed him, and that her children were not his. All next day he was seen sitting in the bar of the inn soaking steadily. Yet on Tuesday morning Mrs. Leman was serving in her shop as usual—a really noble figure, with that lustreless black hair of hers—very silent, and ever sweetening her eyes to her customers. Mrs. Sandford, in one of her bursts of garrulity, complained bitterly of the way her neighbours had "gone on" the night before. But unmoved, ashy, stolid as ever, Sandford worked in the most stony of his fields.

That hot, magnificent day wore to its end; a night of extraordinary beauty fell. In the gold moonlight the shadows of the
lime-tree leaves lay, blacker than any velvet, piled one on the
other at the foot of the little green. It was very warm. A
cuckoo called on till nearly midnight. A great number of little
moths were out; and the two broad meadows which fell away
from the hamlet down to the stream were clothed in a glamorous
haze of their own moonlit buttercups. Where that marvellous
moonlight spread out across the moor it was all pale witchery;
only the three pine-trees had strength to resist the wan gold
of their fair visitor, and brooded over the scene like the ghosts
of three great gallows. The long white dwelling of " the neighbours," bathed in that vibrating glow, seemed to be exuding
a refulgence of its own. Beyond the stream a night-jar hunted,
whose fluttering harsh call tore the garment of the scent-laden
still air. It was long before sleep folded her wings.

A little past twelve o'clock there was the sound of a double
shot. By five o'clock the next morning the news had already
travelled far; and before seven quite a concourse had gathered
to watch two mounted constables take Leman on Sandford's
pony to Bideford Gaol. The dead bodies of Sandford and Mrs.
Leman lay—so report ran—in the locked bedroom at Leman's
end of the neighbours' house. Mrs. Sandford, in a state of
collapse, was being nursed at a neighbouring cottage. The
Leman children had been taken to the Rectory. Alone of the
dwellers in those two cottages, Sandford's spaniel sat in a
gleam of early sunlight under the eastern porch, with her nose
fixed to the crack beneath the door.

It was vaguely known that Leman had " done for 'em "; of
the how, the why, the when, all was conjecture. Nor was it
till the assizes that the story of that night was made plain,
from Leman's own evidence, read from a dirty piece of paper:

" I, George Leman, make this confession—so help me God!
When I came up to bed that evening, I was far gone in liquor
and so had been for two days off and on, which Sandford knows.
My wife was in bed. I went up, and I said to her: ' Get up! '
I said; ' do what I tell you for once! ' ' I will not! ' she said.
So I pulled the bedclothes off her. When I saw her all white
like that, with her black hair, it turned me queer, and I ran
downstairs and got my gun, and loaded it. When I came upstairs again, she was against the door. I pushed, and she pushed
back. She didn't call out, or say one word—but pushed; she

was never one to be afraid. I was the stronger, and I pushed-in the door. She stood up against the bed, defying me with her mouth tight shut, the way she had; and I put up my gun to shoot her. It was then that Sandford came running up the stairs and knocked the gun out of my hand with his stick. He hit me a blow over the heart with his fist, and I fell down against the wall and couldn't move. And he said: 'Keep quiet!' he said, 'you dog!' Then he looked at her. 'And as for you,' he said, 'you bring it on yourself! You can't bow down, can't you? *I'll* bow you down for once!' And he took and raised his stick. But he didn't strike her; he just looked at her in her nightdress, which was torn at the shoulders, and her black hair ragged. She never said a word, but smiled at him. Then he caught hold of her by the arms, and they stood there. I saw her eyes; they were black as two sloes. He seemed to go all weak of a sudden, and white as the wall. It was like as they were struggling which was the better of them, meaning to come on to one another at the end. I saw what was in them as clear as I see this paper. I got up and crept round, and I took the gun and pointed it, and pulled the triggers one after the other, and they fell dead, first him, then her; they fell quietly, neither of them made a noise. I went out and lay down on the grass. They found me there when they came to take me. This is all I have to write, but it is true that I was far gone in liquor, which I had of him. . . ."

1909.

STROKE OF LIGHTNING

THIS was before the war, and conditions were such that the
tragedies and comedies of our private lives seemed still to have
importance.

I had not seen my friend Frank Weymouth for some years,
before coming across him and his wife that Christmas at the big
hotel in Heliopolis. He was always a sunny fellow with a
spilt-wine look about him, which not even a house-mastership
at a Public School had been able to overcome: his wife, whom
I had only met twice before, surprised me a little. I remembered a quiet, rather dark, little person with a doubting eye;
but this was a very kitten of a woman, brimful of mischief and
chaff, and always on the go—reaction, no doubt, from the en-
forced decorum of a house where she was foster-mother of
forty boys, in an atmosphere of being under glass, and the
scrutiny of intensive propriety. In our Egyptian hotel, with
its soft, clever Berberine servants, its huge hall, palm-garden
and cosmopolitan guests, its golf-course with little dark, scurrying Arab caddies, and the desert at its doors, Jessie Weymouth
frolicked and rolled her large dark eyes, scratched and caressed
us with her little paws. Life had suddenly got into her, and
left its tail outside for her to chase. She dragged us all along
in her gay pursuit of it; and Weymouth roused my admiration
by his smiling acquiescence in her outrageous " goings-on." He
knew, I suppose, that she was devoted to him, and her bark
no bite. His " term " had been a hard one; he was in a mood
of lying-back, physically run down, mentally flattened out. To
soak in idleness and the sun was all he seemed to care about.

I forget who first conceived our desert trip, but it was Jessie
Weymouth who fostered it. The Weymouths were not rich, and
a desert trip costs money. They, myself, and a certain Brecon-
ridge couple had agreed to combine, when the Breconridges were
suddenly summoned home by their daughter's illness. Jessie

Weymouth danced with disappointment. "I shall die if we don't go now," she cried; "we simply must scare up somebody."

We scared up the Radolins—an Austrian couple in our hotel whom we had been meeting casually after dinner. He was a Count, in a bank at Constantinople, and she, I think, the daughter of a Viennese painter. They used to interest me from being so very much the antithesis of the Weymouths. He was making the most of his holiday, dancing, playing golf, riding; while she seemed extraordinarily listless, pale, and, as it were, dragged along by her lively husband. I would notice her lounging alone in the gorgeous hall, gazing apparently at nothing. I could not make up my mind about her looks. Her figure was admirable, so were her eyes—ice-green, with dark lashes. But that air of tired indifference seemed to spoil her face. I remember doubting whether it were not going to spoil our trip. But Jessie Weymouth could not be denied, and Radolin, we all admitted, was good company.

We started, then, from Mena House, like all desert excursionists on New Year's Day. We had only a fortnight before us, for the Weymouths were due back in England on the twentieth.

Our dragoman was a merry scoundrel by disposition and an Algerian Bedouin by race. Besides him we had twelve Arabs, a Greek cook, seven camels, four donkeys, and five tents. We took the usual route for the Fayoum. I remember our start so well. In front, Jessie Weymouth on a silver-grey donkey, and our scoundrel on his pet camel. Then Radolin, Weymouth and I on the other three donkeys, and Hélène Radolin perched up, remote and swaying, on the other riding camel. The pack camels had gone on ahead. All day we dawdled along, following the river towards Samara, where we camped that night at a due distance from the evil-smelling village. I had the middle tent, Weymouths to my right, Radolins to my left. Everything was well done by our merry scoundrel, and dinner, thanks to him, Jessie Weymouth and Radolin, a lively enough feast. Still, these first three days, skirting cultivation, were disappointing. But on the fourth we were well out on the lonely sands, and the desert air had begun to go to our heads. That night we camped among bare hills under a wonderful starry sky, cold and clear as crystal. Our scoundrel surpassed himself at dinner; Jessie Weymouth and Radolin were like madcaps, Weymouth his old sunny self. Only Hélène Radolin preserved her languor, not offensively, but as though she had lost the habit of gaiety.

That night I made up my mind, however, that she really was a beautiful woman. The long days in the sun had given her colour, taken the tired look out of her face; and at least twice during the evening I caught Weymouth's eyes fixed on her as if he, too, had made that discovery.

The pranks of Jessie Weymouth and Radolin reached their limit at dinner, and they finished by rushing out into the night to the top of a neighbouring hillock.

Sitting in my tent doorway, counting the stars, I was joined by our scoundrel. The fellow had been in England and knew about Western freedom and the manners of our women.

" She certainly is a good one, Mrs. Weymut," he said to me. " Mr. Weymut a very quiet man. I think he will be tired of her flirts, but he never say nothing—too bloody gentle. The Count he is a good one too, but the Countess—ah! she made of ice! We get some fresh fruit to-morrow at the Fayoum." He went on to his men, two hundred yards away among the camels.

It was wonderfully silent. The light from stars and a half-moon powdered the sands; no wind at all, yet deliciously cold —the desert in good mood; no influence quite so thrilling to pulses, yet so cooling to fevers; no sound, no movement in all the night!

" Isn't it heavenly? Good-night!"

Hélène Radolin was passing me in her fur. The look on her face, the movement of her body, seemed to belong to the lonely silence. She went into her tent. I sat on, smoking. And presently, outside the dining tent, I saw Weymouth, his head thrown back, drawing in deep breaths. By the light of the lantern over the tent door, he had a look as if inspired by a curious happy wonder. Then he too went to his tent. Ten minutes later the madcaps returned, Mrs. Weymouth in front, very quiet; her face, indeed, wore a rather mortified expression, as if she had fallen a little in her own estimation. They went into their tents, and I heard voices a moment, to left and right; then the stillness and the powdering light enveloped all.

Next day, bored with donkey-riding, I walked with the Arabs and saw little of my companions. Weymouth and the Countess, I think, were on the two riding camels, Radolin and Mrs. Weymouth on their donkeys. We came to the edge of the Fayoum about five o'clock. That camping ground was narrow. In tents, when jammed together, one can't avoid hearing at least the

tone of neighbouring talk, and I was struck by a certain
acrimony in the Weymouth tent. Jessie Weymouth seemed complaining that Frank hadn't spoken to her all day.

" I suppose," she said, " you didn't like my running out with
Countie last night ? "

Weymouth's voice, quite good-humoured, answered:

" Oh! not a bit; why should I mind ? "

By the ensuing silence I seemed to realise that Jessie Weymouth was disappointed. Perhaps I hadn't really a feeling of
suspense that evening, but, in reminiscence, it seems to me I
had. Dinner was certainly a disharmonic feast: little Mrs.
Weymouth audacious and rueful; Weymouth and the Countess
subdued, Radolin artificial; our scoundrel and myself had to
make the running. That fellow was needle-sharp, though not
always correct in his conclusions.

" Mrs. Weymut got a fly in her little eye," he said to me as
I was turning in. " I make it all right to-morrow; I get a
dancer at Sennourès. Oho, she is a good one! She make the
married couples 'appy. We get some fresh eggs too."

Severe silence in the tents to right and left that night!

A whole day's travelling through the crops of the Fayoum
brought us to the camping ground outside Sennourès, among
a grove of palm trees—charming spot, but lacking the clear,
cold spirituality of the desert night.

The dancer was certainly " a good one." What a baggage—
all lithe, supple enticement, and jangle of shivering beads!
The excitement of the Arabs, the shocked goggling eyes of
Jessie Weymouth—quite a little Puritan when it came to the
point!—the laughter of our scoundrel, Hélène Radolin's aloof-
ness, which kept even that daughter of Egypt in her place, were
what impressed me during the performance.

Towards the end the Egyptian made a dead set at Weymouth,
and, getting nothing out of him except his smile, became quite
cross. Leaning down to our scoundrel and slinking her eyes
round at the Countess, she murmured something malicious. Our
laughing scoundrel patted her, and we broke up. In ten minutes our camp was empty—dancer, Arabs, all had gone off
to the village. I went out and stood in darkness among the
palm trees, listening to the shivering of their leaves.

Inside the dining tent Radolin was playing the guitar. The
sound was soothing after the vibrant Arab music. Presently I
saw Weymouth come out of the tent. He stood under the lamp

at the entrance, looking back; his face was fully lighted for me, but invisible, I think, to those within. I shall never forget the look on it. Adoration incarnate!

'Hallo!' I thought, 'what's this?' And just then Hélène Radolin came out too. She passed him quietly; he did not attempt to speak or follow; but she saw. Oh! yes, she saw; then vanished into her tent. And Weymouth stood, rooted, as if struck by lightning, while, on and on, behind him rose the thrum of that guitar and all around us the shivering of the palm leaves in a gusty breeze.

Quite the custom, I believe, in these days to laugh at this sort of thing—at such sudden leaps of an irresponsible force; to suggest that they are old-fashioned, overrated—literary, in fact. The equality of the sexes—they say—the tendency of women towards brains and trousers, have diminished Venus; and yet, I fancy what happened to my friend Weymouth may still happen to young gentlemen who talk as if love had no fevers and no proprietary instincts; as if, when you burn for a woman, you are willing to leave her to another, or share her with him without fuss. Of course there are men who have no blood in their veins; but my friend Weymouth unfortunately had; not for nothing was the sunny, spilt-wine look about his hair and cheeks and dark-blue eyes.

For the rest of our desert trip the situation hopelessly promoted that adoration. Little Jessie Weymouth certainly did her best to help. She was the only one of us blind to what had happened. Her perceptions, you see, were blunted by the life of strenuous duty which she and Weymouth led in term time, and by the customary exhaustion of her husband during the holidays. She could not imagine him otherwise than sober. But now—if ever a man were drunk! The thing became so patent that it was quite painful to see her continued blindness. Not till sunset of the second day, with the Fayoum behind us, in our high camp on the desert's edge, did she sense her tragedy. *Those two* were sitting in camp-chairs close together, watching the sun go down. Our Arabs, presented with a ram to soothe their grief at abandoning the joys of the Fayoum, were noisily preparing the animal to the idea of being eaten. Our scoundrel and Radolin were absent; I was sketching; Jessie Weymouth lying down in her tent. Those two were alone— their faces turned towards each other, their hands, perhaps, touching. A strange violet was in the light over the bare hills:

how much they saw of it, I know not, nor what they were saying to each other, when Jessie Weymouth came out of her tent, stretching and yawning, and, like the kitten she was, went stealing up behind to startle them. Three yards away, unseen, unheard, I saw her stop. Her lips opened, her eyes went wide with amazement. Suddenly she covered them with her hands, turned round and stole back into her tent.

Five minutes later out she came again, with bright, hard spots of colour in her cheeks. I saw her run up to them, her feverish attempts at gaiety; and that to those two she simply did not exist. We none of us existed for them. They had found a world of their own, and we were shadows in the unreal world which they had left. You know the pink-flowered daphne, the scent of whose blossoms is very sweet, heavy, and slightly poisonous; sniff it too much and a kind of feverish fire will seize on you. Those two had sniffed the daphne!

Walls have a singular value for civilised beings. In my thin tent between the thin tents of those two couples, prevented by lack of walls from any outlet to their feelings, I seemed to hear the smothered reproaches, the smothered longings. It was the silence of those two suddenly stricken lovers that was so impressive. I, literally, did not dare to speak to Weymouth while we were all mixed up like that. This English schoolmaster had lost, as if by magic, all power of seeing himself as others saw him. Not that those two " carried on "—nothing so normal; they just seemed to have stepped into quiet oblivion of everything but each other.

Even our scoundrel was puzzled. " In my house, when my wife behave bad, I beat her," he said to me; " when I behave bad she scratch my face." But there it was—we had no walls; Hélène Radolin could not be beaten, Weymouth could not have his face scratched. It was most awkward.

Things come to an end, and I never breathed more freely than when Mena House delivered us from that frightful close companionship.

As if by common consent, we dined at separate tables. After dinner I said to Weymouth:

" Come up and see the Sphinx by moonlight."

He came, still in his dream. We reached the Sphinx in silence, and sat down over against her on the sand. At last I said:

" What are you going to do now, old man? "

"I can't leave her." It was as if we had discussed the thing
a dozen times already.

"But you have to be back on the twentieth?"

"I know."

"My dear fellow, it's ruination. And Jessie?"

"She must do what she likes."

"This is madness, Frank!"

"Perhaps. I can't go; that's all."

"What about *her*?"

"I don't know. I only know that where she goes I must."

I just sat staring at the blunt shadow of the Sphinx's broken
profile on the moonlit sand. The strange actionless, desert love-
dream was at an end indeed! Something definite—horrible,
perhaps—must happen now! And I stammered out:

"For God's sake, old boy, think of your wife, your work,
yourself—be reasonable! It isn't worth it, really!"

"Perhaps not. This has nothing to do with reason."

From a master at an English Public School the remark appeared to me fantastic. And, suddenly, he got up, as if he
had been bitten. He was realising suddenly the difference that
walls make. His face had a tortured look. The woman he
loved, walled up with the man she had married! Behind us
the desert, hundreds of miles of clean, savage sand, and in it
we humans—tame and spiritual! Before us walls, and we
humans—savage, carnal again! Queer! I doubt if he saw the
irony; but he left me sitting there and went hurrying back
to the hotel.

I stayed on a little with the riddle of the Ages, feeling it
simple compared with this riddle of the moment. Then I followed him down. Would it resolve itself in terms of L.S.D.?
After all, these four people had to live—could they afford to
play fast and loose with the realities? Hélène Radolin had no
money, I knew; Weymouth his mastership and a few hundreds
saved; Jessie Weymouth a retired Colonel for a father; Radolin
his banking partnership.

A night of walls had its effect. Radolin took his wife back
to Heliopolis next day. The Weymouths remained at Mena
House: in three days they were due to sail.

I well remember thinking: 'There, you see, it doesn't do
to exaggerate. This was a desert mirage and will pass like one.
People are *not* struck by lightning!' But in a mood of morbid
curiosity I went out to Heliopolis.

In the tramcar on the way I felt a sort of disappointment—
Hélène Radolin was a Roman Catholic, Frank Weymouth an
English gentleman. The two facts put such a stopper on what
I wanted stopped. And we all have a sneaking love for the
romantic, or—shall we say?—dramatic.

Well! The Radolins were gone. They had started that
morning for Constantinople. In the Oriental hall where all
this had begun, I sat, browsing over my Turkish coffee, seeing
again my friend Weymouth, languid and inert; his little wife's
flirtatious liveliness; Radolin so *debonair;* Hélène Radolin,
silent, her ice-green eyes slightly reddened in the lids as if she
had been crying. The white-garbed Berberines slipped by;
Greek gentlemen entertained their dubious ladies; Germans
raised a guttural racket; the orchestra twanged out the latest
tango. Nothing was changed but those figures of my vision.
And suddenly one of them materialised—Weymouth was standing as if lost, where the lobby opened into the hall. From
his face it was clear to me that he knew they were gone; before
I could join him he went out hastily. I am sorry now that I
did not follow.

That evening at Mena House I was just beginning to undress when Jessie Weymouth tapped on my door.

" Have you seen Frank? "

I told her where I had seen him in the afternoon.

" That woman! " she cried. " He's not come back."

I assured her that the Radolins were gone away home. She
stared at me and began to cry. She cried and cried, and I
did not try to stop her. She was not only desolate and miserable, but bitter and angry. ' So long as she can be angry,'
I thought, ' she'll get over it. One is not angry under a death-
blow.'

At last she had cried her misery out, but not her anger or
dismay. What was she to do? I tried to persuade her that
Frank would turn up in time for them to start to-morrow evening. He was probably trying to work the thing out of his
system; she must look on it as a fever, a kind of illness. She
laughed wildly, scornfully, and went out.

Weymouth did not turn up, but the morning brought me a
letter, enclosing a cheque for £300, a note to his wife, and a
sealed envelope addressed to the headmaster of his Public
School.

The letter to me ran as follows:—

" Old man, I admit that I am behaving like a cad but it's either this or the sweet waters of oblivion; and there's less scandal this way. I have made up some story for my chief; please post it. The cheque is for all my substance except some fifty pounds. Take care of it for my wife; she'll get another five hundred, about, out of the turnover of our house. She will go to her father, no doubt, and forget me, I hope. Do, please, like a good fellow, see her safely on board. It's not likely that I shall ever come back to England. The future is quite dark, but where *she* is there I must be. Poste restante Constantinople will find me, so far as I know at present. Goodbye and bless you.

" Your affectionate,
" F. W."

I did see Jessie Weymouth on board her ship, and a precious job it was.

A week later I, too, started for Constantinople, partly because I had promised Mrs. Weymouth, partly because I could not reconcile myself to the vision of my friend in the grip of his passion, without a job, almost without money.

The Radolins inhabited an old house on the far shore almost opposite the Rumeli Hissar. I called on them without warning, and found Hélène Radolin alone. In a room all Turkish stuffs and shadowy lights, she looked very different from her desert self. She had regained her pale languor, but her face had a definite spirit, lacking when I first saw her. She spoke quite freely.

" I love him; but it is madness. I have tried to send him away; but he will not go. You see, I am a Catholic; my religion means much to me. I must not go away with him. Take him back to England with you; I cannot bear to see him ruin his life like this for me."

I confess to looking at her with the wonder whether it was religion or the lack of L.S.D.

" Ah!" she said. " You don't understand; you think I am afraid of poverty with him. No! I am afraid of losing my soul, and his."

The way she said that was extraordinarily impressive. I asked her if she saw him.

"Yes; he comes. I have to let him. I cannot bear the look on his face when I say ' No.' " She gave me his address.

He had a garret in a little Greek hotel just above Galata— a ramshackle place, chosen for its cheapness. He did not seem surprised to see me. But I was startled. His face, shrunken and lined, had a bitter, burnt-up look, which deepened the set and colour of his eyes till they looked almost black. A long bout of disease will produce just that effect.

"If she didn't love me," he said, " I could bear it. But she does. Well! So long as I can see her, I shall stand it; and she'll come—she'll come to me at last."

I repeated her words to me; I spoke of his wife, of England —no memory, no allusion, no appeal touched him.

I stayed a month and saw him nearly every day; I did not move him by one jot. At the end of that month I should never have known him for the Frank Weymouth who had started out with us from Mena House on New Year's Day. Changed! He was! I had managed to get him a teaching job through a man I knew at the Embassy—a poor enough job—a bare subsistence. And watching my friend day by day, I began to have a feeling of hatred for that woman. Yet I knew that her refusal to in- dulge their passion was truly religious. She really did see her lost soul and his, whirling entwined through purgatory like the souls of Paolo and Francesca in Watts' picture. Call it superstition, or what you will, her scruples were entirely genuine, and, from a certain point of view, quite laudable.

As for Radolin, he took it all precisely as if there were noth- ing to take; smooth and *debonair* as ever—a little harder about the mouth and eyes, and that was all.

The morning before I went home I made my way once more up the evil-smelling stairs to my friend's garret. He was stand- ing at the window, looking down over the bridge—that tragic bridge at Galata where unfortunates used to trade, perhaps still trade, the sight of their misfortunes. We stood there side by side.

"Frank," I said, " do you ever look at yourself in the glass? This can't go on."

No smile can be so bitter as a smile that used to be sunny.

"So long as I can see her, I shall last out."

"You surely don't want a woman to feel she's lost her soul, and is making you lose yours? She's perfectly sincere, in that."

"I know. I've given up asking. So long as I can see her, that's all."

It was mania!

That afternoon I took a boat over to the Radolins'. It was April—the first real day of spring, balmy and warm. The Judas trees of the Rumeli Hissar were budding, the sun laying on the water the tints of opal; and all the strange city of mosques and minarets, Western commerce and Oriental beggary, was wonderfully living under that first spring sun. I brought my boat up to the Radolins' landing stage, and got out. I mounted the steps, greened over by the wash of the water, and entered their little garden courtyard. I had never come this way before, and stood for a moment looking through the mimosas and bougainvilleas for a door that would satisfy formality. There was a grille to the left, but to reach it I would have to pass in front of the wide ground-floor window, whence I had sometimes looked out over the water to the Rumeli Hissar. My shoes made no noise on the marble path, but what I saw in the room stopped me from trying to pass.

Hélène Radolin was sitting perfectly still in a low chair sideways to the window, her hands on her lap, her eyes fixed on the tiled floor, where a streak of sunlight fell. In the curve of her grand piano, resting his elbows on it, Weymouth was leaning back, equally still, gazing down at her. That was all. But the impression I received of life arrested, of frozen lava, was in a way terrible. I stole back down the steps into my boat, and out on to the opal-tinted waters.

I have nothing more to tell you of this business. The war came down on us all soon after. Rumours I have heard, but know nothing, as they say, of my own knowledge. Yet it has seemed to me worth while to set down this record of a "stroke of lightning," in days when people laugh at such absurdities.

1921.

SPINDLEBERRIES

THE celebrated painter, Scudamore—whose studies of Nature had been hung on the line for so many years that he had forgotten the days when, not yet in the Scudamore manner, they depended from the sky—stood where his cousin had left him so abruptly. His lips, between comely grey moustache and comely pointed beard, wore a mortified smile, and he gazed rather dazedly at the spindleberries fallen on to the flagged courtyard from the branch she had brought to show him. Why had she thrown up her head as if he had struck her, and whisked round so that those dull-pink berries quivered and lost their rain-drops, and four had fallen? He had but said: " Charming! I'd like to use them! " And she had answered: " God ! " and rushed away. Alicia really was crazed; who would have thought that once she had been so adorable? He stooped and picked up the four berries—a beautiful colour, that dull pink! And from below the coatings of success and the Scudamore manner a little thrill came up; the stir of emotional vision. Paint! What good? How express? He went across to the low wall which divided the courtyard of his expensively restored and beautiful old house from the first flood of the River Arun wandering silvery in pale winter sunlight. Yes, indeed! How express Nature, its translucence and mysterious unities, its mood never the same from hour to hour? Those brown-tufted rushes over there against the gold grey of light and water— those restless, hovering, white gulls. A kind of disgust at his own celebrated manner welled up within him—the disgust expressed in Alicia's " God! " Beauty! What use—how express it? Had she been thinking the same thing?

He looked at the four pink berries glistening on the grey stone of the wall and memory stirred. What a lovely girl she had been, with her grey-green eyes shining under long lashes, the rose-petal colour in her cheeks and the too-fine dark hair —now so very grey—always blowing a little wild. An enchant-

383

ing, enthusiastic creature! He remembered, as if it had been but last week, that day when they started from Arundel Station by the road to Burpham, when he was twenty-nine and she twenty-five, both of them painters and neither of them famed—a day of showers and sunlight in the middle of March, and Nature preparing for full spring! How they had chattered at first; and when their arms touched, how he had thrilled, and the colour had deepened in her rain-wet cheeks; and then, gradually, they had grown silent; a wonderful walk, which seemed leading so surely to a more wonderful end. They had wandered round through the village and down past the chalk-pit and Jacob's ladder, into the field path and so to the river bank. And he had taken her ever so gently round the waist, still silent, waiting for that moment when his heart would leap out of him in words and hers—he was sure—would leap to meet it. The path entered a thicket of blackthorn with a few primroses close to the little river running full and gentle. The last drops of a shower were falling, but the sun had burst through, and the sky above the thicket was cleared to the blue of speedwell flowers. Suddenly she had stopped and cried: "Look, Dick! Oh, look! It's heaven!" A high bush of blackthorn was lifted there, starry white against the blue and that bright cloud. It seemed to sing, it was so lovely; the whole of spring was in it. But the sight of her ecstatic face had broken down all his restraint, and tightening his arm round her he had kissed her lips. He remembered still the expression of her face, like a child's startled out of sleep. She had gone rigid, gasped, started away from him, quivered and gulped, and broken suddenly into sobs. Then, slipping from his arm, she had fled. He had stood at first, amazed and hurt, utterly bewildered; then, recovering a little, had hunted for her full half an hour before at last he found her sitting on wet grass, with a stony look on her face. He had said nothing, and she nothing, except to murmur: "Let's go on; we shall miss our train!" And all the rest of that day and the day after, until they parted, he had suffered from the feeling of having tumbled down off some high perch in her estimation. He had not liked it at all; it had made him very angry. Never from that day to this had he thought of it as anything but a piece of wanton prudery. Had it—had it been something else?

He looked at the four pink berries, and, as if they had uncanny power to turn the wheel of memory, he saw another vision of his cousin five years later. He was married by then, and already hung on the line. With his wife he had gone down to Alicia's country cottage. A summer night, just dark and very warm. After many exhortations she had brought into the little drawing-room her last finished picture. He could see her now placing it where the light fell, her tall, slight form already rather sharp and meagre, as the figures of some women grow at thirty, if they are not married; the nervous, fluttering look on her charming face, as though she could hardly bear this inspection; the way she raised her shoulder just a little as if to ward off an expected blow of condemnation. No need! It had been a beautiful thing, a quite surprisingly beautiful study of night. He remembered with what a really jealous ache he had gazed at it—a better thing than he had ever done himself. And, frankly, he had said so. Her eyes had shone with pleasure.

"Do you really like it? I tried so hard!"

"The day you show that, my dear," he had said, "your name's made!" She had clasped her hands and simply sighed: "Oh, Dick!" He had felt quite happy in her happiness, and presently the three of them had taken their chairs out, beyond the curtains, on to the dark verandah, had talked a little, then somehow fallen silent. A wonderful warm, black, grape-bloom night, exquisitely gracious and inviting; the stars very high and white, the flowers glimmering in the garden-beds, and against the deep, dark blue, roses hanging, unearthly, stained with beauty. There was a scent of honeysuckle, he remembered, and many moths came fluttering by toward the tall, narrow chink of light between the curtains. Alicia had sat leaning forward, elbows on knees, ears buried in her hands. Probably they were silent because she sat like that. Once he heard her whisper to herself: "Lovely, lovely! Oh, God! How lovely!" His wife, feeling the dew, had gone in, and he had followed; Alicia had not seemed to notice. But when she too came in, her eyes were glistening with tears. She said something about bed in a queer voice; they had taken candles and gone up. Next morning, going to her little studio to give her advice about that picture, he had been literally horrified to see it streaked with lines of white—Alicia, standing before it, was dashing her brush in broad smears across and across. She heard him and turned round. There was a hard red spot in either cheek, and she said in a quivering voice: "It was blasphemy.

That's all!" And turning her back on him she had gone
on smearing it with white. Without a word, he had turned tail
in simple disgust. Indeed, so deep had been his vexation at
that wanton destruction of the best thing she had ever done
or was ever likely to do, that he had avoided her for years.
He had always had a horror of eccentricity. To have planted
her foot firmly on the ladder of fame and then deliberately
kicked it away; to have wantonly foregone this chance of
making money—for she had but a mere pittance! It had
seemed to him really too exasperating, a thing only to be explained by tapping one's forehead. Every now and then he still
heard of her, living down there, spending her days out in the
woods and fields, and sometimes even her nights, they said, and
steadily growing poorer and thinner and more eccentric; becoming, in short, impossibly difficult, as only Englishwomen
can. People would speak of her as "such a dear," and talk
of her charm, but always with that shrug which is hard to
bear when applied to one's relations. What she did with the
productions of her brush he never inquired, too disillusioned
by that experience. Poor Alicia!

The pink berries glowed on the grey stone, and he had yet
another memory. A family occasion when Uncle Martin Scudamore departed this life, and they all went up to bury him and
hear his will. The old chap, whom they had looked on as a
bit of a disgrace, money-grubbing up in the little grey York-
shire town which owed its rise to his factory, was expected to
make amends by his death, for he had never married—too sunk
in industry, apparently, to have the time. By tacit agreement,
his nephews and nieces had selected the Inn at Bolton Abbey,
nearest beauty spot, for their stay. They had driven six miles
to the funeral, in three carriages. Alicia had gone with him
and his brother, the solicitor. In her plain black clothes she
looked quite charming, in spite of the silver threads already
thick in her fine dark hair, loosened by the moor wind. She
had talked of painting to him with all her old enthusiasm, and
her eyes had seemed to linger on his face as if she still had a
little weakness for him. He had quite enjoyed that drive.
They had come rather abruptly on the small grimy town clinging to the river banks, with old Martin's long, yellow-brick
house dominating it, about two hundred yards above the mills.
Suddenly, under the rug, he felt Alicia's hand seize his with a
sort of desperation, for all the world as if she were clinging

to something to support her. Indeed, he was sure she did not know it was his hand she squeezed. The cobbled streets, the muddy-looking water, the dingy, staring factories, the yellow, staring house, the little dark-clothed, dreadfully plain work-people, all turned out to do a last honour to their creator; the hideous new grey church, the dismal service, the brand-new tombstones—and all of a glorious autumn day! It was inexpressibly sordid—too ugly for words! Afterwards the will was read to them seated decorously on bright mahogany chairs in the yellow mansion, a very satisfactory will, distributing in perfectly adjusted portions, to his own kinsfolk and nobody else, a very considerable wealth. Scudamore had listened to it dreamily, with his eyes fixed on an oily picture, thinking, 'My God! What a thing!' and longing to be back in the carriage smoking a cigar to take the reek of black clothes and sherry—sherry!—out of his nostrils. He happened to look at Alicia. Her eyes were closed; her lips, always sweet-looking, quivered amusedly. And at that very moment the will came to her name. He saw those eyes open wide, and marked a beautiful pink flush, quite like that of old days, come into her thin cheeks. 'Splendid!' he had thought; 'it's really jolly for her. I *am* glad! Now she won't have to pinch. Splendid!' He shared with her to the full the surprised relief showing in her still beautiful face.

All the way home in the carriage he felt at least as happy over her good fortune as over his own, which had been substantial. He took her hand under the rug and squeezed it, and she answered with a long, gentle pressure, quite unlike the clutch when they were driving in. That same evening he strolled out to where the river curved below the Abbey. The sun had not quite set, and its last smoky radiance slanted into the burnished autumn woods. Some white-faced Herefords were grazing in lush grass, the river rippled and gleamed all over golden scales. About that scene was the magic which had so often startled the hearts of painters, the wistful gold—the enchantment of a dream. For some minutes he had gazed with delight which had in it a sort of despair. A little crisp rustle ran along the bushes; the leaves fluttered, then hung quite still. And he heard a voice—Alicia's—speaking. "The lovely, lovely world!" And moving forward a step, he saw her standing on the river bank, braced against the trunk of a birch tree, her head thrown back, and her arms stretched wide apart as though to clasp the lovely world she had apostrophised.

To have gone up to her would have been like breaking up a lovers' interview, and he turned round instead and went away.

A week later he heard from his brother that Alicia had refused her legacy. " I don't want it," her letter had said simply; " I couldn't bear to take it. Give it to those poor people who live in that awful place." Really eccentricity could go no further! They decided to go down and see her. Such mad neglect of her own good must not be permitted without some effort to prevent it. They found her very thin and charming, humble, but quite obstinate in her refusal. " Oh! I couldn't really! I should be so unhappy. Those poor little stunted people who made it all for him! That little, awful town! I simply couldn't be reminded. Don't talk about it, please. I'm quite all right as I am." They had threatened her with lurid pictures of the workhouse and a destitute old age. To no purpose; she would not take the money. She had been forty when she refused that aid from heaven—forty, and already past any hope of marriage. For though Scudamore had never known for certain that she had ever wished or hoped for marriage, he had his theory—that all her eccentricity came from wasted sexual instinct. This last folly had seemed to him monstrous enough to be pathetic, and he no longer avoided her. Indeed, he would often walk over to tea in her little hermitage. With Uncle Martin's money he had bought and restored the beautiful old house over the River Arun, and was now only five miles from Alicia's, across country. She, too, would come tramping over at all hours, floating in with wild flowers or ferns, which she would put into water the moment she arrived. She had ceased to wear hats, and had by now a very doubtful reputation for sanity about the countryside. This was the period when Watts was on every painter's tongue, and he seldom saw Alicia without a disputation concerning that famous symbolist. Personally, he had no use for Watts, resenting his faulty drawing and crude allegories, but Alicia always maintained with her extravagant fervour that he was great because he tried to paint the soul of things. She especially loved a painting called " Iris " —a female symbol of the rainbow, which indeed, in its floating eccentricity, had a certain resemblance to herself. " Of course he failed," she would say; " he tried for the impossible and went on trying all his life. Oh! I can't bear your tales and catchwords, Dick; what's the good of them! Beauty's too big, too deep! " Poor Alicia! She was sometimes very wearing.

He never knew quite how it came about that she went abroad with them to Dauphiné in the autumn of 1904—a rather disastrous business. Never again would he take anyone travelling who did not know how to come in out of the cold. It was a painter's country, and he had hired a little *château* in front of Glandaz mountain—himself, his wife, their eldest girl, and Alicia. The adaptation of his famous manner to that strange scenery, its browns and French greys and filmy blues, so preoccupied him that he had scant time for becoming intimate with these hills and valleys. From the little gravelled terrace in front of the annexe, out of which he had made a studio, there was an absorbing view over the pantiled old town of Die. It glistened below in the early or late sunlight, flat-roofed and of pinkish yellow, with the dim, blue River Drôme circling one side, and cut, dark cypress trees dotting the vineyarded slopes. And he painted it continually. What Alicia did with herself they none of them very much knew, except that she would come in and talk ecstatically of things and beasts and people she had seen. One favourite haunt of hers they did visit—a ruined monastery high up in the amphitheatre of the Glandaz mountain. They had their lunch up there, a very charming and remote spot, where the watercourses and ponds and chapel of the old monks were still visible, though converted by the farmer to his use. Alicia left them abruptly in the middle of their praises, and they had not seen her again till they found her at home when they got back. It was almost as if she had resented laudation of her favourite haunt. She had brought in with her a great bunch of golden berries, of which none of them knew the name; berries almost as beautiful as these spindleberries glowing on the stone of the wall. And a fourth memory of Alicia came.

Christmas Eve, a sparkling frost, and every tree round the little *chateau* rimed so that they shone in the starlight as though dowered with cherry blossom. Never were more stars in clear black sky above the whitened earth. Down in the little town a few faint points of yellow light twinkled in the mountain wind keen as a razor's edge. A fantastically lovely night—quite "Japanese," but cruelly cold. Five minutes on the terrace had been enough for all of them except Alicia. She—unaccountable, crazy creature—would not come in. Twice he had gone out to her, with commands, entreaties, and extra wraps; the third time he could not find her. She had deliberately avoided his onslaught and slid off somewhere to keep this mad

vigil by frozen starlight. When at last she did come in she
reeled as if drunk. They tried to make her really drunk, to
put warmth back into her. No good! In two days she was
down with double pneumonia; it was two months before she
was up again—a very shadow of herself. There had never
been much health in her since then. She floated like a ghost
through life, a crazy ghost, who would steal away, goodness
knew where, and come in with a flush in her withered cheeks,
and her grey hair wild blown, carrying her spoil—some flower,
some leaf, some tiny bird or little soft rabbit. She never painted
now, never even talked of it. They had made her give up her
cottage and come to live with them, literally afraid that she
would starve herself to death in her forgetfulness of everything.
These spindleberries even! Why probably, she had been right up
this morning to that sunny chalk-pit in the lew of the Downs
to get them, seven miles there and back, when you wouldn't
think she could walk seven hundred yards, and as likely as not
had lain there on the dewy grass looking up at the sky, as
he had come on her sometimes. Poor Alicia! And once he had
been within an ace of marrying her! A life spoiled! By what,
if not by love of beauty? But who would have ever thought
that the intangible could wreck a woman, deprive her of love,
marriage, motherhood, of fame, of wealth, of health? And yet
—by George!—it had!

Scudamore flipped the four pink berries off the wall. The
radiance and the meandering milky waters; that swan against
the brown tufted rushes; those far, filmy Downs—there was
beauty! *Beauty!* But, damn it all—moderation! Moderation! And, turning his back on that prospect, which he had
painted so many times, in his celebrated manner, he went in,
and up the expensively restored staircase to his studio. It had
great windows on three sides, and perfect means for regulating
light. Unfinished studies melted into walls so subdued that
they looked like atmosphere. There were no completed pictures—they sold too fast. As he walked over to his easel his
eye was caught by a spray of colour—the branch of spindleberries set in water, ready for him to use, just where the pale
sunlight fell so that their delicate colour might glow and the
few tiny drops of moisture still clinging to them shine. For
a second he saw Alicia herself as she must have looked, setting
them there, her transparent hands hovering, her eyes shining,
that grey hair of hers all fine and loose. The vision vanished!

But what had made her bring them after that horrified "God!" when he spoke of using them? Was it her way of saying: "Forgive me for being rude"? Really she was pathetic, that poor devotee! The spindleberries glowed in their silver-lustre jug, sprayed up against the sunlight. They looked triumphant —as well they might, who stood for that which had ruined— or was it saved?—a life! Alicia! She had made a pretty mess of it, and yet who knew what secret raptures she had felt with her subtle lover, Beauty, by starlight and sunlight and moon-light, in the fields and woods, on the hilltops, and by riverside? Flowers, and the flight of birds, and the ripple of the wind, and all the shifting play of light and colour which made a man despair when he wanted to use them; she had taken them, hugged them to her with no afterthought, and been happy! Who could say that she had missed the prize of life? Who could say it? . . . Spindleberries! A bunch of spindleberries to set such doubts astir in him! Why, what was beauty but just the extra value which certain forms and colours, blended, gave to things—just the extra value in the human market! Nothing else on earth, nothing! And the spindleberries glowed against the sunlight, delicate, remote!

Taking his palette, he mixed crimson lake, white, and ultra-marine. What was that? Who sighed, away out there behind him? Nothing!

'Damn it all!' he thought; 'this is childish. This is as bad as Alicia!' And he set to work to paint in his celebrated manner—spindleberries.

1918.

SALTA PRO NOBIS

(A Variation)

"THE dancer, my Mother, is very sad. She sits with her head on her hands. She looks into the emptiness. It is frightful to watch. I have tried to make her pray, my Mother, but the poor girl—she does not know how; she has no belief. She refuses even to confess herself. She is pagan—but quite pagan. What could one do for her, my Mother—to cheer her a little during these hours? I have tried to make her tell me of her life. She does not answer. She sits and looks always into the emptiness. It does me harm in the heart to see her. Is there nothing one can do to comfort her a little before she dies? To die so young—so full of life; for her who has no faith! To be shot—so young, so beautiful; but it is frightful, my Mother!"

When she had finished speaking thus, the little elderly Sister raised her hands, and crossed them quietly on her grey-clothed breast. Her eyes, brown and mild, looked up, questioning the face before her, wax pale under its coif and smooth grey hair. Straight, thin, as it were bodiless, beneath the grey and white of her garb, the Mother Superior stood pondering. The spy-woman in her charge, a dancer with gypsy blood they said—or was it Moorish?—who had wormed secrets from her French naval lover, and sold them to the Germans in Spain. At the trial they said there was no doubt. And they had brought her to the Convent saying, " Keep her for us till the fifteenth. She will be better with you than in prison." To be shot—a woman! It made one shiver! And yet—it was war! It was for France!

Looking down at the little Sister with the soft brown eyes, the Mother Superior answered:

" One must see, my daughter. Take me to her cell."

Along the corridor they passed, and went in gently. The dancer was sitting on her bed, with legs crossed under her.

393

There was no colour in her skin, save the saffron sprinkled
into it by Eastern blood. The face was oval, the eyebrows
slanted a little up; black hair formed on her forehead a V reversed; her lips, sensuous but fine, showed a gleam of teeth.
Her arms were crossed, as though compressing the fire within
her supple body. Her eyes, colour of Malaga wine, looked
through and beyond the whitened walls, through and beyond
her visitors, like the eyes of a caged leopard.

The Mother Superior spoke:

" What can we do for you, my daughter? "

The daughter shrugged her body from the waist; one could
see its supple shivering beneath her silk garment.

" You suffer, my daughter. They tell me you do not pray.
It is a pity."

The dancer smiled—that quickly passing smile had sweetness, as of something tasted, of a rich tune, of a long kiss;
she shook her head.

" One would not say anything to trouble you, my daughter;
one feels pity for your suffering. One comprehends. Is there
a book you would read; some wine you would like; in a word,
anything which could distract you a little? "

The dancer untwined her arms, and clasped them behind her
neck. The movement was beautiful, sinuous—all her body
beautiful; and into the Mother Superior's waxen cheeks a faint
colour came.

" Will you dance for us, my daughter? "

Again the smile, like the taste of a sweet wine, came on the
dancer's face, and this time did not pass.

" Yes," she said, " I will dance for you—willingly. It will
give me pleasure, Madame! "

" That is good. Your dresses shall be brought. This evening in the refectory, after the meal. If you wish music—one
can place a piano. Sister Mathilde is a good musician."

" Yes, music—some simple dances. Madame, could I
smoke? "

" Certainly, my daughter. I will have cigarettes brought to
you."

The dancer stretched out her hand. Between her own, fragile
with thin blue veins, the Mother Superior felt its supple warmth,
and shivered. To-morrow it would be cold and stiff!

" *Au revoir!* then, my daughter. . . . "

" The dancer will dance for us! " This was the word. One

waited, expectant, as for a marvel. One placed the piano; procured music; sat eating the evening meal—whispering. The strangeness of it! The intrusion! The little gay ghosts of memories! Ah! the dramatic, the strange event! Soon the meal was finished; the tables cleared, removed; against the wall, on the long benches sixty grey figures with white coifs waited—in the centre the Mother Superior, at the piano Sister Mathilde.

The little elderly Sister came first; then, down the long whitened refectory, the dancer walking slowly over the dark oak floor. Every head was turned—alone the Mother Superior sat motionless, thinking: ' If only it does not put notions into some light heads!'

The dancer wore a full skirt of black silk, she had silvery shoes and stockings, round her waist was a broad tight network of gold, over her bust tight silvery tissue, with black lace draped; her arms were bare; a red flower was set to one side of her black hair; she held a black and ivory fan. Her lips were just touched with red, her eyes just touched with black; her face was like a mask. She stood in the very centre, with eyes cast down. Sister Mathilde began to play. The dancer lifted her fan. In that dance of Spain she hardly moved from where she stood, swaying, shivering, spinning, poised; only the eyes of her face seemed alive, resting on this face and on that of the long row of faces, where so many feelings were expressed—curiosity and doubt, pleasure, timidity, horror, curiosity. Sister Mathilde ceased playing, the dancer stood still; a little murmur broke along the line of nuns, and the dancer smiled. Then Sister Mathilde began again to play, a Polish dance; for a moment the dancer listened as if to catch the rhythm of music strange to her; then her feet moved, her lips parted, she was sweet and gay, like a butterfly, without a care; and on the lips of the watching faces smiles came, and little murmurs of pleasure escaped.

The Mother Superior sat without moving, her thin lips pressed together, her thin fingers interlaced. Images from the past kept starting out, and falling back, like figures from some curious old musical box. That long-ago time—she was remembering—when her lover was killed in the Franco-Prussian war, and she entered religion. This supple figure from the heathen world, the red flower in the black hair, the whitened face, the sweetened eyes, stirred up remembrance, sweet and yearning,

of her own gay pulses, before they had seemed to die, and she
brought them to the Church to bury them.

The music ceased; began again a Habañera, reviving memories of the pulses after they were buried—secret, throbbing,
dark. The Mother Superior turned her face to left and right.
Had she been wise? So many light heads, so many young
hearts! And yet, why not soothe the last dark hours of this
poor heathen girl? She was happy, dancing. Yes, she was
happy! What power! And what abandonment! It was frightening. She was holding every eye—the eyes even of Sister
Louise—holding them as a snake holds a rabbit's eyes. The
Mother Superior nearly smiled. That poor Sister Louise! And
then, just beyond that face of fascinated horror, the Mother
Superior saw young Sister Marie. How the child was staring
—what eyes, what lips! Sister Marie—so young—just twenty
—her lover dead in the war—but one year dead! Sister Marie
—prettiest in all the Convent! Her hands—how tightly they
seemed pressed together on her lap! And—but yes—it was at
Sister Marie that the dancer looked; at Sister Marie she twirled
and writhed those supple fiery limbs! For Sister Marie the
strange sweet smile came and went on those enticing reddened
lips. In dance after dance—like a bee on a favourite flower
—to Sister Marie the dancer seemed to cling. And the Mother
Superior thought: ' Is this the Blessed Virgin's work I have
done, or—the Devil's? '

Close along the line of nuns the dancer was sweeping now;
her eyes glowed, her face was proud, her body supreme. Sister
Marie! What was it? A look, a touch with the fan! The
music ceased! The dancer blew a kiss. It lighted—where?
" *Gracias, Señoras! Adios!* "

Slowly, swaying, as she had come, she walked away over the
dark floor; and the little old Sister followed.

A sighing sound from the long row of nuns; and—yes—one
sob!

" Go to your rooms, my daughters! Sister Marie! "

The young nun came forward; tears were in her eyes.

" Sister Marie, pray that the sins of that poor soul be forgiven. But yes, my child, it is sad. Go to your room. Pray! "

With what grace the child walked! She, too, had the limbs
of beauty. The Mother Superior sighed. . . .

Morning, cold, grey, a sprinkle of snow on the ground; they
came for the dancer during Mass. A sound of firing! With

trembling lips, the Mother Superior prayed for the soul dancing before her God. . . .

That evening they searched for Sister Marie, but could not find her. After two days a letter came:

" Forgive me, my Mother. I have gone back to life.

" MARIE."

The Mother Superior sat quite still. Life in death! Figures starting out from that old musical box of memory; the dancer's face, red flower in the hair, dark sweetened eyes, lips, touched with flying finger, parted in a kiss!

1922.

THE PACK

"It's only," said H., "when men run in packs that they lose their sense of decency. At least that's my experience. Individual man—I'm not speaking of savages—is more given to generosity than meanness, rarely brutal, inclines in fact to be a gentleman. It's when you add three or four more to him that his sense of decency, his sense of personal responsibility, his private standards, go by the board. I am not at all sure that he does not become the victim of a certain infectious fever. Something physical takes place, I fancy. . . . I happen to be a trustee, with three others, and we do a deal of cheeseparing in the year, which as private individuals we should never dream of."

"That's hardly a fair example," said D., "but on the whole, I quite agree. Single man is not an angel; collective man is a bit of a brute."

The discussion was carried on for several minutes, and then P., who had not yet spoken, said: "They say a pinch of illustration is worth a pound of argument. When I was at the 'Varsity there was a man at the same college with me called Chalkcroft, the son of a high ecclesiastic, a perfectly harmless, well-mannered individual, who had the misfortune to be a Radical, or, as some even thought, a Socialist—anyway, he wore a turn-down collar, a green tie, took part in Union debates on the shady side, and no part in college festivities. He was, in fact, a 'smug'—a man, as you know, who, through some accident of his early environment, incomprehensibly fails to adopt the proper view of life. He was never drunk, not even pleasantly, played no games connected with a ball, was believed to be afraid of a horse or a woman, took his exercise in long walks with a man from another college, or solitarily in a skiff upon the river; he also read books, and was prepared to discuss abstract propositions. Thus, in one way or another he disgusted almost every self-respecting undergraduate. Don't imagine, of course, that his case was unusual; we had many such at M—— in my time; but about this Chalkcroft there was an unjustifiable composure, a quiet sarcasm, which made him conspicuously intolerable. He was thought to be a 'bit above himself,' or, rather, he did not seem conscious, as any proper 'smug' should, that he was a bit below his fellows; on the contrary, his figure, which was slim, and slightly stooping, passed in and about college with serene assurance; his pale face with its traces of reprehensible whisker, wore a faint smile above his detested green tie; besides, he showed no signs of that poverty which is, of course, some justification to 'smugs' for their lack of conformity. And as a matter of fact, he was *not* poor, but had some of the best rooms in college, which was ever a remembered grievance against him. For these reasons, then," went on P., " it was decided one evening to bring him to trial. This salutary custom had originated in the mind of a third-year man named Jefferies, a dark person with a kind of elephant-like unwieldiness in his nose and walk, a biting, witty tongue, and very small eyes with a lecherous expression. He is now a baronet. This gentleman in his cups had quite a pretty malice, and a sense of the dignity of the law. Wandering of a night in the quadrangles, he never had any difficulty in gathering a troop of fellows in search of distraction, or animated by public and other spirits; and, with them whooping and crowing at his heels, it was his beneficial practice to enter the rooms of any person, who for good and sufficient reasons merited trial, and thereupon to conduct the same with all the ceremony due to the dispensation of British justice. I had attended one of these trials before, on a chuckle-headed youth whose buffoonery was really offensive. The ceremony was funny enough, nor did the youth seem to mind, grinning from ear to ear, and ejaculating continually, ' Oh! I say, Jefferies! '

" The occasion of which I am going to speak now was a different sort of affair altogether. We found the man Chalkcroft at home, reading before his fire by the light of three candles. The room was panelled in black oak, and the yellow candle flames barely lit up the darkness as we came whooping in.

" ' Chalkcroft,' said Jefferies, ' we are going to try you.' Chalkcroft stood up and looked at us. He was in a Norfolk jacket, with his customary green tie, and his face was pale.

" He answered: ' Yes, Jefferies? You forgot to knock.'

" Jefferies put out his finger and thumb and delicately plucked Chalkcroft's tie from out of his waistcoat.

" ' You wear a green tie, sir,' he said.

" ' Chalkcroft went the colour of the ashes in the grate; then, slowly, a white-hot glow came into his cheeks.

" ' Don't look at me, sir," said Jefferies; ' look at the jury! ' and he waved his hand at us. ' We are going to try you for——' He specified an incident of a scabrous character which served as the charge on all such humorous occasions, and was likely to be peculiarly offensive to ' smugs,' who are usually, as you know, what is called ' pi.'

" We yelped, guffawed, and settled ourselves in chairs; Jefferies perched himself on a table and slowly swung his thin legs; he always wore very tight trousers. His little black eyes gleamed greedily above his unwieldy nose. Chalkcroft remained standing.

" It was then," pursued P., " that I had my first qualm. The fellow was so still and pale and unmoved; he looked at me, and, when I tried to stare back, his eyes passed me over, quiet and contemptuous. And I remember thinking: ' Why are we all here—we are not a bit the kind of men to do this sort of thing? ' And really we were not. With the exception of Jefferies, who was, no doubt, at times inhabited by a devil, and one Anderson, a little man in a long coat, with a red nose and very long arms, always half-drunk—a sort of desperate character, and long since a schoolmaster—there wasn't one of us who, left to himself, would have entered another man's rooms unbidden (however unpopular he might be, however much of a ' smug '), and insulted him to his face. There was Beal, a very fair, rather good-looking man, with bowed legs and no expression to speak of, known as Boshy Beal; Dunsdale, a heavy, long-faced, freckled person, prominent in every college disturbance, but with a reputation for respectability; Horden (called Jos), a big, clean-cut Kentish man with nice eyes, and fists like hammers; Stickland, fussy, with mild habits; Sevenoax, now in the House of Lords; little Holingbroke, the cox; and my old school-fellow, Fosdyke, whose dignity even then would certainly have forbidden his presence had he not previously dined. Thus, as you see, we were all or nearly all from the ' best ' schools in the country, in the ' best ' set at M——, and naturally, as individuals, quite —oh! quite—incapable of an ungentlemanlike act.

" Jefferies appointed Anderson gaoler, Dunsdale Public Prosecutor, no one counsel for the defence, the rest of us jury, himself judge, and opened the trial. He was, as I have said, a

witty young man, and, dangling his legs, fastening his malevolent black eyes on Chalkcroft, he usurped the functions of us
all. The nature of the charge precludes me from recounting to
you the details of the trial, and, in fact, I have forgotten them,
but as if he were standing here before us, I remember, in the
dim glow of those three candles, Chalkcroft's pale, unmoved,
ironic face; his unvarying, 'Yes, Jefferies'; his one remon-
strance: 'Are you a gentleman, Jefferies?' and our insane
laughter at the answer: 'No, sir, a by-our-Lady judge.' As
if he were standing here before us I remember the expression
on his face at the question: 'Prisoner, are you guilty—yes or
no?' the long pause, the slow, sarcastic: 'As you like, Jefferies.' As if he were standing here before us I remember his calm
and his contempt. He was sentenced to drink a tumbler of his
own port without stopping; whether the sentence was carried
out I cannot tell you; for with one or two more I slipped away.

"The next morning I had such a sense of discomfort that I
could not rest till I had sent Chalkcroft a letter of apology.
I caught sight of him in the afternoon walking across the quad.
with his usual pale assurance, and in the evening I received his
answer. It contained, at the end, this sentence: 'I feel sure
you would not have come if it hadn't been for the others.' It
has occurred to me since that he may have said the same thing
to us all—for anything I know, we may all of us have written."

There was a silence. Then H. said: "The Pack! Ah!
What second-hand devil is it that gets into us when we run
in packs?"

1905.

"THE DOG IT WAS THAT DIED"

UNTIL the Great War was over I had no idea that some of us who stayed at home made the great sacrifice.

My friend Harburn is, or rather was, a Northumbrian or some kind of northerner, a stocky man of perhaps fifty with close-clipped grizzled hair and moustache and a deep-coloured face. He was a neighbour of mine in the country, and we had the same kind of dogs—Airedales, never less than three at a time, so that for breeding purposes we were useful to each other. We often, too, went up to town by the same train. His occupation was one which gave him opportunity of prominence in public life, but until the war he took little advantage of this, sunk in a kind of bluff indifferentism which was almost cynical. I used to look on him as a typically good-natured, blunt Englishman, rather enjoying his cynicism, and appreciating his open-air tendencies—for he was a devotee of golf and fond of shooting when he had the chance; a good companion, too, with an open hand to people in distress. He was unmarried, and dwelled in a bungalow-like house not far from mine and next door to a German family called Holsteig, who had lived in England nearly twenty years. I knew them pretty well also—a very united trio—father, mother, and one son. The father, who came from Hanover, was something in the city, the mother was Scotch, and the son—the one I knew best and liked most—had just left his public school. This youth had a frank, open, blue-eyed face, and thick light hair brushed back without a parting—an attractive, rather Norwegian-looking type. His mother was devoted to him—she was a real West Highlander; slight, with dark hair going grey, high cheekbones, a sweet but ironical smile, and those grey eyes which have second sight in them. I several times met Harburn at their house, for he would go in to play billiards with Holsteig in the evenings, and the whole family were on friendly terms with him. The third morning after we had declared war on

Germany, Harburn, Holsteig, and I went up to town in the
same carriage. Harburn and I talked freely. But Holsteig, a
fair, well-set-up man of about fifty, with a pointed beard and
blue eyes like his son, sat immersed in his paper, till Harburn
said rather suddenly:

"I say, Holsteig, is it true that your boy was going off to
join the German Army?"

Holsteig looked up.

"Yes," he said. "He was born in Germany, so he's liable
to military service. Thank heaven—it isn't possible for him to
go!"

"But his mother?" said Harburn. "She surely wouldn't
have let him."

"She was very miserable, of course, but she thought duty
came first."

"Duty! Good God—my dear man! Half British, and living in this country all his life! I never heard of such a thing!"

Holsteig shrugged his shoulders.

"In a crisis like this what can you do except follow the law
strictly? He is of military age and a German subject. We
were thinking of his honour; but, of course, we're most thankful he can't get over to Germany."

"Well, I'm damned!" said Harburn. "You Germans are
too bally conscientious altogether."

Holsteig did not answer.

I travelled back with Harburn the same evening, and he said
to me:

"Once a German, always a German. Didn't that chap Holsteig astonish you this morning? In spite of living here so
long and marrying a British wife, his sympathies are dead German, you see."

"Well," I replied, "put yourself in his place."

"I can't; I could never have lived in Germany. I say, Cumbermere," he added, "I wonder if the chap's all right?"

"Of course he's all right." Which was the wrong thing to
say to Harburn if one wanted to re-establish his confidence
in the Holsteigs, as I certainly did, for I liked them and was
sure of their good faith. If I had said: "Of course he's a
spy," I should have rallied all Harburn's confidence in Holsteig, for he was naturally contradictious.

I only mention this little passage to show how early Harburn's thoughts began to turn to the subject which afterwards

completely absorbed and inspired him till he—er—died for his country.

I am not sure what paper first took up the question of interning all the Huns; but I fancy the point was raised originally rather from the instinct, deeply implanted in so many journals, to do what would please the public than out of any deep animus. At all events, I remember meeting a sub-editor who told me he had been opening letters of approval all the morning. "Never," said he, "have we had a stunt catch on so quickly. 'Why should that bally German round the corner get my custom?' and so forth. Britain for the British!"

"Rather bad luck," I said, "on people who've paid us the compliment of finding this the best country to live in?"

"Bad luck, no doubt," he replied, "but war's war. You know Harburn, don't you? Did you see that article he wrote? By Jove! he pitched it strong."

When next I met Harburn himself he began talking on this subject at once.

"Mark my words," he said, "I'll have every German out of this country." His grey eyes seemed to glint with the snap and spark as of steel and flint and tinder; and I felt I was in the presence of a man who had brooded so over the German atrocities in Belgium that he was possessed by a sort of abstract hate.

"Of course," I said, "there have been many spies, but——"

"Spies and ruffians," he cried, "the whole lot of them."

"Mow many Germans do you know personally?" I asked him.

"Thank God! not a dozen."

"And are they spies and ruffians?"

He looked at me and laughed, but that laugh was uncommonly like a snarl.

"You go in for fairness," he said, "and all that slop; take 'em by the throat—it's the only way."

It trembled on the tip of my tongue to ask him whether he meant to take the Holsteigs by the throat, but I swallowed it for fear of doing them an injury. I was feeling much the same general abhorrence myself, and had to hold myself in for fear it should gallop over my common sense of justice. But Harburn, I could see, was giving it full rein. His whole manner and personality somehow had changed. He had lost geniality and that good-humoured cynicism which had made him an attractive companion; he was as if gnawed at inwardly,—in a word, he already had a fixed idea.

Now, a cartoonist, like myself, has to be interested in the psychology of men, and I brooded over Harburn, for it seemed to me quite remarkable that one whom I had always associated with good humour and bluff indifference should be thus obsessed. And I found this theory about him: " Here "—I said to myself—" is one of Cromwell's Ironsides, born out of his age. In the slack times of peace he discovered no outlet for the grim within him—his fire could never be lighted by love, therefore he drifted in the waters of indifferentism. Now, suddenly, in this grizzly time he has found himself, a new man, girt and armed by this new passion of hate, stung and uplifted, as it were, by the sight of that which he can smite with a whole heart. It really is most deeply interesting. Who could have dreamed of such a reincarnation; for what on the surface could possibly be less like an ' Ironside ' than Harburn as I've known him up to now? " I used his face for the basis of a cartoon which represented a human weather-vane continually pointing to the East, no matter from what quarter the wind blew. He recognised himself, and laughed when he saw me—rather pleased, in fact; but in that laugh there was a sort of truculence as if the man had the salt taste of blood at the back of his mouth.

" Ah! " said he, " you may joke about it, Cumbermere, but I've got my teeth into the swine! "

And there was no doubt he had—the man had become a force; unhappy Germans—a few of them spies, no doubt, but the great majority as certainly innocent—were being wrenched from their trades and families and piled into internment camps all day and every day—and the faster they were piled in, the higher grew his " stock " as a servant of his country. I'm sure he did not do it to gain credit; the thing was a crusade to him, something sacred—" his bit "; but I believe he also felt for the first time in his life that he was really living, getting out of life the full of its juice. Was he not smiting hip and thigh? He longed, I am sure, to be in the thick of the actual fighting, but age debarred him, and he was not of that more sensitive type which shrinks from smiting the defenceless if it cannot smite anything stronger. I remember saying to him once:

"Harburn, do you ever think of the women and children of your victims?"

He drew his lips back, and I saw how excellent his teeth were.

"The women are worse than the men, I believe," he said. "I'd put them in, too, if I could. As for the children, they're all the better for being without fathers of that kidney."

He really was a little mad on the subject; no more so, of course, than any other man with a fixed idea, but certainly no less.

In those days I was here, there, and everywhere, and had let my country cottage, so I saw nothing of the Holsteigs, and, indeed, had pretty well forgotten their existence. But coming back at the end of 1917 from a long spell with the Red Cross, I found among my letters one from Mrs. Holsteig.

"DEAR MR. CUMBERMERE,

"You were always so friendly to us that I have summoned up courage to write this letter. You know, perhaps, that my husband was interned over a year ago, and repatriated last September; he has lost everything, of course, but so far he is well and able to get along in Germany. Harold and I have been jogging on here as best we can on my own little income—'Huns in our midst' as we are, we see practically nobody. What a pity we cannot all look into each other's hearts, isn't it? I used to think we were a 'fair-play' people, but I have learned the bitter truth, that there is no such thing when pressure comes. It's much worse for Harold than for me; he feels his paralysed position intensely, and would, I'm sure, really rather be 'doing his bit' as an interned than be at large, subject to everyone's suspicion and scorn. But I am terrified all the time that they *will* intern him. You used to be intimate with Mr. Harburn. We have not seen him since the first autumn of the war, but we know that he has been very active in the agitation and is very powerful in this matter. I have wondered whether he can possibly realise what this indiscriminate internment of the innocent means to the families of the interned. Could you not find a chance to try and make him understand? If he and a few others were to stop hounding on the Government, it would cease, for the authorities must know perfectly well that all the dangerous have been disposed of long ago. You have no notion how lonely one feels in one's

native land nowadays; if I should lose Harold, too, I think I
might go under, though that has never been my habit.
                    " Believe me, dear Mr. Cumbermere,
                                " Most truly yours,
                                        " HELEN HOLSTEIG."

On receiving this letter I was moved by compassion, for it
required no stretch of imagination to picture the life of that
lonely British mother and her son; and I thought very carefully over the advisability of speaking to Harburn, and consulted the proverbs: " Speech is silver, but silence is gold—
When in doubt, play trumps." " Second thoughts are best—He
who hesitates is lost." " Look before you leap—Delays are dangerous." They balanced so perfectly that I had recourse to
commonsense, which told me to abstain. But meeting Harburn
at the club a few days later and finding him in a genial mood,
I let impulse prevail.

" By the way," I said, " you remember the Holsteigs? I
had a letter from poor Mrs. Holsteig the other day; she seems
terrified that they'll intern her son, that particularly nice boy.
Don't you think it's time you let up on these unhappy people? "
The moment I reached the word Holsteig I saw I had made a
mistake, and only went on because to have stopped at that
would have been worse still. The hair had bristled up on his
back, as it were, and he said:

" Holsteig! That young pup who was off to join the German
Army if he could? By George, is he at large still? This
Government will never learn. I'll remember him."

" Harburn," I stammered, " I spoke of this in confidence.
The boy is half British and a friend of mine. I thought he was
a friend of yours, too."

" Of mine? " he said. " No, thank you. No mongrels for
me. As to confidence, Cumbermere, there's no such thing in
war time over what concerns the country's safety."

" Good God! " I exclaimed. " You really are crazy on this
subject. That boy—with his bringing-up! "

He grinned. " We're taking no risks," he said, " and making
no exceptions. The British Army or an internment camp. I'll
see that he gets the alternative."

" If you do," I said, rising, " we cease to be friends. I won't
have my confidence abused! "

"Oh! Hang it all," he grumbled, "sit down! We must all do our duty."

"You once complained to Holsteig himself of that German peculiarity."

He laughed. "I did," he said; "I remember—in the train. I've changed since then. That pup ought to be in with all the other swine-hounds. But let it go."

There the matter rested, for he had said: "Let it go," and he was a man of his word. It was, however, a lesson to me not to meddle with men of temperament so different from my own. I wrote to young Holsteig and asked him to come and lunch with me. He thanked me, but could not, of course, being confined to a five-mile radius. Really anxious to see him, I motorbiked down to their house. I found a very changed youth; moody and introspective, thoroughly forced in upon himself, and growing bitter. He had been destined for his father's business, and, marooned as he was by his nationality, had nothing to do but raise vegetables in their garden and read poetry and philosophy, not occupations to take a young man out of himself. Mrs. Holsteig, whose nerves were evidently at cracking point, had become extremely bitter and lost all power of seeing the war as a whole. All the ugly human qualities and hard people which the drive and pressure of a great struggle inevitably bring to the fore seemed viewed by her now as if they were the normal character of her fellow-countrymen, and she made no allowance for the fact that those fellow-countrymen had not commenced this struggle, nor for the certainty that the same ugly qualities and hard people were just as surely to the fore in every other of the fighting countries. The certainty she felt about her husband's honour had made her regard his internment and subsequent repatriation as a personal affront as well as a wicked injustice. Her tall, thin figure and high-cheekboned face seemed to have been scorched and withered by some inner flame; she could not have been a wholesome companion for her boy in that house, empty even of servants. I spent a difficult afternoon in muzzling my sense of proportion, and journeyed back to town sore, but very sorry.

I was off again with the Red Cross shortly after, and did not return to England till August of 1918. I was unwell, and went down to my cottage, now free to me again.

The influenza epidemic was raging, and there I developed a mild attack; when I was convalescent my first visitor was

Harburn, who had come down to his bungalow for a summer holiday. He had not been in the room five minutes before he was off on his favourite topic. My nerves must have been on edge from illness, for I cannot express the disgust with which I listened to him on that occasion. He seemed to me just like a dog who mumbles and chews a mouldy old bone with a sort of fury. There was a kind of triumph about him, too, which was unpleasant, though not surprising, for he was more of a force than ever.

'God save me from the fixed idea!' I thought, when he had gone. That evening I asked my old housekeeper if she had seen young Mr. Holsteig lately.

"Oh! no," she said, "he's been put away this five month. Mrs. Holsteig goes up once a week to see 'im. She's nigh out of her mind, poor lady, the baker says—that fierce she is about the Government for takin' 'im off."

I confess I could not bring myself to go and see her.

About a month after the armistice had been signed I came down to my cottage again. Harburn was in the same train, and he gave me a lift from the station. He was more like his old good-humoured self, and asked me to dinner the next day. It was the first time I had met him since the victory. We had a most excellent repast, and drank the health of the Future in some of his oldest port. Only when we had drawn up to the blazing wood fire in that softly lighted room, with our glasses beside us and two Airedales asleep at our feet, did he come round to his hobby.

"What do you think?" he said, suddenly leaning toward the flames. "Some of these blazing sentimentalists want to release our Huns. But I've put my foot on it; they won't get free till they're out of this country and back in their precious Germany." And I saw the familiar spark and smoulder in his eyes.

"Harburn," I said, moved by an impulse which I couldn't resist, "I think you ought to take a pill."

He stared at me.

"This way madness lies," I went on. "Hate is a damned insidious disease, men's souls can't stand very much of it, you know. You want purging."

He laughed.

"Hate! I thrive on it. The more I hate the brutes the better I feel. Here's to the death of every cursed Hun!"

I looked at him steadily. "I often think," I said, "that there could have been no more unhappy men on earth than Cromwell's Ironsides or the red revolutionaries in France when their work was over and done with."

"What's that to do with me?" he asked, amazed.

"They too smote out of hate and came to an end of their smiting. When a man's occupation is gone——"

"You're drivelling," he said sharply.

"Far from it," I answered, nettled. "Yours is a curious case, Harburn. Most of our professional Hun-haters have found it a good stunt or are merely weak sentimentalists; they can drop it easily enough when it ceases to be a good stunt or a parrot's war cry. You can't. With you it's mania, religion. When the tide ebbs and leaves you high and dry——"

He struck his fist on the arm of his chair, upsetting his glass and awakening the Airedale at his feet.

"I won't let it ebb," he said. "I'm going on with this—mark me!"

"Remember Canute!" I muttered. "May I have some more port?" I had got up to fill my glass when I saw to my astonishment that a woman was standing in the long window which opened on to the verandah. She had evidently only just come in, for she was still holding the curtain in her hand. It was Mrs. Holsteig, with her fine grey hair blown about her face, looking strange and almost ghostly in a grey gown. Harburn had not seen her, so I went quickly towards her, hoping to get her to go out again as silently and speak to me on the verandah; but she held up her hand with a gesture as if she would push me back, and said:

"Forgive my interrupting; I came to speak to that man."

Startled by the sound of her voice, Harburn jumped up and spun round towards it.

"Yes," she repeated quite quietly, "I came to speak to you; I came to put my curse on you. Many have put their curses on you silently; I do so to your face. My son lies between life and death in your prison—*your* prison. Whether he lives or dies I curse you for what you have done to poor wives and mothers—to British wives and mothers. Be for ever accursed! Good-night!"

She let the curtain fall and had vanished before Harburn had time to reach the window. She vanished so swiftly and silently, she had spoken so quietly, that both he and I stood rubbing our eyes and ears.

"Pretty theatrical!" he said at last.

"But quite real," I answered slowly; "you have been cursed by a live Scotswoman. Look at those dogs!"

The two Airedales were standing stock-still with the hair bristling on their backs.

Harburn suddenly laughed, and it jarred the whole room.

"By George!" he said, "I believe that's actionable."

But I was not in that mood and answered tartly:

"If it is, we are all food for judges."

He laughed again, this time uneasily, slammed the window to, and bolted it, and sat down again in his chair.

"He's got the 'flu, I suppose," he said. "She must think me a prize sort of idiot to have come here with such tomfoolery." But our evening was spoiled, and I took my leave almost at once. I went out into the roupy raw December night pondering deeply. Harburn had made light of it, and though I suppose no man likes being cursed to his face in the presence of a friend, I felt his skin was quite tough enough to stand it. Besides, it was too cheap and crude a way of carrying on. Anybody can go into his neighbour's house and curse him—and no bones broken. And yet—what she had said was no doubt true —hundreds of women—of his fellow-countrywomen—must silently have put their curse on one who had been the chief compeller of their misery. Still, he had put *his* curse on the Huns and their belongings, and I felt he was man enough to take what he had given. 'No,' I thought, 'she has only fanned the flame of his hate. But, by Jove! that's just it! Her curse has fortified my prophecy.' It was *of his own state of mind* that he would perish, and she had whipped and deepened that state of mind. And, odd as it may seem, I felt sorry for him, as one is for a dog that goes mad, does what harm he can, and dies. I lay awake that night a long time thinking of him, and of that unhappy half-crazed mother, whose son lay between life and death.

Next day I went to see her, but she was up in London hovering round the cage of her son, no doubt. I heard from her, however, some days later, thanking me for coming and saying he was out of danger. But she made no allusion to that evening visit. Perhaps she was ashamed of it. Perhaps she was demented when she came and had no remembrance thereof.

Soon after this I went to Belgium to illustrate a book on Reconstruction, and found such subjects that I was not back in town till the late summer of 1918. Going into my club one day I came on Harburn in the smoking-room. The curse had not done him much harm, it seemed, for he looked the picture of health.

" Well, how are you? " I said. " You look at the top of your form."

" Never better," he replied.

" Do you remember our last evening together? "

He uttered a sort of gusty grunt and did not answer.

" That boy recovered," I said. " What's happened to him and his mother since? "

" Ironical young brute! I've just had this from him." And he handed me a letter with a Hanover post-mark.

" DEAR MR. HARBURN,

" It was only on meeting my mother here yesterday that I learned of her visit to you one evening last December. I wish to apologise for it, since it was my illness which caused her to so forget herself. I owe you a deep debt of gratitude for having been at least partly the means of giving me the most wonderful experience of my life. In that camp of sorrow— where there was sickness of mind such as I am sure you have never seen or realised, such endless, hopeless mental anguish of poor huddled creatures turning and turning on themselves year after year—I learned to forget myself and to do my little best for them. And I learned, and I hope I shall never forget it, that good will towards his fellow-creatures is all that stands between man and death in life; I was going fast the other way before I was sent there. I thank you from my heart, and beg to remain,

" Very faithfully yours,
" HAROLD HOLSTEIG."

I put it down and said:

" That's not ironical. He means it."

" Bosh ! " said Harburn, with the old spark and smoulder in his eyes. " He's pulling my leg—the swinelet Hun-prig."

" He is not, Harburn; I assure you."

Harburn got up.

" He *is;* I tell you he *is*. Ah! those brutes! Well! I haven't done with them yet."

And I heard the snap of his jaw and saw his eyes fixed fiercely on some imagined object. I changed the subject hurriedly and soon took my depature. But going down the steps an old jingle came into my head and has hardly left it since:

> " The man recovered of the bite,
> The dog it was that died."

1919.

A KNIGHT

At Monte Carlo, in the spring of the year 189—, I used to notice an old fellow in a grey suit and sunburnt straw hat with a black ribbon. Every morning at eleven o'clock, he would come down to the *Place,* followed by a brindled German boarhound, walk once or twice round it, and seat himself on a bench facing the casino. There he would remain in the sun, with his straw hat tilted forward, his thin legs apart, his brown hands crossed between them, and the dog's nose resting on his knee. After an hour or more he would get up, and, stooping a little from the waist, walk slowly round the *Place* and return up hill. Just before three, he would come down again in the same clothes and go into the casino, leaving the dog outside.

One afternoon, moved by curiosity, I followed him. He passed through the hall without looking at the gambling-rooms, and went into the concert. It became my habit after that to watch for him. When he sat in the *Place* I could see him from the window of my room. The chief puzzle to me was the matter of his nationality.

His lean, short face had a skin so burnt that it looked like leather; his jaw was long and prominent, his chin pointed, and he had hollows in his cheeks. There were wrinkles across his forehead; his eyes were brown; and little white moustaches were brushed up from the corners of his lips. The back of his head bulged out above the lines of his lean neck and high, sharp shoulders; his grey hair was cropped quite close. In the Marseilles buffet, on the journey out, I had met an Englishman, almost his counterpart in features—but somehow very different! This old fellow had nothing of the other's alert, autocratic self-sufficiency. He was quiet and undemonstrative, without looking, as it were, insulated against shocks and foreign substances. He was certainly no Frenchman. His eyes, indeed, were brown, but hazel-brown, and gentle—not the red-brown sensual eye of the Frenchman. An American? But was ever an American so passive? A German? His moustache was certainly brushed up, but in a modest, almost pathetic way, not in the least Teutonic. Nothing seemed to fit him. I gave him up, and nicknamed him " the Cosmopolitan."

Leaving at the end of April, I forgot him altogether. In the same month, however, of the following year I was again at Monte Carlo, and going one day to the concert found myself seated next this same old fellow. The orchestra was playing Meyerbeer's " Prophète," and my neighbour was asleep, snoring softly. He was dressed in the same grey suit, with the same straw hat (or one exactly like it) on his knees, and his hands crossed above it. Sleep had not disfigured him—his little white moustache was still brushed up, his lips closed; a very good and gentle expression hovered on his face. A curved mark showed on his right temple, the scar of a cut on the side of his neck, and his left hand was covered by an old glove, the little finger of which was empty. He woke up when the march was over and brisked up his moustache.

The next thing on the programme was a little thing by Poise from *Le joli Gilles,* played by Mons. Corsanego on the violin. Happening to glance at my old neighbour, I saw a tear caught in the hollow of his cheek, and another just leaving the corner of his eye; there was a faint smile on his lips. Then came an interval; and while orchestra and audience were resting, I asked him if he were fond of music. He looked up without distrust, bowed, and answered in a thin, gentle voice: " Certainly. I know nothing about it, play no instrument, could never sing a note; but—fond of it! Who would not be?" His English was correct enough, but with an emphasis not quite American nor quite foreign. I ventured to remark that he did not care for Meyerbeer. He smiled.

" Ah!" he said, " I was asleep? Too bad of me He *is* a little noisy—I know so little about music. There is Bach, for instance. Would you believe it, he gives me no pleasure? A great misfortune to be no musician!" He shook his head.

I murmured, " Bach is too elevating for you perhaps."

" To me," he answered, " any music I *like* is elevating. People say some music has a bad effect on them. I never found any music that gave me a bad thought—no—no—quite the opposite; only sometimes, as you see, I go to sleep. But what a lovely instrument the violin!" A faint flush came on his parched cheeks. " The human soul that has left the body. A curious thing, distant bugles at night have given me the same feeling." The orchestra was now coming back, and, folding his hands, my neighbour turned his eyes towards them. When the concert was over we came out together. Waiting at the entrance was his dog.

"You have a beautiful dog!"

"Ah! yes. *Freda, mia cara, da su mano!*" The dog squatted on her haunches, and lifted her paw in the vague, bored way of big dogs when requested to perform civilities. She was a lovely creature—the purest brindle, without a speck of white, and free from the unbalanced look of most dogs of her breed.

"*Basta! basta!*" He turned to me apologetically. "We have agreed to speak Italian; in that way I keep up the language; astonishing the number of things that dog will understand!" I was about to take my leave, when he asked if I would walk a little way with him—"If you are free, that is." We went up the street with Freda on the far side of her master.

"Do you never 'play' here?" I asked him.

"Play? No. It must be very interesting; most exciting, but as a matter of fact, I can't afford it. If one has very little, one is too nervous."

He had stopped in front of a small hairdresser's shop. "I live here," he said, raising his hat again. "*Au revoir!*—unless I can offer you a glass of tea. It's all ready. Come! I've brought you out of your way; give me the pleasure!"

I have never met a man so free from all self-consciousness, and yet so delicate and diffident—the combination is a rare one. We went up a steep staircase to a room on the second floor. My companion threw the shutters open, setting all the flies buzzing. The top of a plane-tree was on a level with the window, and all its little brown balls were dancing, quite close, in the wind. As he had promised, an urn was hissing on a table; there was also a small brown teapot, some sugar, slices of lemon, and glasses. A bed, washstand, cupboard, tin trunk, two chairs, and a small rug were all the furniture. Above the bed a sword in a leather sheath was suspended from two nails. The photograph of a girl stood on the closed stove. My host went to the cupboard and produced a bottle, a glass, and a second spoon. When the cork was drawn, the scent of rum escaped into the air. He sniffed at it and dropped a teaspoonful into both glasses.

"This is a trick I learned from the Russians after Plevna; they had my little finger, so I deserved something in exchange." He looked round; his eyes, his whole face, seemed to twinkle. "I assure you it was worth it—makes all the difference. Try!" He poured off the tea.

"Had you a sympathy with the Turks?"

"The weaker side——" He paused abruptly, then added: "But it was not that." Over his face innumerable crow's feet had suddenly appeared, his eyes twitched; he went on hurriedly, "I had to find something to do just then—it was necessary." He stared into his glass; and it was some time before I ventured to ask if he had seen much fighting.

"Yes," he replied gravely, "nearly twenty years altogether; I was one of Garibaldi's *Mille* in '60."

"Surely you are not Italian?"

He leaned forward with his hands on his knees. "I was in Genoa at that time learning banking; Garibaldi was a wonderful man! One could not help it." He spoke quite simply. "You might say it was like seeing a little man stand up to a ring of great hulking fellows; I went, just as you would have gone, if you'd been there. I was not long with them—*our* war began; I had to go back home." He said this as if there had been but one war since the world began. "In '61," he mused, "till '65. Just think of it! The poor country. Why, in my State, South Carolina—I was through it all—nobody could be spared there—we were one to three."

"I suppose you have a love of fighting?"

"H'm!" he said, as if considering the idea for the first time. "Sometimes I fought for a living, and sometimes—because I was obliged; one must try to be a gentleman. But won't you have some more?"

I refused more tea and took my leave, carrying away with me a picture of the old fellow looking down from the top of the steep staircase, one hand pressed to his back, the other twisting up those little white moustaches, and murmuring, "Take care, my dear sir, there's a step there at the corner."

"To be a gentleman!" I repeated in the street, causing an old French lady to drop her parasol, so that for about two minutes we stood bowing and smiling to each other, then separated full of the best feeling.

II

A week later I found myself again seated next him at a concert. In the meantime I had seen him now and then, but only
in passing. He seemed depressed. The corners of his lips
were tightened, his tanned cheeks had a greyish tinge, his eyes
were restless; and, between two numbers of the programme, he
murmured, tapping his fingers on his hat, " Do you ever have
bad days? Yes? Not pleasant, are they? "

Then something occurred from which all that I have to tell
you followed. There came into the concert-hall the heroine
of one of those romances, crimes, follies, or irregularities, call
it what you will, which had just attracted the " world's " stare.
She passed us with her partner, and sat down in a chair a few
rows to our right. She kept turning her head round, and at
every turn I caught the gleam of her uneasy eyes. Some one
behind us said: " The brazen baggage! "

My companion turned full round, and glared at whoever it
was who had spoken. The change in him was quite remarkable. His lips were drawn back from his teeth; he frowned;
the scar on his temple had reddened.

" Ah! " he said to me. " The hue and cry! Contemptible!
How I hate it! But you wouldn't understand—I——" he
broke off, and slowly regained his usual air of self-obliteration;
he even seemed ashamed, and began trying to brush his moustaches higher than ever, as if aware that his heat had robbed
them of neatness.

" I'm not myself, when I speak of such matters," he said
suddenly; and began reading his programme, holding it upside
down. A minute later, however, he said in a peculiar voice:
" There are people to be found who object to vivisecting animals; but the vivisection of a woman, who minds that? Will
you tell me it's right, that because of some tragedy like this
—believe me, it is always a tragedy—we should hunt down a
woman? That her fellow-women should make an outcast of her?
That we, who are *men,* should make a prey of her? If I thought
that——" Again he broke off, staring very hard in front of
him. " It is *we* who make them what they are; and even if that
is not so—why, if I thought there was a woman in the world
I could not take my hat off to—I—I—couldn't sleep at night."
He got up from his seat, put on his old straw hat with trembling

fingers, and, without a glance back, went out, stumbling over
the chair-legs.

I sat there, horribly disturbed; the words, " One must try
to be a gentleman ! " haunting me. When I came out, he was
standing by the entrance with one hand on his hip and the other
on his dog. In that attitude of waiting he was such a patient
figure; the sun glared down and showed the threadbare nature
of his clothes and the thinness of his brown hands, with their
long fingers and nails yellow from tobacco. Seeing me he
came up the steps again, and raised his hat.

" I am glad to have caught you; please forget all that."

I asked him if he would do me the honour of dining at my
hotel.

" Dine ? " he repeated with the sort of smile a child gives if
you offer him a box of soldiers; " with the greatest pleasure. I
seldom dine out, but I think I can muster up a coat. Yes—
yes—and at what time shall I come? At half-past seven, and
your hotel is——! Good! I shall be there. *Freda, mia cara,*
you will be alone this evening. You do not smoke *caporal,* I
fear. I find it fairly good; though it has too much bite." He
walked off with Freda, puffing at his thin roll of *caporal.*

Once or twice he stopped, as if bewildered or beset by some
sudden doubt or memory; and every time he stopped, Freda
licked his hand. They disappeared round the corner of the
street, and I went to my hotel to see about dinner. On the way
I met Jules le Ferrier, and asked him to come too.

" My faith, yes ! " he said, with the rosy pessimism characteristic of the French editor. " Man must dine ! "

At half-past six we assembled. My " Cosmopolitan " was in
an old frock-coat braided round the edges, buttoned high and
tight, defining more than ever the sharp lines of his shoulders
and the slight kink of his back; he had brought with him, too,
a dark-peaked cap of military shape, which he had evidently
selected as more fitting to the coat than a straw hat. He
smelled slightly of some herb.

We sat down to dinner, and did not rise for two hours. He
was a charming guest, praised everything he ate—not with
commonplaces, but in words that made you feel it had given him
real pleasure. At first, whenever Jules made one of his caustic
remarks, he looked quite pained, but suddenly seemed to make
up his mind that it was bark, not bite; and then at each of
them he would turn to me and say, " Aha ! that's good—isn't

it?" With every glass of wine he became more gentle and
more genial, sitting very upright, and tightly buttoned-in; while
the little white wings of his moustache seemed about to leave
him for a better world.

In spite of the most leading questions, however, we could
not get him to talk about himself, for even Jules, most cynical of
men, had recognised that he was a hero of romance. He would
answer gently and precisely, and then sit twisting his moustaches, perfectly unconscious that we wanted more. Presently, as the wine went a little to his head, his thin, high voice
grew thinner, his cheeks became flushed, his eyes brighter; at
the end of dinner he said: " I hope I have not been noisy."

We assured him that he had not been noisy enough. " You're
laughing at me," he answered. " Surely I've been talking all
the time!"

" *Mon Dieu!* " said Jules, " we have been looking for some
fables of your wars; but nothing—nothing, not enough to feed
a frog!"

The old fellow looked troubled.

" To be sure!" he mused. " Let me think! there is that
about Colhoun at Gettysburg; and there's the story of Garibaldi
and the Miller." He plunged into a tale, not at all about himself, which would have been extremely dull, but for the conviction in his eyes, and the way he stopped and commented.
" So you see," he ended, " that's the sort of man Garibaldi
was! I could tell you another tale of him." Catching an introspective look in Jules's eye, however, I proposed taking our
cigars over to the *café* opposite.

" Delightful!" the old fellow said: " We shall have a band
and the fresh air, and clear consciences for our cigars. I cannot like this smoking in a room where there are ladies dining."

He walked out in front of us, smoking with an air of great
enjoyment. Jules, glowing above his candid shirt and waistcoat, whispered to me, " Mon cher Georges, how he is good!"
then sighed, and added darkly: " The poor man!"

We sat down at a little table. Close by, the branches of a
plane-tree rustled faintly; their leaves hung lifeless, speckled
like the breasts of birds, or black against the sky; then, caught
by the breeze, fluttered suddenly.

The old fellow sat, with head thrown back, a smile on his face,
coming now and then out of his enchanted dreams to drink
coffee, answer our questions, or hum the tune that the band

was playing. The ash of his cigar grew very long. One of those bizarre figures in Oriental garb, who, night after night, offer their doubtful wares at a great price, appeared in the white glare of a lamp, looked with a furtive smile at his face, and glided back, discomfited by its unconsciousness. It was a night for dreams! A faint, half-Eastern scent in the air, of black tobacco and spice; few people as yet at the little tables, the waiters leisurely, the band soft! What was he dreaming of, that old fellow, whose cigar-ash grew so long? Of youth, of his battles, of those things that must be done by those who try to be gentlemen; perhaps only of his dinner; anyway of something gilded in vague fashion as the light was gilding the branches of the plane-tree.

Jules pulled my sleeve: "He sleeps." He had smilingly dropped off; the cigar-ash—that feathery tower of his dreams —had broken and fallen on his sleeve. He awoke, and fell to dusting it.

The little tables round us began to fill. One of the bandsmen played a czardas on the czymbal. Two young Frenchmen, talking loudly, sat down at the adjoining table. They were discussing the lady who had been at the concert that afternoon.

"It's a bet," said one of them, "but there's the present man. I take three weeks, that's enough—*elle est déclassée; ce n'est que le premier pas*——"

My old friend's cigar fell on the table. "Monsieur," he stammered, "you speak of a lady so, in a public place?"

The young man stared at him. "Who is this person?" he said to his companion.

My guest took up Jules's glove that lay on the table; before either of us could raise a finger, he had swung it in the speaker's face. "Enough!" he said, and, dropping the glove, walked away.

We all jumped to our feet. I left Jules and hurried after him. His face was grim, his eyes those of a creature who has been struck on a raw place. He made a movement of his fingers which said plainly, "Leave me, if you please!"

I went back to the *café*. The two young men had disappeared, so had Jules, but everything else was going on just as before; the bandsman still twanging out his czardas; the waiters serving drinks; the Orientals trying to sell their carpets. I paid the bill, sought out the manager, and apologised. He shrugged his shoulders, smiled and said: "An eccentric, your friend, *nicht wahr?*" Could he tell me where Mr. le Ferrier was? He could not. I left to look for Jules; could not find him, and returned to my hotel disgusted. I was sorry for my old guest, but vexed with him too; what business had he to carry his Quixotism to such an unpleasant length? I tried to read. Eleven o'clock struck; the casino disgorged a stream of people; the *Place* seemed fuller of life than ever; then slowly it grew empty and quite dark. The whim seized me to go out. It was a still night, very warm, very black. On one of the seats a man and woman sat embraced, on another a girl was sobbing, on a third—strange sight—a priest dozed. I became aware of some one at my side; it was my old guest.

"If you are not too tired," he said, "can you give me ten minutes?"

"Certainly; will you come in?"

"No, no; let us go down to the Terrace. I shan't keep you long."

He did not speak again till we reached a seat above the pigeon-shooting grounds; there in a darkness denser for the string of lights still burning in the town, we sat down.

"I owe you an apology," he said; "first in the afternoon, then again this evening—your guest—your friend's glove. I have behaved as no gentleman should." He was leaning forward with his hands on the handle of a stick. His voice sounded broken and disturbed.

"Oh!" I muttered. "It's nothing!"

"You are very good," he sighed; "but I feel that I must explain. I consider I owe this to you, but I must tell you I should not have the courage if it were not for another reason. You see I have no friend." He looked at me with an uncertain smile. I bowed, and a minute or two later he began. . . .

III

"You will excuse me if I go back rather far. It was in '74, when I had been ill with Cuban fever. To keep me alive they had put me on board a ship at Santiago, and at the end of the voyage I found myself in London. I had very little money; I knew nobody. I tell you, sir, there are times when it's hard for a fighting man to get anything to do. People would say to me: 'Afraid we've nothing for a man like you in our business.' I tried people of all sorts; but it was true—I had been

fighting here and there since '60, I wasn't fit for anything
————" He shook his head. " In the South, before the war,
they had a saying, I remember, about a dog and a soldier having the same value. But all this has nothing to do with what
I have to tell you." He sighed again and went on, moistening
his lips: " I was walking along the Strand one day, very disheartened, when I heard my name called. It's a queer thing,
that, in a strange street. By the way," he put in with dry ceremony, " you don't know my name, I think; it is Brune—Roger
Brune. At first I did not recognise the person who called me.
He had just got off an omnibus—a square-shouldered man with
heavy moustaches, and round spectacles. But when he shook
my hand I knew him at once. He was a man called Dalton,
who was taken prisoner at Gettysburg; one of you Englishmen
who came to fight with us—a major in the regiment where I
was captain. We were comrades during two campaigns. If I
had been his brother he couldn't have seemed more pleased to
see me. He took me into a bar for the sake of old times. The
drink went to my head, and by the time we reached Trafalgar
Square I was quite unable to walk. He made me sit down on a
bench. I was in fact—drunk. It's disgraceful to be drunk,
but there was some excuse. Now I tell you, sir" (all through
his story he was always making use of that expression, it
seemed to infuse fresh spirit into him, to help his memory in
obscure places, to give him the mastery of his emotions; it was
like the piece of paper a nervous man holds in his hand to
help him through a speech), " there never was a man with a
finer soul than my friend Dalton. He was not clever, though
he had read much; and sometimes perhaps he was too fond of
talking. But he was a gentleman; he listened to me as if I had
been a child; he was not ashamed of me—and it takes a gentleman not to be ashamed of a drunken man in the streets of
London; God knows what things I said to him while we were
sitting there! He took me to his home and put me to bed
himself; for I was down again with fever." He stopped, turned
slightly from me, and put his hand up to his brow. " Well, then
it was, sir, that I first saw her. I am not a poet and I cannot tell you what she seemed to me. I was delirious, but I
always knew when she was there. I had dreams of sunshine
and cornfields, of dancing waves at sea, young trees—never the
same dreams, never anything for long together; and when I
had my senses I was afraid to say so for fear she would go

away. She'd be in the corner of the room, with her hair hanging about her neck, a bright gold colour; she never worked and never read, but sat and talked to herself in a whisper, or looked at me for a long time together out of her blue eyes, a little frown between them, and her upper lip closed firm on her lower lip, where she had an uneven tooth. When her father came, she'd jump up and hang on to his neck until he groaned, then run away, but presently come stealing back on tiptoe. I used to listen for her footsteps on the stairs, then the knock, the door flung back or opened quietly—you never could tell which; and her voice, with a little lisp, 'Are you better to-day, Mr. Brune? What funny things you say when you're delirious! Father says you've been in heaps of battles?'"

He got up, paced restlessly to and fro, and sat down again. " I remember every word as if it were yesterday, all the things she said, and did; I've had a long time to think them over, you see. Well, I must tell you, the first morning that I was able to get up, I missed her. Dalton came in her place, and I asked him where she was. ' My dear fellow,' he answered, ' I've sent Eilie away to her old nurse's inn down on the river; she's better there at this time of year.' We looked at each other, and I saw that he had sent her away because he didn't trust me. I was hurt by this. Illness spoils one. He was right, he was quite right, for all he knew about me was that I could fight and had got drunk; but I am very quick-tempered. I made up my mind at once to leave him. But I was too weak—he had to put me to bed again. The very next morning he came and proposed that I should go into partnership with him. He kept a fencing-school and pistol-gallery. It seemed like the finger of God; and perhaps it was—who knows?" He fell into a reverie, and taking out his *caporal,* rolled himself a cigarette; having lighted it, he went on suddenly: " There, in the room above the school, we used to sit in the evenings, one on each side of the grate. The room was on the second floor, I remember, with two windows, and a view of nothing but the houses opposite. The furniture was covered up with chintz. The things on the bookshelf were never disturbed, they were Eilie's—half-broken cases with butterflies, a dead frog in a bottle, a horse-shoe covered with tinfoil, some shells too, and a cardboard box with three speckled eggs in it, and these words written on the lid: ' Misselthrush from Lucy's tree—second family, only one blown.' " He smoked fiercely, with puffs that were like sharp sighs.

"Dalton was wrapped up in her. He was never tired of talking to me about her, and I was never tired of hearing. We had a number of pupils; but in the evening when we sat there, smoking—our talk would sooner or later come round to her. Her bedroom opened out of that sitting-room; he took me in once and showed me a narrow little room the width of a passage, fresh and white, with a photograph of her mother above the bed, and an empty basket for a dog or cat." He broke off with a vexed air, and resumed sternly, as if trying to bind himself to the narration of his more important facts: "She was then fifteen—her mother had been dead twelve years—a beautiful face, her mother's; it had been her death that sent Dalton to fight with us. Well, sir, one day in August, very hot weather, he proposed a run into the country, and who should meet us on the platform when we arrived but Eilie, in a blue sunbonnet and frock—flax blue, her favourite colour. I was angry with Dalton for not telling me that we should see her; my clothes were not quite—my hair wanted cutting. It was black then, sir," he added, tracing a pattern in the darkness with his stick. "She had a little donkey-cart; she drove, and, while we walked one on each side, she kept looking at me from under her sunbonnet. I must tell you that she never laughed—her eyes danced, her cheeks would go pink, and her hair shake about on her neck, but she never laughed. Her old nurse, Lucy, a very broad, good woman, had married the proprietor of the inn in the village there. I have never seen anything like that inn; sweetbriar up to the roof! And the scent—I am very susceptible to scents!" His head drooped, and the cigarette fell from his hand. A train passing beneath sent up a shower of sparks. He started, and went on: "We had our lunch in the parlour—I remember that room very well, for I spent the happiest days of my life afterwards in that inn. . . . We went into a meadow after lunch, and my friend Dalton fell asleep. A wonderful thing happened then. Eilie whispered to me, 'Let's have a jolly time.' She took me for the most glorious walk. The river was close by. A lovely stream, your river Thames, so calm and broad; it is like the spirit of your people. I was bewitched; I forgot my friend, I thought of nothing but how to keep her to myself. It was such a day! There are days that are the devil's, but that was truly one of God's. She took me to a little pond under an elm-tree, and we dragged it, we two, an hour, for a kind of tiny red worm to feed some creature that she had. We found them in the mud, and while she was bending over, the curls got in her eyes. If you could have seen her then, I think, sir, you would have said she was like the first sight of spring. . . . We had tea afterwards, all together, in the long grass under some fruit-trees. If I had the knack of words, there are things that I could say——" He bent, as though in deference to those unspoken memories. " Twilight came on while we were sitting there. A wonderful thing is twilight in the country! It became time for us to go. There was an avenue of trees close by—like a church with a window at the end, where golden light came through. I walked up and down it with her. ' Will you come again?' she whispered, and suddenly she lifted up her face to be kissed. I kissed her as if she were a little child. And when we said good-bye, her eyes were looking at me across her father's shoulder, with surprise and sorrow in them. ' Why do you go away?' they seemed to say. . . . But I must tell you," he went on hurriedly, " of a thing that happened before we had gone a hundred yards. We were smoking our pipes, and I, thinking of her—when out she sprang from the hedge and stood in front of us. Dalton cried out, ' What are you here for again, you mad girl!' She rushed up to him and hugged him; but when she looked at me, her face was quite different—careless, defiant, as one might say —it hurt me. I couldn't understand it, and what one doesn't understand frightens one.

IV

" Time went on. There was no swordsman, or pistolshot like me in London, they said. We had as many pupils as we liked—it was the only part of my life when I have been able to save money. I had no chance to spend it. We gave lessons all day, and in the evening were too tired to go out. That year I had the misfortune to lose my dear mother. I became a rich man—yes, sir, at that time I must have had not less than six hundred a year.

" It was a long time before I saw Eilie again. She went abroad to Dresden with her father's sister to learn French and German. It was in the autumn of 1875 when she came back to us. She was seventeen then—a beautiful young creature." He paused, as if to gather his forces for description, and went on.

" Tall, as a young tree, with eyes like the sky. I would not say she was perfect, but her imperfections were beautiful to me. What is it makes you love—ah! sir, that is very hidden and mysterious. She had never lost the trick of closing her lips tightly when she remembered her uneven tooth. You may say that was vanity, but in a young girl—and which of us is not vain, eh? 'Old men and maidens, young men and children!'

" As I said, she came back to London to her little room, and in the evenings was always ready with our tea. You mustn't suppose she was housewifely; there is something in me that never admired housewifeliness—a fine quality, no doubt, still ——" He sighed.

" No," he resumed, " Eilie was not like that, for she was never quite the same two days together. I told you her eyes were like the sky—that was true of all of her. In one thing, however, at that time, she always seemed the same—in love for her father. For me! I don't know what I should have expected; but my presence seemed to have the effect of making her dumb: I would catch her looking at me with a frown, and then, as if to make up to her own nature—and a more loving nature never came into this world, that I shall maintain to my dying day— she would go to her father and kiss him. When I talked with him she pretended not to notice, but I could see her face grow cold and stubborn. I am not quick, and it was a long time before I understood that she was jealous, she wanted him all to herself. I've often wondered how she could be his daughter, for he was the very soul of justice and a slow man too—and she was as quick as a bird. For a long time after I saw her dislike of me, I refused to believe it—if one does not want to believe a thing there are always reasons why it should not seem true, at least so it is with me, and I suppose with all selfish men.

" I spent evening after evening there, when, if I had not thought only of myself, I should have kept away. But one day I could no longer be blind.

" It was a Sunday in February. I always had an invitation on Sundays to dine with them in the middle of the day. There was no one in the sitting-room; but the door of Eilie's bedroom was open. I heard her voice: 'That man, always that man!' It was enough for me, I went down again without coming in, and walked about all day.

" For three weeks I kept away. To the school of course I

came as usual, but not upstairs. I don't know what I told Dalton—it did not signify what you told him, he always had a theory of his own, and was persuaded of its truth—a very single-minded man, sir.

"But now I come to the most wonderful days of my life. It was an early spring that year. I had fallen away already from my resolution, and used to slink up—seldom, it's true—and spend the evening with them as before. One afternoon I came up to the sitting-room; the light was failing—it was warm, and the windows were open. In the air was that feeling which comes to you once a year, in the spring, no matter where you may be, in a crowded street, or alone in a forest; only once —a feeling like—but I cannot describe it.

"Eilie was sitting there. If you don't know, sir, I can't tell you what it means to be near the woman one loves. She was leaning on the window-sill, staring down into the street. It was as though she might be looking out for some one. I stood, hardly breathing. She turned her head, and saw me. Her eyes were strange. They seemed to ask me a question. But I couldn't have spoken for the world. I can't tell you what I felt—I dared not speak, or think, or hope. I have been in nineteen battles—several times in positions of some danger, when the lifting of a finger perhaps meant death; but I have never felt what I was feeling at that moment. I knew something was coming; and I was paralysed with terror lest it should not come!" He drew a long breath.

"The servant came in with a light and broke the spell. All that night I lay awake and thought of how she had looked at me, with the colour coming slowly up in her cheeks.

"It was three days before I plucked up courage to go again; and then I felt her eyes on me at once—she was making a 'cat's cradle' with a bit of string, but I could see them stealing up from her hands to my face. And she went wandering about the room, fingering at everything. When her father called out: 'What's the matter with you, Eilie?' she stared at him like a child caught doing wrong. I looked straight at her then, she tried to look at me, but she couldn't; and a minute later she went out of the room. God knows what sort of nonsense I talked—I was too happy.

"Then began our love. I can't tell you of that time. Often and often Dalton said to me: 'What's come to the child? Nothing I can do pleases her.' All the love she had given him was now for me; but he was too simple and straight to see what was going on. How many times haven't I felt criminal towards him! But when you're happy, with the tide in your favour, you become a coward at once. . . .

"Well, sir," he went on, "we were married on her eighteenth birthday. It was a long time before Dalton became aware of our love. But one day he said to me with a very grave look: "'Eilie has told me, Brune; I forbid it. She's too young, and you're—too old!' I was then forty-five, my hair as black and thick as a rook's feathers, and I was strong and active. I answered him: 'We shall be married within a month!' We parted in anger. It was a May night, and I walked out far into the country. There's no remedy for anger, or, indeed, for anything, so fine as walking. Once I stopped—it was on a common, without a house or light, and the stars shining like jewels. I was hot from walking, I could feel the blood boiling in my veins—I said to myself: 'Old, are you?' And I laughed like a fool. It was the thought of losing her—I wished to believe myself angry, but really I was afraid; fear and anger in me are very much the same. A friend of mine, a bit of a poet, sir, once called them 'the two black wings of self.' And so they are, so they are! . . . The next morning I went to Dalton again, and somehow I made him yield. I'm not a philosopher, but it has often seemed to me that no benefit can come to us in this life without an equal loss somewhere, but does that stop us? No, sir, not often. . . .
"We were married on the 30th of June, 1876, in the parish church. The only people present were Dalton, Lucy, and Lucy's husband—a big, red-faced fellow, with blue eyes and a golden beard parted in two. It had been arranged that we should spend the honeymoon down at their inn on the river. My wife, Dalton and I, went to a restaurant for lunch. She was dressed in grey, the colour of a pigeon's feathers." He paused, leaning forward over the crutch handle of his stick; trying to conjure up, no doubt, that long-ago image of his young bride in her dress " the colour of a pigeon's feathers," with her blue eyes and yellow hair, the little frown between her brows, the firmly shut red lips, opening to speak the words, " For better, for worse, for richer, for poorer, in sickness and in health."

"At that time, sir," he went on suddenly, "I was a bit of a dandy. I wore, I remember, a blue frock-coat, with white trousers, and a grey top hat. Even now I should always prefer to be well dressed. . . .

"We had an excellent lunch, and drank Veuve Clicquot, a wine that you cannot get in these days! Dalton came with us to the railway station. I can't bear partings; and yet, they must come.

"That evening we walked out in the cool under the aspen trees. What should I remember in all my life if not that night—the young bullocks snuffling in the gateways—the campion flowers all lighted up along the hedges—the moon with a halo—bats, too, in and out among the stems, and the shadows of the cottages as black and soft as that sea down there. For a long time we stood on the river-bank beneath a lime-tree. The scent of the lime flowers! A man can only endure about half his joy; about half his sorrow. Lucy and her husband," he went on, presently, "his name was Frank Tor—a man like an old Viking, who ate nothing but milk, bread, and fruit—were very good to us! It was like Paradise in that inn—though the commissariat, I am bound to say, was limited. The sweetbriar grew round our bedroom windows; when the breeze blew the leaves across the opening—it was like a bath of perfume. Eilie grew as brown as a gipsy while we were there. I don't think any man could have loved her more than I did. But there were times when my heart stood still; it didn't seem as if she understood how much I loved her. One day, I remember, she coaxed me to take her camping. We drifted down stream all the afternoon, and in the evening pulled into the reeds under the willow-boughs and lit a fire for her to cook by—though, as a matter of fact, our provisions were cooked already—but you know how it is; all the romance was in having a real fire. 'We won't pretend,' she kept saying. While we were eating our supper a hare came to our clearing—a big fellow—how surprised he looked! 'The tall hare,' Eilie called him. After that we sat by the ashes and watched the shadows, till at last she roamed away from me. The time went very slowly; I got up to look for her. It was past sundown. I called and called. It was a long time before I found her—and she was like a wild thing, hot and flushed, her pretty frock torn, her hands and face scratched, her hair down, like some beautiful creature of the woods. If one loves, a little thing will scare one. I didn't think she had noticed my fright;

but when we got back to the boat she threw her arms round my neck, and said, 'I won't ever leave you again.'

"Once in the night I woke—a water-hen was crying, and in the moonlight a kingfisher flew across. The wonder on the river —the wonder of the moon and trees, the soft bright mist, the stillness! It was like another world, peaceful, enchanted, far holier than ours. It seemed like a vision of the thoughts that come to one—how seldom! and go if one tries to grasp them. Magic—poetry—sacred!" He was silent a minute, then went on in a wistful voice: "I looked at her, sleeping like a child, with her hair loose, and her lips apart, and I thought: 'God do so to me, if ever I bring her pain!' How was I to understand her? the mystery and innocence of her soul?—The river has had all my light and all my darkness, the happiest days, and the hours when I've despaired; and I like to think of it, for, you know, in time bitter memories fade, only the good remain. . . . Yet the good have their own pain, a different kind of aching, for we shall never get them back. Sir," he said, turning to me with a faint smile, "it's no use crying over spilt milk. . . . In the neighbourhood of Lucy's inn, the Rose and Maybush— Can you imagine a prettier name? I have been all over the world, and nowhere found names so pretty as in the English country. There, too, every blade of grass, and flower, has a kind of pride about it; knows it will be cared for; and all the roads, trees, and cottages, seem to be certain that they will live for ever. . . . But I was going to tell you: Half a mile from the inn was a quiet old house which we used to call the 'Convent'—though I believe it was a farm. We spent many afternoons there, trespassing in the orchard—Eilie was fond of trespassing; if there were a long way round across somebody else's property, she would always take it. We spent our last afternoon in that orchard, lying in the long grass. I was reading *Childe Harold* for the first time—a wonderful, a memorable poem! I was at that passage—the bull-fight—you remember:

"'Thrice sounds the clarion; lo! the signal falls,
    The din expands, and expectation mute'—

when suddenly Eilie said: 'Suppose I were to leave off loving you?' It was as if some one had struck me in the face. I jumped up, and tried to take her in my arms, but she slipped away; then she turned, and began laughing softly. I laughed too. I don't know why. . . .

VI

" We went back to London the next day; we lived quite close to the school, and about five days a week Dalton came to dine with us. He would have come every day, if he had not been the sort of man who refuses to consult his own pleasure. We had more pupils than ever. In my leisure I taught my wife to fence. I have never seen any one so lithe and quick; or so beautiful as she looked in her fencing dress, with embroidered shoes.

" I was completely happy. When a man has obtained his desire he becomes careless and self-satisfied; I was watchful, however, for I knew that I was naturally a selfish man. I studied to arrange my time and save my money, to give her as much pleasure as I could. What she loved best in the world just then was riding. I bought a horse for her, and in the evenings of the spring and summer we rode together; but when it was too dark to go out late, she would ride alone, great distances, sometimes spend the whole day in the saddle, and come back so tired she could hardly walk upstairs—I can't say that I liked that. It made me nervous, she was so headlong —but I didn't think it right to interfere with her. I had a good deal of anxiety about money, for though I worked hard and made more than ever, there never seemed enough. I was anxious to save—I hoped, of course—but we had no child, and this was a trouble to me. She grew more beautiful than ever, and I think was happy. Has it ever struck you that each one of us lives on the edge of a volcano? There is, I imagine, no one who has not some affection or interest so strong that he counts the rest for nothing, beside it. No doubt a man may live his life through without discovering that. But some of us ——! I am not complaining; what is—is." He pulled the cap lower over his eyes, and clutched his hands firmly on the top of his stick. He was like a man who rushes his horse at some hopeless fence, unwilling to give himself time, for fear of craning at the last moment. " In the spring of '78, a new pupil came to me, a young man of twenty-one who was destined for the army. I took a fancy to him, and did my best to turn him into a good swordsman; but there was a kind of perverse recklessness in him; for a few minutes one would make great impression, then he would grow utterly careless. 'Francis,' I would say, 'if I were you I should be ashamed.' 'Mr. Brune,' he would answer, 'why should I be ashamed? I didn't make myself.' God knows, I wish to do him justice, he had a heart —one day he drove up in a cab, and brought in his poor dog, who had been run over, and was dying. For half an hour he shut himself up with its body, we could hear him sobbing like a child; he came out with his eyes all red, and cried: 'I know where to find the brute who drove over him,' and off he rushed. He had beautiful Italian eyes; a slight figure, not very tall; dark hair, a little dark moustache; and his lips were always a trifle parted—it was that, and his walk, and the way he dropped his eyelids, which gave him a peculiar, soft, proud look. I used to tell him that he'd never make a soldier! 'Oh!' he'd answer, 'that'll be all right when the time comes!' He believed in a kind of luck that was to do everything for him, when the time came. One day he came in as I was giving Eilie her lesson. This was the first time they saw each other. After that he came more often, and sometimes stayed to dinner with us. I won't deny, sir, that I was glad to welcome him; I thought it good for Eilie. Can there be anything more odious," he burst out, "than such a self-complacent blindness? There are people who say, 'Poor man, he had such faith!' Faith, sir! Conceit! I was a fool—in this world one pays for folly. . . .

"The summer came; and one Saturday in early June Eilie, I, and Francis—I won't tell you his other name—went riding. The night had been wet; there was no dust, and presently the sun came out—a glorious day! We rode a long way. About seven o'clock we started back—slowly, for it was still hot, and there was all the cool of night before us. It was nine o'clock when we came to Richmond Park. A grand place, Richmond Park; and in that half-light wonderful, the deer moving so softly, you might have thought they were spirits. We were silent too—great trees have that effect on me. . . .

"Who can say when changes come? Like a shift of the wind, the old passes, the new is on you. I am telling you now of a change like that. Without a sign of warning, Eilie put her horse into a gallop. 'What are you doing?' I shouted. She looked back with a smile, then he dashed past me too. A hornet might have stung them both: they galloped over fallen trees, under low-hanging branches, up hill and down. I had to watch that madness! My horse was not so fast. I rode like a demon; but fell far behind. I am not a man who takes things

A KNIGHT

quietly. When I came up with them at last, I could not speak
for rage. They were riding side by side, the reins on the horses'
necks, looking in each other's faces. 'You should take care.' I
said. 'Care!' she cried; 'life is not all taking care!' My
anger left me. I dropped behind, as grooms ride behind their
mistresses. . . . Jealousy! No torture is so ceaseless or so black.
. . . In those minutes a hundred things came up in me—a hundred memories, true, untrue, what do I know? My soul was
poisoned. I tried to reason with myself. It was absurd to
think such things! It was unmanly. . . . Even if it were true,
one should try to be a gentleman! But I found myself laughing; yes, sir, laughing at that word." He spoke faster, as if
pouring his heart out not to a live listener, but to the night.
"I could not sleep that night. To lie near her with those
thoughts in my brain was impossible! I made an excuse, and
sat up with some papers. The hardest thing in life is to see a
thing coming and be able to do nothing to prevent it. What
could I do? Have you noticed how people may become utter
strangers without a word? It only needs a thought. . . . The
very next day she said: 'I want to go to Lucy's.' 'Alone?'
'Yes.' I had made up my mind by then that she must do just
as she wished. Perhaps I acted wrongly; I do not know what one
ought to do in such a case; but before she went I said to her:
'Eilie, what is it?' 'I don't know,' she answered; and I kissed
her—that was all. . . . A month passed; I wrote to her nearly
every day, and I had short letters from her, telling me very
little of herself. Dalton was a torture to me, for I could not
tell him; he had a conviction that she was going to become a
mother. 'Ah, Brune!' he said, 'my poor wife was just like
that.' Life, sir, is a somewhat ironical affair! . . . *He*—I find
it hard to speak his name—came to the school two or three times
a week. I used to think I saw a change, a purpose growing up
through his recklessness; there seemed a violence in him as if
he chafed against my blade. I had a kind of joy feeling I had
the mastery, and could toss the iron out of his hand any minute
like a straw. I was ashamed, and yet I gloried in it. Jealousy
is a low thing, sir—a low, base thing! When he asked me
where my wife was, I told him; I was too proud to hide it.
Soon after that he came no more to the school.

"One morning, when I could bear it no longer, I wrote and
said I was coming down. I would not force myself on her, but
I asked her to meet me in the orchard of the old house we

called the convent. I asked her to be there at four o'clock. It
has always been my belief that a man must neither beg anything of a woman, nor force anything from her. Women are
generous—they will give you what they can. I sealed my letter,
and posted it myself. All the way down I kept on saying to
myself, ' She must come—surely she will come!'

VII

" I was in high spirits, but the next moment trembled like
a man with ague. I reached the orchard before my time. She
was not there. You know what it is like to wait? I stood still
and listened; I went to the point whence I could see farthest: I
said to myself, ' a watched pot never boils; if I don't look for
her she will come.' I walked up and down with my eyes on the
ground. The sickness of it! A hundred times I took out my
watch. Perhaps it was fast, perhaps hers was slow—I can't tell
you a thousandth part of my hopes and fears. There was a
spring of water in one corner. I sat beside it, and thought of
the last time I had been there—and something seemed to burst
in me. It was five o'clock before I lost all hope; there comes a
time when you're glad that hope is dead, it means rest. ' That's
over,' you say, ' now I can act.' But what was I to do? I lay
down with my face to the ground; when one's in trouble, it's
the only thing that helps—something to press against and
cling to what can't give way. I lay there for two hours, knowing
all the time that I should play the coward. At seven o'clock I
left the orchard and went towards the inn; I had broken my
word, but I felt happy. I should see her—and, sir, nothing—
nothing seemed to matter beside that. Tor was in the garden
snipping at his roses. He came up, and I could see that he
couldn't look me in the face. ' Where's my wife?' I said. He
answered, ' Let's get Lucy.' I ran indoors. Lucy met me with
two letters; the first—my own—unopened; and the second,
this:—

" ' I have left you. You were good to me, but now—it is
no use.
                                                      EILIE.'

" She told me that a boy had brought a letter for my wife
the day before, from a young gentleman in a boat. When Lucy
delivered it she asked, ' Who is he, Miss Eilie? What will Mr.
Brune say?' My wife looked at her angrily, but gave her no
answer—and all that day she never spoke. In the evening she

was gone, leaving this note on the bed. . . . Lucy cried as if
her heart would break. I took her by the shoulders and put
her from the room; I couldn't bear the noise. I sat down and
tried to think. While I was sitting there Tor came in with a
letter. It was written on the notepaper of an inn twelve miles
up the river: these were the words:—

" ' Eilie is mine. I am ready to meet you where you like.' "

He went on with a painful evenness of speech. "When I
read those words, I had only one thought—to reach them; I ran
down to the river, and chose out the lightest boat. Just as I
was starting, Tor came running. 'You dropped this letter,
sir,' he said. 'Two pairs of arms are better than one.' He
came into the boat. I took the sculls and I pulled out into
the stream. I pulled like a madman; and that great man, with
his bare arms crossed, was like a huge, tawny bull sitting there
opposite me. Presently he took my place, and I took the rudder
lines. I could see his chest, covered with hair, heaving up and
down, it gave me a sort of comfort—it meant that we were
getting nearer. Then it grew dark, there was no moon, I
could barely see the bank: there's something in the dark which
drives one into oneself. People tell you there comes a moment
when your nature is decided—' saved ' or ' lost ' as they call it
—for good or evil. That is not true, your self is always with
you, and cannot be altered; but, sir, I believe that in a time of
agony one finds out what are the things one can do, and what
are those one cannot. You get to *know* yourself, that's all.
And so it was with me. Every thought and memory and passion
was so clear and strong! I wanted to kill him. I wanted to
kill myself. But her—no! We are taught that we possess
our wives, body and soul, we are brought up in that faith, we
are commanded to believe it—but when I was face to face with
it, those words had no meaning; that belief, those commands,
they were without meaning to me, they were—vile. Oh yes, I
wanted to find comfort in them, I *wanted* to hold on to them
—but I couldn't. You may force a body; how can you force
a soul? No, no—cowardly! But I wanted to—I wanted to
kill him and force her to come back to me! And then, suddenly,
I felt as if I were pressing right on the most secret nerve of my
heart. I seemed to see her face, white and quivering, as if I'd
stamped my heel on it. They say this world is ruled by force;

it may be true—I know I have a weak spot in me. . . . I couldn't bear it. At last I jumped to my feet and shouted out, 'Turn the boat round!' Tor looked up at me as if I had gone mad. And I *had* gone mad. I seized the boat-hook and threatened him; I called him fearful names. 'Sir,' he said, 'I don't take such names from any one!' 'You'll take them from me,' I shouted; 'turn the boat round, you idiot, you hound, you fish!' . . . I have a terrible temper, a perfect curse to me. He seemed amazed, even frightened; he sat down again suddenly and pulled the boat round. I fell on the seat, and hid my face. I believe the moon came up; there must have been a mist too, for I was cold as death. In this life, sir, we cannot hide our faces—but by degrees the pain of wounds grows less. Some will have it that such blows are mortal; it is not so. Time is merciful.

"In the early morning I went back to London. I had fever on me—and was delirious. I dare say I should have killed myself if I had not been so used to weapons—they and I were too old friends, I suppose—I can't explain. It was a long while before I was up and about. Dalton nursed me through it; his great heavy moustache had grown quite white. We never mentioned her; what was the good? There were things to settle of course, the lawyer—this was unspeakably distasteful to me. I told him it was to be as she wished, but the fellow *would* come to me, with his—there, I don't want to be unkind. I wished him to say it was my fault, but he said—I remember his smile now—he said, that was impossible, would be seen through, talked of collusion—I don't understand these things, and what's more, I can't bear them, they are—dirty.

"Two years later, when I had come back to London, after the Russo-Turkish war, I received a letter from her. I have it here." He took an old, yellow sheet of paper out of a leathern pocket-book, spread it in his fingers, and sat staring at it. For some minutes he did not speak.

"In the autumn of that same year she died in childbirth. He had deserted her. Fortunately for him, he was killed on the Indian frontier, that very year. If she had lived she would have been thirty-two next June; not a great age. . . . I know I am what you call a crank; doctors will tell you that you can't be cured of a bad illness, and be the same man again. If you are bent, to force yourself straight must leave you weak in another place. I *must* and will think well of women—everything done, and everything said against them is a stone on

her dead body. Could *you* sit, and listen to it?" As though
driven by his own question, he rose, and paced up and down. He
came back to the seat at last.

"That, sir, is the reason of my behaviour this afternoon, and
again this evening. You have been so kind, I wanted—I wanted
to tell you. She had a little daughter—Lucy has her now. My
friend Dalton is dead; there would have been no difficulty about
money, but I am sorry to say that he was swindled—disgrace-
fully. It fell to me to administer his affairs—he never knew it,
but he died penniless; he had trusted some wretched fellows—
had an idea they would make his fortune. As I very soon found,
they had ruined him. It was impossible to let Lucy—such a
dear woman—bear that burden. I have tried to make provision;
but, you see," he took hold of my sleeve, "I, too, have not been
fortunate; in fact, it's difficult to save a great deal out of
£190 a year; but the capital is perfectly safe—and I get £47
10s. a quarter, paid on the nail. I have often been tempted to
reinvest at a greater rate of interest, but I've never dared.
Anyway, there are no debts—I've been obliged to make a rule
not to buy what I couldn't pay for on the spot. Now I am
really plaguing you—but I wanted to tell you—in case—anything should happen to me." He seemed to take a sudden scare,
stiffened, twisted his moustache, and muttering, "Your great
kindness! Shall never forget!" turned hurriedly away.

He vanished; his footsteps and the tap of his stick grew
fainter and fainter. They died out. He was gone. Suddenly
I got up and hastened after him. I soon stopped—what was
there to say?

VIII

The following day I was obliged to go to Nice, and did not
return till midnight. The porter told me that Jules le Ferrier
had been to see me. The next morning, while I was still in
bed, the door was opened, and Jules appeared. His face was
very pale; and the moment he stood still drops of perspiration
began coursing down his cheeks.

"Georges!" he said, "he is dead. There, there! How
stupid you look! My man is packing. I have half an hour
before the train; my evidence shall come from Italy. I have
done my part, the rest is for you. Why did you have that
dinner? The Don Quixote! The idiot! The *poor* man!

Don't move! Have you a cigar? Listen! When you followed him, I followed the other two. My infernal curiosity! Can you conceive a greater folly? How fast they walked, those two! feeling their cheeks, as if he had struck them both, you know; it was funny. They soon saw me, for their eyes were all round about their heads; they had the mark of a glove on their cheeks." The colour began to come back into Jules's face; he gesticulated with his cigar and became more and more dramatic. "They waited for me. '*Tiens!*' said one, 'this gentleman was with him. My friend's name is M. le Baron de ——. The man who struck him was an odd-looking person; kindly inform me whether it is possible for my friend to meet him?' Eh!" commented Jules, "he was offensive! Was it for me to give our dignity away? 'Perfectly, monsieur!' I answered. 'In that case,' he said, 'please give me his name and address.' . . . I could not remember his name, and as for the address, I never knew it! . . . I reflected. 'That,' I said, 'I am unable to do, for special reasons.' 'Aha!' he said, 'reasons that will prevent our fighting him, I suppose?' 'On the contrary,' I said, 'I will convey your request to him; I may mention that I have heard he is the best swordsman and pistol-shot in Europe. Good-night!' I wished to give them something to dream of, you understand. . . . Patience, my dear! Patience! I was coming to you, but I thought I would let them sleep on it— there was plenty of time! But yesterday morning I came into the *Place,* and there he was on the bench, with a big dog. I declare to you be blushed like a young girl. 'Sir,' he said, 'I was hoping to meet you; last evening I made a great disturbance. I took an unpardonable liberty'—and he put in my hand an envelope. My friend, what do you suppose it contained—a pair of gloves! Señor Don Punctilioso, *hein?* He was the devil, this friend of yours; he fascinated me with his gentle eyes and his white moustachettes, his humility, his flames—poor man! . . . I told him I had been asked to take him a challenge. 'If anything comes of it,' I said, 'make use of me!' 'Is that so?' he said. 'I am most grateful for your kind offer. Let me see— it is so long since I fought a duel. The sooner it's over the better. Could you arrange to-morrow morning? Weapons? Yes; let them choose.' . . . You see, my friend, there was no hanging back here; *nous voilà en train.*"

Jules took out his watch. "I have sixteen minutes. It is lucky for you that you were away yesterday, or you would be in my shoes now. I fixed the place, right hand of the road to Roquebrune, just by the railway cutting, and the time—five-thirty of the morning. It was arranged that I should call for him. Disgusting hour; I have not been up so early since I fought Jacques Tirbaut in '85. At five o'clock I found him ready and drinking tea with rum in it—singular man! he made me have some too, brrr! He was shaved, and dressed in that old frock-coat. His great dog jumped into the carriage, but he bade her get out, took her paws on his shoulders, and whispered in her ear some Italian words; a charm, *hein!* and back she went, the tail between the legs. We drove slowly, so as not to shake his arm. He was more gay than I. All the way he talked to me of you: how kind you were! how good you had been to him! 'You do not speak of yourself!' I said. 'Have you no friends, nothing to say? Sometimes an accident will happen!' 'Oh!' he answered, 'there is no danger; but if by any chance—well, there is a letter in my pocket.' 'And if you should kill *him?*' I said. 'But I shall not,' he answered slyly: 'do you think I am going to fire on him? No, no, he is too young.' 'But,' I said, 'I am not going to stand that!' 'Yes,' he replied, 'I owe him a shot; but there is no danger—not the least danger.' We had arrived; already they were there. Ah! bah! You know the preliminaries, the politeness—this duelling, you know, it is absurd, after all. We placed them at twenty paces. It is not a bad place. There are pine-trees round, and rocks; at that hour it was cool and grey as a church. I handed him the pistol. How can I describe him to you, standing there, smoothing the barrel with his fingers! 'What a beautiful thing a good pistol!' he said. 'Only a fool or a madman throws away his life,' I said. 'Certainly,' he replied, 'certainly; but there is no danger,' and he regarded me, raising his moustachette.

"There they stood then, back to back, with the mouths of their pistols to the sky. '*Un!*' I cried, '*deux! tirez!*' They turned, I saw the smoke of his shot go straight up like a prayer; his pistol dropped. I ran to him. He looked surprised, put out his hand, and fell into my arms. He was dead. Those fools came running up. 'What is it?' cried one. I made him a bow. 'As you see,' I said; 'you have made a pretty shot. My friend fired in the air. Messieurs, you had better breakfast in Italy.' We carried him to the carriage, and covered him with a rug; the others drove for the frontier. I brought him to his room. Here is his letter." Jules stopped; tears were running down his face. "He is dead; I have closed his eyes. Look here, you know, we are all of us cads—it is the rule; but this—this, perhaps, was the exception." And without another word he rushed away. . . .

Outside the old fellow's lodging a dismounted *cocher* was standing disconsolate in the sun. "How was I to know they were going to fight a duel?" he burst out on seeing me. "He had white hair—I call you to witness he had white hair. This is bad for me: they will ravish my licence. Aha! you will see—this is bad for me!" I gave him the slip and found my way upstairs. The old fellow was alone, lying on the bed, his feet covered with a rug as if he might feel cold; his eyes were closed, but in this sleep of death, he still had that air of faint surprise. At full length, watching the bed intently, Freda lay, as she lay nightly when he was really asleep. The shutters were half open: the room still smelt slightly of rum. I stood for a long time looking at the face: the little white fans of moustache brushed upwards even in death, the hollows in his cheeks, the quiet of his figure; he was like some old knight. . . . The dog broke the spell. She sat up, and resting her paws on the bed, licked his face. I went downstairs—I couldn't bear to hear her howl. This was his letter to me, written in a pointed handwriting:

"MY DEAR SIR,—Should you read this, I shall be gone. I am ashamed to trouble you—a man should surely manage so as not to give trouble; and yet I believe you will not consider me importunate. If, then, you will pick up the pieces of an old fellow, I ask you to have my sword, the letter enclosed in this, and the photograph that stands on the stove buried with me. My will and the acknowledgments of my property are between the leaves of the Byron in my tin chest; they should go to Lucy Tor—address thereon. Perhaps you will do me the honour to retain for yourself any of my books that may give you pleasure. In the *Pilgrim's Progress* you will find some excellent recipes for Turkish coffee, Italian and Spanish dishes, and washing wounds. The landlady's daughter speaks Italian, and she would, I know, like to have Freda; the poor dog will miss me. I have read of old Indian warriors taking their horses and dogs with them to the happy hunting-grounds. Freda would come—noble animals are dogs! She eats once a day—a good large meal—and requires much salt. If you have animals of your own, sir, don't forget—all animals require salt. I have no debts, thank

God! The money in my pockets would bury me decently—not that there is any danger. And I am ashamed to weary you with details—the least a man can do is not to make a fuss—and yet he must be found ready.—Sir, with profound gratitude, your servant,

"ROGER BRUNE."

Everything was as he had said. The photograph on the stove was that of a young girl of nineteen or twenty, dressed in an old-fashioned style, with hair gathered backward in a knot. The eyes gazed at you with a little frown, the lips were tightly closed; the expression of the face was eager, quick, wilful, and, above all, young.

The tin trunk was scented with dry fragments of some herb, the history of which in that trunk man knoweth not. . . . There were a few clothes, but very few, all older than those he usually wore. Besides the Byron and *Pilgrim's Progress* were Scott's *Quentin Durward*, Captain Marryat's *Midshipman Easy*, a pocket Testament, and a long and frightfully stiff book on the art of fortifying towns, much thumbed, and bearing date 1863. By far the most interesting thing I found, however, was a diary, kept down to the preceding Christmas. It was a pathetic document, full of calculations of the price of meals; resolutions to be careful over this or that; doubts whether he must not give up smoking; sentences of fear that Freda had not enough to eat. It appeared that he had tried to live on ninety pounds a year, and send the other hundred pounds home to Lucy for the child; in this struggle he was always failing, having to send less than the amount—the entries showed that this was a nightmare to him. The last words, written on Christmas Day, were these: "What is the use of writing this, since it records nothing but failure!"

The landlady's daughter and myself were at the funeral. The same afternoon I went into the concert-room, where I had spoken to him first. When I came out Freda was lying at the entrance, looking into the faces of every one that passed, and sniffling idly at their heels. Close by the landlady's daughter hovered, a biscuit in her hand, and a puzzled, sorry look on her face.

September, 1900.

THE JURYMAN

I

"Don't you see, brother, I was reading yesterday the Gospel about Christ, the little Father; how He suffered, how He walked on the earth. I suppose you have heard about it?"

"Indeed, I have," replied Stepanuitch; "but we are people in darkness; we can't read."—TOLSTOI.

MR. HENRY BOSENGATE, of the London Stock Exchange, seated himself in his car that morning during the Great War with a sense of injury. Major in a Volunteer Corps; member of all the local committees; lending this very car to the neighbouring hospital, at times even driving it himself for their benefit; subscribing to funds, so far as his diminished income permitted—he was conscious of being an asset to the country, and one whose time could not be wasted with impunity. To be summoned to sit on a jury at the local assizes, and not even the grand jury at that! It was in the nature of an outrage.

Strong and upright, with hazel eyes and dark eyebrows, pinkish-brown cheeks, a forehead white, well-shaped, and getting high, with greyish hair glossy and well-brushed, and a trim moustache, he might have been taken for that colonel of Volunteers which indeed he was in a fair way of becoming.

His wife had followed him out under the porch, and stood bracing her supple body clothed in lilac linen. Red rambler roses formed a sort of crown to her dark head; her ivory-coloured face had in it just a suggestion of the Japanese.

Mr. Bosengate spoke through the whirr of the engine:

"I don't expect to be late, dear. This business is ridiculous. There oughtn't to *be* any crime in these days."

His wife—her name was Kathleen—smiled. She looked very pretty and cool, Mr. Bosengate thought. To one bound on this dull and stuffy business everything he owned seemed pleasant—the geranium beds beside the gravel drive, his long, red-brick house mellowing decorously in its creepers and ivy, the little clock-tower over stables now converted to a garage, the dovecote, masking at the other end the conservatory which adjoined the billiard-room. Close to the red-brick lodge his two children, Kate and Harry, ran out from under the acacia trees, and waved to him, scrambling bare-legged on to the low, red, ivy-covered wall which guarded his domain of eleven acres. Mr. Bosengate waved back, thinking: 'Jolly couple—by Jove, they are!' Above their heads, through the trees, he could see right away to some Downs, faint in the July heat haze. And he thought: 'Pretty a spot as one could have got, so close to town!'

Despite the war he had enjoyed these last two years more than any of the ten since he built "Charmleigh" and settled down to semi-rural domesticity with his young wife. There had been a certain piquancy, a savour added to existence, by the country's peril, and all the public service and sacrifice it demanded. His chauffeur was gone, and one gardener did the work of three. He enjoyed—positively enjoyed—his committee work; even the serious decline of business and increase of taxation had not much worried one continually conscious of the national crisis and his own part therein. The country had wanted waking up, wanted a lesson in effort and economy; and the feeling that he had not spared himself in these strenuous times had given a zest to those quiet pleasures of bed and board which, at his age, even the most patriotic could retain with a good conscience. He had denied himself many things—new clothes, presents for Kathleen and the children, travel, and that pine-apple house which he had been on the point of building when the war broke out; new wine, too, and cigars, and membership of the two Clubs which he had never used in the old days. The hours had seemed fuller and longer, sleep better earned—wonderful, the things one could do without when put to it! He turned the car into the high road, driving dreamily, for he was in plenty of time. The war was going pretty well now; he was no fool optimist, but now that conscription was in force, one might reasonably hope for its end within a year. Then there would be a boom, and one might let oneself go a little. Visions of theatres and supper with his wife at the Savoy afterwards, and cosy night drives back into the sweet-smelling country behind your own chauffeur once more teased a fancy which even now did not soar beyond the confines of domestic pleasures. He pictured his wife in new dresses by Jay—she was fifteen years younger than himself, and "paid for dressing" as they said. He had always delighted—as men older than their wives will—in the admiration she excited from others not privileged to enjoy her charms. Her rather queer and ironical beauty, her cool irreproachable wifeliness, was a constant balm to him. They would give dinner parties again, have their friends down from town, and he would once more enjoy sitting at the foot of the dinner table while Kathleen sat at the head, with the light soft on her ivory shoulders, behind flowers she had arranged in that original way of hers, and fruit which he had grown in his hot-houses; once more he would take legitimate interest in the wine he offered to his guests—once more stock that Chinese cabinet wherein he kept cigars. Yes—there was a certain satisfaction in these days of privation, if only from the anticipation they created.

The sprinkling of villas had become continuous on either side of the high road; and women going to shop, tradesmen's boys delivering victuals, young men in khaki, began to abound. Now and then a limping or bandaged form would pass—some bit of human wreckage! and Mr. Bosengate would think mechanically: 'Another of those poor devils! Wonder if we've had his case before us!'

Running his car into the best hotel garage of the little town, he made his way leisurely over to the court. It stood back from the market-place, and was already lapped by a sea of persons having, as in the outer ring at race meetings, an air of business at which one must not be caught out, together with a soaked or flushed appearance. Mr. Bosengate could not resist putting his handkerchief to his nose. He had carefully drenched it with lavender water, and to this fact owed, perhaps, his immunity from the post of foreman on the jury—for, say what you will about the English, they have a deep instinct for affairs.

He found himself second in the front row of the jury box, and through the odour of " Sanitas " gazed at the judge's face expressionless up there, for all the world like a be-wigged bust. His fellows in the box had that appearance of falling between two classes characteristic of jurymen. Mr. Bosengate was not impressed. On one side of him the foreman sat, a prominent upholsterer, known in the town as " Gentleman Fox." His dark and beautifully brushed and oiled hair and moustache, his radiant linen, gold watch and chain, the white piping to his waistcoat, and a habit of never saying " Sir " had long marked him out from commoner men; he undertook to bury people too, to save them trouble; and was altogether superior. On the other side Mr. Bosengate had one of those men who, except when they sit on juries, are never seen without a little brown bag, and the appearance of having been interrupted in a drink. Pale and shiny, with large loose eyes shifting from side to side, he had an underdone voice and uneasy, flabby hands. Mr. Bosengate disliked sitting next to him. Beyond this commercial traveller sat a dark pale young man with spectacles; beyond him again, a short old man with grey moustache, mutton chops, and innumerable wrinkles; and the front row was completed by a chemist. The three immediately behind, Mr. Bosengate did not thoroughly master; but the three at the end of the second row he learned in their order of an oldish man in a grey suit, given to winking; an inanimate person with the mouth of a moustachioed codfish, over whose long bald crown three wisps of damp hair were carefully arranged; and a dried, dapperish, clean-shorn man, whose mouth seemed terrified lest it should be surprised without a smile. Their first and second verdicts were recorded without the necessity for withdrawal, and Mr. Bosengate was already sleepy when the third case was called. The sight of khaki revived his drooping attention. But what a weedy-looking specimen! This prisoner had a truly nerveless, pitiable, dejected air. If he had ever had a military bearing it had shrunk into him during his confinement. His ill-shaped brown tunic, whose little brass buttons seemed trying to keep smiling, struck Mr. Bosengate as ridiculously short, used though he was to such things. 'Absurd,' he thought—'Lumbago! Just where they ought to be covered!' Then the officer and gentleman stirred in him, and he added to himself: 'Still, there must be some distinction made!' The little soldier's visage had once perhaps been tanned, but was now the colour of dark dough; his large brown eyes with white showing below the iris, as so often in the eyes of very nervous people—wandered from face to face, of judge, counsel, jury, and public. There were hollows in his cheeks, his dark hair looked damp; around his neck he wore a bandage. The commercial traveller on Mr. Bosengate's left turned, and whispered: "Felo de se! My hat! what a guy!" Mr. Bosengate pretended not to hear—he could not bear that fellow!—and slowly wrote on a bit of paper: "Owen Lewis." Welsh! Well, he looked it—not at all an English face. Attempted suicide—not at all an English crime! Suicide implied surrender, a putting-up of hands to Fate—to say nothing of the religious aspect of the matter. And suicide in khaki seemed to Mr. Bosengate particularly abhorrent; like turning tail in face of the enemy; almost meriting the fate of a deserter. He looked at the prisoner, trying not to give way to this prejudice. And the prisoner seemed to look at him, though this, perhaps, was fancy.

The counsel for the prosecution, a little, alert, grey, decided man, above military age, began detailing the circumstances of the crime. Mr. Bosengate, though not particularly sensitive to atmosphere, could perceive a sort of current running through the court. It was as if jury and public were thinking rhythmically in obedience to the same unexpressed prejudice of which he himself was conscious. Even the Cæsar-like pale face up there, presiding, seemed in its ironic serenity responding to that current.

"Gentlemen of the jury, before I call my evidence, I direct your attention to the bandage the accused is still wearing. He gave himself this wound with his Army razor, adding, if I may say so, insult to the injury he was inflicting on his country. He pleads not guilty; and before the magistrates he said that absence from his wife was preying on his mind"—the advocate's close lips widened— "Well, gentlemen, if such an excuse is to weigh with us in these days, I'm sure I don't know what's to happen to the Empire."

'No, by George!' thought Mr. Bosengate.

The evidence of the first witness, a room-mate who had caught the prisoner's hand, and of the sergeant, who had at once been summoned, was conclusive, and he began to cherish a hope that they would get through without withdrawing, and he would be home before five. But then a hitch occurred. The regimental doctor failed to respond when his name was called; and the judge having for the first time that day showed himself capable of human emotion, intimated that he would adjourn until the morrow.

Mr. Bosengate received the announcement with equanimity. He would be home even earlier! And gathering up the sheets of paper he had scribbled on, he put them in his pocket and got up. The would-be suicide was being taken out of the court —a shambling drab figure with shoulders hunched. What good were men like that in these days! What good! The prisoner looked up. Mr. Bosengate encountered in full the gaze of those large brown eyes, with the white showing underneath. What a suffering, wretched, pitiful face! A man had no business to give you a look like that! The prisoner passed on down the stairs, and vanished. Mr. Bosengate went out and across the market-place to the garage of the hotel where he had left his car. The sun shone fiercely and he thought: 'I must do some watering in the garden.' He brought the car out, and was about to start the engine, when some one passing said: "Good evenin'. Seedy-lookin' beggar that last prisoner, ain't he? We don't want men of that stamp." It was his neighbour on the jury, the commercial traveller, in a straw hat, with a little brown bag already in his hand and the froth of an interrupted drink on his moustache. Answering curtly: "Good evening!" and thinking: 'Nor of yours, my friend!' Mr. Bosengate started the car with unnecessary clamour. But as if brought back to life by the commercial traveller's remark, the prisoner's figure seemed to speed along too, turning up at Mr. Bosengate his pitifully unhappy eyes. Want of his wife!—queer excuse that for trying to put it out of his power ever to see her again. Why! Half a loaf, even a slice, was better than no bread. Not many of that neurotic type in the Army—thank Heaven! The lugubrious figure vanished, and Mr. Bosengate pictured instead the form of his own wife bending over her "Gloire de Dijon" roses in the rosery, where she generally worked a little before tea now that they were short of gardeners. He saw her, as often he had seen her raise herself and stand, head to one side, a gloved hand on her slender hip, gazing as it were ironically from under drooped lids at buds which did not come out fast enough. And the word '*Caline*,' for he was something of a French scholar, shot through his mind: 'Kathleen—*Caline!*' If he found her there when he got in, he would steal up on the grass and—ah! but with great care not to crease her dress or disturb her hair! 'If only she weren't quite so self-contained,' he thought. 'It's like a cat you can't get near, not really near!'

The car, returning faster than it had come down that morning, had already passed the outskirt villas, and was breasting the hill to where, among fields and the old trees, Charmleigh lay apart from commoner life. Turning into his drive, Mr. Bosengate thought with a certain surprise: 'I wonder what she *does* think of! I wonder!' He put his gloves and hat down in the outer hall and went into the lavatory to dip his face in cool water and wash it with sweet-smelling soap—delicious revenge on the unclean atmosphere in which he had been stewing so many hours. He came out again into the hall dazed by soap and the mellowed light, and a voice from half-way up the stairs said: "Daddy! Look!" His little daughter was standing up there with one hand on the banisters. She scrambled on to them and came sliding down, her frock up to her eyes, and her holland knickers to her middle. Mr. Bosengate said mildly:

"Well, that's elegant!"

"Tea's in the summer-house. Mummy's waiting. Come on!"

With her hand in his, Mr. Bosengate went on, through the drawing-room, long and cool, with sunblinds down, through the billiard-room, high and cool, through the conservatory, green and sweet-smelling, out on to the terrace and the upper lawn. He had never felt such sheer exhilarated joy in his home surroundings, so cool, glistening and green under the July sun; and he said:

"Well, Kit, what have you all been doing?"

"I've fed my rabbits and Harry's; and we've been in the attic; Harry got his leg through the skylight."

Mr. Bosengate drew in his breath with a hiss.

"It's all right, Daddy; we got it out again, it's only grazed the skin. And we've been making swabs—I made seventeen—Mummy made thirty-three, and then she went to the hospital. Did you put many men in prison?"

Mr. Bosengate cleared his throat. The question seemed to him untimely.

"Only two."

"What's it like in prison, Daddy?"

Mr. Bosengate, who had no more knowledge than his little daughter, replied in an absent voice:

"Not very nice."

They were passing under a young oak tree, where the path wound round to the rosery and summer-house. Something shot down and clawed Mr. Bosengate's neck. His little daughter began to hop and suffocate with laughter.

"Oh, Daddy! Aren't you caught! I led you on purpose!"

Looking up, Mr. Bosengate saw his small son lying along a low branch above him—like the leopard he was declaring himself to be (for fear of error), and thought blithely: 'What an active little chap it is!'

"Let me drop on your shoulders, Daddy—like they do on the deer."

"Oh, yes! Do be a deer, Daddy!"

Mr. Bosengate did not see being a deer; his hair had just been brushed. But he entered the rosery buoyantly between his offspring. His wife was standing precisely as he had imagined her, in a pale blue frock open at the neck, with a narrow black band round the waist, and little accordion pleats below. She looked her coolest. Her smile, when she turned her head, hardly seemed to take Mr. Bosengate seriously enough. He placed his lips below one of her half-drooped eyelids. She even smelled of roses. His children began to dance round their mother, and Mr. Bosengate, firmly held between them, was also compelled to do this, until she said:

"When you've quite done, let's have tea!"

It was not the greeting he had imagined coming along in the car. Earwigs were plentiful in the summer-house—used perhaps twice a year, but indispensable to every country residence —and Mr. Bosengate was not sorry for the excuse to get out again. Though all was so pleasant, he felt oddly restless, rather suffocated; and lighting his pipe, began to move about among the roses, blowing tobacco at the greenfly; in war-time one was never quite idle! And suddenly he said:

"We're trying a wretched Tommy at the assizes."

His wife looked up from a rose.

"What for?"

"Attempted suicide."

"Why did he?"

"Can't stand the separation from his wife."

She looked at him, gave a low laugh, and said:

"Oh dear!"

Mr. Bosengate was puzzled. Why did she laugh? He looked round, saw that the children were gone, took his pipe from his mouth, and approached her.

"You look very pretty," he said. "Give me a kiss!"

His wife bent her body forward from the waist, and pushed her lips out till they touched his moustache. Mr. Bosengate felt a sensation as if he had arisen from breakfast without having eaten marmalade. He mastered it and said:

"That jury are a rum lot."

His wife's eyelids flickered. "I wish women sat on juries."

"Why?"

" It would be an experience."

Not the first time she had used that curious expression! Yet her life was far from dull, so far as he could see; with the new interests created by the war, and the constant calls on her time made by the perfection of their home life, she had a useful and busy existence. Again the random thought passed through him: ' But she never tells me anything!' And suddenly that lugubrious khaki-clad figure started up among the rose bushes. "We've got a lot to be thankful for!" he said abruptly. "I must go to work!" His wife, raising one eyebrow, smiled. "And I to weep!" Mr. Bosengate laughed—she had a pretty wit! And stroking his comely moustache where it had been kissed, he moved out into the sunshine. All the evening, throughout his labours, not inconsiderable, for this jury business had put him behind time, he was afflicted by that restless pleasure in his surroundings; would break off in mowing the lower lawn to look at the house through the trees; would leave his study and committee papers to cross into the drawing-room and sniff its dainty fragrance; paid a special good-night visit to the children having supper in the schoolroom; pottered in and out from his dressing-room to admire his wife while she was changing for dinner; dined with his mind perpetually on the next course; talked volubly of the war; and in the billiard-room afterwards, smoking the pipe which had taken the place of his cigar, could not keep still, but roamed about, now in conservatory, now in the drawing-room, where his wife and the governess were still making swabs. It seemed to him that he could not have enough of anything. About eleven o'clock he strolled out —beautiful night, only just dark enough—under the new arrangement with Time—and went down to the little round fountain below the terrace. His wife was playing the piano. Mr. Bosengate looked at the water and the flat dark water-lily leaves which floated there; looked up at the house, where only narrow chinks of light showed, because of the Lighting Order. The dreamy music drifted out; there was a scent of heliotrope. He moved a few steps back, and sat in the children's swing under an old lime tree. Jolly—blissful—in the warm, bloomy dark! Of all hours of the day, this before going to bed was perhaps the pleasantest. He saw the light go up in his wife's bedroom, unscreened for a full minute, and thought: ' Aha! If I did my duty as a special, I should " strafe " her for that.' She came to the window, her figure lighted, hands up to the back of her

head, so that her bare arms gleamed. Mr. Bosengate wafted her
a kiss, knowing he could not be seen. 'Lucky chap!' he mused;
'she's a great joy!' Up went her arm, down came the blind—
the house was dark again. He drew a long breath. 'Another
ten minutes,' he thought, 'then I'll go in and shut up. By
Jove! The limes are beginning to smell already!' And, the
better to take in that acme of his well-being, he tilted the
swing, lifted his feet from the ground, and swung himself toward the scented blossoms. He wanted to whelm his senses in
their perfume, and closed his eyes. But instead of the domestic
vision he expected, the face of the little Welsh soldier, hare-
eyed, shadowy, pinched and dark and pitiful, started up with
such disturbing vividness that he opened his eyes again at once.
Curse! The fellow almost haunted one! Where would he be
now—poor little devil! lying in his cell, thinking—thinking of
his wife! Feeling suddenly morbid, Mr. Bosengate arrested
the swing and stood up. Absurd!—all his well-being and mood
of warm anticipation had deserted him! 'A d——d world!' he
thought. 'Such a lot of misery! Why should I have to sit in
judgment on that poor beggar, and condemn him?' He moved
up on to the terrace and walked briskly, to rid himself of this
disturbance before going in. 'That commercial traveller chap,'
he thought, 'the rest of those fellows—they see nothing!' And,
abruptly turning up the three stone steps, he entered the conservatory, locked it, passed into the billiard-room, and drank his
barley water. One of the pictures was hanging crooked; he
went up to put it straight. Still life. Grapes and apples, and
lobsters! They struck him as odd for the first time. Why
lobsters? The whole picture seemed dead and oily. He turned
off the light, and went upstairs, passed his wife's door, into his
own room, and undressed. Clothed in his pyjamas he opened
the door between the rooms. By the light coming from his own
he could see her dark head on the pillow. Was she asleep?
No—not asleep, certainly. The moment of fruition had come;
the crowning of his pride and pleasure in his home. But he
continued to stand there. He had suddenly no pride, no
pleasure, no desire; nothing but a sort of dull resentment against
everything. He turned back, shut the door, and slipping between the heavy curtains and his open window, stood looking
out at the night. 'Full of misery!' he thought. 'Full of
d——d misery!'

II

Filing into the jury box next morning, Mr. Bosengate collided slightly with a short juryman, whose square figure and square head of stiff yellow-red hair he had only vaguely noticed the day before. The man looked angry, and Mr. Bosengate thought: ' An ill-bred dog, that! '

He sat down quickly, and, to avoid further recognition of his fellows, gazed in front of him. His appearance on Saturdays was always military, by reason of the route march of his Volunteer Corps in the afternoon. Gentleman Fox, who belonged to the corps too, was also looking square; but that commercial traveller on his other side seemed more *louche*, and as if surprised in immorality, than ever; only the proximity of Gentleman Fox on the other side kept Mr. Bosengate from shrinking. Then he saw the prisoner being brought in, shadowy and dark behind the brightness of his buttons, and he experienced a sort of shock, this figure was so exactly that which had several times started up in his mind. Somehow he had expected a fresh sight of the fellow to dispel and disprove what had been haunting him, had expected to find him just an outside phenomenon, not, as it were, a part of his own life. And he gazed at the carven immobility of the judge's face, trying to steady himself, as a drunken man will, by looking at a light. The regimental doctor, unabashed by the judge's comment on his absense the day before, gave his evidence like a man who had better things to do, and the case for the prosecution was forthwith rounded in by a little speech from counsel. The matter—he said—was clear as daylight. Those who wore His Majesty's uniform, charged with the responsibility and privilege of defending their country, were no more entitled to desert their regiments by taking their own lives than they were entitled to desert in any other way. He asked for a conviction. Mr. Bosengate felt a sympathetic shuffle passing through all feet; the judge was speaking:

" Prisoner, you can either go into the witness box and make your statement on oath, in which you may be cross-examined on it; or you can make your statement there from the dock, in which case you will not be cross-examined. Which do you elect to do? "

" From here, my lord."

Seeing him now full face, and, as it might be, come to life

in the effort to convey his feelings, Mr. Bosengate had suddenly a quite different impression of the fellow. It was as if his khaki had fallen off, and he had stepped out of his own shadow, a live and quivering creature. His pinched clean-shaven face seemed to have an irregular, wilder, hairier look, his large nervous brown eyes darkened and glowed; he jerked his shoulders, his arms, his whole body, like a man suddenly freed from cramp or a suit of armour. He spoke, too, in a quick, crisp, rather high voice, pinching his consonants a little, sharpening his vowels, like a true Welshman.

" My lord and misters the jury," he said: " I was a hairdresser when the call came on me to join the army. I had a little home and a wife. I never thought what it would be like to be away from them, I surely never did; and I'm ashamed to be speaking it out like this—how it can squeeze and squeeze a man, how it can prey on your mind when you're nervous like I am. 'Tis not everyone that cares for his home—there's a lots o' them never wants to see their wives again. But for me 'tis like being shut up in a cage, it is!" Mr. Bosengate saw daylight between the skinny fingers of the man's hand thrown out with a jerk. " I cannot bear it shut up away from wife and home like what you are in the army. So when I took my razor that morning I was wild—an' I wouldn't be here now but for that man catching my hand. There was no reason in it, I'm willing to confess. It was foolish; but wait till you get feeling like what I was, and see how it draws you. Misters the jury, don't send me back to prison; it is worse still there. If you have wives you will know what it is like for lots of us; only some is more nervous than others. I swear to you, sirs, I could not help it——" Again the little man flung out his hand, his whole thin body shook and Mr. Bosengate felt the same sensation as when he drove his car over a dog—" Misters the jury, I hope you may never in your lives feel as I've been feeling."

The little man ceased, his eyes shrank back into their sockets, his figure back into its mask of shadowy brown and gleaming buttons, and Mr. Bosengate was conscious that the judge was making a series of remarks; and, very soon, of being seated at a mahogany table in the jury's withdrawing room, hearing the voice of the man with hair like an Irish terrier's saying: " Didn't he talk through his hat, that little blighter!" Conscious, too, of the commercial traveller, still on his left— always on his left!—mopping his brow, and muttering: " Phew!

It's hot in there to-day!" when an effluvium, as of an inside accustomed to whisky, came from him. Then the man with the underlip and the three plastered wisps of hair said:

"Don't know why we withdrew, Mr. Foreman!"

Mr. Bosengate looked round to where, at the head of the table, Gentleman Fox sat, in defensive gentility and the little white piping to his waistcoat. "I shall be happy to take the sense of the jury," he was saying blandly.

There was a short silence, then the chemist murmured:

"I should say he must have what they call claustrophobia."

"Clauster fiddlesticks! The feller's a shirker, that's all. Missed his wife—pretty excuse! Indecent, I call it!"

The speaker was the little wire-haired man; and emotion, deep and angry, stirred in Mr. Bosengate. That ill-bred little cur! He gripped the edge of the table with both hands.

"I think it's d——d natural!" he muttered. But almost before the words had left his lips he felt dismay. What had he said—he, nearly a colonel of volunteers—endorsing such a want of patriotism! And hearing the commercial traveller murmuring: "'Ear, 'ear!" he reddened violently.

The wire-headed man said roughly:

"There's too many of these blighted shirkers, and too much pampering of them."

The turmoil in Mr. Bosengate increased; he remarked in an icy voice:

"I agree to no verdict that'll send the man back to prison."

At this a real tremor seemed to go round the table, as if they all saw themselves sitting there through lunch time. Then the large grey-haired man given to winking, said:

"Oh! Come, sir—after what the judge said! Come, sir! What do you say, Mr. Foreman?"

Gentleman Fox—as who should say 'This is excellent value, but I don't wish to press it on you!'—answered:

"We are only concerned with the facts. Did he or did he not try to shorten his life?"

"Of course he did—said so himself," Mr. Bosengate heard the wire-haired man snap out, and from the following murmur of assent he alone abstained. Guilty! Well—yes! There was no way out of admitting that, but his feelings revolted against handing "that poor little beggar" over to the tender mercy of his country's law. His whole soul rose in arms against agreeing with that ill-bred little cur, and the rest of this job-lot.

He had an impulse to get up and walk out, saying: " Settle it your own way. Good-morning."

" It seems, sir," Gentleman Fox was saying, " that we're all agreed to guilty, except yourself. If you will allow me, I don't see how you can go behind what the prisoner himself admitted."

Thus brought up to the very guns, Mr. Bosengate, red in the face, thrust his hands deep into the side pockets of his tunic, and, staring straight before him, said:

" Very well; on condition we recommend him to mercy."

" What do you say, gentlemen; shall we recommend him to mercy? "

" 'Ear 'ear! " burst from the commercial traveller, and from the chemist came the murmur:

" No harm in that."

" Well, I think there is. They shoot deserters at the front, and we let this fellow off. I'd hang the cur."

Mr. Bosengate stared at that little wire-haired brute. " Haven't you *any* feeling for others? " he wanted to say. " Can't you see that this poor devil suffers tortures? " But the sheer impossibility of doing this before ten other men brought a slight sweat out on his face and hands; and in agitation he smote the table a blow with his fist. The effect was instantaneous. Everybody looked at the wire-haired man, as if saying: " Yes, you've gone a bit too far there! " The " little brute " stood it for a moment, then muttered surlily:

" Well, commend 'im to mercy if you like; I don't care."

" That's right; they never pay any attention to it," said the grey-haired man, winking heartily. And Mr. Bosengate filed back with the others into court.

But when from the jury box his eyes fell once more on the hare-eyed figure in the dock, he had his worst moment yet. Why should this poor wretch suffer so—for no fault, no fault; while he, and these others, and that snapping counsel, and the Cæsar-like judge up there, went off to their women and their homes, blithe as bees, and probably never thought of him again? And suddenly he was conscious of the judge's voice:

" You will go back to your regiment, and endeavour to serve your country with better spirit. You may thank the jury that you are not sent to prison, and your good fortune that you were not at the front when you tried to commit this cowardly act. You are lucky to be alive."

A policeman pulled the little soldier by the arm; his drab

figure, with eyes fixed and lustreless, passed down and away.
From his very soul Mr. Bosengate wanted to lean out and say:
"Cheer up, cheer up! *I* understand."

It was nearly ten o'clock that evening before he reached home,
motoring back from the route march. His physical tiredness
was abated, for he had partaken of a snack and a whisky and
soda at the hotel but mentally he was in a curious mood. His
body felt appeased, his spirit hungry. To-night he had a yearning, not for his wife's kisses, but for her understanding. He
wanted to go to her and say: "I've learnt a lot to-day—found
out things I never thought of. Life's a wonderful thing, Kate,
a thing one can't live all to oneself; a thing one shares with
everybody, so that when another suffers, one suffers too. It's
come to me that what one *has* doesn't matter a bit—it's what
one does, and how one sympathises with other people. It came
to me in the most extraordinary vivid way, when I was on that
jury watching that poor little rat of a soldier in his trap; it's
the first time I've ever felt—the—the spirit of Christ, you know.
It's a wonderful thing, Kate—wonderful! We haven't been close
—really close, you and I, so that we each understand what the
other is feeling. It's all in that, you know; understanding—
sympathy—it's priceless. When I saw that poor little devil
taken down and sent back to his regiment to begin his sorrows
all over again—wanting his wife, thinking and thinking of her
just as you know I would be thinking and wanting you, I
felt what an awful outside sort of life we lead, never telling
each other what we really think and feel, never being really close.
I daresay that little chap and his wife keep nothing from each
other—live each other's lives. That's what *we* ought to do.
Let's get to feeling that what really matters is—understanding
and loving, and not only just saying it as we all do, those
fellows on the jury, and even that poor devil of a judge—what
an awful life, judging one's fellow-creatures! When I left
that poor little Tommy this morning, and ever since, I've longed
to get back here quietly to you and tell you about it, and make
a beginning. There's something wonderful in this, and I want
you to feel it as I do, because you mean such a lot to me."

This was what he wanted to say to his wife, not touching, or
kissing her, just looking into her eyes, watching them soften and
glow as they surely must, catching the infection of his new
ardour. And he felt unsteady, fearfully unsteady with the

desire to say it all as it should be said: swiftly, quietly, with the truth and fervour of his feeling.

The hall was not lit up, for daylight still lingered under the new arrangement. He went towards the drawing-room, but from the very door shied off to his study and stood irresolute under the picture of a " Man catching a flea " (Dutch school), which had come down to him from his father. The governess would be in there with his wife! He must wait. Essential to go straight to Kathleen and pour it all out, or he would never do it. He felt as nervous as an undergraduate going up for his *vivâ voce*. This thing was so big, so astoundingly and unexpectedly important. He was suddenly afraid of his wife, afraid of her coolness and her grace, and that something Japanese about her—of all those attributes he had been accustomed to admire; most afraid, as it were, of her attraction. He felt young to-night, almost boyish; would she see that he was not really fifteen years older than herself, and she not really a part of his collection, of all the admirable appointments of his home; but a companion spirit to one who wanted a companion badly? In this agitation of his soul he could keep still no more than he could last night in the agitation of his senses; and he wandered into the dining-room. A dainty supper was set out there, sandwiches, and cake, whisky and cigarettes—even an early peach. Mr. Bosengate looked at this peach with sorrow rather than disgust. The perfection of it was of a piece with all that had gone before this new and sudden feeling. Its delicious bloom seemed to heighten his perception of the hedge around him, that hedge of the things he so enjoyed, carefully planted and tended these many years. He passed it by uneaten, and went to the window. Out there all was darkening, the fountain, the lime tree, the flower-beds, and the fields below, with the Jersey cows who would come to your call; darkening slowly, losing form, blurring into soft blackness, vanishing, but there none the less—all there—the hedge of his possessions. He heard the door of the drawing-room open, the voices of his wife and the governess in the hall, going up to bed. If only they didn't look in here! If only——! The voices ceased. He was safe now—had but to follow in a few minutes, to make sure of Kathleen alone. He turned round and stared down the length of the dark dining-room, over the rosewood table, to where in the mirror above the sideboard at the far end, his figure bathed, a stain, a mere blurred shadow; he made his way down to it along the table edge, and stood before himself as close as he could get. His throat and the roof of his mouth felt dry with nervousness; he put out his finger and touched his face in the glass. ' You're an ass! ' he thought. ' Pull yourself together, and get it over. She will see; of course she will! ' He swallowed, smoothed his moustache, and walked out. Going up the stairs, his heart beat painfully; but he was in for it now, and marched straight into her room.

Dressed only in a loose blue wrapper, she was brushing her dark hair before the glass. Mr. Bosengate went up to her and stood there silent, looking down. The words he had thought of were like a swarm of bees buzzing in his head yet not one would fly from between his lips. His wife went on brushing her hair under the light which shone on her polished elbows. She looked up at him from beneath one lifted eyebrow.

" Well, dear—tired ? "

With a sort of vehemence the single word " No " passed out. A faint, a quizzical smile flitted over her face; she shrugged her shoulders ever so gently. That gesture—he had seen it before! And in desperate desire to make her understand, he put his hand on her lifted arm.

" Kathleen, stop—listen to me ! " His fingers tightened in his agitation and eagerness to make his great discovery known. But before he could get out a word he became conscious of that cool round arm, conscious of her eyes half-closed, sliding round at him, of her half-smiling lips, of her neck under the wrapper. And he stammered:

" I want—I must—Kathleen, I——"

She lifted her shoulders again in that little shrug. " Yes—I know; all right ! "

A wave of heat and shame, and of God knows what came over Mr. Bosengate; he fell on his knees and pressed his forehead to her arm; and he was silent, more silent than the grave. Nothing —nothing came from him but two long sighs. Suddenly he felt her hand stroke his cheek—compassionately, it seemed to him. She made a little movement towards him; her lips met his, and he remembered nothing but that. . . .

In his own room Mr. Bosengate sat at his wide-open window, smoking a cigarette; there was no light. Moths went past, the moon was creeping up. He sat very calm, puffing the smoke out into the night air. Curious thing—life ! Curious world ! Curious forces in it—making one do the opposite of what one

wished; always—always making one do the opposite, it seemed!
The furtive light from the creeping moon was getting hold of
things down there, stealing in among the boughs of the trees.
'There's something ironical,' he thought, 'which walks about.
Things don't come off as you think they will. I meant, I tried
—but one doesn't change like that all of a sudden, it seems.
Fact is, life's too big a thing for me! All the same, I'm not the
man I was yesterday—not quite!' He closed his eyes, and in
one of those flashes of vision which come when the senses are
at rest, he saw himself as it were far down below—down on the
floor of a street narrow as a grave, high as a mountain, a deep
dark slit of a street—walking down there, a black midget of a
fellow, among other black midgets—his wife, and the little
soldier, the judge, and those jury chaps—*fantoches* straight up
on their tiny feet, wandering down there in that dark, infinitely
tall, and narrow street. 'Too much for one!' he thought. 'Too
high for one—no getting on top of it. We've got to be kind, and
help one another, and not expect too much, and not think too
much. That's—all!' And, squeezing out his cigarette, he
took six deep breaths of the night air, and got into bed.

1916.

TIMBER

SIR ARTHUR HIRRIES, Baronet, of Hirriehugh, in a northern
county, came to the decision to sell his timber in that state of
mind—common during the War—which may be called patrio-
profiteering. Like newspaper proprietors, writers on strategy,
shipbuilders, owners of works, makers of arms and the rest of
the working classes at large, his mood was: " Let me serve my
country, and if thereby my profits are increased, let me put up
with it, and invest in National Bonds."

With an encumbered estate and some of the best coverts in
that northern county, it had not become practical politics to
sell his timber till the Government wanted it at all costs. To
let his shooting had been more profitable, till now, when a
patriotic action and a stroke of business had become synony-
mous. A man of sixty-five, but not yet grey, with a reddish
tinge in his moustache, cheeks, lips, and eyelids, slightly knock-
kneed, and with large, rather spreading feet, he moved in the
best circles in a somewhat embarrassed manner. At the enhanced price, the timber at Hirriehugh would enfranchise him
for the remainder of his days. He sold it therefore one day of
April when the War news was bad, to a Government official on
the spot. He sold it at half-past five in the afternoon, practically for cash down, and drank a stiff whisky and soda to wash
away the taste of the transaction; for, though no sentimentalist,
his great-great-grandfather had planted most of it, and his
grandfather the rest. Royalty too had shot there in its time;
and he himself (never much of a sportsman) had missed more
birds in the rides and hollows of his fine coverts than he cared
to remember. But the country was in need, and the price
considerable. Bidding the Government official good-bye, he
lighted a cigar, and went across the Park to take a farewell
stroll among his timber.

He entered the home covert by a path leading through a
group of pear trees just coming into bloom. Smoking cigars and

drinking whisky in the afternoon in preference to tea, Sir
Arthur Hirries had not much sense of natural beauty. But
those pear trees impressed him, greenish white against blue
sky and fleecy thick clouds which looked as if they had snow
in them. They were deuced pretty, and promised a good year
for fruit, if they escaped the late frosts, though it certainly
looked like freezing to-night! He paused a moment at the
wicket gate to glance back at them—like scantily-clothed
maidens posing on the outskirts of his timber. Such, however,
was not the vision of Sir Arthur Hirries, who was considering
how he should invest the balance of the cash down after paying
off his mortgages. National Bonds—the country was in need!

Passing through the gate he entered the ride of the home
covert. Variety lay like colour on his woods. They stretched
for miles, and his ancestors had planted almost every kind of
tree—beech, oak, birch, sycamore, ash, elm, hazel, holly, pine; a
lime tree and a hornbeam here and there, and further in among
the winding coverts, spinneys and belts of larch. The evening
air was sharp, and sleet showers came whirling from those
bright clouds; he walked briskly, drawing at his richly fragrant
cigar, the whisky still warm within him. He walked thinking,
with a gentle melancholy slowly turning a little sulky, that he
would never again be pointing out with his shooting stick to
such or such a guest where he was to stand to get the best birds
over him. The pheasants had been let down during the War,
but he put up two or three old cocks who went clattering and
whirring out to left and right; and rabbits crossed the rides
quietly to and fro, within easy shot. He came to where Royalty
had stood fifteen years ago during the last drive. He remembered Royalty saying: "Very pretty shooting at that last stand,
Hirries; birds just about as high as I like them." The ground
indeed rose rather steeply there, and the timber was oak and
ash, with a few pines sprinkled into the bare greyish
twiggery of the oaks, always costive in spring, and the just
greening feather of the ashes.

'They'll be cutting those pines first,' he thought—strapping
trees, straight as the lines of Euclid, and free of branches, save
at their tops. In the brisk wind those tops swayed a little and
gave forth soft complaint. 'Three times my age,' he thought;
'prime timber.' The ride wound sharply and entered a belt
of larch, whose steep rise entirely barred off the rather sinister
sunset—a dark and wistful wood, delicate dun and grey, whose

green shoots and crimson tips would have perfumed the evening coolness, but for the cigar smoke in his nostrils. ' They'll have this spinney for pit props.' he thought; and, taking a cross ride through it, he emerged in a heathery glen of birch trees. No forester, he wondered if they would make anything of those whitened, glistening shapes. His cigar had gone out now, and he leaned against one of the satin-smooth stems, under the lacery of twig and bud, sheltering the flame of a relighting match. A hare lopped away among the bilberry shoots; a jay, painted like a fan, squawked and flustered past him up the glen. Interested in birds, and wanting just one more jay to complete a fine stuffed group of them, Sir Arthur, though devoid of a gun, followed, to see where " The beggar's " nest was. The glen dipped rapidly, and the character of the timber changed, assuming greater girth and solidity. There was a lot of beech here— a bit he did not know, for though taken in by the beaters, no guns could be stationed there because of the lack of undergrowth. The jay had vanished, and light had begun to fail. ' I must get back,' he thought, ' or I shall be late for dinner.' He debated for a moment whether to retrace his steps or to cut across the beeches and regain the home covert by a loop. The jay, reappearing to the left, decided him to cross the beech grove. He did so, and took a narrow ride up through a dark bit of mixed timber with heavy undergrowth. The ride, after favouring the left for a little, bent away to the right; Sir Arthur followed it hurriedly, conscious that twilight was gathering fast. It must bend again to the left in a minute! It did, and then to the right, and, the undergrowth remaining thick, he could only follow on, or else retrace his steps. He followed on, beginning to get hot in spite of a sleet shower falling through the dusk. He was not framed by Nature for swift travelling— his knees turning in and his toes turning out—but he went at a good bat, uncomfortably aware that the ride was still taking him away from home, and expecting it at any minute to turn left again. It did not, and hot, out of breath, a little bewildered, he stood still in three-quarter darkness, to listen. Not a sound save that of wind in the tops of the trees, and a faint creaking of timber, where two stems had grown athwart and were touching.

The path was a regular will-o'-the-wisp. He must make a bee line of it through the undergrowth into another ride! He had never before been amongst his timber in the dusk, and he found the shapes of the confounded trees more weird, and as if menacing, than he had ever dreamed of. He stumbled quickly on in and out of them among the undergrowth, without coming to a ride.

'Here I am stuck in this damned wood!' he thought. To call these formidably encircling shapes "a wood" gave him relief. After all, it was *his* wood, and nothing very untoward could happen to a man in his own wood, however dark it might get; he could not be more than a mile and a half at the outside from his dining-room! He looked at his watch, whose hands he could just see—nearly half-past seven! The sleet had become snow, but it hardly fell on him, so thick was the timber just here. But he had no overcoat, and suddenly he felt that first sickening little drop in his chest, which presages alarm. Nobody knew he was in this damned wood! And in a quarter of an hour it would be black as your hat! He *must* get on and out! The trees amongst which he was stumbling produced quite a sick feeling now in one who hitherto had never taken trees seriously. What monstrous growths they were! The thought that seeds, tiny seeds or saplings, planted by his ancestors, could attain such huge impending and imprisoning bulk—ghostly great growths mounting up to heaven and shutting off this world, exasperated and unnerved him. He began to run, caught his foot in a root and fell flat on his face. The cursed trees seemed to have a down on him! Rubbing elbows and forehead with his snow-wetted hands, he leaned against a trunk to get his breath, and summon the sense of direction to his brain. Once as a young man he had been "bushed" at night in Vancouver Island; quite a scary business! But he had come out all right, though his camp had been the only civilised spot within a radius of twenty miles. And here he was, on his own estate, within a mile or two of home, getting into a funk. It was childish! And he laughed. The wind answered, sighing and threshing in the tree tops. There must be a regular blizzard blowing now, and, to judge by the cold, from the north—but whether north-east or north-west was the question. Besides, how keep definite direction without a compass, in the dark? The timber, too, with its thick trunks, diverted the wind into keen, directionless draughts. He looked up, but could make nothing of the two or three stars that he could see. It was a mess! And he lighted a second cigar with some difficulty, for he had begun to shiver. The wind in this

blasted wood cut through his Norfolk jacket and crawled about
his body, which had become hot from his exertion, and now
felt clammy and half-frozen. This would mean pneumonia, if
he didn't look out! And, half feeling his way from trunk to
trunk, he started on again, but for all he could tell he might be
going round in a circle, might even be crossing rides without
realising, and again that sickening drop occurred in his
chest. He stood still and shouted. He had the feeling of
shouting into walls of timber, dark and heavy, which threw
the sound back at him.

'Curse you!' he thought; 'I wish I'd sold you six months
ago!' The wind fleered and mowed in the tree tops; and he
started off again at a run in that dark wilderness; till, hitting
his head against a low branch, he fell stunned. He lay several minutes unconscious, came to himself deadly cold, and
struggled up on to his feet.

'By Jove!' he thought, with a sort of stammer in his
brain; 'this is a bad business! I may be out here all night!'
For an unimaginative man, it was extraordinary what vivid
images he had just then. He saw the face of the Government
official who had bought his timber, and the slight grimace with
which he had agreed to the price. He saw his butler, after the
gong had gone, standing like a stuck pig by the sideboard, waiting for him to come down. What would they do when he didn't
come? Would they have the *nous* to imagine that he might
have lost his way in the coverts, and take lanterns and search
for him? Far more likely they would think he had walked over
to "Greenlands" or "Berrymoor," and stayed there to dinner.
And, suddenly, he saw himself slowly freezing out here, in the
snowy night, among this cursed timber. With a vigorous shake,
he butted again into the darkness among the tree trunks. He
was angry now—with himself, with the night, with the trees;
so angry that he actually let out with his fist at a trunk against
which he had stumbled, and scored his knuckles. It was humiliating; and Sir Arthur Hirries was not accustomed to hu-
miliation. In anybody else's wood—yes; but to be lost like this
in one's own coverts! Well, if he had to walk all night, he
would get out! And he plunged on doggedly in the darkness.

He was fighting with his timber now, as if the thing were
alive and each tree an enemy. In the interminable stumbling
exertion of that groping progress his angry mood gave place to
half-comatose philosophy. Trees! His great-great-grandfather

had planted them! His own was the fifth man's life, but the
trees were almost as young as ever; they made nothing of a
man's life! He sniggered: And a man made nothing of theirs!
Did they know they were going to be cut down? All the better
if they did, and were sweating in their shoes. He pinched
himself—his thoughts were becoming so queer! He remembered
that once, when his liver was out of order, trees had seemed to
him like solid, tall diseases—bulbous, scarred, cavernous, witch-
armed, fungoid emanations of the earth. Well, so they were!
And he was among them, on a snowy pitch-black night, engaged in this death-struggle! The occurrence of the word death
in his thoughts brought him up all standing. Why couldn't he
concentrate his mind on getting out; why was he mooning
about the life and nature of trees instead of trying to remember
the conformation of his coverts, so as to re-kindle in himself
some sense of general direction? He struck a number of matches
to get a sight of his watch again. Great heaven! He had been
walking nearly two hours since he last looked at it; and in
what direction? They said a man in a fog went round and
round because of some kink in his brain! He began now to
feel the trees, searching for a hollow trunk. A hollow would
be some protection from the cold—his first conscious confession
of exhaustion. He was not in training, and he was sixty-five.
The thought: 'I can't keep this up much longer,' caused a second explosion of sullen anger. Damnation! Here he was—
for all he could tell—standing where he had sat perhaps a
dozen times on his spread shooting stick; watching sunlight on
bare twigs, or the nose of his spaniel twitching beside him,
listening to the tap of the beaters' sticks, and the shrill, drawn-
out: "Marrk! Cock over!" Would they let the dogs out, to
pick up his tracks? No! ten to one they would assume he was
staying the night at the Summertons', or at Lady Mary's, as he
had done before now, after dining there. And suddenly his
strained heart leaped. He had struck a ride again! His mind
slipped back into place like an elastic let-go, relaxed, quivering
gratefully. He had only to follow this ride, and somewhere,
somehow, he would come out. And be hanged if he would let
them know what a fool he had made of himself! Right or left
—which way? He turned so that the flying snow came on his
back, hurrying forward between the denser darkness on either
hand, where the timber stood in walls, moving his arms across
and across his body, as if dragging a concertina to full stretch,

to make sure that he was keeping in the path. He went what seemed an interminable way like this, till he was brought up all standing by trees, and could find no outlet, no continuation. Turning in his tracks, with the snow in his face now, he retraced his steps till once more he was brought up short by trees. He stood panting. It was ghastly—ghastly! And in a panic he dived this way and that to find the bend, the turning, the way on. The sleet stung his eyes, the wind fleered and whistled, the boughs sloughed and moaned. He struck matches, trying to shade them with his cold, wet hands, but one by one they went out, and still he found no turning. The ride must have a blind alley at either end, the turning be down the side somewhere! Hope revived in him. Never say die! He began a second retracing of his steps, feeling the trunks along one side, to find a gap. His breath came with difficulty. What would old Brodley say if he could see him, soaked, frozen, tired to death, stumbling along in the darkness among this cursed timber—old Brodley who had told him his heart was in poor case! . . . A gap? Ah! No trunks—a ride at last! He turned, felt a sharp pain in his knee and pitched forward. He could not rise—the knee dislocated six years ago was out again. Sir Arthur Hirries clenched his teeth. Nothing more could happen to him! But after a minute—blank and bitter—he began to crawl along the new ride. Oddly he felt less discouraged and alarmed on hands and knee—for he could use but one. It was a relief to have his eyes fixed on the ground, not peering at the tree trunks; or perhaps there was less strain for the moment on his heart. He crawled, stopping every minute or so to renew his strength. He crawled mechanically, waiting for his heart, his knee, his lungs to stop him. The earth was snowed over, and he could feel its cold wetness as he scraped along. Good tracks to follow, if anybody struck them! But in this dark forest——! In one of his halts, drying his hands as best he could, he struck a match, and sheltering it desperately, fumbled out his watch. Past ten o'clock! He wound the watch, and put it back against his heart. If only he could wind his heart! And squatting there he counted his matches—four! 'Well,' he thought grimly, 'I won't light them to show me my blasted trees. I've got a cigar left; I'll keep them for that.' And he crawled on again. He must keep going while he could!

He crawled till his heart and lungs and knee struck work; and, leaning his back against a tree, sat huddled together, so exhausted that he felt nothing save a sort of bitter heartache. He even dropped asleep, waking with a shudder, dragged from a dream armchair at the Club into this cold, wet darkness and the blizzard moaning in the trees. He tried to crawl again, but could not, and for some minutes stayed motionless, hugging his body with his arms. 'Well,' he thought vaguely, 'I *have* done it!' His mind was in such lethargy that he could not even pity himself. His matches: could he make a fire? But he was no woodsman, and, though he groped around, could find no fuel that was not soaking wet. He scraped a hole and with what papers he had in his pockets tried to kindle the wet wood. No good! He had only two matches left now, and he remembered his cigar. He took it out, bit the end off, and began with infinite precautions to prepare for lighting it. The first burned, and the cigar drew. He had one match left, in case he dozed and let the thing go out. Looking up through the blackness he could see a star. He fixed his eyes on it, and leaning against the trunk, drew the smoke down into his lungs. With his arms crossed tightly on his breast he smoked very slowly. When it was finished—what? Cold, and the wind in the trees until the morning! Halfway through the cigar, he dozed off, slept a long time, and woke up so cold that he could barely summon vitality enough to strike his last match. By some miracle it burned, and he got his cigar to draw again. This time he smoked it nearly to its end, without mentality, almost without feeling, except the physical sense of bitter cold. Once with a sudden clearing of the brain, he thought faintly: 'Thank God, I sold the —— trees, and they'll all come down!' The thought drifted away in frozen incoherence, drifted out like his cigar smoke into the sleet; and with a faint grin on his lips he dozed off again. . . .

An under-keeper found him at ten o'clock next morning, blue from cold, under a tall elm tree, within a mile of his bed, one leg stretched out, the other hunched up toward his chest, with its foot dug into the undergrowth for warmth, his head huddled into the collar of his coat, his arms crossed on his breast. They said he must have been dead at least five hours. Along one side snow had drifted against him; but the trunk had saved his back and other side. Above him, the spindly top boughs of that tall tree were covered with green-gold clusters of tiny crinkled elm flowers, against a deep blue sky—gay as a song of perfect praise. The wind had dropped, and after the cold of the night the birds were singing their clearest in the sunshine.

They did not cut down the elm tree under which they found his body, with the rest of the sold timber, but put a little iron fence round it, and a little tablet on its trunk.

1920.

SANTA LUCIA

RETURNING from the English church at Monte Carlo towards his hotel, old Trevillian paused at a bend in the road to rest his thin calves. Through a mimosa tree the sea was visible, very blue, and Trevillian's eyes rested on it with the filmy brown stare of old age.

Monte Carlo was changed, but that blue, tideless, impassive sea was the same as on his first visit forty-five years ago, and this was pleasant to one conservative by nature. Since then he had married; made money, and inherited more; " raised," as Americans called it, a family—all, except his daughter Agatha, out in the world; had been widowed, and developed old man's cough. He and Agatha now left The Cedars, their country house in Hertfordshire, for the Riviera with the annual regularity of swallows. Usually they stayed at Nice or Cannes; but this year, because a friend of Agatha's was the wife of the English chaplain, they had chosen Monte Carlo.

It was near the end of their stay, and the April sun hot.

Trevillian passed a thin hand down his thin brown hairy face, where bushy eyebrows were still dark, but the pointed beard white; and the effect, under a rather wide-brimmed brown hat, almost too Spanish for an English Bank Director. He was fond of saying that some of the best Cornish families had Spanish blood in their veins, whether Iberian or Armadesque he did not specify. The theory in any case went well with his formalism, growing more formal every year.

Agatha having stayed in with a cold, he had been to service by himself. A poor gathering! The English out here were a rackety lot! Among the congregation to whom he had that morning read the Lessons he had noted, for instance, that old blackguard Telford, who had run off with two men's wives in his time, and was now living with a French woman, they said. What on earth was *he* doing in church? And that ostracised couple, the Gaddenhams, who had the villa near Roque-

brune? She used his name, but they had never been married—
for Gaddenham's wife was still alive. And, more seriously, had
he observed Mrs. Rolfe, who before the war used to come with
her husband—now in India—to The Cedars, to shoot the coverts
in November. Young Lord Chesherford was hanging about her,
they said. That would end in a scandal to a certainty! Never
without uneasiness did he see that woman, with whom his daughter was on terms of some intimacy. Grass widows were dangerous, especially in a place like this. He must give Agatha a
hint. Such doubtful people, he felt, had no business to attend
divine service; yet it was difficult to disapprove of people coming to church, and after all—most of them did not! A man
of the world, however strong a Churchman, could, of course,
rub shoulders with anyone; but it was different when they came
near one's womenfolk, or into the halls of one's formal beliefs.
To encroach like that showed no sense of the fitness of things.
He must certainly speak to Agatha!

The road had lain uphill, and he took breaths of the mimosa-
scented air, carefully regulating them so as not to provoke his
cough. He was about to proceed on his way when a piano organ
across the road burst into tune. The man who turned the
handle was the usual moustachioed Italian, with restive eyes
and a game leg; the animal who drew it the customary little
grey donkey; the singer, the proverbial dark girl with an orange
head-kerchief; the song she sang, the immemorial " Santa
Lucia." Her brassy voice blared out the full metallic a's which
seemed to hit the air, as hammers hit the wires of a czymbal.
Trevillian had some music in his soul; he often started out for
the Casino concert, though he generally arrived in the playing-
rooms, not indeed to adventure more than a five-franc piece or
two, for he disapproved of gambling, but because their motley
irregularity titillated his formalism, made him feel like a boy
a little out of school. He could distinguish, however, between
several tunes, and knew this to be neither " God save the King,"
" Rule, Britannia," " Tipperary," nor " Funiculi-Funicula! "
Indeed, it had to him a kind of separate ring, a resonance oddly
intimate, as if in some other life it had been the beating—
the hammering rhythm of his heart. Queer sensation—quite a
queer sensation! And he stood, blinking. Of course, he knew
that tune now that he heard the words—Santa Lucia; but in
what previous existence had its miauling awakened something
deep, hot, almost savage within him, sweet and luring like a

strange fruit or the scent of a tropical flower? "San-ta Luici-i-a! San-ta Luci-i-a!" Lost! And yet so close to the fingers of his recollection that they itched! The girl stopped singing and came across to him—a gaudy baggage, with her orange scarf, her beads, the whites of her eyes, and all those teeth! These Latins, emotional, vibrant, light-hearted and probably light-fingered—an inferior race! He felt in his pocket, produced a franc, and moved on slowly.

But at the next bend in the road he halted again. The girl had recommenced, in gratitude for his franc—" Santa Luci-ia! " What was it buried in him, under the fallen leaves of years and years?

The pink clusters of a pepper tree drooped from behind a low garden wall right over him, while he stood there. The air tingled with its faint savorous perfume, true essence of the South. And again that conviction of a previous existence, of something sweet, burning, poignant, caught him in the Adam's apple veiled by his beard. Was it something he had dreamed? Was that the matter with him now—while the organ wailed, the girl's song vibrated? Trevillian's stare lighted on the prickly pears and aloes above the low pink wall. The savagery of those plants jerked his mind forward almost to the pitch of —what? A youth passed, smoking a maize-coloured cigarette, leaving a perfume of Latakia, that tobacco of his own youth, when he too smoked cigarettes made of its black, strong fragrant threads. He gazed blankly at the half-obliterated name on the dilapidated garden gate, and spelled it aloud: " V lla Be u S te. Villa Beau Site! Beau——! By God! I've got it!"

At the unbecoming vigour of his ejaculation, a smile of release, wrinkling round his eyes, furrowed his thin brown cheeks. He went up to the gate. What a coincidence! The very——! He stood staring into a tangled garden, through the fog of forty-five years, resting his large prayer-book with its big print on the top rail of the old green gate; then, looking up and down the road like a boy about to steal cherries, he lifted the latch and passed in.

Nobody lived here now, he should say. The old pink villa, glimpsed some sixty yards away at the end of that little wilderness, was shuttered, and its paint seemed peeling off. Beau Site! That *was* the name! And this the gate he had been wont to use into this lower garden, invisible from the house. And—yes—here was the little fountain, broken and discoloured now, with the same gargoyle face, and water still dripping from its mouth! And here—the old stone seat his cloak had so often covered. Grown over now—all of it; unpruned the lilacs, mimosas, palms making that dry rustling when the breeze crept into them. He opened his prayer-book, laid it on the seat, and carefully sat down—he never sat on unprotected stone. He had passed into another world, screened from any eye by the overgrown shrubs and tangled foliage. And, slowly, while he sat there the frost of nearly half a century thawed.

Yes! Little by little, avidly, yet as it were unwillingly, he remembered—sitting on his prayer-book, out of the sun, under the flowering tangled trees.

He had been twenty-six, just after he went into the family bank—he recollected—such a very sucking partner. A neglected cold had given him the first of those bronchial attacks of which he was now reaping the aftermath. Those were the days when, in the chill of a London winter, he would—dandy-like—wear thin underclothes and no overcoat. Still coughing at Easter, he had taken three weeks off and a ticket to Mentone. A cousin of his was engaged to a Russian girl whose family had a villa there, and he had pitched his tent in a little hotel almost next door. The Russians of *that* day were the Russians of the Turgenev novels, which Agatha had made him read. A simple, tri-lingual family of gentlefolk, the Rostakovs, father, mother, and two daughters—what was it they had called *him*—Philip Philipovitch? Monsieur Rostakov, with his beard, his witty French stories, imperfectly understood by young Trevillian, his zest for food and drink, his thick lips, and, as they said, his easy morals—quite a dog in his way! And Madame, née Princesse Nogárin (a Tartar strain in her, his cousin said); " spirituelle," somewhat worn out by Monsieur Rostakov and her belief in the transmigration of souls. And Varvara, the eldest daughter— the one engaged; only seventeen, with deep-grey, truthful eyes, a broad grave face, dark hair, and a candour—by George!— which had almost frightened him. And the little one, Katrina, blue-eyed, snub-nosed, fair-haired, with laughing lips, yet very serious too—charming little creature, whose death from typhoid three years later had given him quite a shock! Delightful family, seen through the mists of time. And now, in all the world you couldn't find a Russian family like that—gone, vanished from the face of the earth! Their estates had been—ah! —somewhere in South Russia, and a house near Yalta. Cos-

mopolitan, yet very Russian, with their samovar, and their "Za-
kouskas"—a word he had never learned to spell—and Rostakov's little glasses of white vodka, and those caviare sandwiches
that the girls and he used to take on their picnics to Gorbio,
and Castellar, and Belle Enda, riding donkeys, and chaperoned
by that amiable young German lady, their governess. . . . Germans, in those days—how different they were! How different
the whole of life! The girls riding in their wide skirts, under
parasols, the air unspoiled by the fumes of petrol, the carriages
with their jangling-belled little horses and bright harness;
priests in black, soldiers in bright trousers and yellow shakoes;
and beggars—plenty. The girls would gather wild flowers,
and press them afterwards; and in the evening Varvara would
look at him with her grave eyes and ask him whether he believed in a future life. He had no beliefs to speak of, then,
if he remembered rightly; they had come with increasing income, family, and business responsibilities. It had always seemed
to hurt her that he thought of sport and dress, and not of his
soul. The Russians, in those days, seemed so tremendously
concerned about the soul—an excellent thing, of course, but
not what one talked of. Still, that first fortnight had been quite
idyllic. He remembered one Sunday afternoon—queer how
such a little thing could stay in the mind—on the beach near
Cap Martin, flicking sand off his boots with his handkerchief,
and Varvara saying: "And then to your face again, Philip
Philipovitch?" She was always saying things which made him
feel uncomfortable. And in the little letter which Katrina wrote
him a year later, with blue forget-me-nots all about the paper,
she had reminded him of how he had blushed! Charming
young girls—simple—no such, nowadays! The dew was off.
They had thought Monte Carlo a vulgar place—what would
they think of it now, by Jove! Even Rostakov only went there
on the quiet—a *viveur*, that fellow, who would always be living
a double life. Trevillian recollected how, under the spell of
that idyllic atmosphere, and afraid of Varvara's eyes, he himself had put off from day to day his visit to the celebrated
haunt, until one evening when Madame Rostakov had *migraine*
and the girls were at a party, he had sauntered to the station
and embarked on a Monte Carlo train. How clearly it came
back to him—the winding path up through the Gardens, a beautiful still evening, scented and warm, the Casino orchestra
playing the Love music from " Faust "—the one opera that

knew well. The darkness, strange with exotic foliage, glimmering with golden lamps—none of this glaring white electric
light—had deeply impressed him, who, for all his youthful
dandyism, had Puritanism in his blood and training. It was
like going up to—well, not precisely heaven! And in his white
beard old Trevillian uttered a slight cackle. Anyway, he had
entered " the rooms " with a beating heart. He had no money
to throw away in those days; by Jove! no! His father had
kept him strictly to an allowance of four hundred a year, and
his partnership was still in the apprentice stage. He had only
some ten or twenty pounds to spare. But to go back to England
and have his fellows say: " What? Monte Carlo, and never
played? " was not to be thought of.

His first sensation in the " rooms " was disappointing. The
decorations were florid, the people foreign, queer, ugly! For
some time he stood still listening to the chink of rake against
coin, and the nasal twang of the croupiers' voices. Then he
had gone up to a table to watch the game, which he had never
played. That, at all events, was the same as now; that, and the
expression on the gamblers' faces—the sharp, blind, crab-like
absorption like no other human expression. And what a lot of
old women! A nervous excitement had crept into his brain
while he stood there, an itch into his fingers. But he was
shy. All these people played with such deadly calm, seemed
so utterly familiar with it all. At last he had reached over the
shoulder of a dark-haired woman sitting in front of him, put
down a five-franc piece and called out the word: " Vingt." A
rake shovelled it forward on to the number with an indifferent
click. The ball rolled: " Quatorze, Rouge pair et manque."
His five-franc piece was raked away; but he—Philip Trevillian
—had gambled at Monte Carlo, and at once he had seemed to
see Varvara's eyes with something of amusement in their candour, and to hear her voice: " But to gamble! How silly,
Philip Philipovitch'! " Then the man sitting to his left got up,
and he had slipped down into the empty chair. Once seated he
knew that he must play. So he pushed another five-franc piece
on to black, and received its counterpart. Now he was quits;
and continuing that simple stake with varying success he began
taking in the faces of his neighbours. On his left he had an
old Englishman in evening dress, ruddy, with chubby lips, who
played in gold pieces and seemed winning rather heavily; opposite, in a fabulous shawl, a bird-like old woman, with a hook

nose, and a man who looked like a Greek bandit in a frock
coat. To his right was the dark-haired woman over whose
shoulder he had leaned. An agreeable perfume, as of jasmine
blossoms, floated from her. She had some tablets, and six or
seven gold pieces before her, but seemed to have stopped playing. Out of the tail of his eye Trevillian scrutinised her profile. She was by far the most attractive woman he had seen in
here. And he felt, suddenly, uninterested in the fate of his
five-franc pieces. Under the thin dark brows a little drawn
down, he could see that her eyes were dark and velvety. Her
face was rather pointed, delicate, faintly powdered in the foreign fashion. She wore a low dress, but with a black lace scarf
thrown over her gleaming shoulders, and something that glim-
mered in her dark hair. She was not English; but what he
could not tell. He won twice running on black, left his stake
untouched, and was conscious that she pushed one of her own
gold pieces on to the black. Again black won; again he left his
stake, and she hers. To be linked with her by that following of
his luck was agreeable to young Trevillian. The devil might
care—he would leave his winnings down! Again, and again,
till he had won eight times on black, he left his stake, and his
neighbour followed suit. A pile of gold was mounting in front
of each of them. The eyes of the hawk-like old woman opposite, like those of a crustacean in some book of Natural History, seemed pushed out from her face; a little hard smile on
her thin lips seemed saying: " Wait, it will all go back! " The
jasmine perfume from his neighbour grew stronger, as though
disengaged by increasing emotion; he could see her white neck
heave under its black lace. She reached her hand out as though
to gather in her winnings. In bravado Trevillian sat unmoving. Her eyes slid round to his, she withdrew her hand. The
little ball rolled. Black! He heard her sigh of relief; she
touched his arm. " *Retirez!* " she whispered, " *retirez,* Monsieur! " and, sweeping in her winnings, she got up. Trevillian
hesitated just a moment, then with the thought: ' If I stay,
I lose sight of her! ' he too reached out, and, gathering in his
pile, left the table. Starting with a five-franc piece, in nine
successful coups he had won just over a hundred pounds. His
neighbour, who had started with a louis, in seven coups—he calculated rapidly—must have won the same. " *Seize, Rouge pair
et manque!* " Just in time! Elated, Trevillian turned away.
There was the graceful figure of his dark neighbour, threading

the throng; and without deliberate intention, yet longing not to lose sight of her, he followed. A check in her progress brought him so close, however, that he was at infinite pains to seem unconscious. She turned and saw him. " Ah! *Merci, Monsieur!* I tank you moch." " It's for me to thank you! " he stammered. The dark lady smiled. " I have the instinct," she said in her broken English, " for others—not for myself. I am unlucky. It is the first time you play, Sare? I tought so. Do not play again. Give me that promise; it will make me 'appy."

· Her eyes were looking into his. Never in his life had he seen anything so fascinating as her face with its slightly teasing smile; her figure in the lacy black dress swinging out Spanish fashion from the hips, and the scarf flung about her shoulders. He had made the speech, then, which afterwards seemed to him so foreign.

" Charmed to promise anything that will make you happy, Madame."

She clasped her hands like a pleased child.

" That is a bargain; now I have repaid you."

" May I find your carriage? "

" I am walkin', Monsieur."

With desperate courage, he had murmured:

" Then may I escort you? "

" But certainly."

Sitting on his prayer-book, Trevillian burrowed into the past. What had he felt, thought, fancied, in those moments while she had gone to get her cloak? Who and what was she? Into what whirlpool drawing him? How nearly he had bolted—back to the idyllic, to Varvara's searching candour, and Katrina's laughing innocence, before she was there beside him, lace veiling her hair, face, eyes, like an Eastern woman, and her fingers had slipped under his sleeve. . . . What a walk! What sense of stepping into the unknown; strange intimacy, and perfect ignorance! Perhaps every man had some such moment in his life—of pure romance; of adventuring at all and any cost! He had restrained the impulse to press that slender hand closely to his side, had struggled to preserve the perfect delicacy worthy of the touching confidence of so beautiful a lady. Italian, Spanish, Polish, Bohemian? Married, widowed? She told him nothing—he asked no questions. Instinct or shyness kept him dumb, but with a whirling brain. And the night above them had seemed the starriest ever seen, the sweetest scented, the most abandoned by all except himself and her. They had come to the gate of this very garden; and, opening it, she had said:

"Here is my home. You have been perfect for me, Monsieur."

Her lightly resting fingers were withdrawn. Trevillian remembered—with a sort of wonder—how he had kissed those fingers.

"I am always at your service, Madame."

Her lips had parted; her eyes had an arch sweetness he had never seen before or since in woman.

"Every night I play. *Au revoir!*"

He had listened to her footsteps on the path—watched lights go up in the house which looked so empty now behind him, watched them put out again; and, retracing his steps, had learned by heart their walk from the Casino, till he was sure he could not miss his way to that garden gate by day or night. . . . A fluster of breeze came into the jungle where he sat, and released the dry rustle of the palm tree leaves. *"On fait des folies!"* as the French put it. Loose lot—the French! Queer, what young men would go through when they were "making madnesses." And, plucking a bit of lilac, old Trevillian put it to his nose, as though seeking explanation for the madnesses of youth. What had he been like then? Thin as a lath, sunburnt—he used to pride himself on being sunburnt—a little black moustache; a dandy about clothes! The memory of his youthful looks warmed him, sitting there, chilly from old age. . . .

"On fait des folies!" All next day he had been restless, uneasy at the Villa Rostakov under the question in Varvara's eyes—and Lord knew what excuse he had made for not going there that evening! Ah! And what of his solemn resolutions to find out all about his dark lady, not to run his head into some foreign noose, not to compromise her or himself? They had all gone out of his head the moment he set eyes on her again, and he had never learned anything but her name, Iñez, in all those three weeks; nor told anything of himself—as if both had felt the knowledge would destroy romance. When had he known himself of interest to her—the second night—the third? The look in her eyes; the pressure of her arm against his own! On this very seat, with his cloak spread to guard her from the chill, he had whispered his turbulent avowals! Not free! No such woman could be free. What did it matter? Disinheri-

tance—Ostracism—Exile! All such considerations had burned like straws in the fire he had felt, sitting by her in the darkness, his arm about her, her shoulder pressed to his. With mournful mockery she had gazed at him, kissed his forehead, slipped away up the dark garden. God! What a night after that! Wandering, up and down, along by the sea—devoured! Funny to look back on—deuced funny! A woman's face to have such power! And with a little shock he remembered that never in all the few weeks of that mad business had he seen her face by daylight! Of course, he had left Mentone at once—no offering his madness up to the candid eyes of those two girls, to the cynical stare of that old *viveur* Rostakov! But no going home, though his leave was up; he was his own master yet awhile, thanks to his winnings. And then—the deluge! Literally—a night when the rain came down in torrents, drenching him through cape and clothes while he stood waiting for her. It was after that drenching night which had kept them apart that she had returned his passion. . . . A wild young devil! the madness of those nights, beneath these trees by the old fountain! How he used to sit waiting on this bench in the darkness with heart fluttering, trembling, aching with expectancy! . . . Gad! how he had ached and fluttered on that seat! What fools young men could be! And yet, in all his life had there been weeks so wildly sweet as those? Weeks the madness of which could stir in him still this strange youthful warmth. Rubbing his veined thin hands together, he held them out into a streak of sunlight and closed his eyes. . . . There, coming through the gate into the deeper shadow, dark in her black dress—always black—the gleam of her neck when she bent and pressed his head to it! Through the rustling palm leaves the extinct murmuring of their two voices, the beating of their two hearts. . . . Madness indeed! His back gave a little crick. He had been very free from lumbago lately! Confound it—a premonitory twinge! Close to his feet, a lizard rustled out into the patch of sunlight, motionless but for tongue and eyes, looked at him with head to one side—queer quick dried-looking little object! . . . And then, the end! What a Jezebel of cruelty he had thought her! Now he could see its wisdom and its mercy. By George! She had blown their wild weeks out like a candle flame! Vanished! Vanished into the unknown as she had come from the unknown; left him to go, haggard

and burnt-up, back to England and Bank routine, to the social
and moral solidity of a pillar of society. . . .

Like that lizard whisking its tail and vanishing beneath the
dead dry leaves, so she had vanished—as if into the earth.
Could she ever have felt for him as he for her? Did women
ever know such consuming fires? Trevillian shrugged his thin
shoulders. She had seemed to; but—how tell? Queer cattle
—women!

Two nights he had sat here—waiting—sick with anxiety and
longing. A third day he had watched outside the villa, closed,
shuttered, abandoned—not a sound from it, not a living thing,
but one white and yellow cat. He pitied himself even now,
thinking of that last vigil. For three days more he had hung
around, haunting Casino, garden, villa—— No sign—no sign!
. . .

Trevillian rose; his back had given him another twinge. He
examined the seat and his open prayer-book. Had he overlapped
it on to damp stone? He frowned, smoothing superstitiously
the pages a little creased and over-flattened by his weight. Closing the book he went towards the gate. Had those passionate
hours been the best or the worst of his life? He did not know.

He moved out into the hot sunshine and up the road. Round
the corner he came suddenly abreast of the old villa. 'It was
here I stood,' he thought: 'Just here.' What was that cater-
wauling? Ah! The girl and the organ—there they were again!
What! Why, of course! That long-ago morning a barrel organ
had come while he stood there in despair. He could see it
still, grinding away, with a monkey on it, and a woman singing
that same silly tune. With a dry dusty feeling he turned and
walked on. What had he been thinking of before? Oh! Ah!
The Rolfe woman, and that young fool Chesherford. Yes, he
would certainly warn Agatha; certainly warn her! They were
a loose lot out here!

1921.

THE MOTHER STONE

IT was after dinner, and five elderly Englishmen were discussing the causes of the war.

"Well," said Travers, a big, fresh-coloured grey-beard, with little twinkling eyes and very slow speech, "you gentlemen know more about it than I do, but I bet you I can lay my finger on the cause of the war at any minute."

There was an instant clamour of jeering. But a man called Askew, who knew Travers well, laughed and said: "Come, let's have it!" Travers turned those twinkling little eyes of his slowly round the circle, and with heavy, hesitating modesty began:

"Well, Mr. Askew, in was in '67 or '68 that this happened to a great big fellow of my acquaintance named Ray—one of those fellers, you know, that are always on the lookout to make their fortunes and never do. This Ray was coming back south one day after a huntin' trip he'd been in what's now called Bechuanaland, and he was in a pretty bad way when he walked one evenin' into the camp of one of those wanderin' Boers. That class of Boer has disappeared now. They had no farms of their own, but just moved on with their stock and their boys; and when they came to good pasture they'd outspan and stay there till they'd cleared it out—and then trek on again. Well, this old Boer told Ray to come right in and take a meal; and Heaven knows what it was made of, for those old Boers they'd eat the devil himself without onion sauce, and relish him. After the meal the old Boer and Ray sat smokin' and yarnin' in the door of the tent, because in those days these wanderin' Boers used tents. Right close by in the front the children were playin' in the dust, a game like marbles with three or four round stones, and they'd pitch 'em up to another stone they called the Moer-Klip, or Mother Stone—one, two, and pick up; two, three, and pick up—you know the game of marbles. Well, the sun was settin', and presently Ray noticed this Moer-Klip that they were pitchin' 'em up to shinin'; and he looked at it, and he

485

said to the old Boer: ' What's that stone the children are playin'
with?' And the old Boer looked at him and looked at the
stone, and said: ' It's just a stone,' and went on smokin'.

"Well, Ray went down on his knees and picked up the stone
and weighed it in his hand. About the size of a hazel-nut it
was and looked—well, it looked like a piece of alum; but the
more he looked at it the more he thought: ' By Jove, I believe it's a diamond!'

"So he said to the old Boer: ' Where did the children get
this stone?' And the old Boer said: ' Oh! the shepherd picked
it up somewhere.' And Ray said: ' *Where* did he pick it up?'
And the old Boer waved his hand, and said: ' Over the kopje,
there, beyond the river. How should I know, brother?—a
stone is a stone!' So Ray said: ' You let me take this stone
away with me.' And the old Boer went on smokin', and he said:
' One stone's the same as another. Take it, brother.' And
Ray said: ' If it's what I think, I'll give you half the price I
get for it.'

"The old Boer smiled and said: ' That's all right, brother;
take it, take it!'

"The next morning Ray left this old Boer, and, when he was
going, he said to him: ' Well,' he said, ' I believe this is a valuable stone!' And the old Boer smiled because he knew one
stone was the same as another.

"The first place Ray came to was C——, and he went to
the hotel; and in the evenin' he began talkin' about the stone,
and they all laughed at him, because in those days nobody had
heard of diamonds in South Africa. So presently he lost his
temper and pulled out the stone and showed it round; but nobody thought it was a diamond, and they all laughed at him the
more. Then one of the fellers said: ' If it's a diamond it ought
to cut glass.'

"Ray took the stone, and, by Jove! he cut his name on the
window, and there it is—I've seen it—on the bar window of
that hotel. Well, next day, you bet, he travelled straight back
to where the old Boer told him the shepherd had picked up the
stone, and he went to a native chief called Jointje, and said to
him: ' Jointje,' he said, ' I go a journey. While I go, you go
about and send all your " boys " about, and look for all the
stones that shine like this one; and when I come back, if you
find me plenty, I give you gun.' And Jointje said: ' That all
right, boss.'

" And Ray went down to Cape Town and took the stone to a jeweller, and the jeweller told him it was a diamond of about 30 or 40 carats, and gave him five hundred pound for it. So he bought a waggon and a span of oxen to give to the old Boer, and went back to Jointje. The niggers had collected skinfuls of stones of all kinds, and out of all the skinfuls Ray found three or four diamonds. So he went to work and got another feller to back him, and between them they made the Government move. The rush began, and they found that place near Kimberley; and after that they found De Beers, and after that Kimberley itself."

Travers stopped and looked around him.

" Ray made his fortune, I suppose ? "

" No, Mr. Askew; the unfortunate feller made next to nothin'. He was one of those fellers that never do any good for themselves."

" But what has all this to do with the war ? "

Again Travers looked round, and more slowly than ever said:

" Without that game of marbles, would there have been a Moer-Klip—without the Moer-Klip, would there have been a Kimberley—without Kimberley, would there have been a Rhodes —without a Rhodes would there have been a Raid—without a Raid, would the Boers have started armin'—if the Boers hadn't armed, would there have been a Transvaal War ? And if there hadn't been the Transvaal War, would there have been the incident of those two German ships we held up, and all the general feelin' in Germany that gave the Kaiser the chance to start his Navy programme in 1900 ? And if the Germans hadn't built their Navy, would their heads have swelled till they challenged the world, and should we have had this war ? "

He slowly drew a hand from his pocket and put it on the table. On the little finger was blazing an enormous diamond.

" My father," he said, " bought it of the jeweller."

The Mother Stone glittered and glowed, and the five Englishmen fixed their eyes on it in silence. Some of them had been in the Boer War, and three of them had sons in this. At last one of them said:

" Well, that's seeing God in a dew-drop with a vengeance. What about the old Boer ? "

" Well," he said, " Ray told me the old feller just looked at him as if he thought he'd done a damn silly thing to give him a waggon; and he nodded his old head and said, laughin' in his beard: 'Wish you good luck, brother, with your stone.' You couldn't humbug that old Boer; he knew one stone was the same as another."

1914.

PEACE MEETING

COLIN WILDERTON, coming from the west on his way to the Peace Meeting, fell in with John Rudstock, coming from the north, and they walked on together. After they had commented on the news from Russia and the inflation of money, Rudstock said abruptly:

"We shall have a queer meeting, I expect."

"God knows!" answered Wilderton.

And both smiled, conscious that they were uneasy, but predetermined not to show it under any circumstances. Their smiles were different, for Rudstock was a black-browed man with dark beard and strong, thick figure, and Wilderton a very light-built, grey-haired man, with kindly eyes and no health. He had supported the war an immense time, and had only recently changed his attitude. In common with all men of warm feelings, he had at first been profoundly moved by the violation of Belgium. The horrors of the German advance through that little country and through France, to which he was temperamentally attached, had stirred in him a vigorous detestation, freely expressed in many ways. Extermination, he had felt all those early months, was hardly good enough for brutes who could commit such crimes against humanity and justice; and his sense of the need for signal defeat of a noxious force riding rough-shod over the hard-won decency of human life had survived well into the third year of the war. He hardly knew himself when his feeling had begun—not precisely to change, but to run, as it were, in a different channel. A man of generous instincts, artistic tastes and unsteady nerves too thinly coated with that God-given assurance which alone fits a man for knowing what is good for the world, he had become gradually haunted by the thought that he was not laying down his own life, but only the lives of his own and other people's sons. And the consideration that he was laying them down for the benefit of their own future had lost its grip on him. At mo-

ments he was still able to see that the war he had so long
supported had not yet attained sufficient defeat of the Prus-
sian military machine to guarantee that future; but his pity and
distress for all these young lives cut down without a chance to
flower had grown till he had become, as it were, a gambler.
What good—he would think—to secure the future of the young
in a Europe which would soon have no young? Every country
was suffering hideously—the criminal country not least, thank
God! Suppose the war were to go for another year, two, three
years, and then stop from sheer exhaustion of both sides, while
all the time these boys were being killed and maimed, for nothing more, perhaps, than could be obtained to-day. What then?
True the Government promised victory, but they never promised it within a year. Governments did not die; what if they
were to go on promising it a year hence, till everybody else
was dead! Did history ever show that victory in the present
could guarantee the future? Besides, even if not so openly de-
feated as was desirable, this damnable Prussianism had got
such a knock that it could never again do what it had in the
past. These last, however, were but side reflections, toning
down for him the fact that his nerves could no longer stand this
vicarious butchery of youth. And so he had gradually become
that "traitor to his country, a weak-kneed, peace-by-negotiation
man." Physically his knees really were weak, and he used to
smile a wry smile when he read the expression.

John Rudstock, of vigorous physique, had opposed the war,
on principle, from the start, not because, any more than Wilderton, he approved of Prussianism, but because, as an essentially
combative personality, he opposed everything supported by a
majority; the greater the majority, the more bitterly he opposed
it; and no one would have been more astonished than he at hearing that this was his principle. He preferred to put it that he
did not believe in opposing force by force. In peace-time he was
a "stalwart," in war-time a "renegade."

The street leading to the chapel which had been engaged
seemed quiet enough. Designed to make an impression on public opinion, every care had been taken that the meeting should
not attract the public eye. God's protection had been enlisted,
but two policemen also stood at the entrance, and half a dozen
others were suspiciously near by. A thin trickle of persons,
mostly women, were passing through the door. Colin Wilderton, making his way up the aisle to the platform, wrinkled his

nose, thinking: 'Stuffy in here.' It had always been his
misfortune to love his neighbours individually, but to dislike
them in a bunch. On the platform some fifteen men and
women were already gathered. He seated himself modestly in
the back row, while John Rudstock, less retiring, took his place
at the chairman's right hand. The speakers began with a preci-
pitancy hardly usual at a public meeting. Wilderton listened,
and thought: 'Dreadfully *cliché;* why can't someone say
straight out that boys enough have been killed?' He had
become conscious, too, of a muttering noise, as of the tide coming in on a heavy wind; it broke suddenly into component parts
—human voices clamouring outside. He heard blows raining
on the door, saw sticks smashing in the windows. The audience had risen to its feet, some rushing to defend the doors,
others standing irresolute. John Rudstock was holding up the
chair he had been sitting on. Wilderton had just time to think:
'I thought so,' when a knot of young men in khaki burst into
the chapel, followed by a crowd. He knew he was not much
good in a scrimmage, but he placed himself at once in front
of the nearest woman. At that moment, however, some soldiers,
pouring through a side-door, invaded the platfrom from behind, and threw him down the steps. He arrived at the bottom with a bump, and was unable to get up because of the
crowd around him. Someone fell over him; it was Rudstock,
swearing horribly. He still had the chair in his hand, for it hit
Wilderton a nasty blow. The latter saw his friend recover his
feet and swing the weapon, and with each swing down went
some friend or foe, until he had cleared quite a space round
him. Wilderton, still weak and dizzy from his fall, sat watching this Homeric battle. Chairs, books, stools, sticks were flying at Rudstock, who parried them, or diverted their course
so that they carried on and hit Wilderton, or crashed against
the platform. He heard Rudstock roar like a lion and saw him
advance, swinging his chair; down went two young men in
khaki, down went a third in mufti; a very tall young soldier,
also armed with a chair, dashed forward, and the two fought
in single combat. Wilderton had got on his feet by now, and,
adjusting his eyeglass, for he could see little without, he caught
up a hymn-book, and, flinging it at the crowd with all his force,
shouted: " Hoobloodyray ! " and followed with his fists clenched.
One of them encountered what must have been the jaw of an
Australian, it was so hard against his hand; he received a vicious

punch in the ribs and was again seated on the ground. He could still hear his friend roaring, and the crash of chairs meeting in mid-air. Something fell heavily on him. It was Rudstock—he was insensible. There was a momentary lull, and peering up as best he could from underneath the body, Wilderton saw that the platform had been cleared of all its original inhabitants, and was occupied mainly by youths in navy blue and khaki. A voice called out:

" Order! Silence! "

Rubbing Rudstock's temples with brandy from a flask which he had had the foresight to slip into his pocket, he listened as best he could, with the feet of the crowd jostling his anatomy.

" Here we are, boys," the voice was saying, " and here we'll always be when these treacherous blighters try their games on. No peace, no peace at any price! We've got to show them that we won't have it. Leave the women alone—though they ought to be ashamed of themselves; but for the men—the skunks— shooting's too good for them. Let them keep off the course or we'll make them. We've broken up this meeting, and we'll break up every meeting that tries to talk of peace. Three cheers for the old flag! "

During the cheers which followed Wilderton was discovering signs of returning consciousness in his friend; for Rudstock had begun to breathe heavily. Pouring some brandy into his mouth, he propped him up as best he could against a wooden structure, which he suddenly perceived to be the chapel's modest pulpit, A thought came to his dazed brain. If he could get up into that, as if he had dropped from Heaven, they might almost listen to him. He disengaged his legs from under Rudstock and began crawling up the steps on hands and knees. Once in the pulpit he sat on the floor below the level of visibility, getting his breath and listening to the cheers. Then, smoothing his hair, he rose, and waited for the cheers to stop. He had calculated rightly. His sudden appearance, his grey hair, eyeglass and smile deceived them for a moment. There was a hush.

" Boys! " he said, " listen to me a second. I want to ask you something. What on earth do you think we came here for? Simply and solely because we can't bear to go on seeing you killed day after day, month after month, year after year. That's all, and it's Christ's truth. Amen! "

A strange gasp and mutter greeted this little speech; then a dull voice called out:

" Pro-German ! "

Wilderton flung up his hand.

" The Germans to hell ! " he said simply.

The dull voice repeated :

" Pro-German ! " And the speaker on the platform called out : " Come out of that ! When we want you to beg us off we'll let you know."

Wilderton spun round to him.

" You're all wonderful ! " he began, but a hymn-book hit him fearfully on the forehead, and he sank down into the bottom of the pulpit. This last blow, coming on the top of so many others, had deprived him of intelligent consciousness ; he was but vaguely aware of more speeches, cheers and tramplings, then of a long hush, and presently found himself walking out of the chapel door between Rudstock and a policeman. It was not the door by which they had entered, and led to an empty courtyard.

" Can you walk ? " said the policeman.

Wilderton nodded.

" Then walk off ! " said the policeman, and withdrew again into the house of God.

The two walked, holding each other's arms, a little unsteadily at first. Rudstock had a black eye and a cut on his ear, the blood from which had stained his collar and matted his beard. Wilderton's coat was torn, his forehead bruised, his cheek swollen, and he had a pain in his back which prevented him from walking very upright. They did not speak, but in an archway did what they could, with pins and handkerchiefs and by turning up Rudstock's coat collar, to regain something of respectability. When they were once more under way Rudstock said coldly :

" I heard you. You should have spoken for yourself. I came, as you know, because I don't believe in opposing force by force. At the next meeting we hold I shall make that plainer."

Wilderton murmured :

" Yes, yes ; I saw you—I'm sure you will. I apologise ; I was carried away."

Rudstock went on in a deep voice :

" As for those young devils, they may die to a man if they like ! Take my advice and let them alone."

Wilderton smiled on the side which was not swollen.

"Yes," he said sadly, "it does seem difficult to persuade them to go on living. Ah, well!"

"Ah, well" he said again, five minutes later, "they're wonderful—poor young beggars! I'm very unhappy, Rudstock!"

"I'm not," said Rudstock, "I've enjoyed it in a way! Good-night!"

They shook hands, screwing up their mouths with pain, for their fists were badly bruised, and parted, Rudstock going to the north, Wilderton to the west.

1917.

A STRANGE THING

NOT very long ago, during a sojourn in a part of the West Country never yet visited by me, I went out one fine but rather cold March morning for a long ramble. I was in one of those disillusioned moods which come to writers bankrupt of ideas, bankrupt of confidence, a prey to that recurrent despair, the struggle with which makes the profession of the pen—as a friend once said to me—" a manly one." ' Yes,' I was thinking, for all that the air was so brisk, and the sun so bright, ' nothing comes to me nowadays, no flashes of light, none of those suddenly shaped visions that bring cheer and warmth to a poor devil's heart, and set his brain and pen to driving on. A bad business!' And my eyes, wandering over the dip and rise, the woods, the moor, the rocks of that fine countryside, took in the loveliness thereof with the profound discontent of one who, seeing beauty, feels that he cannot render it. The high lane-banks had just been pollarded; one could see right down over the fields and gorse and bare woods tinged with that rosy brown of beech and birch twigs, and the dusty saffron of the larches. And suddenly my glance was arrested by something vivid, a sort of black and white excitement in the air. ' Aha!' I thought, ' a magpie. Two! Good! Is it an omen?' The birds had risen at the bottom of a field, their twining, fluttering voyage—most decorative of all bird flights—was soon lost in the wood beyond, but something it had left behind—in my heart; I felt more hopeful, less inclined to think about the failure of my spirit, better able to give myself up to this new country I was passing through. Over the next rise in the very winding lane I heard the sound of brisk church bells, and not three hundred yards beyond came to a village green, where knots of men dressed in the dark clothes, light ties and bowler hats of village festivity, and of women smartened up beyond belief, were gathered, chattering, round the yard of an old, grey, square-towered church.

'What's going on?' I thought. 'It's not Sunday, not the birthday of a potentate, and surely they don't keep saint days in this manner. It must be a wedding. Yes—there's a favour! Let's go in and see!' And, passing the expectant groups, I entered the church and made my way up the aisle. There was already a fair sprinkling of folk all turned round towards the door, and the usual licensed buzz and whisper of a wedding congregation. The church, as seems usual in remote parishes, had been built all those centuries ago to hold a population in accordance with the expectations of its tenet, "Be fruitful and multiply." But the whole population could have been seated in a quarter of its space. It was lofty and unwarmed save by excitement and the smell of bear's-grease. There was certainly more animation than I had ever seen or savoured in a truly rural district.

The bells, which had been ringing with a sort of languid joviality, fell now into the hurried crashing which marks the approach of a bride, and the people I had passed outside came thronging in. I perceived a young man—little more than a boy—who by his semi-detachment, the fumbling of his gloved hands, and the sheepishness of the smile on his good-looking, open face, was obviously the bridegroom. I liked the looks of him—a cut above the usual village bumpkin—something free and kind about his face. But no one was paying him the least attention. It was for the bride they were waiting; and I myself began to be excited. What would this young thing be like? Just the ordinary village maiden with tight cheeks and dress, coarse veil, high colour, and eyes like a rabbit's; or something —something like that little Welsh girl on the hills whom I once passed and whose peer I have never since seen? Bending forward, I accosted an apple-faced woman in the next pew. "Can you tell me who the bride is?"

Regarding me with the grey, round, defensive glance that one bestows on strangers, she replied:

"Aw, don't 'ee know? 'Tes Gwenny Mara—prettiest, brightest maid in these parts." And jerking her thumb towards the neglected bridegroom, she added: "He's a lucky young chap. She'm a sunny maid, for sure, and a gude maid, tu."

Somehow the description did not reassure me, and I prepared for the worst.

A bubble, a stir, a rustle!

Like everyone else, I turned frankly round. She was coming

up the aisle on the arm of a hard-faced, rather gipsy-looking man dressed in a farmer's very best.

I can only tell you that to see her coming down the centre of that grey church amongst all those dark-clothed people was like watching the dance of a sunbeam. Never had I seen a face so happy, sweet, and radiant. Smiling, eager, just lost enough to her surroundings, her hair unconquerably golden through the coarse veil; her dancing eyes clear and dark as a great pool —she was the prettiest sight. One could only think of a young apple tree with the spring sun on its blossom. She had that kind of infectious brightness which comes from very simple goodness. It was quite a relief to have taken a fancy to the young man's face and to feel that she was passing into good hands.

The only flowers in the church were early daffodils, but those first children of the sun were somehow extraordinarily appropriate to the wedding of this girl. When she came out she was pelted with them, and with that miserable confetti, without which not even the simplest souls can pass to bliss, it seems. There are things in life which make one feel good—sunshine, most music, all flowers, many children, some animals, clouds, mountains, bird-songs, blue sky, dancing, and here and there a young girl's face. And I had the feeling that all of us there felt good for the mere seeing of her.

When she had driven away, I found myself beside a lame old man with whiskers and delightful eyes, who continued to smile after the carriage had quite vanished. Noticing, perhaps, that I, too, was smiling, he said: " 'Tes a funny thing, tu, when a maid like that gets married—makes you go all of a tremble— so it du." And to my nod he added: " Brave bit o' sunshine —we'll miss her hereabout; not a doubt of it. We ain't got another one like that."

" Was that her father?" I asked, for the want of something to say. With a sharpish look at my face he shook his head.

"No, she ain't got no parents, Mr. Mara bein' her uncle, as you may say. No, she ain't got no parents," he repeated, and there was something ill at ease, yet juicy, about his voice, as though he knew things that he would not tell.

Since there was nothing more to wait for, I went up to the little inn and ordered bread and cheese. The male congregation was wetting its whistle noisily within, but, as a stranger, I had the verandah to myself, and, finishing my simple lunch in the

March sunlight, I paid and started on. Taking at random one
of the three lanes which debouched from the bottom of the
green, I meandered on between high banks, happy in the consciousness of not knowing at all where it would lead me—that
essential of a country ramble. Except one cottage in a bottom
and one farm on a rise, I passed nothing, nobody. The spring
was late in these parts, the buds had hardly formed as yet on
any trees, and now and then between the bursts of sunlight
a few fine specks of snow would come drifting past me on the
wind. Close to a group of pines at a high corner the lane
dipped sharply down to a long farmhouse standing back in its
yard, where three carts were drawn up and an empty waggon-
ette with its shafts in the air. And suddenly, by some broken
daffodils on the seats and confetti on the ground, I perceived
that I had stumbled on the bride's home, where the wedding
feast was, no doubt, in progress.

Gratifying but by no means satisfying my curiosity by gazing
at the lichened stone and thatch of the old house, at the pigeons,
pigs, and hens at large between it and the barns, I passed on
down the lane, which turned up steeply to the right beside a
little stream. To my left was a long larch wood, to my right
rough fields with many trees. The lane finished at a gate below
the steep moorside crowned by a rocky tor. I stood there leaning on the top bar, debating whether I should ascend or no.
The bracken had, most of it, been cut in the autumn, and not
a hundred yards away the furze was being swaled; the little
blood-red flames and the blue smoke, the yellow blossoms of the
gorse, the sunlight, and some flecks of drifting snow were
mingled in an amazing tangle of colour.

I had made up my mind to ascend the tor and was pushing
through the gate when suddenly I saw a woman sitting on a
stone under the wall bordering the larch wood. She was holding her head in her hands, rocking her body to and fro, and
her eyes were evidently shut, for she had not noticed me. She
wore a blue serge dress, her hat reposed beside her, and her dark
hair was straggling about her face. That face, all blowsy and
flushed, was at once wild and stupefied. A face which has been
beautiful, coarsened and swollen by life and strong emotion, is
a pitiful enough sight. Her dress, hat, and the way her hair
had been done were redolent of the town, and of that unname-
able something which clings to women whose business it is to

attract men. And yet there was a gipsyish look about her, as
though she had not always been of the town.

The sight of a woman's unrestrained distress in the very
heart of untouched nature is so rare that one must be peculiar
to remain unmoved. And there I stood, not knowing what on
earth to do. She went on rocking herself to and fro, her stays
creaking, and a faint moaning sound coming from her lips;
and suddenly she drooped over her lap, her hands fallen to her
sides, as though she had gone into a kind of coma. How go
on and leave her thus? Yet how intrude on what did not
seem to me mere physical suffering?

In that quandary I stood and watched. This corner was
quite sheltered from the wind, the sun almost hot, and the
breath of the swaling reached one in the momentary calms. For
three full minutes she had not moved a finger, till, beginning
to think she had really fainted, I went up to her. From her
drooped body came a scent of heat and of stale violet powder,
and I could see, though the east wind had outraddled them,
traces of rouge on her cheeks; their surface had a sort of swollen defiance, but underneath, as it were, a wasted look. Her
breathing sounded faint and broken.

Mustering courage, I touched her on the arm. She raised
her head and looked up. Her eyes were the best things she
had left; they must have once been very beautiful. Blood-shot
now from the wind, their wild, stupefied look passed after a
moment into the peculiar, half-bold, half-furtive stare of women
of a certain sort. She did not speak, and in my embarrassment
I drew out the flask of port I always take with me on my
rambles, and stammered:

"I beg your pardon—are you feeling faint? Would you
care——?" And, unscrewing the top, I held out the flask.
She stared at it a moment blankly, then taking it, said:

"That's kind of you. I feel to want it, tu." And, putting
it to her lips, she drank, tilting back her head. Perhaps it was
the tell-tale softness of her u's, perhaps the naturally strong
lines of her figure thus bent back, but somehow the plumage of
the town bird seemed to drop off her suddenly.

She handed back the flask, as empty as it had ever been, and
said, with a hard smile:

"I daresay you thought me funny sittin' 'ere like that."

"I thought you were ill."

She laughed without the faintest mirth, and muttered:

"I did go on, didn't I?" Then, almost fiercely, added: "I got some reason, too. Seein' the old place again after all these years." Her dark eyes, which the wine seemed to have cleared and boldened, swept me up and down, taking me in, making sure, perhaps, whether or no she had ever seen me, and what sort of a brute I might be. Then she said: "I was born here. Are you from these parts?" I shook my head. "No, from the other side of the county."

She laughed. Then, after a moment's silence, said abruptly: "I been to a weddin'—first I've seen since I was a girl."

Some instinct kept me silent.

"My own daughter's weddin', but nobody didn't know me —not likely."

I had dropped down under the shelter of the wall on to a stone opposite, and at those words looked at her with interest indeed. She—this coarsened, wasted, suspiciously-scented woman of the town—the mother of that sweet, sunny child I had just seen married? And again instinctively silent about my own presence at the wedding, I murmured:

"I thought I saw some confetti in that farmyard as I came up the lane."

She laughed again.

"Confetti—that's the little pink and white and blue things —plenty o' that,"; and she added fiercely: "My own brother didn' know me—let alone my girl. How should she?—I haven't seen her since she was a baby—she was a laughin' little thing;" and she gazed past me with that look in the eyes as of people who are staring back into the bygone. "I guess we was laughin' when we got her. 'Twas just here—summer-time. I 'ad the moon in my blood that night, right enough." Then, turning her eyes on my face, she added: "That's what a girl *will* 'ave, you know, once in a while, and like as not it'll du for her. Only thirty-five now, I am, an' pretty nigh the end o' my tether. What can you expect?—I'm a gay woman. Did for me right enough. Her father's dead, tu."

"Do you mean," I said, "because of your child?"

She nodded. "I suppose you can say that. They made me bring an order against him. He wouldn't pay up, so he went and enlisted, an' in tu years 'e was dead in the Boer War—so it killed him right enough. But there she is, a sweet sprig if ever there was one. That's a strange thing, isn't it?" And she stared straight before her in a sudden silence. Nor could *I* find anything to say, slowly taking in the strangeness of this thing. That girl, so like a sunbeam, of whom the people talked as though she were a blessing in their lives—her coming into life to have been the ruin of the two who gave her being!

The woman went on dully: " Funny how I knew she was goin' to be married—'twas a farmer told me—comes to me regular when he goes to Exeter market. I always knew he came from near my old home. ' There's a weddin' on Tuesday,' 'e says, ' I'd like to be the bridegroom at. Prettiest, sunniest maid you ever saw;' an' he told me where she come from, so I knew. He found me a bit funny that afternoon. But he don't know who I am, though he used to go to school with me; I'd never tell, not for worlds." She shook her head vehemently. " I don't know why I told you; I'm not meself to-day, and that's a fact." At her half-suspicious, half-appealing look, I said quickly:

" I don't know a soul about here. It's all right."

She sighed. " It was kind of you; and I feel to want to talk sometimes. Well, after he was gone, I said to myself: ' I'll take a holiday and go an' see my daughter married.' " She laughed —" I never had no pink and white and blue little things myself. That was all done up for me that night I had the moon in me blood. Ah! my father was a proper hard man. 'Twas bad enough before I had my baby; but after, when I couldn't get the father to marry me, an' he cut an' run, proper life they led me, him and stepmother. Cry! Didn' I cry—I was a soft-hearted thing—never went to sleep with me eyes dry—never. 'Tis a cruel thing to make a young girl cry."

I said quietly: " Did you run away, then? "

She nodded. " Bravest thing I ever did. Nearly broke my 'eart to leave my baby; but 'twas that or drownin' meself. I was soft then. I went off with a young fellow—bookmaker that used to come over to the sports meetin', wild about me—but he never married me "—again she uttered her hard laugh— " knew a thing worth tu o' that." Lifting her hand towards the burning furze, she added: " I used to come up here an' help 'em light that when I was a little girl." And suddenly she began to cry. It was not so painful and alarming as her first distress, for it seemed natural now.

At the side of the cart-track by the gate was an old boot thrown away, and it served me for something to keep my eyes engaged. The dilapidated black object among the stones and wild plants on that day of strange mixed beauty was as incongruous as this unhappy woman herself revisiting her youth. And there shot into my mind a vision of this spot as it might have been that summer night when she had " the moon in her blood "—queer phrase—and those two young creatures in the tall soft fern, in the warmth and the darkened loneliness, had yielded to the impulse in their blood. A brisk fluttering of snowflakes began falling from the sky still blue, drifting away over our heads towards the blood-red flames and smoke. They powdered the woman's hair and shoulders, and with a sob and a laugh she held up her hand, and began catching them as a child might.

" 'Tis a funny day for my girl's weddin'," she said. Then with a sort of fierceness added: " She'll never know her mother —she's in luck there, tu!" And, grabbing her feathered hat from the ground, she got up. " I must be gettin' back for my train, else I'll be late for an appointment."

When she had put her hat on, rubbed her face, dusted and smoothed her dress, she stood looking at the burning furze. Restored to her town plumage, to her wonted bravado, she was more than ever like that old discarded boot, incongruous.

" I'm a fool ever to have come," she said; " only upset me —and you don't want no more upsettin' than you get, that's certain. Good-bye, and thank you for the drink—it lusened my tongue praaper, didn't it?" She gave me a look—not as a professional—but a human, puzzled look. " I told you my baby was a laughin' little thing. I'm glad she's still like that. I'm glad I've seen her." Her lips quivered for a second; then, with a faked jauntiness, she nodded. " So long!" and passed through the gate down into the lane.

I sat there in the snow and sunlight some minutes after she was gone. Then, getting up, I went and stood by the burning furze. The blowing flames and the blue smoke were alive and beautiful; but behind them they were leaving blackened skeleton twigs.

' Yes,' I thought, ' but in a week or two the little green grass-shoots will be pushing up underneath into the sun. So the world goes! Out of destruction! It's a strange thing!'

1916.

THE NIGHTMARE CHILD

I SET down here not precisely the words of my friend, the country doctor, but the spirit of them:

"You know there are certain creatures in this world whom one simply dare not take notice of, however sorry one may be for them. That has often been borne in on me. I realised it, I think, before I met that little girl. I used to attend her mother for varicose veins—one of those women who really ought not to have children, since they haven't the very least notion of how to bring them up. The wife of a Sussex agricultural labourer called Alliner, she was a stout person, with most peculiar prominent epileptic eyes, such eyes as one usually associates with men of letters or criminals. And yet there was nothing in her. She was just a lazy, slatternly, easy-going body, rather given to drink. Her husband was a thin, dirty, light-hearted fellow, who did his work and offended nobody. Her eldest daughter, a pretty and capable girl, was wild, got into various kinds of trouble, and had to migrate, leaving two illegitimate children behind her with their grandparents. The younger girl, the child of this story, who was called Emmeline, of all names—pronounced Em'leen, of course—was just fifteen at the time of my visits to her mother. She had eyes like a hare's, a mouth which readily fell open, and brown locks caught back from her scared and knobby forehead. She was thin, and walked with her head poked a little forward, and she so manœuvred her legs and long feet, of which one turned in rather and seemed trying to get in front of the other, that there was something clod-hopperish in her gait. Once in a way you would see her in curl-papers, and then indeed she was plain, poor child! She seemed to have grown up without ever having had the least attention paid to her. I don't think she was ill-treated—she was simply not treated at all. At school they had been kind enough, but had regarded her as almost deficient. Seeing that her father was paid about fifteen shillings a week, that her mother had no conception of housekeeping,

and that there were two babies to be fed, they were, of course,
villainously poor, and Em'leen was always draggle-tailed and
badly shod. One side of her too-short dress seemed ever to
hang lower than the other, her stockings always had one hole
at least, and her hats—such queer hats—would seem about to
fly away. I have known her type in the upper classes pass
muster as 'eccentric' or 'full of character.' And even in
Em'leen there was a sort of smothered natural comeliness, trying
pathetically to push through, and never getting a chance. She
always had a lost-dog air, and when her big hare's eyes clung
on your face it seemed as if she only wanted a sign to make her
come trailing at your heels, looking up for a pat or a bit of
biscuit.

"She went to work, of course, the moment she left school.
Her first place was in a small farm where they took lodgers,
and her duties were to do everything, without, of course, knowing how to do anything. She had to leave because she used to
take soap and hair-pins, and food that was left over, and was
once seen licking a dish. It was just about then that I attended
her mother for those veins in her unwieldy legs, and the child
was at home, waiting to secure some other fate. It was impossible not to look at that little creature kindly and to speak
to her now and then; she would not exactly light up, because
her face was not made that way, but she would hang towards
you as if you were a magnet, and you had at once the uncomfortable sensation that you might find her clinging, impossible
to shake off. If one passed her in the village, too, or coming
down from her blackberrying in the thickets on the Downs—
their cottage lay just below the South Downs—one knew that
she would be lingering along, looking back till you were out
of sight. Somehow one hardly thought of her as a girl at all;
she seemed so far from all human hearts, so wandering in a
queer lost world of her own, and to imagine of what she could
be thinking was as impossible as it is with animals. Once I
passed her and her mother dawdling slowly in a lane, then heard
the dot-and-go-one footsteps pattering after me, and the childish
voice, rather soft and timid, say behind my shoulders: 'Would
you please buy some blackberries, sir?' She was almost pretty
at that moment, flushed and breathless at having actually spoken
to me, but her eyes hanging on my face brought a sort of
nightmare feeling at once of being unable to get rid of her.

"Isn't it a cruel thing, when you come to think of it, that

there should be born into the world poor creatures—children, dogs, cats, horses—who want badly to love and be loved, and yet whom no one can quite put up with, much less feel affection for!

"Well, what happened to her is what will always happen to such as those, one way or another, in a world where the callous abound; for, however unlovable a woman or girl, she has her use to a man, just as a dog or a horse has to a master who cares nothing for it.

"Soon after I bought those blackberries I went out to France on military duty. I got my leave a year later and went home. It was late September, very lovely weather, and I took a real holiday walking or lying about up on the Downs, and only coming down at sunset. On one of those days when you really enter heaven, so pure are the lines of the hills, so cool the blue, the green, the chalk-white colouring under the smile of the afternoon sun—I was returning down that same lane, when I came on Em'leen sitting in a gap on the bank, with her di-shevelled hat beside her, and her chin sunk on her hands. My appearance seemed to drag her out of a heavy dream—her eyes awoke, became startled, rolled furtively; she scrambled up, dropped her little old school curtsey, then all confused, faced the bank as if she were going to climb it. She was taller, her dress longer, her hair gathered up, and it was very clear what was soon going to happen to her. I walked on in a rage. At her age—barely sixteen even yet! I am a doctor accustomed to most things, but this particular crime against children of that hopeless sort does make my blood boil. Nothing, not even passion to excuse it—who could feel passion for that poor child? —nothing but the cold, clumsy lust of some young ruffian. Yes, I walked on in a rage, and went straight to her mother's cottage. That wretched woman was incapable of moral indigna-tion, or else the adventures of her elder daughter had exhausted her powers of expression. 'Yes,' she admitted, 'Em'leen had got herself into trouble too; but she would not tell, she wouldn't say nothin' against nobody. It was a bad business, surely, an' now there would be three o' them, an' Alliner was properly upset, that he was!' That was all there was to be had out of *her*. One felt that she knew or suspected more, but her fingers had been so burned over the elder girl that anything to her was better than a fuss.

"I saw Alliner; he was a decent fellow, though dirty, dis-

tressed in his simple, shallow-pated way, and more obviously
ignorant than his wife. I spoke to the school-mistress, a shrewd
and kindly married woman.

"Poor Emmeline! Yes, she had noticed. It was very sad
and wicked! She hinted, but would not do more than hint, at
the son of the miller, but he was back again, fighting in France
now, and, after all, her evidence amounted to no more than his
reputation with girls. Besides, one is very careful what one
says in a country village. I, however, was so angry that I should
not have been careful if I could have got hold of anything at
all definite.

"I did not see the child again before my leave was up. The
very next news I heard of her was from a newspaper—Emmeline
Alliner, sixteen, had been committed for trial for causing the
death of her illegitimate child by exposure. I was on the sick
list in January, and went home to rest. I had not been there
two days before I received a visit from a solicitor of our assize
town, who came to ask me if I would give evidence at the
girl's trial as to the nature of her home surroundings. I
learned from him the details of the lugubrious business. It
seems that she had slipped out one bitter afternoon in December,
barely a fortnight after her confinement, carrying her baby.
There was snow on the ground and it was freezing hard, but
the sun was bright, and it was that, perhaps, which tempted
her. She must have gone up towards the Downs by the lane
where I had twice met her; gone up, and stopped at the very
gap in the bank where she had been sitting lost in that heavy
dream when I saw her last. She appears to have subsided
there in the snow, for there she was found by the postman just
as it was getting dark; leaning over her knees as if stupefied,
with her chin buried in her hands—and the baby stiff and dead
in the snow beside her. When I told the lawyer how I had
seen her there ten weeks before, and of the curious dazed state
she had been in, he said at once: 'Ah! the exact spot! That's
very important; it looks uncommonly as if it were there that
she came by her misfortune. What do you think? It's almost
evidence that she'd lost sense of her surroundings, baby and
all. I shall ask you to tell us about that at the trial. She's a
most peculiar child; I can't get anything out of her. I keep
asking her for the name of the man, or some indication of how
it came about, but all she says is: "Nobody—nobody!" Another case of immaculate conception! Poor little creature!

She's very pathetic, and that's her best chance. Who could condemn a child like that?'

"And so, indeed, it turned out. I spared no feelings in my evidence. The mother and father were in court, and I hope Mrs. Alliner liked my diagnosis of her maternal qualities. My description of how Em'leen was sitting when I met her in September tallied so exactly with the postman's account of how he met her that I could see the jury were impressed. And then there was the figure of the child herself, lonely there in the dock. The French have a word, *hébétée*. Surely there never was a human object to which it applied better. She stood like a little tired pony, whose head hangs down, half-sleeping after exertion; and those hare eyes of hers were glued to the judge's face, for all the world as if she were worshipping him. It must have made him extraordinarily uncomfortable. He summed up very humanely, dwelling on the necessity of finding intention in her conduct towards the baby; and he used some good strong language against the unknown man. The jury found her not guilty, and she was discharged. The schoolmistress and I, anticipating this, had found her a refuge with some sisters of mercy who ran a sort of home not far away, and to that we took her, without a 'by your leave' to the mother.

"When I came home the following summer I found an opportunity of going to look her up. She was amazingly improved in face and dress, but she had attached herself to one of the sisters—a broad, fine-looking woman—to such a pitch that she seemed hardly alive when out of her sight. The sister spoke of it to me with real concern.

"'I really don't know what to do with her,' she said; 'she seems incapable of anything unless I tell her; she only feels things through me. It's really quite trying, and sometimes very funny, poor little soul! but it's tragic for her. If I told her to jump out of her bedroom window, or lie down in that pond and drown, she'd do it without a moment's hesitation. She can't go through life like this; she must learn to stand on her own feet. We must try and get her a good place, where she can learn what responsibility means and get a will of her own.'

"I looked at the sister, so broad, so capable, so handsome, and so puzzled, and I thought. 'Yes, I know exactly. She's on your nerves; and where in the world will you find a place for her where she won't become a sort of nightmare to someone

with her devotion, or else get it taken advantage of again?'
And I urged them to keep her a little longer. They did; for
when I went home for good, six months later, I found that she
had only just gone into a place with an old lady patient of mine
in a small villa on the outskirts of our village. She used to
open the door to me when I called there on my rounds once a
week. She retained vestiges of the neatness which had been
grafted on her by the sister, but her frock was already beginning
to sag down on one side and her hair to look ill-treated. The
old lady spoke to her with a sort of indulgent impatience, and
it was clear that the girl's devotion was not concentrated upon
her. I caught myself wondering what would be its next object,
never able to help the feeling that if I gave a sign it would
be myself. You may be sure I gave no sign. What's the good?
I hold the belief that people should not force themselves to
human contacts or relationships which they cannot naturally
and without irritation preserve. I've seen these heroic attempts
come to grief so often; in fact, I don't think I've ever seen one
succeed, not even between blood relations. In the long run
they merely pervert and spoil the fibre of the attempter without
really benefiting the attemptee. Behind healthy relationships
between human beings, or even between human beings and
animals, there must be at least some rudimentary affinity.
That's the tragedy of poor little souls like Em'leen. Where on
earth can they find the affinity which makes life good? The
very fact that they must worship is their destruction. It was a
soldier—or so they said—who had brought her to her first grief;
I had seen her adoring the judge at the trial, then the handsome
uniformed sister. And I, as the village doctor, was a sort of
tin-pot deity in those parts, so I was very careful to keep my
manner to her robust and almost brusque.

"And then one day I passed her coming from the post office;
she was looking back, her cheeks were flushed, and she was
almost pretty. There by the inn a butcher's cart was drawn
up. The young butcher, new to our village (he had a stiff
knee and had been discharged from the army), was taking out
a leg of mutton. He had a dare-devil face and eyes that had
seen much death. He had evidently been chatting with her, for
he was still smiling, and even as I passed him he threw her a
jerk of the head.

"Two Sundays after that I was coming down past Wiley's
copse at dusk and heard a man's coarse laugh. There, through

a tiny gap in the nut-bushes, I saw a couple seated. He had his leg stiffly stretched out and his arm round the girl, who was leaning towards him; her lips were parted, and those hare's eyes of hers were looking up into his face. Adoration!

"I don't know what it was my duty to have done; I only know that I did nothing, but slunk on with a lump in my throat.

"Adoration! There it was again! Hopeless! Incurable devotions to those who cared no more for her than for a slice of suet-pudding to be eaten hot, gulped down, forgotten, or loathed in the recollection. And there they are, these girls, one to almost every village of this country—a nightmare to us all. The look on her face was with me all that evening and in my dreams.

"I know no more, for two days later I was summoned north to take up work in a military hospital."

1917.

A REVERSION TO TYPE

WE sat smoking after dinner in a country house. Someone was saying: "They're either too conceited, too much in earnest, too much after advertisement, too effeminate, or too dirty—I never found literary men amusing."

There was a murmur of approval, till a sallow man who had not spoken all the evening, except to ask for matches, emerged from the shadow of his chair. . . .

"You're wrong," he said. "The most diverting thing I ever came across was in connection with two literary men. It happened some years ago at an Italian inn, in a place where there were ruins. I was travelling with poor B——, and at that inn we came across a literary man, a regular Classicist, looking up items for an historical romance. He was very good company—a prosperous, clever, satirical creature, who wore a moustache, and thought it wicked not to *change* for dinner. In spite of this, he had his limitations—but we all have *them,* even we sitting here. This inn was a queer place—at a crossing of two roads in the midst of brown hills—with blistered eucalyptus trees throwing ragged shadows on it, and two old boar-spears fastened up over the door. We were the only people there, and it was very hot. We used to dine outside the entrance, in the shade of the eucalyptus trees. There was a wonderful tap of wine; and, after toiling over ruins in the sun all day, we used to punish it—the Classicist especially; it sharpened his wit and thickened his tongue. He was a man of culture, great believer in physical sports, and knew all about everybody's ancestors—was himself fifteen degrees removed from a murderer of Thomas A'Becket, and a friend of the champion tennis-player. We got on very well; he was quite amusing and affable.

"It was about sunset on the fourth evening when the other literary person turned up. He came just as we were going to dinner—a long, weedy fellow, slouching in under a knapsack, covered with dust, in a battered 'larrikin' hat, unshaved, with

511

eyes as keen as sword-points, a lot of hair, and an emotional mouth, like a girl's. He sprawled down on a bench close to our table, unslung his pack, and appeared to lose himself in the sunset. When our host came out with the soup, he asked for wine and a bed. B—— suggested that he should join us; he accepted, and sat down forthwith. I sat at one end, B—— opposite; this fellow and the Classicist, who wore a smoking jacket, and smelt tremendously of soap, faced each other. From the first moment it was a case of 'two of a trade.' The moment their eyes met, ironical smiles began wandering about their mouths. There was little enough talk till we had broached our third bottle. The Classicist was a noble drinker; this wild man of the ways a nobler, or perhaps more thirsty. I remember the first words they exchanged. The Classicist, in his superior, thick, satirical voice, was deploring 'the unmanly tricks' introduced nowadays into swordsmanship, to the detriment of its dignity and grace.

" ' It would be interesting to know, sir,' said the other, ' when you're fighting for life, what is the good of those " tickle points of niceness "?' The Classicist looked at him: ' You would wish, I should imagine, to " play the game," sir?'

" ' With my enemy's sword through the middle of me?'

" The Classicist answered: ' I should have thought it a matter of " good form "; however, if you don't feel that—of course——'

" ' I have not the good fortune to be a swordsman; but if I were, I should be concerned to express my soul with the point of my sword, not with attitudes.'

" ' Noble aspiration!'

" ' Just as I drink off at a draught this most excellent wine.'

" ' Evidently you are not concerned with flavours?'

" ' Its flavour, sir, is the feeling it gives me—Burn Academy, and all its works!'

" The Classicist turned to me elaborately and asked:

" ' Do you know young D——, the author of ——? You ought to; there's no d—d nonsense about *him*.' The man on the other side of the table laid his soiled hand on his soiled chest. ' A hit. I feel honoured.'

" The Classicist continued his remarks. ' No " expressions of soul " and that sort of thing about D——!'

" ' Oh! happy D——!' murmured our visitor. ' And is the happy D—— an artist in his writings?'

" The Classicist turned and rent him. ' He's a public school man, sir, and a gentleman, which, in my humble opinion, is much better.'

" The newcomer drank. ' That is very interesting. I must read D——. Has he given us any information about the inner meaning of life in public schools? '

" 'No, sir; he is not a prig.'

" 'Indeed! He must have English blood in him, this gentleman! '

" ' He knows the meaning of " good form," anyway.'

" Our visitor clutched his glass and shook it in the air. ' Sir,' he said, ' with all my heart, with all my blood, I revolt against those words " good form "; I revolt against the commercial snobbery that underlies them; I revolt against the meanness and the Pharisaism of them; I revolt——' and still he went on shaking his glass and saying ' I revolt.'

" The Classicist ironically murmured: ' *Sparge rosas! Inania verba!* '

" ' No, sir; " winged words," that I will drive home with my last breath.'

" The Classicist smiled: ' An Emotional,' he began, ' an Emotional . . .'

" Gentlemen, it was time to interfere, so I upset the bottle. The wine streamed across the table. We ordered more. Darkness had gathered; the moon was rising; over the door the reflections of those old boar-spears branched sharp and long on the pale wall; they had an uncanny look, like cross-bones. How those two fellows disliked each other! Whole centuries of antagonism glared out of their eyes. They seemed to sum up in some mysterious way all that's significant and opposed in the artist and the man of action. It was exceedingly funny. They were both learned pigs. But the ancestors of the one might from time immemorable have been burning and stamping on the other, and the ancestors of the other stabbing desperately up at the one. One represented a decent well-fed spirit of satisfaction with things as they are, and the other a ravening shade, whom centuries of starvation had engrained with strife. For all I know they may both have been the sons of chemists. But, anyway, some instinct made each recognise the other as typical of what he had most cause to hate. Very obscure the reasons of such things—very obscure everything to do with origins!

"We ordered another bottle. Any other two men, having discovered such hostility, would have held their tongues; these couldn't—I have noticed it with members of their profession. The Emotionalist proposed a toast: 'I give you,' he said, 'the country most immersed in the slough of commercialism, the country that suffocates truth in its cradle with the smell of money, the country of snobs and stockjobbers!' He drank his own toast with enthusiasm; needless to say, nobody else did. The Classicist showed the first signs of excitement. 'I give you,' he responded, 'the whipping of all high-falutin' upstarts!'

"'Good!' replied the other; 'I drink that too!' It again became necessary to upset something—a glass this time. Presently we tumbled somehow on the subject of the Sagas. Gentlemen, the Sagas were deep in the affections of both those fellows; and nothing could have better roused their hostility to boiling-point than this common affection. You could see it by their faces. To the one a Saga was the quintessence of sport, of manly valour, and aristocratic tyranny; to the other something lawless and beautiful, freedom in a mist of primitive emotions, a will-o'-the-wisp hovering over bogs, a draught of blood and wine.

"Have you ever noticed two men discussing a picture, a book, a person, which one loves and the other hates? What happens? Indifference or mutual contempt—nothing more. But let them chance on that which each loves; then you may cry 'havoc!'

"We left our chairs, and stood about, and in the moonlight those creatures talked. First one went to the table and drained his glass, then the other. Their words were as bitter as bitter; they kept closing and hastily recoiling. They were like two men defending the honour of some woman who belonged to both of them—a priceless possession, which neither would abandon to the other. So, in the age of Sagas, a forbear of the one, some wild heathman, may have hewn a lord in sunder; or, in a foray, the other's ancestor trodden into the earth a turbulent churl. It was being done over again that evening—with words—by two lights of our high civilisation. B—— went to sleep. I woke him, and we left them disputing in the moonlight.

"And now, gentlemen, I come to the diverting part of my story. It may have been a quarter, it may have been half an hour after B—— and I had retired, when the landlord came to call us.

"There, in a pool of moonlight, shadows, blood, and wine, they lay—they had carved each other up with the boar-spears.

"The Classicist was quite dead, with a sneer on his face; the Emotionalist still lived, with a gash right through his chest. There was nothing to be learnt from him, however; before his death he fixed his eyes on me. I bent, thinking to hear words of remorse or terror. But all he said was:

"'The snob!' and died.

"They took alarm at the inn and wanted to smother it up. They called it fever. Well, gentlemen, so it *was*: the ineradicable fever of type. A good many years ago. You must have seen it in the papers. . . ."

The sallow man was silent.

1901.

EXPECTATIONS

NOT many years ago a couple were living in the south of England whose name was Wotchett—Ralph and Eileen Wotchett; a curious name, derived, Ralph asserted, from a Saxon Thegn called Otchar, mentioned in Domesday, or at all events —when search of the book had proved vain—on the edge of that substantial record.

He—possibly the thirtieth descendant of the Thegn—was close on six feet in height and thin, with thirsty eyes, and a smile which had fixed itself in his cheeks, so on the verge of appearing was it. His hair waved and was of a dusty shade bordering on grey. His wife, of the same age and nearly the same height as himself, was of sanguine colouring and a Cornish family, which had held land in such a manner that it had nearly melted in their grasp. All that had come to Eileen was a reversion on the mortgageable value of which she and Ralph had been living for some time. Ralph Wotchett also had expectations. By profession he was an architect, but, perhaps because of his expectations, he had always had bad luck. The involutions of the reasons why his clients died, became insolvent, abandoned their projects, or otherwise failed to come up to the scratch, were followed by him alone in the full of their maze-like windings. The house they inhabited, indeed, was one of those he had designed for a client, but the "fat chough" had refused to go into it for some unaccountable reason; he and Eileen were only perching there, however, on the edge of settling down in some more permanent house when they came into their expectations.

Considering the vicissitudes and disappointments of their life together, it was remarkable how certain they remained that they would at last cross the bar and reach the harbour of comfortable circumstances. They had, one may suppose, expectations in their blood. The germ of getting "something for nothing" had infected their systems, so that, though they were not selfish or greedy people, and well knew how to rough it, they dreamed so of what they had not that they continually got rid of what they had in order to obtain more of it. If, for example, Ralph received an order, he felt so strongly that this was the chance of his life if properly grasped, that he would almost as a matter of course increase and complicate the project till it became unworkable, or in his zeal omit some vital calculation such as a rise in the price of bricks; nor would anyone be more surprised than he at this, or more certain that all connected with the matter had been "fat choughs" except—himself. On such occasions Eileen would get angry, but if anyone suggested that Ralph had over-reached himself, she would get still angrier. She was very loyal, and unfortunately rather flyaway both in mind and body; before long she always joined him in his feeling that the whole transaction had been just the usual "skin-game" on the part of Providence to keep them out of their expectations. It was the same in domestic life. If Ralph had to eat a breakfast, which would be almost every morning, he had so many and such imaginative ways of getting from it a better breakfast than was in it that he often remained on the edge of it, as it were. He had special methods of cooking, so as to extract from everything a more than ordinary flavour, and these took all the time that he would have to eat the results in. Coffee he would make with a whole egg, shell and all, stirred in; it had to be left on the hob for an incomparable time, and he would start to catch his train with his first cup in his hand; Eileen would have to run after him and take it away. They were, in fact, rather like a kitten which knows it has a tail, and will fly round and round all day with the expectation of catching that desirable appendage. Sometimes indeed, by sheer perseverance, of which he had a great deal in a roundabout way, Ralph would achieve something, but, when this happened, something else, not foreseen by him, had always happened first, which rendered that accomplishment nugatory and left it expensive on his hands. Nevertheless, they retained their faith that some day they would get ahead of Providence and come into their own.

In view of not yet having come into their expectations, they had waited to have children; but two had rather unexpectedly been born. The babes had succumbed, however, one to preparation for betterment too ingenious to be fulfilled, the other

to fulfillment itself, a special kind of food having been treated
so ingeniously that it had undoubtedly engendered poison. And
they remained childless.

They were about fifty when Ralph received one morning a
solicitor's letter announcing the death of his godmother, Aunt
Lispeth. When he read out the news they looked at their plates
a full minute without speaking. Their expectations had ma-
tured. At last they were to come into something in return for
nothing. Aunt Lispeth, who had latterly lived at Ipswich in a
house which he had just not built for her, was an old maid.
They had often discussed what she would leave them—though
in no mean or grasping spirit, for they did not grudge the
"poor old girl" her few remaining years, however they might
feel that she was long past enjoying herself. The chance would
come to them some time, and when it did, of course, must be
made the best of. Then Eileen said:

"You must go down at once, Ralph!"

Donning black, Ralph set off hurriedly, and just missed his
train; he caught one, however, in the afternoon, and arrived that
evening in Ipswich. It was October, drizzling and dark; the
last cab moved out as he tried to enter it, for he had been
detained by his ticket, which he had put for extra readiness in
his glove, and forgotten—as if the ticket collector couldn't have
seen it there, the "fat chough!" He walked up to his aunt's
house, and was admitted to a mansion where a dinner-party
was going on. It was impossible to persuade the servant
that this was his aunt's, so he was obliged to retire to an hotel
and wire to Eileen to send him the right address—the "fat
choughs" in the street did not seem to know it. He got her
answer the following midday, and, going to the proper number,
found the darkened house. The two servants who admitted
him described the manner of their mistress's death and showed
him up into her room. Aunt Lispeth had been laid out daintily.
Ralph contemplated her with the smile which never moved from
his cheeks and with a sort of awe in his thirsty eyes. The
poor old girl! How thin, how white! It had been time she
went! A little stiffened twist in her neck where her lean head
had fallen to one side at the last had not been set quite straight,
and there seemed the ghost of an expression on her face, almost
cynical; by looking closer he saw that it came from a gap in the
white lashes of one eye, giving it an air of not being quite closed,

as though she were trying to wink at him. He went out rather hastily, and, ascertaining that the funeral was fixed for noon next day, paid a visit to the solicitor.

There he was told that the lawyer himself was sole executor, and he—Ralph—residuary legatee. He could not help a feeling of exultation, for he and Eileen were at that time particularly hard pressed. He restrained it, however, and went to his hotel to write to her. He received a telegram in answer next morning at ten o'clock: " For goodness' sake leave all details to lawyer. —Eileen," which he thought very peculiar. He lunched with the lawyer after the funeral, and they opened his aunt's will. It was quite short and simple, made certain specific bequests of lace and jewellery, left a hundred pounds to her executor, the lawyer, and the rest of her property to her nephew, Ralph Wotchott. The lawyer proposed to advertise for debts in the usual way, and Ralph, with considerable control, confined himself to urging all speed in the application for probate and disposal of the estate. He caught a late train back to Eileen. She received his account distrustfully; she was sure he had put his finger in the pie, and if he had it would all go wrong. Well, if he hadn't, he soon would! It was really as if loyalty had given way in her now that their expectations were on the point of being realised.

They had often discussed his aunt's income, but they went into it again that night, to see whether it could not by fresh investment be increased. It was derived from Norwich and Birmingham Corporation Stocks, and Ralph proved that by going into industrial concerns the four hundred a year could quite safely be made into six. Eileen agreed that this would be a good thing to do, but nothing definite was decided. Now that they had come into money they did not feel so inclined to move their residence, though both felt that they might increase their scale of living, which had lately been at a distressingly low ebb. They spoke, too, about the advisability of a small car. Ralph knew of one—a second-hand Ford—to be had for a song. They ought not—he thought—to miss the chance. He would take occasion to meet the owner casually and throw out a feeler. It would not do to let the fellow know that there was any money coming to them, or he would put the price up for a certainty. In fact, it would be better to secure the car before the news got about. He secured it a few days later for eighty

pounds, including repairs, which would take about a month. A
letter from the lawyer next day informed them that he was
attending to matters with all speed; and the next five weeks
passed in slowly realising that at last they had turned the corner
of their lives and were in smooth water. They ordered, among
other things, the materials for a fowl-house, long desired, which
Ralph helped to put up; and a considerable number of fowls,
for feeding which he had a design which would enable them to
lay a great many more eggs in the future than could reasonably
be expected from the amount of food put into the fowls. He
also caused an old stable to be converted into a garage. He
still went to London two or three times a week, to attend to
business which was not, as a rule, there. On his way from St.
Pancras to Red Lion Square, where his office was, he had long
been attracted by an emerald pendant with pearl clasp in a
jeweller's shop window. He went in now to ask its price.
Fifty-eight pounds—emeralds were a rising market. The expression rankled in him, and going to Hatton Garden to enquire
into its truth, he found the statement confirmed. "The chief
advantage of having money," he thought, "is to be able to buy
at the right moment." He had not given Eileen anything for a
long time, and this was an occasion which could hardly be
passed over. He bought the pendant on his way back to St.
Pancras, the draft in payment absorbing practically all his
balance. Eileen was delighted with it. They spent that evening
in the nearest approach to festivity that they had known for
several years. It was, as it were, the crown of the long waiting
for something out of nothing. All those little acerbities which
creep into the manner of two married people who are always
trying to round the corner fell away, and they sat together in
one large chair, talking and laughing over the countless tricks
which Providence—"that fat chough"—had played them.
They carried their lightheartedness to bed.

They were awakened next morning by the sound of a car.
The Ford was being delivered with a request for payment.
Ralph did not pay; it would be "all right," he said. He stabled
the car and wrote to the lawyer that he would be glad to have
news and an advance of £100. On his return from town in
the evening two days later he found Eileen in the dining-room
with her hair wild and an opened letter before her. She looked
up with the word: "Here!" and Ralph took the letter.

"Lodgers and Wayburn,
          "Solicitors, Ipswich.

"Dear Mr. Wotchett,

"In answer to yours of the fifteenth, I have obtained probate, paid all debts, and distributed the various legacies. The sale of furniture took place last Monday. I now have pleasure in enclosing you a complete and, I think, final account, by which you will see that there is a sum in hand of forty-three pounds due to you as residuary legatee. I am afraid this will seem a disappointing result, but as you were doubtless aware (though I was not when I had the pleasure of seeing you), the greater part of your aunt's property passed under a deed of settlement, and it seems she had been dipping heavily into the capital of the remainder for some years past.

"Believe me,
          "Faithfully yours,
               "Edward Lodgers."

For a minute the only sounds were the snapping of Ralph's jaws and Eileen's rapid breathing. Then she said:

"You never said a word about a settlement. I suppose you got it muddled as usual!"

Ralph did not answer, too deep in his anger with the old woman who had left that "fat chough" a hundred pounds to provide him—Ralph—with forty-three.

"You always believe what you want to believe!" cried Eileen; "I never saw such a man."

Ralph went to Ipswich on the morrow. After going into everything with the lawyer, he succeeded in varying the account by fifteen shillings, considerably more than which was absorbed by the fee for this interview, his fare, and hotel bill. The conduct of his aunt, in having caused him to get it into his head that there was no settlement, and in living on her capital, gave him pain quite beyond the power of expression; and more than once he recalled with a shudder that slightly quizzical look on her dead face. He returned to Eileen the following day with his brain racing round and round. Getting up next morning, he said:

"I believe I can get a hundred for that car; I'll go up and see about it."

"Take this, too," said Eileen, handing him the emerald pendant. Ralph took it with a grunt.

"Lucky," he muttered; "emeralds are a rising market. I bought it on purpose."

He came back that night more cheerful. He had sold the car for sixty-five pounds, and the pendant for forty-two pounds —a good price, for emeralds were now on the fall! With the cheque for forty-three pounds, which represented his expectations, he proved that they would only be fourteen pounds out on the whole business when the fowls and fowlhouse had been paid for; and they would have the fowls—the price of eggs was going up. Eileen agreed that it was the moment to develop poultry-keeping. They might expect good returns. And holding up her face she said:

"Give me a kiss, dear Ralph!"

Ralph gave it, with his thirsty eyes fixed, expectant, on something round the corner of her head, and the smile, which never moved, on his cheeks.

After all, there was her reversion! They would come into it some day.

1919.

A WOMAN

A TRAVELLER was writing to his friend: . . . "We were sitting on the *stoep*. Above the pines the long line of Table Mountain was like a violet shadow two shades deeper than the sky. We had no light except the ' Cross,' and a swarm of other stars; it was a rare night, dark crystal.

"There had been a dance, and the girls had gone to bed; all the shutters were closed, the old house against our backs looked very silent, and flat, and long. Only the door was open, and we sat round it. The sparks from our pipes writhed about in the air, or, falling on to the *stoep,* expired like the words dropping from our mouths. You know the kind of talk. In the morning we had played cricket amongst the trees—a hit into the vineyards, ' five and out '—girls and all. In the afternoon we had played tennis, on a half-made court—the girls too. In the evening we had danced. Some had hitched up, and departed. Some had gone to bed. We four were left, and old Juno, the pointer, with her head on her paws, and her nose wrinkling at the squeaking of some tiny beast in the darkness. Little Byng, with his waistcoat unbuttoned, was sitting quite square above his parted legs; round-faced little man, no neck to speak of, straw-coloured hair, and eyes without lashes, just like a dissipated egg. You know him, Billy Byng, best-hearted little man, they say, in Cape Colony. Young Sanley—married to one of the Detwell girls, sleeping a healthy sleep already indoors—such a neat, smooth chap; great Scott! yes, and how commonplace! with his pale moustache, and his high white forehead, and his slim nose, and his well-cut clothes, and his tidy made-up tie. And our host—you know him; a little too alert, a little too dark, a little too everything, but a right good fellow; engaged to the other Detwell girl, who was perhaps thinking of him, and perhaps wasn't, in her bed just over our heads. Well, we were talking; profaning things a bit; not much, you know, couldn't lay claim to original profanity;

525

just tarbrushing the surface. We were all a bit bored, rather sleepy, and accordingly, just a little too jovial. Even Juno, who's at least as wise as any human, was pondering somewhat gloomily over her master's intention of taking us to shoot pheasants at daybreak—'before it was too hot.' We had been there before; we knew it—that pheasant shooting, up stony slopes in a tangle of cover, with the chance of a couple of shots, at most, producing one disembowelled bird. Every now and then one of us would get up, walk to the edge of the *stoep,* stare into the dark vineyard, stretch as if he were going to make a move, and after all yield to our host's: 'Just one more, boys!'

"All of a sudden young Sanley murmured:

"'I heard footsteps.'

"'Some nigger,' said our host.

"And then at the far end of the *stoep* a woman appeared, walked straight into our midst, and sat down. It was pretty startling and absurd. Little Byng seemed absolutely trans-fixed; he blinked his lashless eyes, and seemed to twitch all over his face. Sanley got very pale and nervously tapped the table. Our host alone kept the use of his tongue.

"'Corrie!' he said.

"'Why not? Give me a drink, Jack Allen.'

"Our host in a kind of surreptitious way poured brandy into a glass and added seltzer.

"The woman held out her hand for it, and as she tilted her chin to drink, the cloak fell from her shoulders, and we could see her neck and arms gleaming out of her evening dress.

"'Thanks!' she said; 'I wanted that.' Then she bent over the table and leaned her face on her hand. Well, no one spoke, and we all cast secret looks back at the house. Sanley reached out his hand quietly and drew the door to.

"The woman said:

"'I saw the bowls of your pipes, and heard your voices. You're not too lively now.'

"Her voice wasn't loud; but it sounded wilfully coarsened. Her lips were slightly parted above her forefinger crooked across her chin. Her nostrils seemed to broaden as she looked at us, in a sort of distrustful way. She wore no hat, and her hair was like a little black patch of the night over her brow. Her eyes; how can I describe them? They seemed to see every-thing, and to see nothing. They were so intent, and mournful, and defiant; hard, if you like, tragic, too. I remembered, now, where I had met her—though I hadn't been ten days in the Colony—at the supper party of a man called Brown, after the theatre; very vulgar and noisy.

" The most notorious woman in Cape Town! Her house had been pointed out to me, too, just at the corner of the Malay quarter; a little house, painted mauve, with large red flowers starring its front.

" The most notorious woman in Cape Town! I looked at our host. He was biting his fingers. At Byng. His mouth was a little open, as if he were about to make a very sage remark. Sanley struck me as looking altogether too pitiably decent.

" Our host broke the silence.

" ' How? Where? Eh! What?'

" ' Staying down there at Charlie Lennard's; what a beast! Oh! what a beast!'

" Her eyes rested, wistfully it seemed to me, on each of us in turn.

" ' It's a beautiful night, isn't it?' she said.

" Little Byng kicked out his foot, as if he would have sent something sprawling, and began stuttering out:

" ' I beg pardon—I beg pardon.' I saw the old pointer thrust her nose against the woman's knees. Something moved, back in the house; we all looked round with a start. Then the woman began to laugh, almost noiselessly, as though she had an unholy understanding of our minds, as if she would never leave off. I saw Sanley tear at his hair, and stealthily smooth it down again. Our host frowned horribly, and thrust his hands so deep into his pockets that it seemed to me they must go through the linings. Little Byng almost bounded up and down in his chair. Then, just as suddenly, the woman stopped laughing; there was dead silence. You could only hear the squeaking of the tiny beast. At last the woman said:

" ' Doesn't it smell good to-night? It's quiet, too. . . . Here! let me have another drink!' She took the glass our host held out: 'Your very good health,' she said, 'my respectable friends!'

" Our host suddenly resumed his seat, crossed his arms, and sighed. A pitiful little noise he made of it.

" ' I'm not going to hurt you,' she said; ' I wouldn't hurt a fly to-night—— It smells like home. Look!' She held out the edge of her skirts to us. ' Dew! I'm dripping; isn't it sweet?'

" Her voice had lost all coarseness—it might have been your

mother or sister speaking; it was ever so queer, and little Byng
sputtered out: 'Too bad! too bad!' but whether to her, or of
her, or to us—no one knew.

"'I've walked miles to-night,' she said. 'Haven't had such
a walk since I was a girl.' There was a kind of tone in her
voice that hurt me horribly; and suddenly young Sanley rose.

"'Excuse me, Allen!' he stammered: 'it's very late. Going
to turn in.' I caught the gleam of his eyes on the woman.

"'Oh! are you going?' she said. There was a sort of regret,
a sort of something innocent and unconscious in her voice that
seemed regularly to pierce a bag of venom in that smooth young
man.

"'Madam, I am. My wife——' He stopped, groped for the
door, pulled it open, smiled his mean tidy smile, and vanished.

"The woman had risen, and she gave a sort of laugh.

"'*His wife!* Oh! Well, I wish her happiness. Ah! my
God! I *do* wish her happiness—I *do;* and yours, Jack Allen;
and yours, if you have one. Billy Byng, you remember me—
you remember when I first—to-night, I thought—I thought
——' She hid her face. One by one we slunk off the *stoep,* and
left her, sobbing her heart out before the house.

"God knows what she was thinking of! God knows what sort
of things lurk round us, and leap out—thank Heaven! not
often—from the darkness, as that did!

"I crept back later to the edge of the vineyard.

"There she was still, and, beside her, little Byng, with his
toes turned out, bending over her fingers. Then I saw him
draw them under his arm, pat them with his other hand, and,
gazing up at the sky, lead her gently out into the darkness. . . .

1900.

A HEDONIST

RUPERT K. VANESS remains freshly in my mind because he was so fine and large, and because he summed up in his person and behaviour a philosophy which, budding before the war, hibernated during that distressing epoch, and is now again in bloom.

He was a New Yorker addicted to Italy. One often puzzled over the composition of his blood. From his appearance it was rich; and his name fortified the conclusion. What the K. stood for, however, I never learned; the three possibilities were equally intriguing. Had he a strain of Highlander with Kenneth or Keith; a drop of German or Scandinavian with Kurt or Knut; a blend of Syrian or Armenian with Khalil or Kassim? The blue in his fine eyes seemed to preclude the last, but there was an encouraging curve in his nostrils, and a raven gleam in his auburn hair, which by the way was beginning to grizzle and recede when I knew him. The flesh of his face, too, had sometimes a tired and pouchy appearance, and his tall body looked a trifle rebellious within his extremely well-cut clothes —but, after all, he was fifty-five. You felt that Vaness was a philosopher, yet he never bored you with his views, and was content to let you grasp his moving principle gradually, through watching what he ate, drank, smoked, wore, and how he encircled himself with the beautiful things and people of this life. One presumed him rich, for one was never conscious of money in his presence. Life moved round him with a certain noiseless ease or stood still at a perfect temperature, like the air in a conservatory round a choice blossom which a draught might shrivel.

This image of a flower in relation to Rupert K. Vaness pleases me, because of that little incident in Magnolia Garden, near Charleston, South Carolina.

Vaness was the sort of man of whom one could never say with safety whether he was revolving round a beautiful young woman or whether the beautiful young woman was revolving round him. His looks, his wealth, his taste, his reputation, invested him with a certain sun-like quality; but his age, the recession of his locks, and the advancement of his waist were beginning to dim his lustre; so that whether he was moth or candle was becoming a moot point. It was moot to me, watching him and Miss Sabine Monroy at Charleston throughout the month of March. The casual observer would have said that she was " playing him up " as a young poet of my acquaintance puts it; but I was not casual. For me Vaness had the attraction of a theorem, and I was looking rather deeply into him and Miss Monroy. That girl had charm. She came, I think, from Baltimore, with a strain in her, they said, of old Southern Creole blood. Tall and what is known as willowy, with dark chestnut hair, very broad dark eyebrows, very soft quick eyes, and a pretty mouth —when she did not accentuate it with lip-salve—she had more sheer quiet vitality than any girl I ever saw. It was delightful to watch her dance, ride, play tennis. She laughed with her eyes; she talked with a savouring vivacity. She never seemed tired or bored. She was—in one hackneyed word—" attractive." And Vaness, the connoisseur, was quite obviously attracted. Of men who professionally admire beauty one can never tell offhand whether they definitely design to add a pretty woman to their collection, or whether their dalliance is just matter of habit. But he stood and sat about her, he drove and rode, listened to music, and played cards with her; he did all but dance with her, and even at times trembled on the brink of that. And his eyes—those fine lustrous eyes of his—followed her about.

How she had remained unmarried to the age of twenty-six was a mystery, till one reflected that with her power of enjoying life she could not yet have had the time. Her perfect physique was at full stretch for eighteen hours out of the twenty-four each day. Her sleep must have been like that of a baby. One figured her sinking into dreamless rest the moment her head touched pillow, and never stirring till she sprang up into her bath.

As I say, for me, Vaness, or rather his philosophy, *erat demonstrandum.* I was philosophically in some distress just then. The microbe of fatalism, already present in the brains of artists before the War, had been considerably enlarged by that depressing occurrence. Could a civilisation basing itself on the production of material advantages, do anything but ensure the desire for more and more material advantages? Could it promote progress even of a material character except in countries whose resources were still much in excess of their population? The war had seemed to me to show that mankind was too combative an animal ever to recognise that the good of all was the good of one. The coarse-fibred, pugnacious, and self-seeking would, I had become sure, always carry too many guns for the refined and kindly. In short, there was not enough altruism to go round—not half, not a hundredth part enough. The simple heroism of mankind, disclosed or rather accentuated by the war, seemed to afford no hope—it was so exploitable by the rhinoceri and tigers of high life. The march of science appeared on the whole to be carrying us backward. I deeply suspected that there had been ages when the populations of this earth, though less numerous and comfortable, had been proportionately more healthy than they were at present. As for religion, I had never had the least faith in Providence rewarding the pitiable by giving them a future life of bliss; the theory seemed to me illogical, for even more pitiable in this life appeared to me the thick-skinned and successful, and these, as we know, in the saying about the camel and the needle's eye, our religion consigns wholesale to hell. Success, power, wealth—those aims of profiteers and premiers, pedagogues and Pandemoniacs, of all, in fact, who could not see God in a dew-drop, hear Him in distant goat-bells, and scent Him in a pepper tree—had always appeared to me akin to dry rot. And yet every day one saw more distinctly that they were the pea in the thimble-rig of life, the hub of a universe which, to the approbation of the majority they represented, they were fast making uninhabitable. It did not even seem of any use to help one's neighbours; all efforts at relief just gilded the pill and encouraged our stubbornly contentious leaders to plunge us all into fresh miseries. So I was searching right and left for something to believe in, willing to accept even Rupert K. Vaness and his basking philosophy. But could a man bask his life right out? Could just looking at fine pictures, tasting rare fruits and wines, the mere listening to good music, the scent of azaleas and the best tobacco, above all the society of pretty women, keep salt in my bread, and ideal in my brain? Could they? That's what I wanted to know.

Everyone who goes to Charleston in the Spring, soon or late, visits Magnolia Garden. A painter of flowers and trees, myself,

I specialise in gardens, and freely assert that none in the world is so beautiful as this. Even before the magnolias come out, it consigns the Boboli at Florence, the Cinnamon Gardens of Colombo, Concepcion at Malaga, Versailles, Hampton Court, the Generaliffe at Granada, and La Mortola to the category of "also ran." Nothing so free, gracious, so lovely and wistful, nothing so richly coloured, yet so ghostlike, exists, planted by the sons of men. It is a kind of Paradise which has wandered down, a miraculously enchanted wilderness. Brilliant with azaleas, or magnolia-pale, it centres round a pool of water, overhung by tall trunks festooned with the grey Florida moss. Beyond anything I have ever seen, it is other-worldly. And I went there day after day, drawn as one is drawn in youth by visions of the Ionian Sea, of the East, or the Pacific Isles. I used to sit paralysed by the absurdity of putting brush to canvas, in front of that dream-pool. I wanted to paint of it a picture like that of the fountain, by Helleu, which hangs in the Luxembourg. But I knew I never should.

I was sitting there one sunny afternoon with my back to a clump of azaleas, watching an old coloured gardener—so old that he had started life as an "owned" negro, they said, and certainly still retained the familiar suavity of the old-time darkie—I was watching him prune the shrubs when I heard the voice of Rupert K. Vaness say, quite close: "There's nothing for me but beauty, Miss Monroy."

The two were evidently just behind my azalea clump, perhaps four yards away, yet as invisible as if in China.

"Beauty is a wide, wide word. Define it, Mr. Vaness."

"An ounce of fact is worth a ton of theory—it stands before me."

"Come now, that's just a get-out. Is beauty of the flesh or of the spirit?"

"What is the spirit, as you call it? I'm a Pagan."

"Oh! so am I. But the Greeks were Pagans."

"Well, spirit is only the refined side of sensual appreciations."

"I wonder!"

"I have spent my life in finding that out."

"Then the feeling this garden rouses in me is purely sensuous?"

"Of course. If you were standing there blind and deaf, without the powers of scent and touch, where would your feeling be?"

" You are very discouraging, Mr. Vaness."

" No, Madam—I face facts. When I was a youngster I had plenty of fluffy aspiration towards I didn't know what—I even used to write poetry."

" Oh! Mr. Vaness, was it good? "

" It was not. I very soon learned that a genuine sensation was worth all the uplift in the world."

" What is going to happen when your senses strike work? "

" I shall sit in the sun and fade out."

" I certainly do like your frankness."

" You think me a cynic, of course; I am nothing so futile, Miss Sabine. A cynic is just a posing ass proud of his attitude. I see nothing to be proud of in my attitude, just as I see nothing to be proud of in the truths of existence."

" Suppose you had been poor? "

" My senses would be lasting better than they are; and when they at last failed, I should die quicker, from want of food and warmth—that's all."

" Have you ever been in love, Mr. Vaness? "

" I am in love now."

" And your love has no element of devotion, no finer side? "

" None. It wants."

" I have never been in love. But, if I were, I think I should want to lose myself, rather than to gain the other."

" Would you? Sabine, *I am in love with you.*"

" Oh! Shall we walk on? "

I heard their footsteps, and was alone again, with the old gardener lopping at his shrubs.

But what a perfect declaration of hedonism; how simple and how solid was this Vaness theory of existence! Almost Assyrian —worthy of Louis Quinze!

And just then the old negro came up.

" It's pleasant settin'," he said in his polite and hoarse half-whisper; " dar ain't no flies yet."

" It's perfect, Richard. This is the most beautiful spot in the world."

" Sure," he answered, softly drawling. " In de war time de Yanks nearly burn d'house heah. Sherman's Yanks. Sure dey did, po'ful angry wi' ole Massa dey was, 'cos he hid up d' silver plate afore he went away. My ole father was de facto-talum den. De Yanks too'm, Suh; dey took'm; and de Major he tell my fader to show'm whar de plate was. My ole fader he look at 'm an' say: 'What yuh take me foh? Yuh take me for a sneakin' nigger? No, Suh, yuh kin do wot yuh like wid dis chile, he ain't goin' to act no Judas. No, Suh!' And de Yankee Major he put'm up against dat tall live oak dar, an' he say: 'Yu darn ungrateful nigger. I'se come all dis way to set yuh free. Now, whar's dat silver plate, or I shoot yuh up, sure!' 'No, Suh,' says my fader, 'shoot away. I'se never goin' t' tell.' So dey begin to shoot, and shot all roun'm to skeer'm up. I was a lil' boy den, an' I see my ole fader wid my own eyes, Suh, standin' thar's bold's Peter. No, Suh, dey didn't never got no word from him; he loved de folk heah; sure he did."

The old man smiled; and in that beatific smile I saw not only his perennial pleasure in the well-known story, but the fact that he too would have stood there with the bullets raining round him, sooner than betray the folk he loved.

"Fine story, Richard. But—very silly obstinate old man, your father, wasn't he?"

He looked at me with a sort of startled anger, which slowly broadened into a grin; then broke into soft hoarse laughter.

"Oh! yes, Suh, sure! Berry silly obstinacious ole man. Yes, Suh, indeed!" And he went off cackling to himself.

He had only just gone when I heard footsteps again behind my azalea clump, and Miss Monroy's voice:

"Your philosophy is that of faun and nymph. But can you play the part?"

"Only let me try." Those words had such a fevered ring that in imagination I could see Vaness all flushed, his fine eyes shining, his well-kept hands trembling, his lips a little protruded.

There came a laugh, high, gay, sweet.

"Very well, then; catch me!" I heard a swich of skirt against the shrubs, the sound of flight; an astonished gasp from Vaness, and the heavy thud thud of his feet, following on the path through the azalea maze. I hoped fervently that they would not suddenly come running past and see me sitting there. My straining ears caught another laugh far off, a panting sound, a muttered oath, a far-away Cooee! And then, staggering, winded, pale with heat and with vexation, Vaness appeared, caught sight of me, and stood a moment—baff! Sweat was running down his face, his hand was clutching at his side, his stomach heaved —a hunter beaten and undignified. He muttered, turned abruptly on his heel, and left me staring at where his fastidious dandyism and all that it stood for had so abruptly come undone.

I know not how he and Miss Monroy got home to Charleston; not in the same car, I guess. As for me, I travelled deep in thought, conscious of having witnessed something rather tragic, not looking forward to my next encounter with Vaness.

He was not at dinner, but the girl was there; radiant as ever; and though I was glad she had not been caught, I was almost angry at the signal triumph of her youth. She wore a black dress with a red flower in her hair, and another at her breast, and had never looked so vital and so pretty. Instead of dallying with my cigar beside cool waters in the lounge of the hotel, I strolled out afterwards on the Battery and sat down beside the statue of a tutelary personage. A lovely evening: from some tree or shrub close by emerged an adorable faint fragrance, and in the white electric light the acacia foliage was patterned out against a thrilling blue sky. If there were no fireflies abroad, there should have been. A night for hedonists indeed!

And, suddenly, in fancy, there came before me Vaness's well-dressed person, panting, pale, perplexed; and beside him, by a freak of vision, stood the old darkie's father, bound to the live oak, with the bullets whistling past, and his face transfigured. There they stood alongside—the creed of pleasure, which depended for fulfilment on its waist measurement; and the creed of love devoted unto death!

' Aha ! ' I thought; ' which of the two laughs *last?* '

And just then I saw Vaness himself beneath a lamp; cigar in mouth, and cape flung back so that its silk lining shone. Pale and heavy, in the cruel white light, his face had a bitter look. And I was sorry—very sorry, at that moment, for Rupert K. Vaness.

1920.

A MILLER OF DEE

MACCREEDY was respectable, but an outcast in his village.

There was nothing against him; on the contrary, he held the post of ferry-man to the people of the Manor, and nightly explained in the bar-parlour that if he had not looked sharp after his rights he would have been a salaried servant: "At a fixed wage, ye'll understand, without a chance to turn an honest penny."

He turned the honest pennies by exacting sixpenny ferry tolls from every person who was not a member of the Manor family. His doctrine, preached nightly, was that the gentry were banded to destroy the rights of the poor; yet, in spite of this, which should have conferred on him popularity, he was subtly and mysteriously felt to be a spiritual alien. No one ever heard him object to this unwritten, unspoken verdict; no one knew, in fact, whether he was aware of it. On still evenings he could be seen sitting in his boat in the Manor pool, under the high-wooded cliff, as if brooding over secret wrongs. He was a singer, too, with a single song, "The Miller of Dee," which he gave on all occasions; the effort of producing it lent his mouth a ludicrous twist under his whitey-brown moustache. People on the Manor terrace above could hear him sing it at night in an extraordinarily flat voice, as he crossed the river back to his cottage below.

No one knew quite where he came from, though some mentioned Ireland; others held a Scotch theory; and one man, who had an imagination, believed him to be of Icelandic origin. This mystery rankled in the breast of the village—the village of white cottages, with its soft, perpetual crown of smoke, and its hard north-country tongue. MacCreedy was close about money, too —no one knew whether he had much money or little.

Early one spring he petitioned for a holiday, and disappeared for a month. He returned with a wife, a young anæmic girl, speaking in a Southern accent. A rather interesting creature, this wife of MacCreedy, very silent, and with a manner that was unconsciously, and, as it were, ironically submissive.

On May mornings her slender figure, which looked as if it might suddenly snap off at the waist, might be seen in the garden, hanging clothes out to dry, or stooping above the vegetables, while MacCreedy watched her in a possessive manner from the cottage doorway. Perhaps she symbolised victory to him, a victory over his loneliness; perhaps he only looked on her as more money in his stocking. She made no friends, for she was MacCreedy's wife, and a Southerner; moreover, Mac-Creedy did not want her to make friends. When he was out it was she who would pull the ferry-boat over, and, after landing the passengers, remain motionless, bowed over her sculls, staring after them, as though loth to lose the sound of their footsteps; then she would pull slowly back across the swirl of silver-brown water, and, tying up the boat, stand with her hand shading her eyes. MacCreedy still went to the "public" at nights, but he never spoke of his wife, and it was noticed that he stared hard with his pug's eyes at anyone who asked after her. It was as though he suspected the village of wanting to take her from him. The same instinct that made him bury his money in a stocking bid him bury his wife. Nobody gave him anything, none should touch his property!

Summer ripened, flushed full, and passed; the fall began. The river came down ruddy with leaves, and often in the autumn damp the village was lost in its soft mist of smoke. MacCreedy became less and less garrulous, he came to the "public" seldom, and in the middle of his drink would put his glass down, and leave, as though he had forgotten something. People said that Mrs. MacCreedy looked unhappy; she ceased to attend church on Sundays. MacCreedy himself had never attended.

One day it was announced in the village that Mrs. Mac-Creedy's mother was ill—that Mrs. MacCreedy had gone away to nurse her; and, in fact, her figure was no more seen about the cottage garden beneath the cliff. It became usual to ask MacCreedy about his mother-in-law, for the question seemed to annoy him. He would turn his head, give a vicious tug at the sculls, and answer, "Oh! aye, a wee bit better!"

Tired perhaps of answering this question, he gave up going to the "public" altogether, and every evening, when the shadows of the woods were closing thick on the water, he could be seen staring over the side of his boat moored in the deep backwater below his cottage; the sound of his favourite song was heard no more. People said: " He misses his wife! " and for the first time since he had been amongst them a feeling for him almost amounting to warmth grew up in the village.

Early one morning, however, the underkeeper, who had an old-time grudge against MacCreedy, after an hour of patient toil, fished Mrs. MacCreedy up from the bottom of the backwater. She was neatly sewn in a sack, weighted with stones, and her face was black. They charged MacCreedy, who wept and said nothing. He was removed to the county gaol.

At his trial he remained dumb, and was found guilty. It was proved among other things that Mrs. MacCreedy had no mother.

While he was waiting to be hanged, he asked for the chaplain, and made the following statement:

" Parson," said he, " I'm not caring what ye have to say—ye will get plenty chance to talk when I'm gone. It's not to you I'm speaking, nor to anybody in particular—I'm just lonely here; it's a luxury to me to see a face that's not that gravy-eyed old warder's. I don't believe ye're any better than me, but if I did, what then? It's meself I've got to make me peace with. Man, d'ye think I'd have kept me independence if I'd ha' be-lived the likes of ye? They never had a good word for me down there, gentry as bad as the rest—the pack of fools! And why didn't they have a good word for me? Just because I'm an independent man. They'll tell ye that I was close; stingy they'll call it—and why was I close? Because I knew they were all against me. Why should I give 'em anything? They were all waitin' to take it from me! They'll say I set no store by my wife; but that's a lie parson—why, she was all I had! As sure as I'm speaking to ye, if I hadn't done what I did I'd have lost her. I was for guessing it all the autumn. I'm not one of those bodies that won't look a thing in the face; ye can't hood-wink me with palaver. I put it to ye, if ye had a diamond wouldn't ye a sight sooner pitch it into the sea than have it stolen? Ye know ye would! Well, she's just dead; and so'll I be when they squeeze the life out of me. Parson, don't ye go and blabber about her doin' wrong. She never did wrong; hadn't the time to. I wouldn't have ye take away her reputation when I'm gone and can't defend her. But there was aye the certainty that she would 'a done it; 'twas coming, d'ye see?

Aye! but I was bound to lose her; and I'll tell ye how I made sure.

" 'Twas one day nigh the end of October; I emptied the ferry till, and I said to my wife: 'Jenny,' I said, 'ye'll do the ferry work to-day; I'm away to the town for a suit o' clothes. Ye will take care,' I said, 'that no one sneaks over without paying ye his proper saxpence.'

" 'Very well, MacCreedy,' she says. With that I put some bread and meat in a bit of paper, and had her ferry me across. Well, I went away up the road till I thought she would have got back; and then I turned round and came softly down again to the watter; but there she was, still sitting where I'd left her. I was put aback by that, parson; ye know what it is when your plans get upset. 'Jenny,' I said to her, as if I came for that very purpose, 'ye'll look sharp after them fares?'

" 'Yes,' she says, 'MacCreedy.' And with that she turns the boat round. Well, presently I came down again and hid in some bushes on the bank, and all day I stayed there watching. Have ye ever watched a rabbit trap? She put four people across the river, and every time I saw them pay her. But late in the afternoon that man—the devil himself, the same I was lookin' after—came down and called out 'Ferry!' My wife she brought the ferry over, and I watched her close when he stepped in. I saw them talking in the boat, and I saw him take her hands when he left it. There was nothing more to see, for he went away. I waited till evening, then out I crept and called 'Ferry!' My wife came down—she was aye ready—and fetched me across. The first thing I did was to go to the till and take out four saxpences. 'Oh,' I said, 'Jenny, ye've had four fares then?'

" 'Yes,' she said, 'just four.'

" 'Sure?' I said.

" 'Sure,' she said, 'MacCreedy.'

" Have ye ever seen the eyes of a rabbit when the fox is nigh her?

" I asked her who they were, and when she told me the names of the first four, and never another name, I knew I'd lost her. She got to bed presently, and after she was in bed I waited, sitting by the fire. The question I put to meself was this: 'Will I let them have her? Will I let them tak' her away?' The sweat ran off me. I thought maybe she'd forgotten to name him, but there was her eyes; and then, where was his saxpence? In this life, parson, there's some things ye cannot get over.

"'No, I said to meself, 'either ye've took up with him or else ye're goin' to tak' up with him, or ye'd ha' had his saxpence.' I felt myself heavier than lead. 'Ye'd ha' had his saxpence,' I said to meself; 'ther's no gettin' over that.' I would have ye know that my wife was an obedient woman, she aye did what she was told, an' if it hadn't been for a vera good reason she'd ha' had his saxpence; there's no manner of doubt about it. I'm not one of those weak-minded bodies who believe that marriages are sacred; I'm an independent man. What I say is, every man for himself, an' every woman too, and the less of cant the better. I don't want ye to have the chance to take away me reputation when I'm gone, with any such foolish talk. 'Twasn't the marriage; 'twas just the notion of their stealing her. I never owed any man of them a penny, or a good turn— him least of all; and was I to see them steal her and leave me bare? Just as they'd ha' stolen my saxpences; the very money out of me pocket, if I'd ha' let them. I asked ye, was I to do that? Was I to see meself going back to loneliness before me own eyes? 'No,' I said to meself; 'keep yourselves to your-selves, I'll keep meself to mine!' I went and took a look at her asleep, and I could fancy her with a smile as if she were glad to ha' done with me—going off with him to those others up at the village to make a mock of me. I thought, 'Ye've got to do something, MacCreedy, or ye'll just be helping them to steal her from yerself.' But what could I do? I'm a man that looks things through and through, and sees what's logical. There was only one logic to this; but, parson, I cried while I was putting the pillow to her face. She struggled very little, poor thing—she was aye an obedient woman. I sewed her body up in a sack, and all the time I thought: 'There goes MacCreedy!' But I cannot say that I regretted it exactly. Human nature's no so very simple. 'Twas the hanging about the spot after, that was the ruin of me; if ye've got things valuable hidden up, ye're bound to hang around them, ye feel so lonely."

On the morning of his execution MacCreedy ate a good breakfast, and made a wan attempt to sing himself his favourite song:

"I care for nobody—no, not I,
And nobody cares for me!"

1903.

LATE—299

I

i §

IT was disconcerting to the governor. The man's smile was so
peculiar. Of course these educated prisoners—doctors, solicitors,
parsons—one could never say good-bye to them quite without
awkwardness; couldn't dismiss them with the usual: "Shake
hands! Hope you'll keep straight, and have luck." No! With
the finish of his sentence a gentleman resumed a kind of
equality, ceased to be a number, ceased even being a name without prefix, to which the law and the newspapers with their un-
failing sense of what was proper at once reduced a prisoner on,
or even before, his conviction. No. 299 was once more Dr.
Philip Raider, in a suit of dark-grey tweeds, lean and limber,
with grey hair grown again in readiness for the outer world,
with deep-set shining eyes, and that peculiar smile—a difficult
subject. The governor decided suddenly to say only, "Well,
good-bye, Dr. Raider," and, holding out his hand, he found it
remain in contact with nothing.

So the fellow was going out in defiant mood—was he! The
governor felt it rather hard after more than two years, and his
mind retracted his recollections of this prisoner: An illegal
operation case! Not a good "mixer"—not that his prisoners
were allowed to mix; still, always reassuring to know that they
would if not strenuously prevented! Record—Exemplary.
Chaplain's report—Nothing doing, or words to that effect. Work
—Bookbinding. Quite! But chief memory that of a long loose
figure loping round at exercise, rather like a wolf. And there
he stood! The tall governor felt at the moment oddly short.
He raised his hand from its posture of not too splendid isola-
tion, and put the closure with a gesture. No. 299's lips moved:

"Is that all?"

Accustomed to being "sir'd" to the last, the governor reddened. But the accent was so refined that he decided not to mention it.

"Yes, that's all."

"Thank you. Good morning."

The eyes shone from under the brows, the smile curled the lips under the long, fine, slightly hooked nose; the man loped easily to the door. He carried his hands well. He made no noise going out. Damn! The fellow had looked so exactly as if he had been thinking: 'You poor devil!' The governor gazed round his office. Highly specialised life, no doubt! The windows had bars; it was here that he saw refractory prisoners in the morning, early. And, thrusting his hands into his pockets, he frowned. . . .

Outside, the head warder, straight, blue-clothed, grizzled, walked ahead, with a bunch of keys.

"All in order," he said to the blue-clothed janitor, "No. 299—going out. Anyone waiting for him?"

"No, sir."

"Right. Open!"

The door clanged under the key.

"Good day to you," said the head warder.

The released prisoner turned his smiling face and nodded; turned it to the janitor, nodded again, and walked out between them, putting on a grey felt hat. The door clanged under the key.

"Smiling!" remarked the janitor.

"Ah! Cool customer," said the head warder. "Clever man, though, I'm told."

His voice sounded resentful, a little surprised, as if he had missed the last word by saying it. . . .

Hands in pockets, the released prisoner walked at leisure in the centre of the pavement. An October day of misty sunshine, and the streets full of people seeking the midday meal. Chancing to glance at this passer-by, their eyes glanced away at once, as a finger flies from a too-hot iron. . . .

2 §

On the platform the prison chaplain, who had a day off and was going up to town, saw a face under a grey hat which seemed vaguely familiar.

"Yes," said a voice, " Late—299. Raider."

The chaplain felt surprise.

"Oh! Ah!" he stammered. " You went out to-day, I think. I hope you——"

" Thanks, very much."

The train came clattering in. The chaplain entered a third-class compartment; Late—299 followed. The chaplain experienced something of a shock. Extremely unlike a prisoner! And this prisoner, out of whom he had, so to speak, had no change whatever these two years past, had always made him feel uncomfortable. There he sat opposite, turning his paper, smoking a cigarette, as if on terms of perfect equality. Lowering his own journal, the chaplain looked out of the window, trying to select a course of conduct; then, conscious that he was being stared at, he took a flying look at his *vis-à-vis*. The man's face seemed saying: ' Feel a bit awkward, don't you? But don't worry. I've no ill-feeling. You have a devilish poor time.'

Unable to find the proper reply to this look, the chaplain remarked:

" Nice day. Country's looking beautiful."

Late—299 turned those shining eyes of his toward the landscape. The man had a hungry face in spite of his smile, and the chaplain asked:

" Will you have a sandwich? "

" Thanks. . . ."

" Forgive my inquiring," said the chaplain presently, blowing crumbs off his knees, "but what will you do now? I hope you're going to——" How could he put it? "Turn over a new leaf" ? " Make good " ? " Get going " ? He could not put it, and instead took the cigarette which Late—299 was offering him. The man was speaking too; his words seemed to come slowly through the smoke, as if not yet used to a tongue.

" These last two years have been priceless."

" Ah! " said the chaplain hopefully.

" I feel right on top."

The chaplain's spirit drooped.

" Do you mean," he said, "that you don't regret—that you aren't—er—— "

" Priceless! "

The man's face had a lamentable look—steely, strangely smiling. No humility in it at all. He would find society did

not tolerate such an attitude. No, indeed! He would soon discover his place.

"I'm afraid," he said kindly, "that you'll find society very
unforgiving. Have you a family?"

"Wife, son, and daughter."

"How will they receive you?"

"Don't know, I'm sure."

"And your friends? I only want to prepare you a little."

"Fortunately I have private means."

The chaplain stared. What a piece of luck—or was it a
misfortune?

"If I'd been breakable, your prison would have broken me.
Have another cigarette?"

"No, thank you."

The chaplain felt too sad. He had always said nothing could
be done with them so long as their will-power was unbroken.
Distressing to see a man who had received this great lesson still
so stiff-necked! And, lifting his journal, he tried to read. But
those eyes seemed boring through the print. It was most uncomfortable. Oh! most! . . .

II

1 §

In the withdrawing-room of a small house near Kew
Gardens, Mrs. Philip Raider was gazing at a piece of pinkish
paper in her hand, as if it had been one of those spiders of
which she had so constitutional a horror. Opposite her chair
her son had risen, and against the wall her daughter had
ceased suddenly to play Brahm's Variations on a theme by
Haydn.

"He says to-night!"

The girl dropped her hands from the keys. "To-night? I
thought it was next month. Just like father—without a word
of warning!"

The son mechanically took out his pipe, and began polishing
its bowl. He was fresh-faced, fair, with a small head.

"Why didn't he tell us to meet him in London? He must
know we've got to come to an arrangement."

The daughter, too, got up, leaning against the piano—a
slight figure, with bushy, dark, short hair.

" What are we to do, Mother ? "

" Jack must go round, and put Mabel and Roderick off for this evening."

" Yes, and what then, if he's going to stay here ? Does he know that I'm engaged, and Beryl too ? "

" I think I told him in my last letter."

" What are *you* going to do, Mother ? "

" It's come so suddenly—I don't know."

" It's indecent ! " said the boy violently.

His sister picked up the dropped telegram. " ' Earl's Court, five four.' He may be here any minute. Jack, do hurry up ! Doesn't he realise that nobody knows down here ? "

Mrs. Raider turned to the fire.

" Your father will only have realised his own feelings."

" Well, he's got to realise. I'll make him——! "

" Dr. Raider, ma'am."

Late—299 stood, smiling, in front of the door which the maid had closed behind him.

" Well, Bertha ? " he said. " Ah, Beryl ! Well, Jack ! " His daughter alone replied.

" *Well,* Father, you might have let us know beforehand ! "

Late—299 looked from one face to the other.

" Never tell children they're going to have a powder. How are you all ? "

" Perfectly well, thank you. How are you ? "

" Never better. Healthy life—prison ! "

As if walking in her sleep, Mrs. Raider came across the room. She put out her hand with a groping gesture. Late—299 did not take it.

" Rather nice here," he said. " Can I have a wash ? "

" Jack, show your father the lavatory."

" The bathroom, please."

The son crossed from the window, glanced at his father's smiling face, and led the way.

Mrs. Raider, thin, pale, dark, spoke first. " Poor Philip ! "

" It's impossible to pity father, Mother ; it always was. Except for his moustache being gone, I don't see much change, anyway. It's you I pity. He simply can't stay here. Why ! everybody thinks you're a widow."

" People generally know more than they seem to, Beryl."

" Nobody's ever given us a hint. Why couldn't he have consulted us ? "

" He didn't think of us when he did that horrible thing. And it was so gratuitous, unless——! Mother, sometimes I've thought he had to do it; that he was her—her lover as well as her doctor!"

Mrs. Raider shook her head.

" If it had been that, he'd have told me. Your father is always justified in his own eyes."

" What am I to do about Roddy?"

" We must just wait."

" Here's Jack! Well?"

" He's having a bath as hot as he can bear it. All he said was: 'This is the first thing you do when you go in, and the first thing you do when you come out—symmetrical, isn't it?' I've got to take him up a cup of coffee. It's really too thick! The servants can't help knowing that a Dr. Raider who gets into the bath the moment he comes to call must be our father."

" It's comic."

" Is it? He doesn't show a sign of shame. He'll call it from the housetops. I thought, of course, he'd go abroad."

" We all thought that."

" If he were down in the mouth, one could feel sorry for him. But he looks as pleased as Punch with himself. And it's such a beasty sort of crime—how am I to put it to Mabel? If I just say he's been in prison, she'll think it's something even worse. Mother, do insist on his going at once. We can tell the servants he's an uncle—who's been in contact with small-pox."

" *You* take him the coffee, Mother—oh! you can't, if he's to be an uncle! Jack, tell him nobody here knows, and mother can't stand it, and hurry up! It's half-past six now."

The son passed his fingers through his brushed-back hair; his face looked youthful, desperate.

" Shall I?"

Mrs. Raider nodded.

" Tell him, Jack, that I'll come out to him, wherever he likes to go; that I always expected him to arrange that, that this is—too difficult——" She covered her lips with her hand.

" All right, Mother! I'll jolly well make him understand. But don't laugh out about it to the servants yet. Suppose it's we who have to go? It's his house!"

" Is it, Mother?"

" Yes; I bought it with his money under the power of attorney he left."

" Oh! Isn't that dreadful? "

" It's *all* dreadful, but we must consider *him.*"

The girl shook back her fuzzy hair.

" It does seem rather a case of ' coldly received.' But father's always been shut up in himself. He can't expect us suddenly to slobber over him. If he's had a horrible time, so have we."

" Well, shall I go? "

" Yes, take him the coffee. Be quick, my dear boy, and be nice to him! "

The son said with youthful grimness, " Oh! I'll be nice! " and went.

" Mother, don't look like that! "

" How should I look? Smiling? "

" No, don't smile—it's like him. Cry it off your chest."

2 §

Late—299 was sitting in the bath, smiling through steam and the smoke of his cigarette, at his big toe. Raised just above the level of the water, it had a nail blackened by some weight that had dropped on it. He took the coffee-cup from his son's hand.

" For two years and nine months I've been looking forward to this—but it beats the band, Jack."

" Father—I ought to——"

" Good coffee, tobacco, hot water—greatest blessings earth affords. Half an hour in here, and—spotless, body and soul! "

" Father——! "

" Yes, is there anything you want to add? "

" We've been here two years."

" Not so long as I was there. Do you like it? "

" Yes."

" I didn't. Are you studying medicine? "

" No. Botany."

" Good. You won't have to do with human beings."

" I've got the promise of a job in the gardens here at the beginning of next year. I'm—I'm engaged."

" Excellent. I believe in marrying young."

" Beryl's engaged too."

" Your mother isn't by any chance? "

" Father ! "

" My dear fellow, one expects to have been dropped. Why suppose one's family superior to other people's? *Pas si bête!*"

Gazing at that smiling face where prison pallor was yielding to the heat, above the neck whose sinews seemed unnaturally sharp and visible, the boy felt a spasm of remorse.

" We've never had a proper chance to tell you how frightfully sorry we've been for you. Only, we don't understand even now why you did such a thing."

" Should I have done it if I'd thought it would have been spotted? A woman going to the devil; a small risk to oneself —and there we were! Never save anyone at risk to yourself, Jack. I'm sure you agree."

The boy's face went very red. How could he ever get out what he had come to say?

" I have no intention of putting my tail between my legs. D'you mind taking this cup? "

" Will you have another, Father? "

" No, thanks. What time do you dine? "

" Half-past seven."

" You might lend me a razor. I was shaved this morning with a sort of bill-hook."

" I'll get you one."

Away from that smiling stranger in the bath, the boy shook himself. He must and would speak out!

When he came back with the shaving gear, his father was lying flat, deeply immersed, with closed eyes. And, setting his back against the door, he blurted out: " Nobody knows down here. They think mother's a widow."

The eyes opened, the smile resumed control.

" Do you really think that? "

" I do; I know that Mabel—the girl I'm engaged to—has no suspicion. She's coming to dinner; so is Roddy Blades—Beryl's *fiancé.*"

" Mabel, and Roddy Blades—glad to know their names. Give me that big towel, there's a good fellow. I'm going to wash my head."

Handing him the towel, the boy turned. But at the door he stopped. " Father——! "

" Quite. These natural relationships are fixed, beyond redemption."

The boy turned and fled.

His mother and sister stood waiting at the foot of the stairs.
" Well? "
" It's no good. I simply can't tell him we want him to go."
" No, my dear. I understand."
" Oh! but Mother——! Jack, you must."
" I can't, I'm going to put them off." Seizing his hat, he ran.
He ran between small houses in the evening mist, trying to in-
vent. At the corner of the long row of little villas, he rang a
bell.
" Can I see Miss Mabel? "
" She's dressing, sir. Will you come in? "
" No. I'll wait here."
In the dark porch he tried hard to rehearse himself. Aw-
fully sorry! Somebody had come—unexpectedly—on business!
Yes! On what business?
" Hallo, Jack! "
A vision in the doorway—a fair head, a rosy, round, blue-
eyed face above a swansdown collar.
" Look here, darling—shut the door."
" Why? What is it? Anything up? "
" Yes, something pretty badly up. You can't come to-
night, Mabel."
" Don't squeeze so hard! Why not? "
" Oh! well—there—there's a reason! "
" I know. Your father's come out! "
" What? How——? "
" But of course. We all know about it. We must be awfully
nice to him."
" D'you mean to say that Roddy and everybody—— We
thought nobody knew."
" Bless you, yes! Some people feel one way, and some the
other. I feel the other."
" Do you know what he did? "
" Yes; I got hold of the paper. I read the whole trial."
" Why didn't you tell me? "
" Why didn't *you?* "
" It was too beastly. Well? "
" I think it was a shame."
" But you can't have that sort of thing allowed."
" Why not? "
" Where would the population be? "
" Well, we're overpopulated. Everybody says so."

"That's quite another thing. This is the law."

"Look here! If you want to argue, come in. It's jolly cold."

"I don't want to argue; I must go and tell Roddy. It's an awful relief about you, darling. Only—you don't know my father."

"Then I can't come?"

"Not to-night. Mother——"

"Yes, I expect she's frightfully glad."

"Oh! yes—yes! She—yes!"

"Well, good-night. And look here—you go back. *I'll* tell Roddy. No! Don't rumple me!"

Running back between small houses, the boy thought: "Good God! How queer! How upside down! She—she——! It's awfully modern!"

3 §

Late—299 sat in the firelight, a glass beside him, a cigarette between his smiling lips. The cinders clicked; the clock struck. Eleven! He pitched the stump of his cigarette into the ashes, stretched himself, and rose. He went upstairs and opened the first door. The room was dark. A faint voice said:

"Philip?"

"Yes."

The light sprang out under his thumb. His wife was sitting up in bed, her face pale, her lips moving:

"To-night—must you?"

Late—299 moved to the foot of the bed; his lips still smiled, his eyes gazed hungrily.

"Not at all. We learn to contain ourselves in prison. No vile contacts? Quite so. Good-night!"

The voice from the bed said faintly:

"Philip, I'm so sorry; it's the suddenness—I'm——"

"Don't mention it." The light failed under his thumb. The door fell to. . . .

Three people lay awake, one sleeping. The three who lay awake were thinking: 'If only he made one feel sorry for him! If only one could love him! His self-control is forbidding—it's not human! He ought to want our sympathy. He ought to sympathise with us. He doesn't seem to feel—for himself, for us, for anything. And to-morrow what will happen? Is

life possible here, now? Can we stand him in the house, about
the place? He's frightening!'

The sleeper, in his first bed of one thousand and one nights,
lay, with eyes pinched up between brows and bony cheeks of
a face as if carved from ivory, and lips still smiling at the
softness under him.

Past dawn the wakeful slept, the sleeper awoke. His eyes
sought the familiar little pyramid of gear on the shelf in the
corner, the bright tins below, the round port-hole, the line of
distemper running along the walls, the closed and solid small-
ness of a cell. And the blood left his heart. They weren't
there! His whole being struggled with such unreality. He
was in a room staring at light coming through chintz curtains.
His arms were not naked. This was a sheet! For a moment
he shivered, uncertain of everything; then lay back, smiling at
a papered ceiling.

III

1 §

" It can't go on, Mother. It simply can't. I feel an absolute
worm whenever I'm with him. I shall have to clear out, like
Beryl. He has just one object all the time—to make everyone feel small and mean."

" Remember what he's been through! "

" I don't see why *we* should be part of his revenge. We've
done nothing, except suffer through him."

" He doesn't want to hurt us or anyone."

" Well, whenever people talk to him, they dry up, at once,
as if he'd skinned them. It's a disease."

" One can only pity him."

" He's perfectly happy, Mother. He's getting his own back."

" If only that first night——"

" We tried. It's no good. He's absolutely self-sufficient.
What about to-morrow night? "

" We can't leave him on Christmas Day, Jack."

" Then we must take him to Beryl's. I can't stick it here.
Look! There he goes! "

Late—299 passed the window where they stood, loping easily,
a book under his arm.

" He must have seen us. We mightn't exist! . . ."

2 §

Late—299, with the book under his arm, entered Kew Gardens and sat down on a bench. A nursery governess with her charges came and settled down beside him.

"Peter, Joan, and Michael," said Late 299, "quite in the fashion."

The governess stirred uneasily; the gentleman looked funny, smiling there!

"And what are you teaching them?"

"Reading, writing, and arithmetic, sir, and Bible stories."

"Intelligent? . . . Ah! Not very. Truthful? . . . No! No children are."

The governess twisted her hands. "Peter!" she said, "where's your ball? We must go and look for it."

"But I've got it, Miss Somers."

"Oh! Well, it's too sharp, sitting here. Come along!"

She passed away, and Peter, Joan, and Michael trailed after.

Late—299 smiled on; and a Pekinese, towing a stout old lady, smelled at his trousers.

"It's my cat," said Late—299. "Dogs and cats their pleasure is——"

Picking up the Pekinese, the stout old lady pressed it under her arm as though it were a bagpipe, and hurried on like a flustered goose.

Some minutes passed. A workman and his wife sat down to gaze at the pagoda.

"Queer building!" said Late—299.

"Ah!" said the workman. "Japanese, they say!"

"Chinese, my friend. Good people, the Chinese—no regard for human life."

"What's that? Good—did you say?"

"Quite!"

"Eh?"

The workman's wife peered round him.

"Come on, John! The sun gits in me eyes 'ere."

The workman rose. "'Good,' you said, didn't you? *Good* people?"

"Yes."

The workman's wife drew at his arm. "There, don't get arguin' with strangers. Come on!" The workman was drawn away. . . .

A clock struck twelve. Late—299 got up and left the gardens. Walking between small houses, he rang at the side entrance of a little shop.

" If your father's still blind—I've come to read to him again."

" Please, sir, he'll always be."

" So I supposed."

On a horsehair sofa, below the dyed-red plumes of pampasgrass, a short and stocky man was sitting, whittling at a wooden figure. He sniffed, and turned his sightless eyes toward his visitor; his square face in every line and bump seemed saying: " You don't down me."

" What are you making? " said Late—299.

" Christmas Eve. I'm cuttin' out our Lord. I make 'em rather nice. Would you like this one? "

" Thank you."

" Kep' I's end up well, our Lord, didn't He? 'Love your neighbour as yourself'—that means you got to love yourself. And He did, I think; not against Him, neither."

" Easier to love your neighbours when you can't see them, eh? "

" What's that? D'you mind lendin' me your face a minute? It'll help me a lot with this 'ere. I make 'em lifelike, you know."

Late—299 leaned forward, and the tips of the blind man's fingers explored his features.

" 'Igh cheek-bones, eyes back in the 'ead, supraorbital ridges extra special, rather low forehead slopin' to thick hair. Comin' down, two 'ollers under the cheek-bones, thin nose a bit 'ooky, chin sharpish, no moustache. You've got a smile, 'aven't you? And your own teeth? I should say you'd make a very good model. I don't 'old with 'Im always 'avin' a beard. Would you like the figure 'anging', or carryin' the cross? "

" As you wish. D'you ever use your own face? "

" Not for 'Im—for statesmen, or 'eroes, I do. I done one of Captain Scott with my face. Rather pugnacious, my style; yours is sharp, bit acid, suitable to saints, martyrs, and that. I'll just go over you once more—then I'll 'ave it all 'ere. Sharp neck; bit 'unchy in one shoulder; ears stick up a bit; tallish thin man, ain't you, and throw your feet forward when you walk? Give us your 'and a minute. Bite your fingers, I see. Eyes blue, eh—with pin-points to 'em—yes? Hair a bit reddish before it went piebald—that right? Thank you, much obliged. Now, if you like to read, I'll get on with it."

Late—299 opened the book.

"' . . . But at last in the drift of time Hadleyburg had the ill luck to offend a passing stranger, possibly without knowing it, certainly without caring, for Hadleyburg was sufficient unto itself and cared not a rap for strangers and their opinions. Still, it would have been well to make an exception in this one's case, for he was a bitter man and revengeful.'"

"Ah!" interjected the blind man deeply, "there you 'ave it. Talkin' of feelin's, what gave you a fellow-feelin' for me, if I may ask?"

"I can look at you, my friend, without your seeing me."

"Eh! What about it with other people, then?"

"They can look at me without my seeing them."

"I see! Misanthropical. Any reason for that?"

"Prison."

"What oh! Outcast and rejected of men."

"No. The other way on."

The blind man ceased to whittle and scoop.

"I like independence," he said; "I like a man that can go his own way. Ever noticed cats? Men are like dogs mostly; only once in a way you get a man that's like a cat. What *were* you? if it's not a rude question. In the taxes?"

"Medico."

"What's a good thing for 'eartburn?"

"Which kind?"

"Wind, ain't it? But I see your meanin'. Losin' my sight used to burn my 'eart a lot; but I got over that. What's the use? You couldn't have any worse misfortune. It gives you a feelin' of bein' insured-like."

"You're right," said Late—299, rising to go.

The blind man lifted his face in unison. "Got your smile on?" he said. "Just let me 'ave another feel at it, will you?"

Late—299 bent to the outstretched fingers.

"Yes," said the blind man, "same with you—touched bottom. Next time you come I'll 'ave something on show that'll please you, I think; and thank you for readin'."

"Let me know if it bores you."

"I will," said the blind man, following without movement the footsteps of his visitor that died away.

3 §

Christmas night—wild and windy, a shower spattering down in the street; Late—299 walking two yards before his wife, their son walking two yards behind his mother. A light figure, furred to the ears, in a doorway watching for them.

"Come along, darling. Sorry we had to bring him."

"Of course you had to, Jack!"

"Look! He can't even walk with mother. It's a disease. He went to church to-day, and all through the sermon never took his eyes off—the poor old vicar nearly broke down."

"What was it about?"

"Brotherly love. Mother says he doesn't mean it—but it's like—what's that thing that stares?"

"A basilisk. I've been trying to put myself in his place, Jack. He must have swallowed blood and tears in there—or-dered about like a dog, by common men, for three years nearly. If you don't go under, you must become inhuman. This is better than if he'd come out crawling."

"Perhaps. Look out—the rain! I'll turn your hood up, darling." A spattering shower, the whispering hushed. . . .

A lighted open doorway, a red hall, a bunch of hanging mistletoe, a girl beneath, with bushy hair.

"Happy Christmas, Father!"

"Thanks. Do you want to be kissed?"

"As you like. Well, Mother darling! Hallo, you two! Come in! Roddy, take father's coat."

"How are you sir? Beastly weather!"

"That was the advantage we had in prison. Weather never troubled us. 'Peace and Goodwill' in holly-berries! —Very neat! They used to stick them up in there. Christianity is a really remarkable fraud, don't you think? . . ."

Once again those four in the street, and the bells chiming for midnight service.

"What an evening!"

"Let them get out of hearing, Jack."

"Worse than ever! My God, he'd turn the milk sour! And I thought liquor might make him possible. He drank quite a lot."

"Only a few days now, and then! . . ."

"Do you agree with mother that he doesn't mean it, Mabel?"

"Oh! yes, I do."

" The way he sits and smiles! Why doesn't he get himself
a desert?"

" Perhaps he is. . . ."

<h2 align="center">4 §</h2>

" 'Ere you are!" said the blind man. " Best I can do under
the circs. 'Ad a bit o' trouble with the cross; got it top-
'eavy, I'm afraid; but thought you'd rather carry it."

" Quite a masterpiece!"

" Speaking serious?" said the blind man. " You could improve it with a box o' colours; make it more 'uman like."

" I'll do that."

" I wouldn't touch the face, nor the cross—leave 'em wooden;
but the hair and the dress, and the blood from the crown o'
thorns, might be all the better for a bit o' brightenin'. How's
the man that corrupted 'Adleyburg?'"

Late—299 opened the book.

" '. . . Goodson looked him over, like as if he was hunting
for a place on him that he could despise the most; then he says:
" So you are the Committee of Inquiry, are you?" Sawlsberry
said that was about what he was. " H'm! Do they require
particulars, or do you reckon a kind of *general* answer will
do?" " If they require particulars I will come back, Mr. Goodson; I will take the general answer first." " Very well, then;
tell them to go to hell—I reckon that's general enough. And
I'll give you some advice, Sawlsberry; when you come back
for the particulars, fetch a basket to carry what's left of yourself home in." ' "

The blind man chuckled.

" Ah! I like that Mark Twain. Nice sense o' humour—
nothin' sickly."

" Bark and quinine, eh?"

" Bark and bite," said the blind man. " What do you think
of 'uman nature yourself?"

" Little or nothing."

" And yet there's a bit of all right about it, too. Look at
you and me; we got our troubles, and 'ere we are—jolly as
sandboys! Be self-sufficient, or you've got to suffer. That's
what you feel, ain't it? Am I mistook, or did you nod?"

" I did. Your eyes look as if they saw."

" Bright, are they? You and me could 'ave sat down and

cried 'em out any time—couldn't we? But we didn't. That's why I say there's a bit of all right about us. Put the world from you, and keep your pecker up. When you can't think worse of things than what you do, you'll be 'appy—not before. That's right, ain't it?"

"Quite."

"Took me five years. 'Ow long were you about it?"

"Nearly three."

"Well, you 'ad the advantage of birth and edjucation; I can tell that from your voice—got a thin, mockin' sound. I started in a barber shop, got mine in an accident with some 'air-curlers. What I miss most is not bein' able to go fishin'. No one to take me. Don't you miss cuttin' people up?"

"No."

"Well, I suppose a gent never gets a passion; I'd a perfect passion for fishin'. Never missed Sunday, wet or fine. That's why I learned this carvin'—must 'ave an 'obby to go on with. Are you goin' to write your 'istory? Am I wrong, or did you shake your 'ead?"

"I did. My hobby is watching the show go by."

"That might 'ave suited me at one time—always liked to see the river flowin' down. I'm a bit of a philosopher myself. You ain't, I should say."

"Why not?"

"Well, I've a fancy you want life to come to heel too much —misfortune of bein' a gent, perhaps. Am I right?"

Late—299 closed the book and rose. "Pride!" he said.

"Ah!" said the blind man, groping with his eyes, "that's meat and drink to you. Thought as much. Come again, if I don't worry you."

"And take you fishing?"

"Reelly? You will? Shake 'ands."

Late—299 put out his hand. The blind man's groped up and found it. . . .

5 §

"Wednesday again, is it, partner, if I'm not troublin' you?"

"Wednesday it is."

At the door of his house, with the "catch" in a straw bag, the blind man stood a minute listening to his partner's foot-steps, then felt his way to his horsehair sofa under the pampasgrass. Putting his cold feet up under the rug, he heaved a sigh of satisfaction, and fell asleep.

Between the bare acacias and lilac-bushes of the little villas, Late—299 passed on. Entering his house, he sought his study, and stretched his feet toward the fire, and the cat, smelling him fishy, sprang on to his knee.

"Philip, may I come in?"

"You may."

"The servants have given notice. I wanted to say, wouldn't you like to give this up and go abroad with me?"

"Why this sudden sacrifice?"

"Oh, Philip! You make it so hard for me. What do you really want me to do?"

"Take half my income and go away."

"What will you do, here, alone?"

"Get me a char. The cat and I love chars."

"Philip!"

"Yes?"

"Won't you tell me what's in your heart? Do you want always to be lonely like this?"

Late—299 looked up.

"Reality means nothing to those who haven't lived with it. I do."

"But why?"

"My dear Bertha—that is your name, I think?"

"Oh, God! You *are* terrible!"

"What would you have me—a whining worm? Crawling to people I despise—squirming from false position to false position? Do you want humility? What is it you want?"

"I want you to be human."

"Then you want what you have got. I *am* so human that I'll see the world damned before I take its pity, or eat its salt. Leave me alone. I am content."

"Is there nothing I can do?"

"Yes, stand out of my firelight. . . ."

6 §

Two figures, in the dark outside, before the uncurtained window.

"Look, Mabel!"

"Be careful! He may see. Whisper!"

" The window's shut."

" Oh! Why doesn't he draw the blinds—if he **must** sit like that !

> " ' A desert dark without a sound
>   And not a drop to eat or drink
>   And a dark desert all around!'

Jack, I pity him."

" He doesn't suffer. It's being fond of people makes you suffer. He's got all he wants. Look at him."

The firelight on the face—its points and hollows, its shining eyes, its stillness and intensity, its smile; and on the cat, hunched and settled in the curve of the warm body. And the two young people, shrinking back, pass on between small houses, clutching each other's hands.

1923.

THE SILENCE

I

IN a car of the Naples express a mining expert was diving into a bag for papers. The strong sunlight showed the fine wrinkles on his brown face and the shabbiness of his short, rough beard. A newspaper cutting slipped from his fingers; he picked it up, thinking: 'How the dickens did that get in here?' It was from a colonial print of three years back; and he sat staring, as if in that forlorn slip of yellow paper he had encountered some ghost from his past.

These were the words he read: "We hope that the set-back to civilisation, the check to commerce and development, in this promising centre of our colony may be but temporary; and that capital may again come to the rescue. Where one man was successful, others should surely not fail? We are convinced that it only needs——" . . . And the last words: "For what can be sadder than to see the forest spreading its lengthening shadows, like symbols of defeat, over the untenanted dwellings of men; and where was once the merry chatter of human voices, to pass by in the silence——" . . .

On an afternoon, thirteen years before, he had been in the city of London, at one of those emporia where mining experts perch, before fresh flights, like sea-gulls on some favourite rock. A clerk said to him: "Mr. Scorrier, they are asking for you downstairs—Mr. Hemmings of the New Colliery Company."

Scorrier took up the speaking tube. "Is that you, Mr. Scorrier? I hope you are very well, sir. I am—Hemmings—I am—coming up."

In two minutes he appeared, Christopher Hemmings, secretary of the New Colliery Company, known in the City—behind his back—as "Down-by-the-starn" Hemmings. He grasped Scorrier's hand—the gesture was deferential, yet distinguished. Too handsome, too capable, too important, his figure, the cut of his iron-grey beard, and his intrusively fine eyes conveyed a continual courteous invitation to inspect their infallibilities. He stood, like a City " Atlas," with his legs apart, his coat-tails gathered in his hands, a whole globe of financial matters deftly balanced on his nose. " Look at me ! " he seemed to say. " It's heavy, but how easily I carry it. Not the man to let it down, sir ! "

" I hope I see you well, Mr. Scorrier," he began. " I have come round about our mine. There is a question of a fresh field being opened up—between ourselves, not before it's wanted. I find it difficult to get my Board to take a comprehensive view. In short, the question is : Are you prepared to go out for us, and report on it ? The fees will be all right." His left eye closed. " Things have been very—er—dicky ; we are going to change our superintendent. I have got little Pippin—you know little Pippin ? "

Scorrier murmured, with a feeling of vague resentment : " Oh yes. He's not a mining man ! "

Hemmings replied : " We think that he will do." ' Do you ? ' thought Scorrier ; ' that's good of you ! '

He had not altogether shaken off a worship he had felt for Pippin—" King " Pippin he was always called, when they had been boys at the Camborne Grammar-school. " King " Pippin ! the boy with the bright colour, very bright hair, bright, subtle, elusive eyes, broad shoulders, little stoop in the neck, and a way of moving it quickly like a bird ; the boy who was always at the top of everything, and held his head as if looking for something further to be the top of. He remembered how one day " King " Pippin had said to him in his soft way, " Young Scorrie, I'll do your sums for you" ; and in answer to his dubious, " Is that all right ? " had replied, " Of course—I don't want you to get behind that beast Blake, he's not a Cornishman" (the beast Blake was an Irishman not yet twelve). He remembered, too, an occasion when " King " Pippin with two other boys fought six louts and got a licking, and how Pippin sat for half an hour afterwards, all bloody, his head in his hands, rocking to and fro, and weeping tears of mortification ; and how the next day he had sneaked off by himself, and, attacking the same gang, got frightfully mauled a second time.

Thinking of these things he answered curtly : " When shall I start ? "

" Down-by-the-starn " Hemmings replied with a sort of fearful sprightliness : " There's a good fellow ! I will send instructions; so glad to see you well." Conferring on Scorrier a look —fine to the verge of vulgarity—he withdrew. Scorrier remained seated; heavy with insignificance and vague oppression, as if he had drunk a tumbler of sweet port.

A week later, in company with Pippin, he was on board a liner.

The "King" Pippin of his school-days was now a man of forty-four. He awakened in Scorrier the uncertain wonder with which men look backward at their uncomplicated teens; and staggering up and down the decks in the long Atlantic roll, he would steal glances at his companion, as if he expected to find out from them something about himself. Pippin had still "King" Pippin's bright, fine hair, and dazzling streaks in his short beard; he had still a bright colour and suave voice, and what there were of wrinkles suggested only subtleties of humour and ironic sympathy. From the first, and apparently without negotiation, he had his seat at the captain's table, to which on the second day Scorrier too found himself translated, and had to sit, as he expressed it ruefully, "among the big-wigs."

During the voyage only one incident impressed itself on Scorrier's memory, and that for a disconcerting reason. In the forecastle were the usual complement of emigrants. One evening, leaning across the rail to watch them, he felt a touch on his arm; and, looking round, saw Pippin's face and beard quivering in the lamplight. "Poor people!" he said. The idea flashed on Scorrier that he was like some fine wire sound-recording instrument.

'Suppose he were to snap!' he thought. Impelled to justify this fancy, he blurted out: "You're a nervous chap. The way you look at those poor devils!"

Pippin hustled him along the deck. "Come, come, you took me off my guard," he murmured, with a sly, gentle smile, "that's not fair."

He found it a continual source of wonder that Pippin, at his age, should cut himself adrift from the associations and security of London life to begin a new career in a new country with dubious prospect of success. 'I always heard he was doing well all round,' he thought; 'thinks he'll better himself, perhaps. He's a true Cornishman.'

The morning of arrival at the mines was grey and cheerless; a cloud of smoke, beaten down by drizzle, clung above the forest; the wooden houses straggled dismally in the unkempt

semblance of a street, against a background of endless, silent
woods. An air of blank discouragement brooded over everything; cranes jutted idly over empty trucks; the long jetty oozed
black slime; miners with listless faces stood in the rain; dogs
fought under their very legs. On the way to the hotel they
met no one busy or serene except a Chinee who was polishing a
dish-cover.

The late superintendent, a cowed man, regaled them at lunch
with his forebodings; his attitude toward the situation was like
the food, which was greasy and uninspiring. Alone together
once more, the two new-comers eyed each other sadly.

"Oh dear!" sighed Pippin. "We must change all this,
Scorrier; it will never do to go back beaten. I shall not go
back beaten; you will have to carry me on my shield," and
slyly: "Too heavy, eh? Poor fellow!" Then for a long time
he was silent, moving his lips as if adding up the cost. Suddenly he sighed, and grasping Scorrier's arm said: "Dull, aren't
I? What will you do? Put me in your report, 'New Superintendent—sad, dull dog—not a word to throw at a cat!'" And
as if the new task were too much for him, he sank back in
thought. The last words he said to Scorrier that night were:
"Very silent here. It's hard to believe one's here for life. But
I feel I am. Mustn't be a coward, though!" and brushing
his forehead, as though to clear from it a cobweb of faint
thoughts, he hurried off.

Scorrier stayed on the verandah smoking. The rain had
ceased, a few stars were burning dimly; even above the squalor
of the township the scent of the forests, the interminable forests, brooded. There sprang into his mind the memory of a
picture from one of his children's fairy books—the picture of
a little bearded man on tiptoe, with poised head and a great
sword, slashing at the castle of a giant. It reminded him of
Pippin. And suddenly, even to Scorrier—whose existence was
one long encounter with strange places—the unseen presence
of those woods, their heavy, healthy scent, the little sounds, like
squeaks from tiny toys, issuing out of the gloomy silence,
seemed intolerable, to be shunned, from the mere instinct of
self-preservation. He thought of the evening he had spent in
the bosom of "Down-by-the-starn" Hemmings' family, receiving his last instructions—the security of that suburban villa,
its discouraging gentility; the superior acidity of the Miss Hemmings; the noble names of large contractors, of company pro-

moters, of a peer, dragged with the lightness of gun-carriages across the conversation; the autocracy of Hemmings, rasped up here and there, by some domestic contradiction. It was all so nice and safe—as if the whole thing had been fastened to an anchor sunk beneath the pink cabbages of the drawing-room carpet! Hemmings, seeing him off the premises, had said with secrecy: " Little Pippin will have a good thing. We shall make his salary £—. He'll be a great man—quite a king. Ha-ha!"

Scorrier shook the ashes from his pipe. ' Salary!' he thought, straining his ears; ' I wouldn't take the place for five thousand pounds a year. And yet it's a fine country,' and with ironic violence he repeated, ' a dashed fine country!'

Ten days later, having finished his report on the new mine, he stood on the jetty waiting to go aboard the steamer for home.

" God bless you!" said Pippin. " Tell them they needn't be afraid; and sometimes when you're at home think of me, eh?"

Scorrier, scrambling on board, had a confused memory of tears in his eyes, and a convulsive handshake.

II

It was eight years before the wheels of life carried Scorrier back to that disenchanted spot, and this time not on the business of the New Colliery Company. He went for another company with a mine some thirty miles away. Before starting, however, he visited Hemmings. The secretary was surrounded by pigeon-holes and finer than ever; Scorrier blinked in the full radiance of his courtesy. A little man with eyebrows full of questions, and a grizzled beard, was seated in an arm-chair by the fire.

" You know Mr. Booker," said Hemmings—" one of my directors. This is Mr. Scorrier, sir—who went out for us."

These sentences were murmured in a way suggestive of their uncommon value. The director uncrossed his legs, and bowed. Scorrier also bowed, and Hemmings, leaning back, slowly developed the full resources of his waistcoat.

" So you are going out again, Scorrier, for the other side. I tell Mr. Scorrier, sir, that he is going out for the enemy. Don't find them a mine as good as you found us, there's a good man."

The little director asked explosively: " See our last dividend? Twenty per cent.; eh, what? "

Hemmings moved a finger, as if reproving his director. " I will not disguise from you," he murmured, " that there is friction between us and—the enemy; you know our position too well—just a little too well, eh? ' A nod's as good as a wink.' "

His diplomatic eyes flattered Scorrier, who passed a hand over his brow—and said: " Of course."

" Pippin doesn't hit it off with them. Between ourselves, he's a leetle too big for his boots. You know what it is when a man in his position gets a sudden rise! "

Scorrier caught himself searching on the floor for a sight of Hemmings' boots; he raised his eyes guiltily. The secretary continued: " We don't hear from him quite as often as we should like, in fact."

To his own surprise Scorrier murmured: " It's a silent place! "

The secretary smiled. " Very good! Mr. Scorrier says, sir, it's a silent place; ha—ha! I call that very good! " But suddenly a secret irritation seemed to bubble in him; he burst forth almost violently: " He's no business to let it affect him; now, has he? I put it to you, Mr. Scorrier, I put it to you, sir! "

But Scorrier made no reply, and soon after took his leave: he had been asked to convey a friendly hint to Pippin that more frequent letters would be welcomed. Standing in the shadow of the Royal Exchange, waiting to thread his way across, he thought: ' So you must have noise, must you—you've got some here, and to spare.' . . .

On his arrival in the new world he wired to Pippin asking if he might stay with him on the way up country, and received the answer: " Be sure and come."

A week later he arrived (there was now a railway) and found Pippin waiting for him in a phaeton. Scorrier would not have known the place again; there was a glitter over everything, as if some one had touched it with a wand. The tracks had given place to roads, running firm, straight, and black between the trees under brilliant sunshine; the wooden houses were all painted; out in the gleaming harbour amongst the green of islands lay three steamers, each with a fleet of busy boats; and here and there a tiny yacht floated, like a sea-bird on the water. Pippin drove his long-tailed horses furiously; his eyes brimmed with subtle kindness, as if according Scorrier a continual welcome. During the two days of his stay Scorrier never lost that sense of glamour. He had every opportunity for observing the grip Pippin had over everything. The wooden doors and walls of his bungalow kept out no sounds. He listened to interviews between his host and all kinds and conditions of men. The voices of the visitors would rise at first—angry, discontented, matter-of-fact, with nasal twang, or guttural drawl; then would come the soft patter of the superintendent's feet crossing and recrossing the room. Then a pause, the sound of hard breathing, and quick questions—the visitor's voice again, again the patter, and Pippin's ingratiating but decisive murmurs. Presently out would come the visitor with an expression on his face which Scorrier soon began to know by heart, a kind of pleased, puzzled, helpless look, which seemed to say, "I've been done, I know—I'll give it to myself when I'm round the corner."

Pippin was full of wistful questions about "home." He wanted to talk of music, pictures, plays, of how London looked, what new streets there were, and, above all, whether Scorrier had been lately in the West Country. He talked of getting leave next winter, asked whether Scorrier thought they would "put up with him at home"; then, with the agitation which had alarmed Scorrier before, he added: "Ah! but I'm not fit for home now. One gets spoiled; it's big and silent here. What should I go back to? I don't seem to realise."

Scorrier thought of Hemmings. "'Tis a bit cramped there, certainly," he muttered.

Pippin went on as if divining his thoughts. "I suppose our friend Hemmings would call me foolish; he's above the little weaknesses of imagination, eh? Yes; it's silent here. Sometimes in the evening I would give my head for somebody to talk to—Hemmings would never give his head for anything, I think. But all the same, I couldn't face them at home. Spoiled!" And slyly he murmured: "What would the Board say if they could hear that?"

Scorrier blurted out: "To tell you the truth, they complain a little of *not* hearing from you."

Pippin put out a hand, as if to push something away. "Let them try the life here!" he broke out; "it's like sitting on a live volcano—what with our friends, 'the enemy,' over there; the men; the American competition. I keep it going, Scorrier, but at what a cost—at what a cost!"

"But surely—letters?"

Pippin only answered: "I try—I try!"

Scorrier felt with remorse and wonder that he had spoken the truth. The following day he left for his inspection, and while in the camp of "the enemy" much was the talk he heard of Pippin.

"Why!" said his host, the superintendent, a little man with a face somewhat like an owl's, "d'you know the name they've given him down in the capital—'the King'—good, eh? He's made them 'sit up' all along this coast. I like him well enough —good-hearted man, shocking nervous; but my people down there can't stand him at any price. Sir, he runs this colony. You'd think butter wouldn't melt in that mouth of his; but he always gets his way; that's what riles 'em so; that and the success he's making of his mine. It puzzles me; you'd think he'd only be too glad of a quiet life, a man with his nerves. But no, he's never happy unless he's fighting, something where he's got a chance to score a victory. I won't say he likes it, but, by Jove, it seems he's got to do it. Now that's funny! I'll tell you one thing, though—shouldn't be a bit surprised if he broke down some day; and I'll tell you another," he added darkly, "he's sailing very near the wind, with those large contracts that he makes. I wouldn't care to take his risks. Just let them have a strike, or something that shuts them down for a spell—and mark my words, sir—it'll be all u-p with them. But," he concluded confidentially, "I wish I had his hold on the men; it's a great thing in this country. Not like home, where you can go round a corner and get another gang. You have to make the best you can out of the lot you have; you won't get another man for love or money without you ship him a few hundred miles." And with a frown he waved his arm over the forests to indicate the barrenness of the land.

III

Scorrier finished his inspection and went on a shooting trip into the forest. His host met him on his return. "Just look at this!" he said, holding out a telegram. "Awful, isn't it?" His face expressed a profound commiseration, almost ludicrously mixed with the ashamed contentment that men experience at the misfortunes of an enemy.

The telegram, dated the day before, ran thus: "Frightful explosion New Colliery this morning, great loss of life feared."

Scorrier had the bewildered thought: ' Pippin will want me now.'

He took leave of his host, who called after him: " You'd better wait for a steamer! It's a beastly drive! "

Scorrier shook his head. All night, jolting along a rough track cut through the forest, he thought of Pippin. The other miseries of this calamity at present left him cold; he barely thought of the smothered men; but Pippin's struggle, his lonely struggle with this hydra-headed monster, touched him very nearly. He fell asleep and dreamed of watching Pippin slowly strangled by a snake; the agonised, kindly, ironic face peeping out between two gleaming coils was so horribly real, that he awoke. It was the moment before dawn: pitch-black branches barred the sky; with every jolt of the wheels the gleams from the lamps danced, fantastic and intrusive, round ferns and tree-stems, into the cold heart of the forest. For an hour or more Scorrier tried to feign sleep, and hide from the stillness and overmastering gloom of these great woods. Then softly a whisper of noises stole forth, a stir of light, and the whole slow radiance of the morning glory. But it brought no warmth; and Scorrier wrapped himself closer in his cloak, feeling as though old age had touched him.

Close on noon he reached the township. Glamour seemed still to hover over it. He drove on to the mine. The winding-engine was turning, the pulley at the top of the head-gear whizzing round; nothing looked unusual. ' Some mistake! ' he thought. He drove to the mine buildings, alighted, and climbed to the shaft head. Instead of the usual rumbling of the trolleys, the rattle of coal discharged over the screens, there was silence. Close by, Pippin himself was standing, smirched with dirt. The cage, coming swift and silent from below, shot open its doors with a sharp rattle. Scorrier bent forward to look. There lay a dead man, with a smile on his face.

" How many? " he whispered.

Pippin answered: " Eighty-four brought up—forty-seven still below," and entered the man's name in a pocket-book.

An older man was taken out next: he too was smiling—there had been vouchsafed to him, it seemed, a taste of more than earthly joy. The sight of those strange smiles affected Scorrier more than all the anguish or despair he had seen scored on the faces of other dead men. He asked an old miner how long Pippin had been at work.

"Thirty hours. Yesterday he wer' below; we had to nigh carry mun up at last. He's for goin' down again, but the chaps won't lower mun;" the old man gave a sigh. "I'm waiting for my boy to come up, I am."

Scorrier waited too—there was fascination about those dead, smiling faces. The rescuing of these men who would never again breathe went on and on. Scorrier grew sleepy in the sun. The old miner woke him, saying: "Rummy stuff this here choke-damp; see, they all dies drunk!" The very next to be brought up was the chief engineer. Scorrier had known him quite well, one of those Scotsmen who are born at the age of forty and remain so all their lives. His face—the only one that wore no smile—seemed grieving that duty had deprived it of that last luxury. With wide eyes and drawn lips he had died protesting.

Late in the afternoon the old miner touched Scorrier's arm, and said: "There he is—there's my boy!" And he departed slowly, wheeling the body on a trolley.

As the sun set, the gang below came up. No further search was possible till the fumes had cleared. Scorrier heard one man say: "There's some we'll never get; they've had sure burial."

Another answered him: "'Tis a gude enough bag for me!" They passed him, the whites of their eyes gleaming out of faces black as ink.

Pippin drove him home at a furious pace, not uttering a single word. As they turned into the main street, a young woman starting out before the horses obliged Pippin to pull up. The glance he bent on Scorrier was ludicrously prescient of suffering. The woman asked for her husband. Several times they were stopped thus by women asking for their husbands or sons. "This is what I have to go through," Pippin whispered.

When they had eaten, he said to Scorrier: "It was kind of you to come and stand by me! They take me for a good, poor creature that I am. But shall I ever get the men down again? Their nerve's shaken. I wish I were one of those poor lads, to die with a smile like that!"

Scorrier felt the futility of his presence. On Pippin alone must be the heat and burden. Would he stand under it, or would the whole thing come crashing to the ground? He urged him again and again to rest, but Pippin only gave him one of

his queer smiles. "You don't know how strong I am!" he
said.

IV

He himself slept heavily; and, waking at dawn, went down.
Pippin was still at his desk; his pen had dropped; he was
asleep. The ink was wet; Scorrier's eye caught the opening
words:

"GENTLEMEN,—Since this happened I have not slept."...

He stole away again with a sense of indignation that no one
could be dragged in to share that fight. The London Board-
room rose before his mind. He imagined the portentous gravity
of Hemmings; his face and voice and manner conveying the
impression that he alone could save the situation; the six directors, all men of commonsense and certainly humane, seated behind large turret-shaped inkpots; the concern and irritation
in their voices, asking how it could have happened; their comments: "An awful thing!" "I suppose Pippin is doing the
best he can!" "Wire him on no account to leave the mine
idle!" "Poor devils!" "A fund? Of course, what ought we
to give?" He had a strong conviction that nothing of all this
would disturb the commonsense with which they would go home
and eat their mutton. A good thing too; the less it was taken
to heart the better! But Scorrier felt angry. The fight was so
unfair! A fellow all nerves—with not a soul to help him!
Well, it was his own lookout! He had chosen to centre it all
in himself, to make himself its very soul. If he gave way now,
the ship must go down! By a thin thread, Scorrier's hero-worship still held. 'Man against nature,' he thought, 'I back the
man.' The struggle in which he was so powerless to give aid,
became intensely personal to him, as if he had engaged his own
good faith therein.

The next day they went down again to the pithead; and
Scorrier himself descended. The fumes had almost cleared, but
there were some places which would never be reached. At the
end of the day all but four bodies had been recovered. "In
the day o' judgment," a miner said, "they four'll come out of
here." Those unclaimed bodies haunted Scorrier. He came on
sentences of writing, where men waiting to be suffocated had

written down their feelings. In one place, the hour, the word
"Sleepy," and a signature. In another, "A. F.—done for."
When he came up at last Pippin was still waiting, pocket-book
in hand; they again departed at a furious pace.

Two days later Scorrier, visiting the shaft, found its neighbourhood deserted—not a living thing of any sort was there
except one Chinaman poking his stick into the rubbish. Pippin
was away down the coast engaging an engineer; and on his return, Scorrier had not the heart to tell him of the desertion.
He was spared the effort, for Pippin said: " Don't be afraid—
you've got bad news? The men have gone on strike."

Scorrier sighed. " Lock, stock, and barrel."

" I thought so—see what I have here! " He put before Scorrier a telegram:

" At all costs keep working—fatal to stop—manage this somehow.—HEMMINGS."

Breathing quickly, he added: " As if I didn't know! ' Manage
this somehow '—a little hard! "

" What's to be done? " asked Scorrier.

" You see I am commanded! " Pippin answered bitterly.
" And they're quite right; we *must* keep working—our contracts! Now I'm down—not a soul will spare me! "

The miners' meeting was held the following day on the outskirts of the town. Pippin had cleared the place to make a
public recreation ground—a sort of feather in the company's
cap; it was now to be the spot whereon should be decided the
question of the company's life or death.

The sky to the west was crossed by a single line of cloud like
a bar of beaten gold; tree shadows crept towards the groups
of men; the evening savour, that strong fragrance of the forest, sweetened the air. The miners stood all round amongst the
burnt tree-stumps, cowed and sullen. They looked incapable
of movement or expression. It was this dumb paralysis that
frightened Scorrier. He watched Pippin speaking from his
phaeton, the butt of all those sullen, restless eyes. Would he
last out? Would the wires hold? It was like the finish of a
race. He caught a baffled look on Pippin's face, as if he despaired of piercing that terrible paralysis. The men's eyes had
begun to wander. ' He's lost his hold,' thought Scorrier; ' it's
all up! '

A miner close beside him muttered: " Look out! "

Pippin was leaning forward, his voice had risen, the words fell like a whiplash on the faces of the crowd: "You shan't throw me over; do you think I'll give up all I've done for you? I'll make you the first power in the colony! Are you turning tail at the first shot? You're a set of cowards, my lads!"

Each man round Scorrier was listening with a different motion of the hands—one rubbed them, one clenched them, another moved his closed fist, as if stabbing some one in the back. A grisly-bearded, beetle-browed, twinkling-eyed old Cornishman muttered: "Ah'm not troublin' about that." It seemed almost as if Pippin's object was to get the men to kill him; they had gathered closer, crouching for a rush. Suddenly Pippin's voice dropped to a whisper: "I'm disgraced! Men, are you going back on me?"

The old miner next Scorrier called out suddenly: "Anny that's Cornishmen here to stand by the superintendent?" A group drew together, and with murmurs and gesticulation the meeting broke up.

In the evening a deputation came to visit Pippin; and all night long their voices and the superintendent's footsteps could be heard. In the morning, Pippin went early to the mine. Before supper the deputation came again; and again Scorrier had to listen hour after hour to the sound of voices and footsteps till he fell asleep. Just before dawn he was awakened by a light. Pippin stood at his bedside. "The men go down to-morrow," he said: "What did I tell you? Carry me home on my shield, eh?"

In a week the mine was in full work.

V

Two years later, Scorrier heard once more of Pippin. A note from Hemmings reached him asking if he could make it convenient to attend their Board meeting the following Thursday. He arrived rather before the appointed time. The secretary received him, and, in answer to inquiry, said: "Thank you, we are doing well—between ourselves, we are doing very well."

"And Pippin?"

The secretary frowned. "Ah, Pippin! We asked you to come on his account. Pippin is giving us a lot of trouble. We have not had a single line from him for just two years!" He spoke with such a sense of personal grievance that Scorrier felt quite sorry for him. "Not a single line," said Hemmings, "since that explosion—you were there at the time, I remember! It makes it very awkward; I call it personal to *me*."

"But how——" Scorrier began.

"We get—telegrams. He writes to no one, not even to his family. And why? Just tell me why? We hear *of* him; he's a great nob out there. Nothing's done in the colony without his finger being in the pie. He turned out the last Government because they wouldn't grant us an extension for our railway—shows he can't be a fool. Besides, look at our balance-sheet!"

It turned out that the question on which Scorrier's opinion was desired was, whether Hemmings should be sent out to see what was the matter with the superintendent. During the discussion which ensued, he was an unwilling listener to strictures on Pippin's silence. "The explosion," he muttered at last, "a very trying time!"

Mr. Booker pounced on him. "A very trying time! So it was—to all of us. But what excuse is that?"

Scorrier was obliged to admit that it was none.

"Business is business—eh, what?"

Scorrier, gazing round that neat Board-room, nodded. A deaf director, who had not spoken for some months, said with sudden fierceness: "It's disgraceful!" He was obviously letting off the fume of long-unuttered disapprovals. One perfectly neat, benevolent old fellow, however, who had kept his hat on, and had a single vice—that of coming to the Board-room with a brown paper parcel tied up with string—murmured: "We must make allowances," and started an anecdote about his youth. He was gently called to order by his secretary. Scorrier was asked for his opinion. He looked at Hemmings. "My importance is concerned," was written all over the secretary's face. Moved by an impulse of loyalty to Pippin, Scorrier answered, as if it were all settled: "Well, let me know when you are starting, Hemmings—I should like the trip myself."

As he was going out, the chairman, old Jolyon Forsyte, with a grave, twinkling look at Hemmings, took him aside. "Glad to hear you say that about going too, Mr. Scorrier; we must be careful—Pippin's such a good fellow, and so sensitive; and our friend there—a bit heavy in the hand, um?"

Scorrier did in fact go out with Hemmings. The secretary was sea-sick, and his prostration, dignified but noisy, remained a memory for ever; it was sonorous and fine—the prostration of superiority; and the way in which he spoke of it, taking casual acquaintances into the caves of his experience, was truly interesting.

Pippin came down to the capital to escort them, provided for their comforts as if they had been royalty, and had a special train to take them to the mines.

He was a little stouter, brighter of colour, greyer of beard, more nervous perhaps in voice and breathing. His manner to Hemmings was full of flattering courtesy; but his sly, ironical glances played on the secretary's armour like a fountain on a hippopotamus. To Scorrier, however, he could not show enough affection.

The first evening, when Hemmings had gone to his room, he jumped up like a boy out of school. "So I'm going to get a wigging," he said: "I suppose I deserve it; but if you knew— if you *only* knew! . . . Out here they've nicknamed me 'the King'—they say I rule the colony. It's myself that I can't rule"; and with a sudden burst of passion such as Scorrier had never seen in him: "Why did they send this man here? What can he know about the things that I've been through?" In a moment he calmed down again: "There! this is very stupid; worrying you like this!" and with a long, kind look into Scorrier's face, he hustled him off to bed.

Pippin did not break out again, though fire seemed to smoulder behind the bars of his courteous irony. Intuition of danger had evidently smitten Hemmings, for he made no allusion to the object of his visit. There were moments when Scorrier's common-sense sided with Hemmings—these were moments when the secretary was not present.

'After all,' he told himself, 'it's a little thing to ask—one letter a month. I never heard of such a case.' It was wonderful indeed how they stood it! It showed how much they valued Pippin! What was the matter with him? What was the nature of his trouble? One glimpse Scorrier had when even Hemmings, as he phrased it, received "quite a turn." It was during a drive back from the most outlying of the company's trial mines, eight miles through the forest. The track led through a belt of trees blackened by a forest fire. Pippin was driving. The secretary seated beside him wore an expression of faint alarm, such as Pippin's driving was warranted to evoke from almost any face. The sky had darkened strangely, but pale streaks of light, coming from one knew not where, filtered through the trees. No breath was stirring; the wheels and horses' hoofs made no sound on the deep fern mould. All around, the burnt tree-trunks, leafless and jagged, rose like withered giants, the passages between them were black, the sky black, and black the silence. No one spoke, and literally the only sound was Pippin's breathing. What was it that was so terrifying? Scorrier had a feeling of entombment; that nobody could help him; the feeling of being face to face with Nature; a sensation as if all the comfort and security of words and rules had dropped away from him. And—nothing happened. They reached home and dined.

During dinner he had again that old remembrance of a little man chopping at a castle with his sword. It came at a moment when Pippin had raised his hand with the carving-knife grasped in it to answer some remark of Hemmings' about the future of the company. The optimism in his uplifted chin, the strenuous energy in his whispering voice, gave Scorrier a more vivid glimpse of Pippin's nature than he had perhaps ever had before. This new country, where nothing but himself could help a man—that was the castle! No wonder Pippin was impatient of control, no wonder he was out of hand, no wonder he was silent—chopping away at that! And suddenly he thought: 'Yes, and all the time one knows, Nature must beat him in the end!'

That very evening Hemmings delivered himself of his reproof. He had sat unusually silent; Scorrier, indeed, had thought him a little drunk, so portentous was his gravity; suddenly, however, he rose. It was hard on a man, he said, in his position, with a Board (he spoke as of a family of small children), to be kept so short of information. He was actually compelled to use his imagination to answer the shareholders' questions. This was painful and humiliating; he had never heard of any secretary having to use his imagination! He went further—it was insulting! He had grown grey in the service of the company. Mr. Scorrier would bear him out when he said he had a position to maintain—his name in the City was a high one; and, by George! he was going to keep it a high one; he would allow nobody to drag it in the dust—that ought clearly to be understood. His directors felt they were being treated like children; however that might be, it was absurd to suppose that he (Hemmings) could be treated like a child!

○ ○ ○ The secretary paused; his eyes seemed to bully the room. "If there were no London office," murmured Pippin, "the shareholders would get the same dividends."

Hemmings gasped. "Come!" he said, "this is monstrous!"

"What help did I get from London when I first came here? What help have I ever had?"

Hemmings swayed, recovered, and with a forced smile replied that, if this were true, he had been standing on his head for years; he did not believe the attitude possible for such a length of time; personally he would have thought that he too had a little something to say to the company's position, but no matter! . . . His irony was crushing. . . . It was possible that Mr. Pippin hoped to reverse the existing laws of the universe with regard to limited companies; he would merely say that he must not begin with a company of which he (Hemmings) happened to be secretary. Mr. Scorrier had hinted at excuses; for his part, with the best intentions in the world, he had great difficulty in seeing them. He would go further—he did *not* see them! The explosion! . . . Pippin shrank so visibly that Hemmings seemed troubled by a suspicion that he had gone too far.

"We know," he said, "that it was trying for you——"

"Trying!" burst out Pippin.

"No one can say," Hemmings resumed soothingly, "that we have not dealt liberally." Pippin made a motion of the head. "We think we have a good superintendent; I go further, an excellent superintendent. What I say is: Let's be pleasant! I am not making an unreasonable request!" He ended on a fitting note of jocularity; and, as if by consent, all three withdrew, each to his own room, without another word.

In the course of the next day Pippin said to Scorrier: "It seems I have been very wicked. I must try to do better;" and with a touch of bitter humour, "They are kind enough to think me a good superintendent, you see! After that I must try hard."

Scorrier broke in: "No man could have done so much for them;" and, carried away by an impulse to put things absolutely straight, went on: "But, after all, a letter now and then —what does it amount to?"

Pippin besieged him with a subtle glance. "You too?" he said—"I must indeed have been a wicked man!" and turned away.

Scorrier felt as if he had been guilty of brutality; sorry for Pippin, angry with himself; angry with Pippin, sorry for himself. He earnestly desired to see the back of Hemmings. The secretary gratified the wish a few days later, departing by steamer with ponderous expressions of regard and the assurance of his goodwill.

Pippin gave vent to no outburst of relief, maintaining a courteous silence, making only one allusion to his late guest, in answer to a remark of Scorrier:

"Ah! don't tempt me! mustn't speak behind his back."

VI

A month passed, and Scorrier still remained Pippin's guest. As each mail-day approached he experienced a queer suppressed excitement. On one of these occasions Pippin had withdrawn to his room; and when Scorrier went to fetch him to dinner he found him with his head leaning on his hands, amid a perfect litter of torn paper. He looked up at Scorrier.

"I can't do it," he said, "I feel such a hypocrite; I can't put myself into leading-strings again. Why should I ask these people, when I've settled everything already? If it were a vital matter they wouldn't want to hear—they'd simply wire, 'Manage this somehow!'"

Scorrier said nothing, but thought privately: 'This is mad business!' What was a letter? Why make a fuss about a letter? The approach of mail-day seemed like a nightmare to the superintendent; he became feverishly nervous like a man under a spell; and, when the mail had gone, behaved like a respited criminal. And this had been going on two years! Ever since that explosion. Why, it was monomania!

One day, a month after Hemmings' departure, Pippin rose early from dinner; his face was flushed, he had been drinking wine. "I won't be beaten this time," he said, as he passed Scorrier. The latter could hear him writing in the next room, and looked in presently to say that he was going for a walk. Pippin gave him a kindly nod.

It was a cool, still evening: innumerable stars swarmed in clusters over the forests, forming bright hieroglyphics in the middle heavens, showering over the dark harbour into the sea. Scorrier walked slowly. A weight seemed lifted from his mind, so entangled had he become in that uncanny silence. At last Pippin had broken through the spell. To get that letter sent would be the laying of a phantom, the rehabilitation of common-sense. Now that this silence was in the throes of being broken, he felt curiously tender towards Pippin, without the hero-worship of old days, but with a queer protective feeling. After all, he was different from other men. In spite of his feverish, tenacious energy, in spite of his ironic humour, there was something of the woman in him! And as for this silence, this horror of control—all geniuses had " bees in their bonnets," and Pippin was a genius in his way!

He looked back at the town. Brilliantly lighted it had a thriving air—difficult to believe of the place he remembered ten years back; the sounds of drinking, gambling, laughter, and dancing floated to his ears. ' Quite a city! ' he thought. With this queer elation on him he walked slowly back along the street, forgetting that he was simply an oldish mining expert, with a look of shabbiness, such as clings to men who are always travel-ling, as if their " nap " were for ever being rubbed off. And he thought of Pippin, creator of this glory.

He had passed the boundaries of the town, and had entered the forest. A feeling of discouragement instantly beset him. The scents and silence, after the festive cries and odours of the town, were undefinably oppressive. Notwithstanding, he walked a long time, saying to himself that he would give the letter every chance. At last, when he thought that Pippin must have finished, he went back to the house.

Pippin *had* finished. His forehead rested on the table, his arms hung at his sides; he was stone-dead! His face wore a smile, and by his side lay an empty laudanum bottle.

The letter, closely, beautifully written, lay before him. It was a fine document, clear, masterly, detailed, nothing slurred, nothing concealed, nothing omitted; a complete review of the company's position; it ended with the words: " Your humble servant, RICHARD PIPPIN."

Scorrier took possession of it. He dimly understood that with those last words a wire had snapped. The border-line had been overpassed; the point reached where that sense of propor-tion, which alone makes life possible, is lost. He was certain that at the moment of his death Pippin could have discussed bimetallism, or any intellectual problem, except the one prob-

lem of his own heart; *that,* for some mysterious reason, had
been too much for him. His death had been the work of a
moment of supreme revolt—a single instant of madness on a
single subject! He found on the blotting-paper, scrawled across
the impress of the signature, " Can't stand it! " The comple-
tion of that letter had been to him a struggle ungraspable by
Scorrier. Slavery? Defeat? A violation of Nature? The
death of justice? It were better not to think of it! Pippin
could have told—but he would never speak again. Nature, at
whom, unaided, he had dealt so many blows, had taken her
revenge! . . .

In the night Scorrier stole down, and, with an ashamed face,
cut off a lock of the fine grey hair. ' His daughter might like
it!' he thought. . . .

He waited till Pippin was buried, then, with the letter in his
pocket, started for England.

He arrived at Liverpool on a Thursday morning, and travelling to town, drove straight to the office of the company. The
Board were sitting. Pippin's successor was already being in-
terviewed. He passed out as Scorrier came in, a middle-aged
man with a large, red beard, and a foxy, compromising face.
He also was a Cornishman. Scorrier wished him luck with a
very heavy heart.

As an unsentimental man, who had a proper horror of emotion, whose living depended on his good sense, to look back on
that interview with the Board was painful. It had excited in
him a rage of which he was now heartily ashamed. Old Jolyon
Forsyte, the chairman, was not there for once, guessing perhaps that the Board's view of this death would be too small for
him; and little Mr. Booker sat in his place. Every one had
risen, shaken hands with Scorrier, and expressed themselves
indebted for his coming. Scorrier placed Pippin's letter on the
table, and gravely the secretary read out to his Board the last
words of their superintendent. When he had finished, a director said, " That's not the letter of a madman! " Another answered: " Mad as a hatter; nobody but a madman would have
thrown up such a post." Scorrier suddenly withdrew. He
heard Hemmings calling after him. " Aren't you well, Mr.
Scorrier? aren't you well, sir? "

He shouted back: " Quite sane, I thank you." . . .

The Naples "express" rolled round the outskirts of the town. Vesuvius shone in the sun, uncrowned by smoke. But even as Scorrier looked, a white puff went soaring up. It was the footnote to his memories.

February, 1901.

A FEUD

I

ITS psychic origin, like that of most human loves and hates, was obscure, and yet, like most human hates and loves, had a definite point of physical departure—the moment when Bowden's yellow dog bit Steer's ungaitered leg. Even then it might not have "got going," as they say, but for the village sense of justice which caused Steer to bring his gun next day and solemnly execute the dog. He was the third person the dog had bitten; not even Bowden, who was fond of his whippet, opposed the execution, but the shot left him with an obscure feeling of lost property, a dim sense of disloyalty to his dog. Steer was a Northerner, an Easterner, a man from a part called Lincolnshire, outlandish, like the Frisian cattle he mixed with the Devons on his farm—this, Bowden could not help feeling in the bottom of his soul, was what had moved his dog. Snip had not liked, any more than his master, that thin, spry, red-grey-bearded chap's experimental ways of farming, his habit of always being an hour, a week, a month earlier than Bowden; had not liked his lean, dry activity, his thin legs, his east-wind air. Bowden knew that he would have shot Steer's dog if he himself had been the third person Steer's dog had bitten; but then Steer's dog had *not* bitten Bowden, and Bowden's dog *had* bitten Steer; and this seemed to Bowden to show that his dog knew what was what. And while he was burying the poor brute, he had muttered: " Darn the man! What did he want trapesin' about my yard in his Sunday breeks—seein' what he could get, I suppose! " And with each shovel of earth he threw on the limp yellow body, a sticky resentment had oozed from his spirit and clung, undissolving, round the springs of its action. To inter the dog properly was a long hot job.

' He comes and shoots my dog—of a Sunday too, and leaves me to bury 'un,' he thought, wiping his round, well-coloured face; and he spat as if the ground in front of him were Steer.

When he had finished and rolled a big stone on to the little mound, he went in, and, sitting down moodily in the kitchen, said:

"Girl, draw me a glass o' cider." Having drunk it, he looked up and added: "I've a-burried she up to Crossovers." The dog was male, a lissome whippet unconnected with the business of the farm, and Bowden had called him "she" from puppy-hood. The dark-haired, broad-faced, rather sullen-looking girl whom he addressed flushed, and her grey eyes widened with pain. "'Twas a shame!" she muttered.

"Ah!" said Bowden.

Bowden farmed about a hundred acres of half-and-half sort of land, some good, some poor, just under the down. He was a widower, with a mother and an only son. A broad, easy man, with a dark round head, a rosy face, and immense capacity for living in the moment. Looking at him, you would have said not a man in whom things would rankle. But then to look at a West Countryman you would say so many things that have their lurking negations. He was a native of the natives—his family went back in the parish to times beyond the opening of the register; his ancestors had been churchwardens in remote days. His father, "Daddy Bowden," an easy-going, handsome old fellow, and a bit of a rip, had died at ninety. He himself was well over fifty, but had no grey hair as yet. He took life easy, and let his farm off lightly, keeping it nearly all to pasture, with a conservative grin (Bowden was a Liberal) at the outlandish efforts of his neighbour Steer (a Tory) to grow wheat, bring in Frisian stock, and use new-fangled machines. Steer had originally come to that part of the country as a gentleman's bailiff, and this induced a sort of secret contempt in Bowden, whose forefathers in old days had farmed their own land here round about. Bowden's mother, eighty-eight years old, was a little pocket-woman almost past speech, with dark bright eyes and innumerable wrinkles, who sat all day long in any warmth there was, conserving energy. His son Ned, a youth of twenty-four, bullet-headed like all the Bowdens, was of a lighter colour in hair and eyes. At the moment of history when Steer shot Bowden's dog, he was keeping company with Steer's niece, Molly Winch, who kept house for the confirmed bachelor that Steer was. The other member of Bowden's household, the girl Pansy, was an orphan, some said born under a rose, who came from the other side of the moor and earned fourteen pounds a year. She kept to herself, had dark fine hair, grey eyes, a pale broad face; " broody " she was given somewhat to the " tantrums "; now she would look quite plain; now, when moved or excited, quite pretty. Hers was all the housework, and much of the poultry-feeding, wood-cutting and water-drawing. She was hard-worked, and often sullen because of it.

Having finished his cider, Bowden stood in the kitchen porch looking idly at a dance of gnats. The weather was fine, and the hay was in. It was one of those intervals between harvests which he was wont to take easy, and it would amuse him to think of his neighbour always " puzzivanting " over some " improvement " or other. But it did not amuse him this evening. That chap was for ever trying to sneak ahead of his neighbours! Young Bowden had just milked the cows, and was turning them down the lane. The lad would " slick himself up " and go courting that niece of Steers! The courtship seemed to Bowden suddenly unnatural. A cough made him conscious of the girl Pansy standing behind him with her sleeves rolled up.

" Butiful evenin'," he said—" gude for the corn." When Bowden indulged his sense of the æsthetic he would apologise with some comment that implied commercial benefit or loss; while Steer would pass on with only a dry " Fine evenin'." In talking with Steer one never lost consciousness of his keen " on-the-makeness," as of a progressive individualist who has no means of covering his nature from one's eyes. Bowden one might meet for weeks without realising that beneath his uncontradictious pleasantry was a self-preservative individualism quite as stubborn. To the casual eye, Steer was much more up to date and " civilised "; to one looking deeper, Bowden had been " civilised " much longer. He had grown protective covering in a softer climate, or drawn it outward from an older strain of blood.

" The gnats are dancin'," he said; " fine weather," and the girl Pansy nodded. Watching her turn the handle of the separator, he marked her glance straying down the yard to where Ned was shutting the lane gate. She was a likely-looking wench, with her shapely browned arms, and her black hair fine as silk, which she kept brushing back from her eyes with her free hand, and it gave him a kind of farmyard amusement to see those eyes of hers following his son about. " She's Ned's if he wants her —young hussy! " he thought. " Begad, but it would put Steer's nose out of joint properly, if that girl got in front of his precious niece." To say that this thought was father to a wish would too definitely express the circumambulatory mind of Bowden —a lazy and unprecise thinker; but it lurked and hovered while he took his ash-plant and browsed his way out of the yard, to have a look at the young bull before supper. At the meadow of the coarse water-weed and pasture, where the young red bull was grazing, he stood leaning over the gate, with the swallows flying high. The young bull was "lukin'-up bravely —in another year he would lay over that bull of Steers—ah, he would that! And a dim savagery stirred in Bowden, then passed in the sensuous enjoyment—which a farmer never admits—at the scent, sight, sounds of his fields in fine weather; at the blue above and the green beneath him, the gleam of that thread of water, half-smothered in bulrushes, "daggers," and monkey-flower under the slowly sinking sun; at the song of a lark, and the murmuring in the ash trees; at the glistening ruddy coat of the young bull and the sound of his cropping. Three rabbits ran into the hedge. So that fellow had shot his dog—his dog that had nipped up more rabbits out of corn than any dog he ever owned! He tapped his stick on the gate. The young bull raised a lazy head, gazed at his master, and, flicking his tail at the flies, resumed his pasturing.

"Shot my dog!" thought Bowden. "Shot my dog! Yu wait a bit!"

II

The girl Pansy turned the handle of the separator, and its whining drone mixed with the thoughts and feelings, poignant yet formless, of one who had little say in her own career. There was an ache in her loins, for hay harvest was ever a hard week; and an ache in her heart, because she had no leisure, like Molly Winch and other girls who could find time for the piano and to make their dresses. She touched her hard frieze skirt. She was sick of the ugly thing! And she hastened the separator. She had to feed the calves, and set the supper, before she could change into her Sunday frock and go to evening church—her one weekly festivity. Ned Bowden! Her fancy soared to the monstrous extravagance of herself and Ned walking across the fields to church together, singing out of one hymn-book; Ned, who had given her a look when he passed just now as if he

realised at last that she had been thinking of him for weeks.
A dusky flush crept up in her pale cheeks. A girl must think
of somebody—she wasn't old Mother Bowden, with her hands
on her lap all day, in sunlight or fire-shine, content just to be
warm! And she turned the handle with a sort of frenzy.
Would the milk never finish running through? Ned never saw
her in her frock—her frock sprigged with cornflowers; he went
off too early to his courting, Sunday evenings. In this old
skirt she looked so thick and muddy! And her arms——!
Gazing despairingly at arms browned and roughened, her fancy
took another monstrous flight. She saw herself and Molly
Winch side by side ungarbed. Ah, she would make two of that
Molly Winch! The thought at once pained and pleased her.
It was genteel to be thin and elegant; and yet—instinct told
her—strength and firmness of flesh had been desirable before ever
gentility existed. She let the handle go, and, lifting the pail of
"waste," hurried down with it to the dark byre, whence the
young calves were thrusting their red muzzles. She pushed them
back in turn—greedy little things; smacking their wet noses,
scolding them. Ugh! How mucky it was in there—they ought
to give that byre a good clean-up! She could barely wait for
them to finish their drink, one by one—little slow, eager things—
such was the longing in her to be in time this evening; then,
banging down the empty pail, she ran to set out supper on the
long deal table. In the last of the sunlight old Mother Bowden's
bright eyes seemed to watch her inhumanly. She would never
be done in time—never be done in time!

The beef, the cider, the cheese, the bread, the pickles—what
else? Lettuce! Yes, and it wasn't washed, and Bowden loved
his lettuce! But she couldn't wait—she couldn't! Perhaps
he'd forget it—if she put some cream out! From the cool, dark
dairy, down the little stone passage, she fetched the remains
of the scalded cream.

"Watch the cat, Missis Bowden!" And she ran up the
wriggling narrow stairs.

The room she slept in was like a ship's cabin—no bigger. She
drew the curtain over the porthole-like window, tore off her
things and flung them on the narrow bed. This was her weekly
change. There was a hole in her undergarment, and she tore it
wider in her hurry. "I won't have time for a good wash," she
thought. Taking her one towel, she damped it, rubbed it
over her, and began to dress furiously. The church bell had

begun its dull, hard single chime. The little room was fiery hot, and beads of sweat stood on the girl's brow. Savagely she thought: 'Why can't I have time to be cool, like Molly Winch?' A large spider, a little way out from one corner of the ceiling, seemed watching her, and she shuddered. She couldn't bear spiders—great hairy things! But she had no time to stretch up her hand and kill it. Glancing through a chink left by the drawn curtain, to see whether Ned had come down into the yard, she snatched up her powder-puff—precious possession, nearest approach to gentility—and solemnly rubbed it over face and neck. Now she wouldn't shine, anyway! She fastened on her Sunday hat, a broad-brimmed straw, trimmed with wide-eyed artificial daisies, and stood a moment contemplating her image in a mirror the size of her two hands. The scent of the powder, as of gone-off violets, soothed her nerves. But why was her hair so fine that it wouldn't stay in place?—and why black, instead of goldeny-brown like Molly Winch's hair? Her lip drooped—her eyes looked wide and mournful in the glass. She snatched up her pair of dirty white cotton gloves, took her prayer-book, threw open the door, and stood listening. Dead silence in the house! Ned Bowden's room, with his father's and his old grandmother's, were up the other stairs. She would have liked him to see her coming down—like what the young men did in the magazines, looking up at the young ladies, beautiful and cool, descending slowly. But would he look at her when he had his best on, going to Molly Winch? She went down the wriggling staircase. Gnats were still dancing outside the porch, ducks bathing and preening their feathers in sunlight which had lost all sting. She did not sit down, for fear of being caught too obviously waiting, but stood changing from tired foot to foot, while the scent of powder mingled queerly with the homely odour of the farmyard and the lingering perfume of the hay stacked up close by. The bell stopped ringing. Should she wait? Perhaps he wasn't going to church at all: just going to sit with Molly Winch, or to walk in the lanes with her. Oh no, that Molly Winch was too prim and proper; she wouldn't miss church! And suddenly something stirred within the girl. What would *she* not miss for a walk in the lanes with Ned? It wasn't fair! Some people had everything! The sound of heavy boots from stair to stair came to her ears, and, more swiftly than one would have thought natural to that firm body, she sped through the yard and passed through the door in its high wall to the field path. Scarcely more than a rut, it was strewn with wisps of hay, for they had not yet raked this last field, and the air smelled very sweet. She dawdled, every sense throbbing, aware of his approach behind her, and its measured dwelling on either foot which no Bowden could abandon, even when late for church. He ranged up; his hair was greased, his square figure stuffed handsome into board-like Sunday dittos. His red face shone from soap, his grey eyes shone from surplus energy. From head to foot—he was wonderful! Would he pass her, or fall in alongside? He fell into step. The girl's heart thumped, her cheeks burned under the powder, so that the scent thereof was released. Young Bowden's arm, that felt like iron, bumped her own, and at the thrill which went through her, she half-closed her eyes.

" I reckon we're tu late," he said.

Her widened eyes challenged his stare.

" Don't you want to see Molly Winch, then? "

" No, I don't want any words about that dog."

Quick to see her chance, the girl exclaimed:

" 'Twas a shame—it was; but she'd think more of her uncle's leg than of 'im, I know."

Again his arm pressed hers; he said: " Let's go down into the brake."

The bit of common land below the field was high with furze, where a few brown-gold blossoms were still clinging. A late cuckoo called shrilly from an ash tree below. The breeze stirred a faint rustling out of the hedgerow trees. Young Bowden sat down among the knee-high bracken that smelled of sap, and put his arm about her.

III

In parishes whose farms are scattered and there is no real village, gossip has not quite its proper wings; and the first intimation Steer had that his niece was being slighted came from Bowden himself. Steer was wont to drive the seven miles to market in a small spring cart filled with produce on the journey in, and with groceries on the journey out. He held his east-wind face steadily, with eyes fixed on the ears of his mare. His niece sometimes sat beside him—one of those girls whose china is a little too thin for farm life. She was educated, and played the piano. Steer was proud of her, in spite of his low opinion of her father, who had died of consumption and left Steer's sister in poor circumstances and health. Molly Winch's face, indeed, had refinement; it coloured easily a faint rose-pink, was pointed in the chin, had a slightly tip-tilted nose, and pretty, truthful eyes—a nice face.

Steer's mare usually did the seven miles in just under forty minutes, and he was proud of her, especially when she overhauled Bowden's mare. The two spring carts travelled abreast of each other just long enough for these words to be exchanged:

" Mornin', Bowden! "

" Mornin' !—mornin', Miss Molly, 'aven't seen yu lately; thought yu were visitin' ! "

" No, Mr. Bowden."

" Glad to see yu lukin' up s'well. Reckon Ned's tu busy elsewhere just now."

It was then that Steer's mare drew well ahead.

" My old mare's worth two of his," Steer thought.

Bowden's cart was distant dust before he turned to his niece and said:

" What's the matter with New Bowden? When did you see him last? "

His shrewd light eyes noted her lips quivering, and the stain on her cheeks.

" It's—it's a month now."

" It is—is it? " was all Steer said. But he flicked the mare sharply with his whip, thinking: " What's this? Didn't like that fellow's face—was he makin' game of us? "

Steer was an abstemious man; a tot of sloe gin before he embarked for home was the extent of his usual potations at " The Drake." But that day he took two tots, because of the grin on the face of Bowden, who would sit an hour and more after he had gone, absorbing gin and cider. Was that grin meant for him and for his niece?

A discreet man, too, he let a fortnight pass while he watched out. Ned Bowden did not come to church, nor was he seen at Steer's. Molly looked pale and peaky. And something deep stirred in Steer. " If he don't mean to keep his word to her," he thought, " I'll have the law of him, young pup ! "

People talked no more freely to Steer than he to them; and another week had passed before he had fresh evidence. It came, after a parish meeting, from the schoolmistress, a grey-haired single lady much respected.

"I don't like Molly looking so pale and daverdy, Mr. Steer; I'm grieved about Ned Bowden—I thought he was a steady boy."

"What about him?"

"That girl at Bowden's."

Steer flopped into the depths of consciousness. So everybody round had known, maybe for weeks, that his niece was being jilted for that cross-bred slut; known, and been grinning up their sleeves, had they? He announced to his niece that evening:

"I'm goin' round to Bowden's."

She coloured, then went pale.

"They shan't put it up on you," he said, "I'll see to that. Give me that ring of his—I may want it."

Molly Winch silently slipped off her amethyst engagement ring and gave it to him.

Steer put on his best hat, breeches and gaiters, took a thin stick and set out.

Corn harvest was coming near, and he crossed a field of his own wheat into a field of Bowden's oats. Steer was the only farmer round about who grew wheat. Wheat! In Bowden's view it was all his politics! But Steer was thinking: 'My wheat's lookin' well—don't think much of these oats' (another of his foreign expressions, for oats were "corn" to Bowden); 'he'll have no straw.'

He had not been in Bowden's yard since the day he executed the yellow whippet dog, and his calf twitched—the brute had given it a shrewd nip.

The girl Pansy opened the door to him. And, seeing the flush rise into her pale cheeks, he thought, 'If I were to lay my stick across your back, you'd know it, my girl.'

Bowden had just finished his supper of bacon, beans, and cider, and was smoking his pipe before the embers of a wood fire. He did not get up, and there seemed to Steer something studied and insulting in the way he nodded to a chair. He sat down with his stick across his knees, while the girl went quickly out.

"Butiful evenin'," said Bowden. "Fine weather for the corn. Have a drink o' cider?"

Steer shook his head. The cautious man was making sure of his surroundings before he opened fire. Old Mrs. Bowden sat in her chair by the recessed fire, with her little old back turned

to the room. Bowden's white-headed bobtail was stretched out
with his chin on his paws; a yellow cat crouched, still as the
Sphinx, with half-closed eyes; nothing else was alive, except
the slow-ticking clock.

Steer held up the amethyst ring.

" See this ! "

Undisturbed by meaning or emotion, Bowden turned his face
slowly towards the ring.

" Ah ! What about it ? "

" 'Twas given to my niece for a purpose. Is that purpose
goin' to be fulfilled ? "

" Tidden for me to say. Ask Ned."

Steer closed his hand, slightly covered with reddish hairs.

" I've heard tales," he said, " and if he don' mean to keep
his word I 'll have the law of him. I've always thought my
niece a sight too good for him; but if he thinks he can put a
slight on her he's reckoning without the cost—that's all."

Bowden blew out a cloud of smoke.

" Ned's a man grown."

" Do you abet him ? "

Bowden turned his head lazily.

" Don't you come here bullying me." And again he puffed
out a cloud of smoke. Its scent increased the resentment in
Steer, who was no smoker.

" Like father, like son," he said. " We know what your father
was like."

Bowden took his pipe from his mouth with a fist the size of a
beefsteak.

" With the old lady settin' there ! Get out o' my house ! "

A wave of exasperated blood flooded Steer's thin cheeks.

" You know right well that she hears naught."

Bowden replaced his pipe. " 'Tes no yuse tachin' yu manners,"
he muttered.

Something twitched in Steer's lean throat, where the reddish-
grey hair covered his Adam's apple.

" I'll give your son a week, and then look out."

A chuckle pursued him to the door.

" All right ! " he thought. " We'll see who'll laugh last."

IV

Difficult to say whether morality exists in a man like Bowden, whose blood is racy of the soil, and whose farmyard is so

adjacent. That his son should run riot with the girl Pansy
would have struck him more, perhaps, if Steer had not shot his
dog—the affair so providentially put that fellow's nose out of
joint. It went far, in fact, to assuage his outraged sense of
property, and to dull the feeling that he had betrayed his dog
by not actively opposing village justice. As for the "Law,"
the Bowdens had lived for too many generations in a parish
where no constable was resident to have any belief in its powers.
He often broke the law himself in a quiet way—shooting stray
pheasants and calling them pigeons, not inspecting his rabbit-
traps morning and evening, not keeping quite to date in dipping
his sheep, and so forth. "The Law" could always be evaded.
Besides, what law was Ned breaking? That was Steer's talk!

He was contemptuously surprised, therefore, when, three
weeks later, Ned received a document headed "High Courts of
Justice. Winch *versus* Bowden," claiming five hundred pounds
for breach of promise of marriage. An outlandish trick—with
the war on too! Couldn't Ned please himself as to what girl
he'd take? He was for putting it in the fire. But the more
the two examined the document the more hypnotised they became. Lawyers were no use except to charge money—but,
perhaps a lawyer ought to have a look at it.

On market day, therefore, they took it to Applewhite, of
Applewhite and Carter, who subjected them to a prolonged
catechism. Had Ned engaged himself to the girl? Well, yes,
he supposed he had. How had he broken off the engagement—he
had written to the girl? No! Well, he had received letters
from her asking him what was the matter? Yes, two. Had
he answered them? No. Had he seen the girl and done it by
word of mouth? No! He had not seen the girl for ten weeks.
Was he prepared to see the girl or write to her? He was not.
Was he ready to marry her? No! Why was that?

Ned looked at his father; and Bowden looked at Ned. The
girl Pansy had never been mentioned between them.

Mr. Applewhite repeated his question. Ned did not know.

According to the lawyer, if Ned did not know, nobody did.
What had caused the change in his feelings?

It was Bowden who answered——

"He shot my dog."

"Who?"

"Steer."

Mr. Applewhite was unable to see the connection. If that

was all, he was afraid young Mr. Bowden would either have to marry the girl or " stand to be shot at " himself. And suddenly he looked at Ned. " Is there anything against this girl? " No, there was nothing against her.

" Then why not marry her? "

Again Ned shook his bullet head.

The lawyer smoothed his chin—he was a pleasant fellow—and a good fisherman.

" About this young lady, Miss Winch; excuse my asking, but I suppose you haven't been putting the cart before the horse? "

For the third time Ned shook his head.

No, there had been nothing of that sort. He did not add that if there had he might not have been overmastered by the propinquity of the girl Pansy.

" There's another girl in this, I suppose," said the lawyer suddenly. " Well, I don't want to hear. It's for you to decide what you'll do—marry the girl or defend the action and get the damages reduced—it's a stiff claim. You and your father had better go away, talk it over again, and let me know. If you defend, you'll have to go up to London. In the box, least said is soonest mended. You'll simply say you found you were mistaken, and thought it more honourable to break off at once than to go on. That sometimes goes down rather well with juries, if the man looks straight-forward."

The Bowdens went away. Steer passed them on the journey home. He was alone, driving that mare of his. The Bowdens grinned faintly as he went by. Then Bowden called out two words——

" Stickin' plaster! "

If Steer heard, he gave no sign, but his ears looked very red.

When his hurrying cart was a speck at the top of the steep rise, Bowden turned a little towards his son.

" I want to make that chap sweat," he said.

" Ah! " answered Ned.

But how to make Steer sweat without sweating themselves? That was what exercised the Bowdens, each according to his lights and circumstances, which, of course, were very different. Even in this quandary they did not mention the girl Pansy. To do so would have been to touch on feeling; both felt it better to keep to facts and to devices. It was Bowden who put the finishing touch to a long and devious silence.

" If yu don' du nothin', Ned, I don' see how they can 'ave yu.

Yu've not putt nothin' on paper. How'm they to tell yu don'
mean to marry her? I'd let 'em stew in their own juice. Don't
yu never admit it. Drop word to that lawyer chap that yu'm
not guilty."

Ned nodded, but underneath his stolidity he could not help
feeling that it was not so simple as all that. To him, though
not quite tired of the girl Pansy, his first choice had begun to
be faintly desirable again—her refinement " in the distance enchanted," was regaining some of its attraction to his cooling
blood. What would have been the course of events but for
Steer's next action is, indeed, uncertain.

V

In having the law of "those two fellows," Steer had passed
through an experience with his niece which had considerably
embittered feelings already acid. The girl had shown a " lady-
like " shrinking from pressing a man who had ceased to want
her. There was an absolute difference between her wishes and
her uncle's. He would not have young Bowden marry her for
anything; he just wanted revenge on the Bowdens. She wanted
young Bowden still; but if she couldn't get him, would cry
quietly and leave it at that. The two points of view had been
irreconcilable, till Steer, taking the bit between his teeth, assured
his niece that to bring the action was the only way of inducing
young Bowden to come back to her. This gave him a bad conscience, for he was fond of his niece, and he really felt that to
bring the action would make that fellow Bowden stick his toes
in all the more, and refuse to budge. He thought always of
Bowden first and of the five hundred that would come out of *his*
pocket, not out of Ned's.

Steer owned the local weed-sprayer, which by village custom
was at the service of his neighbours in rotation. This year he
fetched the sprayer back from Pethick's farm just as it was on
the point of going on to Bowden's, without reason given. Bowden, who would not have been above using " that chap's sprayer "
so long as it came to him from Pethrick, in ordinary rotation,
was above sending to Steer's for it. He took the action as a
public proclamation of enmity, and in the Three Stars Inn,
where he went nearly every evening for a glass of cider with a
drop of gin and a clove in it, he said out loud that Steer was a

"colley," and Ned wouldn't be seen dead with that niece of his.

By those words, soon repeated far and wide, he committed his son just when Ned was cooling rapidly towards the girl Pansy, and beginning to think of going to church once more and seeing whether Molly wouldn't look at him again. After all, it was he, not his father, who would have to go into the witness-box; moreover, he had nothing against Molly Winch.

Now that the feud was openly recognised by village tongues, its origin was already lost. No one—hardly even the Bowdens—remembered that Bowden's dog had bitten Steer, and Steer had shot it; so much spicier on the palate was Ned's aberration with the girl Pansy, and its questionable consequences. Corn harvest passed, and bracken harvest; the autumn gales, sweeping in from the Atlantic, spent their rain on the moor; the birch-trees goldened and the beech-trees grew fox-red, and, save that Molly Winch was never seen, that Bowden and Steer passed each other as if they were stocks or stones, and for the interest taken in the girl Pansy's appearance by anyone who had a glimpse of her (not often now, for she was seldom out of the farmyard), the affair might have been considered at an end.

Steer was too secretive and too deadly in earnest to mention the breach-of-promise suit; the Bowdens, at once too defiant of the law and too anxious to forget it. By never mentioning it, even to each other, and by such occasional remarks as: " Reckon that chap's bit off more than he can chu," they consigned it to a future which to certain temperaments never exists until it is the present. They had, indeed, one or two legal reminders, and Ned had twice to see Mr. Applewhite on market days, but between all this and real apprehension was always the slow and stolid confidence that " the Law " could be avoided if you " sat tight and did'n du nothin'."

When, therefore, in late November, Ned received a letter from the lawyer telling him to be at the High Courts of Justice in the Strand, London, at ten-thirty in the morning on the next day but one, prepared to give his evidence, a most peculiar change took place in that bullet-headed youth. His appetite abandoned him; sweat stood on his brow at moments unconnected with honest toil. He gave the girl Pansy black looks; and sat with his prepared evidence before him, wiping the palms of his hands stealthily on his breeches. That which he had never really thought would spring was upon him after all, and panic, such as nothing physical could have caused in him, tweaked his nerves and paralysed his brain. But for his father he would never have come up to the scratch. Born before the halfpenny Press, and unable to ride a bicycle, unthreatened, moreover, by the witness-box, Bowden—after a long pipe—gave out his opinion that it " widden never du to let that chap 'ave it all his own way. There wasn't nothin' to it, if Ned kept a stiff upper lip. 'Twid be an 'oliday-like in London for them both."

So, dressed in their darkest and most board-like tweeds, with black bowler hats, they drove in next day to catch the London train, with a small boy bobbing on a board behind them to drive the mare back home. Deep within each was a resentful feeling that this came of women; and they gave no thought to the feelings of the girl who was the plaintiff in the suit, or of the girl who watched them drive out of the yard. While the train swiftly bore them, stolid and red-faced, side by side, the feeling grew within them that to make a holiday of this would spite that chap Steer. He wanted to make them sweat; if they did not choose to sweat—it was one in the eye for him.

They put up at an hotel with a Devonshire name in Covent Garden, and in the evening visited a music-hall where was a show called the " Rooshian Ballet." They sat a little forward with their hands on their thighs, their ruddy faces, expressionless as waxworks, directed towards the stage, whereon " Les Sylphides " were floating white and ethereal. When the leading *danseuse* was held upside down, Bowden's mouth opened slightly. He was afterwards heard to say that she had " got some legs on her." Unable to obtain refreshment after the performance, owing to the war, they sought the large flasks in their bedroom, and slept, snoring soundly, as though to express even in their slumbers a contempt for the machinations of " that chap, Steer."

VI

Though sorely tried by the " pernickety " nature of his niece, Steer had been borne up by the thought that he had only to hold on a little longer to obtain justice. How he had got her to the starting-post he really did not know, so pitiably had she " jibbed." The conviction that good solid damages would in the end be better for her than anything else had salved and soothed a conscience really affected by her nervous distress. Her pale

face and reddened eyes on the way to the court disturbed him,
and yet he knew they were valuable—she was looking her best
for the occasion. It would be all over—he told her—in an hour,
and then she should go to the seaside—what did she say to
Weston-super-Mare (with one syllable)? She said nothing, and
he had entered the Law Courts with his arm through hers, and
his upper lip very long. The sight of the two Bowdens seated
on a bench in the corridor restored the burning in his heart.
He marked his niece's eyes slide round when they passed young
Bowden. Yes! She would take him even now! He saw Ned
shuffle his feet, and Bowden grin, and he hurried her on—not
for anything would he forego the five hundred out of that
fellow's pocket! At that moment the feud between him and
his neighbour showed naked—those young people were but the
catspaws of it. The custom of the court compelled them all
presently to be sitting in a row, divided faction from faction
by not more than the breadth of a pig. Steer's thin face, racked
by effort to follow the patter of the chap in a wig, acquired a
sort of maniacal fixity; but he kept hold of his niece's arm,
squeezing it half-consciously now and again, and aware of her
shrinking faint look. As for "Those two fellows," they sat
as they might have at an auction, giving nothing away, putting
the whole business in its proper place—monkey tricks that must
fail if they " sat tight and didn't du nothin'." It seemed unjust
to Steer that they should seem unmoved while his niece was
wilting beside him. When she went up, trembling, into the
" dock," a strong scent of camphor floated from Steer, stirred
from his clothes by the heat within him. He could hardly
hear, and they kept telling her to speak up. He saw tears roll
down her cheeks; and the ginger in the greying hair and beard
brightened the while he stared at the Bowdens, who never
moved. They didn't ask her much—not even Bowden's counsel
—afraid to, he could see! And, vaguely through his anger and
discomfort, Steer felt that, with her " ladylikeness," her tears,
her shrinking, she was making a good impression on judge and
jury. It enraged him to see her made to shrink and weep, but
it delighted him too.

She came back to his side and sat down, all shrunk into herself. Bowden's counsel began outlining the defence, and Steer
listened with his mouth a little open—an outrageous defence,
for what did it amount to but a confession that the fellow had
played fast and loose! His client—said counsel—came into

court not to defend this action, but to express his regret as an honourable man for having caused the plaintiff distress, though not, he would submit, any material damage, for, now that they had seen her in the box, it would be absurd to suppose that what was called her "value in the marriage market" had deteriorated. His client had come there to tell them the simple truth that, finding his feelings towards the plaintiff changed, he had considered it more honourable, wise and merciful, to renounce his engageemnt before it was too late, rather than to enter into a union from the start doomed to unhappiness, which the gentlemen of the jury must remember, would, in the nature of men and things, fall far more heavily on the plaintiff than on the defendant himself. Though fully admitting his responsibility for the mistake he had made and the hastiness of which he had been guilty, the defendant believed they would give him credit for his moral courage in stopping before it was too late, and saving the plaintiff from a miserable fiasco.

At the words "moral courage," Steer had righted himself in his seat so suddenly that the judge was seen to blink. "Moral courage!" Wasn't anybody going to tell those dodos there that the fellow had been playing the rip with that cross-bred girl? Wasn't anybody going to tell them that Bowden had put his son up to this to spite him—Steer? A sense of mystification and falsity muddled and enraged him; it was all bluff and blarney, like selling a horse.

With the robust common-sense characteristic—counsel went on—of plain and honest men, the jury would realise that one could not have things both ways in this world—however it might be in the next. The sad records of the Divorce Court showed what was the outcome of hasty and ill-considered marriages. They gave one to think furiously, indeed, whether these actions for breach of promise, with their threat of publicity, were not responsible for much of the work of that dismal tribunal. He would submit that where you had, as here, a young man admitting his error and regretting it, yet manly enough to face this ordeal in order to save the plaintiff—and in less degree himself, of course—from a life of misery, that young man was entitled, if not to credit, at least to just and considerate treatment at the hands of his fellow-citizens, who had themselves all been young, and, perhaps, not always as wise as Solomon. Let them remember what young blood was—a sunny lane in that beautiful Western county, the scent of honeysuckle,

a pretty girl—and then let them lay their hands on their hearts
and say that they themselves might not have mistaken the
emotions of a moment for a lifelong feeling.

" Don't let us be hypocrites, gentlemen, and pretend that we
always carry out that to which in moments of mid-summer madness we commit ourselves. My client will tell you quite simply,
for he is a simple country youth, that he just made a mistake,
which no one regrets more than he, and then I shall leave it
in your hands—confident that, sorry as we all are for the disappointment of this charming girl, you will assess the real values
of the case with the instinct of shrewd and understanding men."

" Well, I'm darned ! "

" H'sh ! Silence in the Court ! "

The mutter, which had been riven from Steer by counsel's
closing words, by no means adequately expressed feelings which
grew with every monosyllable from that " young ruffian " answering the cunning questions of his advocate.

With his sleek bullet-head he looked sheepish enough, but the
thing was being made so easy for him—that was what seemed
villainous to Steer, that and the sight of Bowden's face unmoved, the breadth of two pigs away. When his own counsel
began to cross-examine, Steer became conscious that he had
made a hideous mistake. Why had he not caused his lawyer
to drag in the girl Pansy? What on earth had he been about
to let his natural secretiveness, his pride in his niece, prevent
him using the weapon which would have alienated every sympathy from that young rascal? He tingled with disappointed
anger. So the fellow was not to be shown up properly ! It was
outrageous. And then suddenly his ears pricked. " Now, young
man," counsel was saying, " don't you think that in days like
these you can serve your country better than by going about
breaking girls' hearts? . . .   Kindly answer that question !
. . . Don't waste his Lordship's time. Yes? Speak up, please."

" I'm workin' the land—I'm growin' food for you to eat ! "

" Indeed ! The jury will draw their own conclusions as to
what sort of leniency they can extend to a young man in your
position."

Steer's lips relaxed. That was a nasty one !

Then came the speeches from counsel on both sides, and
everything was said over again, but Steer had lost interest;
disappointment nagged at him, as at a man who has meant to
play a fine innings—and gets out for seven. Now the Judge

was saying everything that everybody had said and a little more besides. The jury must not let themselves this, and let themselves that. Defendant's counsel had alluded to the Divorce Court—they must not allow any such consideration to weigh with them. While the law was what it was, breach-of-promise actions must be decided on their merits. They would consider this, and they would consider that, and return a verdict, and give damages according to their consciences. And out the jury filed. Steer felt lonely while they were absent. On one side of him were those Bowdens, whom he wanted to make sweat; on the other his niece, whom, to judge from her face, he *had* made sweat. He was not a lover of animals, but a dog against his legs would have been a comfort during that long quarter of an hour, while those two enemies of his so stolidly stared before them. Then the jury came back, and the sentiment in his heart stuttered into a form he could have sent through the post. " Oh, Lord, make them sweat! Your humble servant, J. Steer."

" We find for the plaintiff, with damages—three hundred pounds."

Three hundred! And costs—with costs it would come to five! And Bowden had no capital; he was always on the edge of borrowing to get through—yes, it would push him hard! And, grasping his niece's arm, Steer rose and led her out by the right-hand door, while the Bowdens sought the left. In the corridor his lawyer came up. The fellow hadn't half done his job! And Steer was about to say so, when those two passed, walking as though over turnips, and he heard Bowden say:

" Think he'll get that stickin'-plaster—let 'im wait an' see ! "

He was about to answer, when the lawyer laid hold of his lapel.

" Get your niece away, Mr. Steer; she's had enough."

And, without sense of conquest, with nothing but a dull, irritable aching in his heart, Steer took her arm and walked her out of the precincts of the law.

VII

The news that Ned Bowden had " joined up " reached the village simultaneously with the report that Steer had " shot " him in London for three hundred pounds and costs for breaking his promise to Molly Winch. The double sensation was delicious. Honours seemed so easy that no one could see which

had come off best. It was fairly clear, however, that Molly
Winch and the girl Pansy had come off worst. And there was
great curiosity to see them. This was not found possible, for
Molly Winch was at Weston-super-Mare and the girl Pansy
invisible, even by those whose business took them to Bowden's
yard. Bowden himself put in his customary appearance at The
Three Stars, where he said quite openly that Steer would never
see a penny of that money; Steer his customary appearances
at church, where he was a warden, and could naturally say
nothing. Christmas passed, and the New Year wore on through
colourless February and March, when every tree was bare, the
bracken's russet had gone dark-dun, and the hedgerows were
songless.

Steer's victory had lost him his niece; she had displayed in-
vincible reluctance to return as a conquering heroine, and had
gone into an office. Bowden's victory had lost him his son,
whose training would soon be over now, and whose battalion was
in Flanders. Neither of the neighbouring enemies showed by
word or sign that they saw any connection between victory
and loss; but the schoolmistress met them one afternoon at the
end of March seated in their carts face to face in a lane so
narrow that some compromise was essential to the passage of
either. They had been there without movement long enough
for their mares to begin grazing in the hedge on either hand.
Bowden was sitting with folded arms and an expression as of
his own bull on his face. Steer's teeth and eyes were bared very
much like a dog's when it is going to bite.

The schoolmistress, who had courage, took hold of Bowden's
mare and backed her.

"Now, Mr. Steer," she said, "pull in to your left, please.
You can't stay here all day, blocking the lane for everybody."

Steer, who, after all, prized his reputation in the parish,
jerked the reins and pulled into the hedge. And the schoolmistress, without more ado, led Bowden's mare past, foot by
foot. The wheels scraped, both carts jolted slightly; the two
farmers' faces, so close together, moved no muscle, but when
the carts had drawn clear, each, as if by agreement, expector-
ated to his right. The schoolmistress loosed the head of
Bowden's mare and said:

"You ought to be ashamed of yourself, Mr. Bowden; you
and Mr. Steer."

"How's that?" said Bowden.

" How's that, indeed? Everybody knows the state of things between you. No good can come of it. In war-time, too, when we ought all to be united. Why can't you shake hands and be friends? "

Bowden laughed.

" Shake 'ands with that chap? I'd suner shake 'ands with a dead pig. Let 'im get my son back out o' the Army."

The schoolmistress looked up at him.

" Ah! I hope you're going to look after that poor girl when her time comes," she said.

Bowden nodded.

" Never fear! I'd suner my grandchild was hers than that niece of Steers."

The schoolmistress was silent.

" Well," she said at last, " it's an unchristian state of mind."

" Yu go to Steer, Ma'am, an' see whether he'll be more Christianlike. He 'olds the plate out, Sundays."

This was precisely what the good lady did. More, perhaps, from curiosity than in a proselytising mood.

" What! " said Steer, who was installing a beehive. " When that God-darned fellow put his son up to jilting my niece! "

" And you a Christian, Mr. Steer! "

" There's a limit to that, Ma'am," said Steer drily. " In my opinion, not even our Lord could have put up with that chap. Don't you waste your breath trying to persuade me."

" Dear me! " murmured the schoolmistress; " I don't know which of you is worst."

The only people, in fact, who did know were Steer and Bowden, whose convictions about each other increased as the spring came in with song and leaf and sunshine, and there was no son to attend to the sowing and the calving, and no niece to make the best butter in the parish.

Towards the end of May, on a " brave " day, when the wind was lively in the ash-trees, and the buttercups bright gold, the girl Pansy had her hour; and on the following morning Bowden received this letter from his son:

" DEAR FATHER,

" They don't let us tell where we are, so all I can say is there's some crumps come over that stop at nothing, and you could bury a waggon where they hit. The grub is nothing to complain of. Hope you have done well with calves. The green

there is within sight of here wouldn't keep a rabbit going half
a day. The thing I wish to say is: If I have a son by you know
who—call it Edward, after you and me. It makes you think out
here. She would like to hear perhaps that I will marry her if
I come back, so as not to have it on my mind. There is some
German prisoners in our section—big fellows, and proper swine
with their machine-guns, I can tell you. Hope you are well, as
this leaves me. Has that swine Steer given over asking for his
money? I would like to see the old farm again. Tell Granma
to keep warm. No more now from your loving son,

" NED."

After standing for some minutes by the weighing-machine
trying to make head or tail of his own sensations, Bowden took
the letter up to the girl Pansy, lying beside her offspring in her
narrow cabin of a room. In countrymen who never observe
themselves, a letter or event which ploughs up fallow land of
feeling, or blasts the rock of some prejudice, causes a prolonged
mental stammer or hiatus. So Ned wanted to marry the girl
if he came home! The Bowdens were an old family, the girl
cross-bred. It wasn't fitting! And the news that Ned had
it on his mind brought home to Bowden, as never before, the
danger his son was in. With profound instinct he knew that
compunction did not seriously visit those who felt life sure and
strong within them; so that there was a kind of superstition in
the way he took the letter up to the girl. After all, the child
was as much bone of Ned's bone and of his own as if the
girl had been married in church—a boy too. He gave it her
with the words: " Here's a present for yu and Edward the
Seventh."

The village widow, accustomed to attend these simple cases,
stepped outside, and while the girl was reading, Bowden sat
down on the low seat beneath the little window. The ceiling
just touched his head, so that he did not care to remain standing. Her coarse nightgown fell back from her strong arms and
neck, her hair showed black and lustreless on the coarse pillow;
he could not see her face for the letter, but he heard her sigh.
Somehow he felt sorry.

" Shud ought to du yu good," he said.

Dropping the letter, so that her eyes met his, the girl spoke.

" 'Tisn' nothin' to me; Ned don't care for me no more."

Something inexpressibly cheerless in the tone of her voice, and uncannily searching in her dark gaze, disturbed Bowden.

"Cheer up!" he murmured; "yu've got a monstrous baby there, all to yureself."

Going up to the bed, he clucked his tongue and held his finger out to the baby. He did it softly, and with a sort of native aptitude.

"He'm a proper little man." Then he took up the letter, for there "wasn't," he felt, "no yuse in leavin' it there against Ned if an' in case he should change his mind when he came safe 'ome." But, as he went out, he saw the girl Pansy put the baby to her breast, and again he felt that disturbance, as of pity. With a nod to the village widow, who was sitting on an empty grocery-box reading an old paper by the light coming through half a skylight, Bowden descended the twisting stairs to the kitchen. His mother was seated where the sunlight fell, her bright little dark eyes moving among their mass of wrinkles. Bowden stood a moment watching her.

"Well, Granny," he said, "y'um a great-granny now."

The old lady nodded, mumbled her lips a little in a smile, and rubbed one hand on the other. Bowden experienced a shock.

"There ain't no sense in et," he muttered to himself, without knowing too well what he meant.

VIII

Bowden did not attend when, three weeks later, the baby was christened Edward Bowden. He spent the June morning in his cart with a bull calf, taking it to market. The cart did not run well, because the weight of the calf made it jerk and dip. Though used to it all his life, he had never become quite case-hardened to separating calves from their mothers. Bowden had a queer feeling for cattle—more feeling, indeed, than he had for human beings. He always sat sulky when there was a little red beast tied up and swaying there behind him. Somehow he felt for it, as if in some previous existence he might himself have been a red bull calf.

Passing through a village someone called:

"'Eard the nus? They beat the Germans up proper yest'day mornin'."

Bowden nodded. News from the war was now nothing but a

reminder of how that fellow Steer had deprived him of Ned's help and company. The war would be over some day, he supposed, but they didn't seem to get on with it, gaining ground one day and losing it the next, and all the time passing this law and that law interfering with the land. Didn't they know the land couldn't be interfered with—the cuckoos? Steer, of course, was all part of this interference with the land—the fellow grew wheat where anybody could have told him it couldn't be grown!

The day was hot, the road dusty, and that chap Steer hanging about the market like the colley he was—so that Bowden imbibed freely at "The Drake" before making a start for home.

When he entered his kitchen the newly christened baby was lying in a grocery box, padded with a pillow and shawl, just out of the sunlight in which old Mrs. Bowden sat moving her hands as if weaving a spell. Bowden's sheepdog had lodged its nose on the edge of the box, and was sniffing as if to ascertain the difference in the baby. In the background the girl Pansy moved on her varying business; she looked strong again, but pale still, and "daverdy," Bowden thought. He stood beside the box contemplating the "monstrous" baby. It wasn't like Ned, nor anything, so far as he could see. It opened its large grey eyes while he stood there. That colley Steer would never have a grandchild, not even one born like this! The thought pleased him. He clucked to the baby with his tongue, and his sheepdog jealously thrust its head with mass of brushed-back snowy hair under his hand.

"Hullo!" said Bowden. "What's matter wi' yu?"

He went out presently, in the slanting sunlight, to look at some beasts he had on the rough grounds below his fields, and the dog followed. Among the young bracken and the furze not yet in bloom again, he sat down on a stone. The afternoon was glorious beyond all words, now that the sun was low and its glamour had motion, as it were, and flight across the ash-trees, the hawthorn, and the fern. One Maytree close beside him was still freakishly in delicate flower, with a sweet and heavy scent; in the hedge the round, cream-coloured heads of the elder-flower flashed, flat against the glistening air, while the rowans up the gully had passed already from blossom to brown un-rounded berries.

There was all the magic of transition from season to season, even in the song of the cuckoo, which flighted arrowlike to a thorn-tree up the rocky dingle, and started a shrill calling. Bowden counted his beasts, and marked the fine sheen on their red coats. He was drowsy from his hot day, from the cider he had drunk, and the hum of the flies in the fern. Unconsciously he enjoyed a deep and sensuous peace of warmth and beauty. Ned had said there was no green out there! It was unimaginable! No green—not the keep of a rabbit; not a curling young caterpillar-frond of fern; no green tree for a bird to light on! And Steer had sent him out there! Through his drowsiness that thought came flapping its black wings. Steer! who had no son to fight, who was making money hand over fist. It seemed to Bowden that a malevolent fortune protected that stingy chap, who couldn't even take his glass.

There were little blue flowers, speedwell and milkwort, growing plentifully in the rough grass around; Bowden noted, perhaps for the first time, that small natural luxury of which Steer had deprived his son by sending him to where no grass grew.

He rose at length, retracing his slow-lifted tread up the lane, deep-soiled with the dried dung of his cows, where innumerable gnats danced level with the elder-blossom and the ash-leaves. He entered the yard as the village postman was leaving it. The man stopped in the doorway, and turned his red face, white head, and dark eyes blinking in the level sunlight.

"There's a talegram for yu, Mist Bowden," he said, and vanished.

"What's that?" said Bowden dully, and passed in under the porch.

The "talegram" lay unopened on the kitchen table, and Bowden stared at it. Very few such missives had come his way, perhaps not half-a-dozen in his fifty odd years. He took it up—handling it rather as he might have handled a fowl that would peck—and broke it open with his thumb.

"Greatly regret inform you your son killed in action on seventh instant.—War Office."

He read it through again and again before he sat down heavily, dropping it on the table. His round solid face looked still and blind, its mouth just a little open. The girl Pansy came up and stood beside him.

"Here!" he said; "read that."

The girl read it and put her hands up to her ears.

" That idn' no yuse," he said, with surprising quickness.

The girl's pale face crimsoned; she uttered a little wail and ran from the room.

In the whitewashed kitchen the only moving things were the clock's swinging pendulum and old Mrs. Bowden's restless eyes, close to the geranium on the window sill, where the last of the sunlight fell before passing behind the house. Minute after minute ticked away before Bowden made a movement—his head bowed, his shoulders rounded, his knees apart. Then he got up.

" God for ever darn the blasted colley! " he said slowly, gathering up the telegram. " Where's my stick? "

Lurching blindly he walked round the room, watched by the old woman's little dark bright eyes, and went out. He went at his unvaried gait on the path towards Steer's, slowly climbing the two stiles and emerging from the field into Steer's farm-yard.

" Master in? " he said to the boy who stood by the cowbyre.

" No."

" Where is he then? "

" Not 'ome from market yet."

" Oh, he idden, idden he! "

And Bowden turned up into the lane. There was a dull buzzing in his ears, but his nostrils moved, savouring the evening scents, of grass, of cow-dung, dried earth, and hedge-row weeds. His nose was alive, the rest within him all knotted into a sort of bitter tangle round his heart. The blood beat in his temples, and he dwelled heavily on foot and foot. Along this road Steer must come in his cart—God for ever darn him! Beyond his own top pasture he reached the Inn abutting on the road. From the bench in there under the window he could see anyone who passed. The innkeeper and two labourers were all the company as yet. Bowden took his usual mug and sat down on the window seat. He did not speak of his loss, and they did not seem to know of it. He just sat with his eyes on the road. Now and then he responded to some question, now and then got up and had his mug refilled. Someone came in; he noted the lowering of voices. They were looking at him. They knew. But he sat on silent till the inn closed. It was still daylight when he lurched back up the road towards home, in-tent on not missing Steer. The sun had gone down; it was very still. He leaned against the wicket-gate of his top field.

Nobody passed. Twilight crept up. . The moon rose. An owl began hooting. Behind him in the field from a group of beech-trees the shadows stole out ever so faint in the flowery grass and darkened slowly in the brightening moonlight.

Bowden leaned his weight against the wood—one knee crooked, and then the other—in dogged stupefaction. He had begun imagining things, but not very much. No grass, no trees, where his son had been killed, no birds, no animals; what could it be like—all mucky grey in the moonlight—and Ned's face all grey! So he would never see Ned's face any more! That colley, Steer—that colley, Steer! His dead son would never see and hear and smell his home again. Vicarious home-sickness for this native soil and scent and sound—this nest of his fathers from time beyond measuring—swept over Bowden. He thought of the old time when his wife was alive and Ned was born. His wife—why! she had brought him six, and of the lot he had only " saved " Ned, and he was a twin. He remembered how he had told the doctor that he wasn't to worry about the " maiden " so long as he saved the boy. He had wanted the boy to come after him here; and now he was dead, and that—that colley, Steer!

He heard the sound of wheels—a long way off, but coming steadily. Gripping his stick he stood up straight, staring down the road all barred with moonlight and the dusk. Closer came the rumble, the clop-clop of hoofs, till the shape of horse and cart came out of darkness into a bright patch. Steer's right enough! Bowden opened his wicket-gate and waited. The cart came slowly; Bowden saw that the mare was lame, and Steer was leading her. He lurched a yard out from the gate.

" 'Ere," he said, " I want to speak to yu. Come in 'ere! "

The moonlight fell on Steer's thin, bearded face.

" What's that? " he answered.

Bowden turned towards the gate.

" Hitch the mare up; I want to settle my account."

He saw Steer stand quite still, as if debating, then pass the reins over the gate. His voice came sharp and firm:

" Have you got that money, then? "

" Ah! " said Bowden, and drew back under the trees. He saw Steer coming cautiously—the colley—with a stick in his hand. He raised his own.

" That's for Ned," he said, and struck with all his might.

The blow fell short a little; Steer staggered back, raising his stick.

He struck again, but the sticks clashed, and, dropping his own, Bowden lurched at his enemy's throat. He had twice Steer's strength and bulk; half his lean quickness and sobriety. They swayed between the beech-trunks, now in shadow, now in moonlight which greyed their faces, and showed the expression in their eyes, of men out to kill. They struggled chest against chest, striving to throw each other, with short, hard gruntings. They reeled against a trunk, staggered and unclinched, and stood, breathing hard, glaring at each other. All those months of hatred looked out of their eyes, and their hands twitched convulsively. Suddenly Steer went on his knees, and gripping Bowden's legs, strained at them till the heavy, unsteady bulk pitched forward and fell over Steer's back with stunning weight. They rolled on the grass then, all mixed up, till they came apart, and sat facing each other, dazed—Bowden from the drink shaken up within him, Steer from the weight which had pitched upon his spine. They sat as if each knew there was no hurry and they were there to finish this; watching each other, bent a little forward, their legs stuck out in the moonlight, their mouths open, breathing in hard gasps, ridiculous—to each other! And suddenly the church bell began to toll. Its measured sound at first reached only the surface of Bowden's muddled brain, dully devising the next attack; then slid into the chambers of his consciousness. Tolling? Tolling! For whom? His hands fell by his sides. Impulse and inhibition, action and superstition, revenge and mourning gripped each other and rolled about within him. A long minute passed. The bell tolled on. A whinny came from Steer's lame mare outside the gate. Suddenly Bowden staggered up, turned his back on his enemy, and, lurching in the moonlight, walked down the field for home. The clover among the wild grasses smelled sweet; he heard the sound of wheels—Steer had started again! Let him go! 'Twasn't no use—'twidden bring Ned back! He reached the yard door and stood leaning against it. Cold streaming moonlight filled the air, covered the fields; the pollarded aspens shivered above him; on the low rock-wall the striped roses were all strangely coloured; and a moth went by brushing his cheek.

Bowden lowered his head, as if butting at the beauty of the night. The bell had ceased to toll—no sound now but the shiver of the aspens and the murmur of a stream. 'Twas monstrous peaceful—surely!

And in Bowden something went out. He had not the heart to hate.

1921.

A FISHER OF MEN

LONG ago it is, now, that I used to see him issue from the rectory, followed by his dogs, an Irish and a fox terrier. He would cross to the churchyard, and, at the gate, stand looking over the Cornish upland of his cure of souls, towards the sea, distant nearly a mile. About his black thin figure there was one bright spot, a little gold cross, dangling on his vest. His eyes at such moments were like the eyes of fishermen watching from the cliffs for pilchards to come by; but as this fisher of men marked the grey roofs covered with yellow lichen where his human fishes dwelt, red stains would come into his meagre cheeks. His lips would move and he would turn abruptly in at the gate over which was written: "This is the Gate of Heaven."

A certain green spot within that churchyard was kept clear of grave-stones, which thickly covered all the rest of the ground. He never—I believe—failed to look at it, and think: "I will keep that corner free. I will not be buried amongst men who refuse their God!"

For this was his misfortune, which, like a creeping fate, had come on him year by year throughout his twenty years of rectorship. It had eaten into his heart, as is the way with troubles which a man cannot understand. In plain words, his catch of souls had dwindled season by season till, from three hundred when he was first presented to the living, it barely numbered forty. Sunday after Sunday he had conducted his three services. Twice a week from the old pulpit, scanning through the church twilight that ever scantier flock of faces, he had in his dry, spasmodic voice—whose harsh tones, no doubt, were music to himself—pronounced this conduct blessed, and that accursed, in accordance with his creed. Week after week he had told us all the sinfulness of not attending God's House, of not observing the Lord's Day. He had respected every proper ritual and ceremony; never refusing baptism even

615

to the illegitimate, nor burial to any but such as took their own lives; joining in marriage with a certain exceptional alacrity those whose conduct had caused scandal in the village. His face had been set, too, against irreverence; no one, I remember, might come to his church in flannel trousers.

Yet his flock had slowly diminished! Living, unmarried, in the neglected rectory, with his dogs, an old housekeeper, and a canary, he seemed to have no interests, such as shooting, or fishing, to take him away from his parish duties; he asked nothing better than to enter the houses and lives of his parishioners; and as he passed their doors—spare, black, and clean-shaven—he could often be seen to stop, make, as it were, a minatory gesture, and walk on with his hungry eyes fixed straight before him. Year by year, to encourage them, he printed privately and distributed documents containing phrases such as these: "It were better for him that a mill-stone were hanged about his neck, and he were cast into the sea." "But the fearful and unbelieving shall have their part in the lake which burneth with fire and brimstone." When he wrote them, his eyes—I fancy—flared, as though watching such penalties in process of infliction. Had not his parishioners in justice merited those fates?

If, in his walks, he came across a truant, some fisherman or farmer, he would always stop, with his eyes fastened on the culprit's face:

"You don't come to church now; how's that?"

Like true Cornishmen, hoping to avoid unpleasantness, they would offer some polite excuse: They didn't knaw ezactly, zur —the missus 'ad been ailin'; there was always somethin'—like —that! This temporising with the devil never failed to make the rector's eyes blaze, or to elicit from him a short dry laugh: "You don't know what you're saying, man! You must be mad to think you can save your soul that way! This is a Christian country!"

Yet never after one of these encounters did he see the face of that parishioner in his church again. "Let un wait!" they would murmur, "tidden likely we'm gwine to his church t'be spoke to like dogs!"

But, indeed, had they been dogs, the rector would not have spoken to them like that. To dogs his conduct was invariably gentle. He might be seen sometimes beside a field of standing corn, where the heads of his two terriers could be marked spasmodically emerging above the golden stalks, as they hunted a covey of partridges or brood of young pheasants which they had scented. His harsh voice could be heard calling them: "Jim, Jim! Pat, Pat! To heel, you rascals!" But when they came out, their tongues lolling ecstatically, he only stooped and shook his finger at them, and they would lick his hand, or rub themselves against his trousers, confident that he would never strike them. With every animal, with every bird and insect he was like this, so gentle that they trusted him completely. He could often be surprised sitting on a high slate stile, or standing in a dip of the wide road between banks of gorse and bramble, with his head, in its wide hat, rather to one side, while a bullfinch or hedge-sparrow on a branch, not three feet off, would be telling him its little tale. Before going for a walk he would sweep his field-glass over the pale-gold landscape of cornfield, scorched pasturage and sand-dune, to see if any horse seemed needing water, or sheep were lying on its back. He was an avowed enemy, too, of traps and gins, and whenever he met with one, took pains to ensure its catching nothing. Such consistent tenderness to dumb animals was perhaps due to a desire to take their side against farmers who would not come to church; but more, I think, to the feeling that the poor things had no souls, that they were here to-day and gone to-morrow—they could not be saved and must be treated with compassion, unlike those men with immortal spirits entrusted by God specially to his care, for whose wanton disobedience no punishment, perhaps, could be too harsh. It was as if, by endowing him with her authority over other men, the Church had divided him into two.

For the view he took of life was very simple, undisturbed by any sense of irony, unspoiled by curiosity, or desire to link effect with cause, or, indeed, to admit the necessity of cause at all. At some fixed date God had made the earth of matter; this matter He had divided into the inanimate and the animate, unconnected with each other; animate matter He had again divided into men, and animals; in men He had placed souls, making them in His own image. Men again He had divided into the Church and other men; and for the government and improvement of these other men, God had passed Himself into His Church. That Church again had passed herself into her ministers. Thus, on the Church's minister—placed by Providence beyond the fear of being in the wrong—there had been

enjoined the bounden duty of instructing, ruling, and saving at
all costs the souls of men.

This was why, I think, when he encountered in the simple
folk committed to his charge a strange dumb democratic spirit,
a wayward feeling that the universe was indivisible, that power
had not devolved, but had evolved, that things were relative,
not absolute, and so forth—expressed in their simple way, he
had experienced from the first a gnawing irritation which, like a
worm, seemed to have cankered his heart. Gradually one had
seen this canker stealing out into his face and body, into his
eyes and voice, into the very gestures of his lean arms and
hands. His whole form gave the impression of a dark tree
withered and eaten by some desiccating wind, like the stiff oaks
of his Cornish upland, gnarled and riven by the Atlantic gales.

Night and day in the worn old rectory, with its red conservatory, he must have brooded over the wrong done him by his
people, in depriving him of his just due, the power to save their
souls. It was as though an officer, gagged and bound at the
head of his company, should have been forced to watch them
manœuvring without him. He was like a schoolmaster tied
to his desk amongst the pandemonium of his scholars. His
failure was a fact strange and intolerable to him, inexplicable,
tragic—a fact mured up in the mystery which each man's blindness to the nature of his own spirit wraps round his relations
with his fellow beings. He could not doubt that, bereaved by
their own wilful conduct of his ministrations, of the Church
in fact, and, through the Church, of God, his parishioners were
given up to damnation. If they were thus given up to damnation, he, their proper pastor—their rightful leader, the symbol
of the Church, that is of God—was but a barren, withered thing.
This thought he could not bear. Unable to see himself as others
saw him, he searched to find excuses for them. He found none;
for he knew that he had preached no narrow doctrines cursed
with the bigotry which he recognised in the Romish or Non-
conformist faiths. The doctrines and dogmas he was appointed
to administer were of the due and necessary breadth, no more,
no less. He was scrupulous, even against his own personal
feeling, to observe the letter of the encyclicals. Thus, nothing
in the matter of his teaching could account for the gradual
defection of his flock. Nor in the manner of it could he detect
anything that seemed to himself unjustified. Yet, as the tide
ebbed from the base of the grey cliffs, so, without haste, with

deadly certainty, the tide ebbed from his church. What could he, then, believe but that his parishioners meant to be personally offensive to himself?

In the school-house, at the post office, on the green, at choir practice, or on the way to service, wherever he met them, one could see that he was perpetually detecting small slights or incivilities. He had come, I think, almost to imagine that these people, who never came to church, fixed the hours of their births and deaths and marriages maliciously, that they might mock at the inconvenience caused to one who neither could, nor would, refuse to do his duty. It was blasphemy they were committing. In avoiding God's church, yet requiring such services of His minister, they were making God their servant.

One could find him any evening in his study, his chin resting on his hand, the oil-lamp flaring slightly, his dogs curled up beside him, and the cloth cover drawn over the cage of his canary so that the little creature should not suffer from the light. Almost the first words he spoke would show how ceaselessly he brooded. " Nothing," he would say, " ever prospers in this village; I've started this and that! Look at the football club, look at the Bible class—all no good! With people such as these, wanting in all reverence, humility, and love of discipline! You have not had the dealings with them that I have! "

In truth his dealings with them had become notorious throughout the district. A petition, privately subscribed, and presented to the Bishop for his removal, had, of course, met with failure. A rector could not be removed from his living for any reason—it had been purchased for him by his father. Nor could his position as minister be interfered with on any such excuse as that of the mere personal dislike of his parishioners—as well, indeed, seek by petition to remove the Church herself. The knowledge of his unassailable position found expression among his parishioners in dogged looks, and the words: " Well, we don't trouble! "

It was in the twentieth year of his rectorship that a slight collision with the parish council drew from him this letter: " It is my duty to record my intention to attend no more meetings, for I cannot, as a Christian, continue to meet those who obstinately refuse to come to church."

It was then late September, and the harvest festival had been appointed for the following Sunday. The week passed,

but the farmers had provided no offerings for the decoration of
the church; the fishermen, too, accustomed by an old tradition
in that parish to supply some purchased fruit in lieu of their
shining fishes, sent nothing. The boycott had obviously been
preconcerted.

But when the rector stepped that Sunday into the pulpit the
church was fuller than it had been for many years. Men and
women who had long ceased to attend had come, possessed
evidently by an itch to see how "th' old man" would take it.
The eyes of the farmers and fishermen, hardened by the elements, had in them a grim humorous curiosity, such as one
may remark in the eyes of a ring of men round some poor
wretch, whom, moved by a crude sense of justice, they have
baited into the loss of dignity. Their faces, with hardly an
exception, seemed to say: "Sir, we were given neither hand
nor voice in the choosing of you. From the first day you
showed us the cloven hoof. We have never wanted you. If we
must have you, let us at all events get some sport out of
you!"

The rector's white figure rising from the dark pulpit received without movement the shafts of all our glances; his own
deep-set hungering eyes were fixed on the Bible in his hand. He
gave out his text: "The kindly fruits of the earth, in due
season——"

His voice—strangely smooth and low that morning, I remember—began discoursing of the beneficence and kindliness
of God, who had allowed the earth to provide men year by year
with food, according to their needs. It was as though the mellow sentiment of that season of fruition had fallen on his exiled
spirit. But presently he paused, and, leaning forward, looked
man by man, woman by woman, at us all. Those eyes now had
in them the peculiar flare which we knew so well. His voice
rose again: "And how have you met this benefaction, my
brethren, how have you shown your gratitude to God, embodied
in His Church and in me, her appointed representative? Do
you think, then, that God will let you insult Him with impunity? Do you think in your foolish pride that God will suffer you unpunished to place this conspired slight on Him? If
you imagine this, you are woefully mistaken. I know the depths
of your rebellious hearts; I read them like this Book. You
seek, you have always sought, to set my authority at defiance—
a wayward and disobedient generation. But let me tell you:

God, who has set His Holy Church over you, is a just and strong God; as a kind master chastises his dogs for their own good, so will He chastise you. You have sought to drive me out from among you"—and from his pale twisting lips, through the hush, there came a sound like a laugh—"to drive the Church, to drive God Himself, away! You could not have made a grosser error. Do you think that we, in solemn charge of your salvation, are to be moved by such puerile rebellion? Not so! God has appointed us—to God alone we are accountable. Not if every man and woman in the parish, aye, and every child, deserted this church, would I recoil one step from my duty, or resign my charge! As well imagine, forsooth, that your great Church is some poor man-elected leader, subject to your whims, and to be deposed as the fancy takes you! Do you conceive the nature of the Church and of my office to be so mean and petty that I am to feed you with the food you wish me to feed you with, to lead you into such fields as you dictate? No! my brethren, you have not that power! Is the shepherd elected by the sheep? Listen, then, to the truth, or to your peril be it! The Church is a rock set up by God amongst the shifting sands of life. It comes from Heaven, not from this miserable earth. Its mission is to command, yours to obey. If the last man in this Christian country proved a rebel and a traitor, the Church and her ministers would stand immovable, as I stand here, firm in my sacred resolve to save your souls. Go down on your knees, and beg God to forgive you for the wanton insult you have offered Him! . . . Hymn 266: 'Lead, kindly Light, amid the encircling gloom!'"

Through the grey aisles, where so great a silence reigned, the notes of the organ rose. The first verse of that hymn was sung only by the choir and a few women's voices; then one by one the men joined in. Our voices swelled into a shout louder than we had ever heard in the little church before—a mutinous, harsh, roaring sound, as though, in the words of that gentle hymn, each one of this grim congregation were pouring out all the resentment in his heart. The roar emerging through the open door must have startled the passing tourists, and the geese in the neighbouring farm-yard. It ended with a groan like the long-drawn sob of a wave sucking back.

In the village all the next week little except this sermon was discussed. Farmers and fishermen are men of the world. The conditions of their lives, which are guarded only by their own unremitting efforts, which are backed by no authority save their own courage in the long struggle with land and sea, gives them a certain deep philosophy. . Amongst the fishermen there was one white-bearded old fellow who even seemed to see a deep significance in the rector's sermon. "Mun putts hissel' above us, like the Czar o' Roossia," he said, "'tes the sperrit o' the thing that's wrong. Talk o' lovin' kindness, there's none 'bout the Church, 'sfar's I can see, 'tes all: 'Du this, or ye'll be blasted!' This man—he's a regular chip o' the old block!" He spoke, indeed, as though the rector's attitude towards them were a symbol of the Church's attitude to men. Among the farmers such analogies were veiled by the expression of simpler thoughts:

"Yu med ta' a 'arse to the watter, yu can't mak' un drink!"

"Whu wants mun, savin' our souls! Let mun save's own!"

"We'm not gude enough to listen to his prachin', I rackon!"

It was before a congregation consisting of his clerk, two tourists, three old women, one of them stone deaf, and four little girls, that the unfortunate man stood next Sunday morning.

Late that same wild and windy afternoon a jeering rumour spread down in the village: "Th' old man's up to Tresellyn 'Igh Cliff, talkin' to the watters!"

A crowd soon gathered, eager for the least sensation that should break the monotony. Beyond the combe, above the grey roofs of the fishing village, Tressellyn High Cliff rises abruptly. At the top, on the very edge, the tiny black shape of a man could be seen standing with his arms raised above his head. Now he kneeled, then stood motionless for many minutes with hands outstretched; while behind him the white and brown specks of his two terriers were visible, couched along the short grass. Suddenly he could be seen gesticulating wildly, and the speck shapes of the dogs leaping up, and cowering again as if terrified at their master's conduct.

For two hours this fantastic show was witnessed by the villagers with gloating gravity. The general verdict was: "Th' old man's carryin' on praaperly." But very gradually the sight of that tiny black figure appealing to his God—the God of his Church militant which lived by domination—roused the superstition of men who themselves were living in primitive conflict with the elements. They could not but appreciate what was so in keeping with the vengeful spirit of a fighting race. One could see that they even began to be afraid. Then a great burst of rain, sweeping from the sea, smothered all sight of him.

Early next morning the news spread that the rector had been found in his armchair, the two dogs at his feet, and the canary perched on his dead hand. His clothes were unchanged and wet, as if he had sunk into that chair, and passed away, from sheer exhaustion. The body of " the poor unfortunate gentleman "—the old housekeeper told me—was huddled and shrunk together; his chin rested on the little gold cross dangling on his vest.

They buried him in that green spot, apart from his parishioners, which he had selected for his grave, placing on the tombstone these words:

HIC JACET

P——— W———

PASTOR ECCLESIÆ BRITANNICÆ

" GOD IS LOVE "

1908.

MANNA

I

THE Petty Sessions Court at Linstowe was crowded. Miracles do not happen every day, nor are rectors frequently charged with larceny. The interest roused would have relieved all those who doubt the vitality of our ancient church. People who never went outside their farms or plots of garden had walked as much as three miles to see the show. Mrs. Gloyn, the sandy-haired little keeper of the shop where soap and herrings, cheese, matches, boot-laces, bull's-eyes, and the other luxuries of a countryside could be procured, remarked to Mrs. Redland, the farmer's wife, " 'Tis quite a gatherin', like." To which Mrs. Redland replied, " 'Most like church of a Sunday."

More women, it is true, than men were present, because of their greater piety, and because most of them had parted with pounds of butter, chickens, ducks, potatoes, or some such offertory in kind during the past two years, at the instance of the rector. They had a vested interest in this matter, and were present, accompanied by their grief at value unreceived. From Trover, their little village on the top of the hill two miles from Linstowe, with the squat church-tower, beautifully untouched, and the body of the building ruined by perfect restoration, they had trooped in; some even coming from the shore of the Atlantic, a mile beyond, across the Downs, whence other upland square church-towers could be viewed on the sky-line against the grey January heavens. The occasion was in a sense unique, and its piquancy strengthened by that rivalry which is the essence of religion.

For there was no love lost between church and chapel in Trover, and the rector's flock had long been fortified in their power of " parting " by fear lest " chapel " (also present that day in court) should mock at his impecuniosity. Not that his flock approved of his poverty. It had seemed " silly-like " ever

since the news had spread that his difficulties had been caused
by a faith in shares. To improve a secure if moderate position
by speculation would not have seemed wrong if he had succeeded, but failure had made him dependent on their butter,
their potatoes, their eggs and chickens. In that parish, as in
others, the saying "Nothing succeeds like success" was true,
nor had the villagers any abnormal disposition to question the
title-deeds of affluence.

But it is equally true that nothing irritates so much as finding that one of whom you have the right to beg is begging of
you. This was why the rector's tall, thin, black figure, down
which a ramrod surely had been passed at birth; his narrow,
hairless, white and wasted face, with red eye-brows over eyes
that seemed now burning and now melting; his grizzled red
hair under a hat almost green with age; his abrupt and dic-
tatorial voice; his abrupt and mirthless laugh—all were on their
nerves. His barked-out utterances, "I want a pound of butter.
—pay you Monday!" "I want some potatoes—pay you soon!"
had sounded too often in the ears of those who had found his
repayments so far purely spiritual. Now and then one of the
more cynical would remark, "Ah! I told un *my* butter was all
to market." Or, "The man can't 'ave no principles—he didn't
get no chicken out o' me." And yet it was impossible to let him
and his old mother die on them—it would give too much pleasure
"over the way." And they never dreamed of losing him in any
other manner, because they knew his living had been purchased.
Money had passed in that transaction; the whole fabric of the
Church and of society was involved. His professional conduct,
too, was flawless; his sermons long and fiery; he was always
ready to perform those supernumerary duties—weddings, bap-
tisms, and burials—which yielded him what revenue he had,
now that his income from the living was mortgaged up to the
hilt. Their loyalty held as the loyalty of people will when
some great institution of which they are members is endan-
gered.

Gossip said that things were in a dreadful way at the Rectory; the external prosperity of that red-brick building surrounded by laurels which did not flower, heightened ironically
the conditions within. The old lady, his mother, eighty years
of age, was reported never to leave her bed this winter, because they had no coal. She lay there, with her three birds
flying about dirtying the room, for neither she nor her son

would ever let a cage-door be shut—deplorable state of things! The one servant was supposed never to be paid. The tradesmen would no longer leave goods because they could not get their money. Most of the furniture had been sold; and the dust made you sneeze "fit to bust yourself, like."

With a little basket on his arm the rector collected for his household three times a week, pursuing a kind of method, always in the apparent belief that he would pay on Monday, and observing the Sabbath as a day of rest. His mind seemed ever to cherish the faith that his shares were on the point of recovery; his spirit never to lose belief in his divine right to be supported. It was extremely difficult to refuse him; the postman had twice seen him standing on the railway line that ran past just below the village, "with 'is 'at off, as if he was in two minds—like!" This vision of him close to the shining metals had powerfully impressed many good souls who loved to make flesh creep. They would say, "I wouldn' never be surprised if someat' 'appened to 'im one of these days!" Others, less romantic, shook their heads, insisting that "he wouldn' never do nothin' while his old mother lived." Others again, more devout, maintained that "he wouldn' never go against the scriptures, settin' an example like that!"

II

The Petty Sessions Court that morning resembled church on the occasion of a wedding, for the villagers of Trover had put on their black clothes and grouped themselves according to their religious faiths—" Church " in the right, " Chapel " in the left-hand aisle. They presented all that rich variety of type and monotony which the remoter country still affords to the observer; their mouths were almost all a little open and their eyes fixed with intensity on the Bench. The three magistrates —Squire Pleydell in the chair, Dr. Becket on his left, and " the Honble " Calmady on his right—were by most seen for the first time in their judicial capacity; and curiosity was divided between their proceedings and observation of the rector's prosecutor, a small baker from the town whence the village of Trover derived its necessaries. The face of this fellow, like that of a white walrus, and the back of his bald head were of interest to everyone until the case was called and the rector himself entered. In his thin black overcoat he advanced and stood as if a little dazed. Then, turning his ravaged face to the Bench, he jerked out:

"Good morning! Lot of people!"

A constable behind him murmured:

"Into the dock, sir, please."

Moving across, he entered the wooden edifice.

"Quite like a pulpit," he said, and uttered his barking laugh.

Through the court ran a stir and shuffle, as it might be of sympathy with his lost divinity, and every eye was fixed on that tall, lean figure, with the red, grey-streaked hair.

Entering the witness-box, the prosecutor deposed as follows:

"Last Tuesday afternoon, your Honours, I 'appened to be drivin' my cart meself up through Trover on to the cottages just above the dip, and I'd gone in to Mrs. 'Oney's, the laundress, leavin' my cart standin', same as I always do. I 'ad a bit o' gossip, an' when I come out, I see this gentleman walkin' away in front towards the village street. It so 'appens I 'appened to look in the back o' my cart, and I thinks to meself: 'That's funny! There's only two flat rounds—'ave I left two 'ere by mistake?' I call to Mrs. 'Oney an' I says, 'I 'aven't been absent, 'ave I, an' left ye two?' 'No,' she says, 'only one—'ere 'tis! Why?' she says. 'Well,' I says, 'I 'ad four when I come in to you; there's only two now. 'Tis funny!' I says. ''Ave you dropped one?' she says. 'No,' I says, 'I counted 'em.' 'That's funny,' she says; 'perhaps a dog's 'ad it.' ''E may 'ave,' I says, 'but the only thing I see on the road is that there.' An' I pointed to this gentleman. 'Oh!' she says, 'that's the rector.' 'Yes,' I says, 'I ought to know that, seein' 'e's owed me money a matter of eighteen months. I think I'll drive on,' I says. Well, I drove on, and come up to this gentleman. 'E turns 'is 'ead and looks at me. 'Good-afternoon!' he says—like that. 'Good-afternoon, sir,' I says. 'You 'aven't seen a loaf, 'ave you?' 'E pulls the loaf out of 'is pocket. 'On the ground,' 'e says; 'dirty,' 'e says. 'Do for my birds! Ha! ha!' like that. 'Oh!' I says, 'indeed! Now I know!' I says. I kept my 'ead, but I thinks: 'That's a bit too light-'earted. You owes me one pound, eight and tuppence; I've whistled for it gettin' on for two years, but you ain't content with that, it seems! Very well,' I thinks; 'we'll see. An' I don't give a darn whether you're a parson or not!' I charge 'im with takin' my bread."

Passing a dirty handkerchief over his white face and huge

gingery moustache, the baker was silent. Suddenly from the dock the rector called out: " Bit of dirty bread—feed my birds. Ha, ha! "

There was a deathly little silence. Then the baker said slowly:

" What's more, I say he ate it 'imself. I call two witnesses to that."

The chairman, passing his hand over his hard, alert face, that of a master of hounds, asked:

" Did you see any dirt on the loaf? Be careful! "

The baker answered stolidly:

" Not a speck."

Dr. Becket, a slight man with a short grey beard and eyes restive from having to notice painful things, spoke:

" Had your horse moved? "

" 'E never moves."

" Ha, ha! " came the rector's laugh.

The chairman said sharply:

" Well, stand down; call the next witness—Charles Stodder, carpenter. Very well! Go on, and tell us what you know."

But before he could speak the rector called out in a loud voice, " Chapel! "

" Hsssh, sir! " But through the body of the court had passed a murmur of challenge, at it were, from one aisle to the other.

The witness, a square man with a red face, grey hair, whiskers, and moustache, and lively, excitable, dark eyes, watering with anxiety, spoke in a fast, soft voice.

" Tuesday afternoon, your worships, it might be about four o'clock, I was passin' up the village, an' I saw the rector at his gate with a loaf in 'is 'and."

" Show us how."

The witness held his black hat to his side, with the rounded top outwards.

" Was the loaf clean or dirty? "

Sweetening his little eyes, the witness answered:

" I should say 'twas clean."

" Lie! "

The chairman said sternly:

" You mustn't interrupt, sir. You didn't see the bottom of the loaf? "

The witness's little eyes snapped.

" Not eggzactly."

" Did the rector speak to you? "

The witness smiled. " The rector wouldn' never stop me if I was passin'. I collects the rates."

The rector's laugh, so like a desolate dog's bark, killed the bubble of gaity rising in the court; and again that deathly little silence followed.

Then the chairman said:

" Do you want to ask him anything? "

The rector turned. " Why d'you tell lies? "

The witness, screwing up his eyes, said excitedly:

" What lies 'ave I told, please? "

" You said the loaf was clean."

" So 'twas clean, so far as I see."

" Come to church and you won't tell lies."

" Reckon I can learn truth faster in chapel."

The chairman rapped his desk.

" That'll do, that'll do! Stand down! Next witness—Emily Bleaker. Yes? What are you? Cook at the rectory? Very well. What do you know about the affair of this loaf last Tuesday afternoon? "

The witness, a broad-faced, brown-eyed girl, answered stolidly, " Nothin', zurr."

" Ha, ha! "

" Hssh! Did you see the loaf? "

" Noa."

" What are you here for, then? "

" Master asked for a plate and a knaife. He an' old missus ate et for dinner. I see the plate after; there wasn't on'y crumbs on et."

" If you never saw the loaf, how do you know they ate it? "

" Because ther warn't nothin' else in the 'ouse."

The rector's voice barked out:

" Quite right! "

The chairman looked at him fixedly.

" Do you want to ask her anything? "

The rector nodded.

" You been paid your wages? "

" Noa, I 'asn't."

" D'you know why? "

" Noa."

" Very sorry—no money to pay you. That's all."

This closed the prosecutor's case and there followed a pause,

during which the Bench consulted together and the rector eyed
the congregation, nodding to one here and there. Then the
chairman, turning to him, said:

"Now, sir, do you call any witnesses?"

"Yes. My bell-ringer. He's a good man. You can believe him."

The bell-ringer, Samuel Bevis, who took his place in the
witness-box, was a kind of elderly Bacchus, with permanently
trembling hands. He deposed as follows:

"When I passed rector Tuesday arternoon, he calls after
me: 'See this!' 'e says, and up 'e held it. 'Bit o' dirrty bread,'
'e says: 'do for my burrds.' Then on he goes walkin'."

"Did you see whether the loaf was dirty?"

"Yaas, I think 'twas dirrty."

"Don't *think*! Do you *know*?"

"Yaas; 'twas dirrty."

"Which side?"

"Which saide? I think 'twas dirrty on the bottom."

"Are you sure?"

"Yaas; 'twas dirrty on the bottom, for zartain."

"Very well. Stand down. Now, sir, will you give us your
version of this matter?"

The rector, pointing at the prosecutor and the left-hand aisle,
jerked out the words:

"All chapel—want to see me down."

The chairman said stonily:

"Never mind that. Come to the facts, please."

"Certainly! Out for a walk—passed the baker's cart—saw
a loaf fallen in the mud—picked it up—do for my birds."

"What birds?"

"Magpie and two starlings; quite free—never shut the cage
door; well fed."

"The baker charges you with taking it from his cart."

"Lie! Underneath the cart in a puddle."

"You heard what your cook said about your eating it. Did
you?"

"Yes, birds couldn't eat all—nothing in the house—mother
and I—hungry."

"Hungry?"

"No money. Hard up—very! Often hungry. Ha, ha!"

Again through the court that queer rustle passed. The three

magistrates gazed at the accused. Then "the Honble" Calmady said:

"You say you found the loaf under the cart. Didn't it occur to you to put it back? You could see it had fallen. How
else could it have come there?"

The rector's burning eyes seemed to melt.

"From the sky—manna." Staring round the court, he added,
"Hungry—God's elect—to the manna born!" And, throwing
back his head, he laughed. It was the only sound in a silence
as of the grave.

The magistrates spoke together in low tones. The rector stood
motionless, gazing at them fixedly. The people in the court
sat as if at a play. Then the chairman said:

"Case dismissed."

"Thank you."

Jerking out that short thanksgiving, the rector descended from
the dock and passed down the centre aisle, followed by every
eye.

III

From the Petty Sessions Court the congregation wended its
way back to Trover, by the muddy lane, "Church" and
"Chapel," arguing the case. To dim the triumph of the
"Church" the fact remained that the baker had lost his loaf
and had not been compensated. The loaf was worth money;
no money had passed. It was hard to be victorious and yet reduced to silence and dark looks at girding adversaries. The
nearer they came to home, the more angry with "Chapel" did
they grow. Then the bell-ringer had his inspiration. Assembling his three assistants, he hurried to the belfry, and in two
minutes the little old tower was belching forth the merriest
and maddest peal those bells had ever furnished. Out it swung
in the still air of the grey winter day, away to the very sea.

A stranger, issuing from the inn, hearing that triumphant
sound, and seeing so many black-clothed people about, said to
his driver:

"What is it—a wedding?"

"No, zurr, they say 'tis for the rector, like; he've a just been
acquitted for larceny."

On the Tuesday following, the rector's ravaged hairless face appeared in Mrs. Gloyn's doorway, and his voice, creaking like a saw, said:

"Can you let me have a pound of butter? Pay you soon."

What else could he do? Not even to God's elect does the sky always send down manna.

1916.

"CAFARD"

THE soldier, Jean Liotard, lay, face to the earth, by the bank of the River Drôme. He lay where the grass and trees ended, and between him and the shrivelled green current was much sandy foreshore, for summer was at height, and the snows had long finished melting and passing down. The burning sun had sucked up all moisture, the earth was parched, but to-day a cool breeze blew, willow and aspen leaves were fluttering and hissing as if millions of tiny kisses were being given up there; and a few swathes of white cloud were drawn, it seemed—not driven —along the blue. The soldier, Jean Liotard, had fixed his eyes on the ground, where was nothing to see but a few dry herbs. He had "*cafard*," for he was due to leave the hospital to-morrow and go up before the military authorities, for "*prolongation*." There he would answer perfunctory questions, and be told at once: *Au dépôt;* or have to lie naked before them that some "*major*" might prod his ribs, to find out whether his heart, displaced by shellshock, had gone back sufficiently to normal position. He had received one "*prolongation*," and so, wherever his heart now was, he felt sure he would not get another. "*Au dépôt*" was the fate before him, fixed as that river flowing down to its death in the sea. He had "*cafard*" —the little black beetle in the brain, which gnaws and eats and destroys all hope and heaven in a man. It had been working at him all last week, and now he was at a monstrous depth of evil and despair. To begin again the cursed barrack-round, the driven life, until in a month perhaps, packed like bleating sheep in the troop-train, he made that journey to the fighting line again—"*A la hachette—à la hachette!*"

He had stripped off his flannel jacket, and lay with shirt opened to the waist, to get the breeze against his heart. In his brown good-looking face, the hazel eyes, which in these three God-deserted years had acquired a sort of startled gloom, stared out like a dog's, rather prominent, seeing only the thoughts within him—thoughts and images swirling round in a dark

635

whirlpool, drawing his whole being deeper and deeper. He
was unconscious of all the summer hum and rustle—the cooing
of the dove up in that willow tree, the winged enamelled fairies
floating past, the chirr of the cicadas, that little brown lizard
among the pebbles, almost within reach, seeming to listen to the
beating of summer's heart, so motionless it lay; unconscious,
as though in verity he were again deep in some stifling trench,
with German shells whining over him, and the smell of muck
and blood making fœtid the air. He was in the mood which
curses God and dies; for he was devout—a Catholic, and still
went to Mass. And God had betrayed the earth, and Jean Liotard. All the enormities he had seen in his two years at the
front—the mouthless, mangled faces, the human ribs whence
rats would steal; the frenzied, tortured horses, with leg or
quarter rent away, still living; the rotted farms, the dazed and
hopeless peasants; his innumerable suffering comrades; the desert of no-man's land; and all the thunder and moaning of
war; and the reek and the freezing of war; and the driving—
the callous, perpetual driving by some great Force which shovelled warm human hearts and bodies, warm human hopes and
loves by the million into the furnace; and over all, dark sky
without a break, without a gleam of blue or lift anywhere—
all this enclosed him, lying in the golden heat, so that not a
glimmer of life or hope could get at him. Back into it all
again! Back into it, he who had been through forty times
the hell that the "*majors*" ever endured, five hundred times
the hell ever glimpsed at by those *députés,* safe with their fat
salaries and their gabble about victory and the lost provinces
and the future of the world—the *Canaille!* Let them allow
the soldiers, whose lives they spent like water—" *les camarades*"
on both sides—poor devils who bled, and froze, and starved,
and sweated—let them suffer these to make the peace! Ah!
what a peace that would be—its first condition, all the sacred
politicians and pressmen hanging in rows in every country; the
mouth fighters, the pen fighters, the fighters with other men's
blood! Those comfortable citizens would never rest while there
was a young man with whole limbs left in France! Had he not
killed enough Boches that they might leave him and his tired
heart in peace? He thought of his first charge; of how queer
and soft that Boche body felt when his bayonet went through;
and another, and another. Ah! he had "*joliment*" done his
duty that day! And something wrenched at his ribs. They

were only Boches, but their wives and children, their mothers
—faces questioning, faces pleading for them—pleading with
whom? Ah! not with him! Who was he that had taken those
lives, and others since, but a poor devil without a life himself,
without the right to breathe or move except to the orders of a
Force which had no mind, which had no heart, had nothing
but a blind will to go on, it knew not why. If only he survived—it was not possible—but if only he survived, and with
his millions of comrades could come back and hold the reckoning! Some scare-the-crows then would waggle in the wind.
The butterflies would perch on a few mouths empty at last; the
flies enjoy a few silent tongues! Then slowly his fierce unreasoning rancour vanished into a mere awful pity for himself.
Was a fellow never again to look at the sky, and the good soil,
the fruit, the wheat, without this dreadful black cloud above
him; never again make love among the trees, or saunter down
a lighted boulevard, or sit before a *café;* never again attend
Mass without this black dog of disgust and dread sitting on his
shoulders, riding him to death? Angels of pity! Was there
never to be an end? One was going mad under it—yes, mad!
And the face of his mother came before him, just as he had
seen her last, three years ago, when he left his home in the now
invaded country to join his regiment—his mother who, with
all his family, was in the power of the Boche. He had gone
gaily, and she had stood like stone, her hand held over her eyes,
in the sunlight, watching him while the train ran out. Usually
the thought of the cursed Boches holding in their heavy hands
all that was dear to him was enough to sweep his soul to a
clear, definite hate, which made all this nightmare of war seem
natural and even right; but now it was not enough—he had
"*cafard.*" He turned on his back. The sky above the mountains might have been black for all the joy its blue gave him.
The butterflies, those drifting flakes of joy, passed unseen. He
was thinking: No rest, no end, except by walking over bodies,
dead, mangled bodies of poor devils like himself, poor hunted
devils, who wanted nothing but never to lift a hand in combat
again so long as they lived, who wanted—as he wanted—nothing but laughter and love and rest! *Quelle vie!* A carnival of
leaping demonry! A dream—unutterably bad! 'And when
I go back to it all,' he thought, 'I shall go all shaven and
smart, and wave my hand as if I were going to a wedding, as
we all do. *Vive la France!* Ah! what mockery! Can't a poor

devil have a dreamless sleep!' He closed his eyes, but the
sun struck hot on them through the lids, and he turned over
on his face again and looked longingly at the river—they said
it was deep in mid-stream; it still ran fast there! What was
that down by the water? Was he really mad? And he uttered
a queer laugh. There was his black dog—the black dog off
his shoulders, the black dog which rode him, yea, which had become his very self, just going to wade in! And he called out:
"*Hé! le copain!*" It was not his dog, for it stopped drinking, tucked its tail in, and cowered at the sound of his voice.
Then it came from the water and sat down on its base among
the stones and looked at him. A real dog. But what a guy!
What a thin wretch of a little black dog! It sat and stared—
a mongrel who might once have been pretty. It stared at
Jean Liotard with the pathetic gaze of a dog so thin and hungry
that it earnestly desires to go to men and get fed once more,
but has been so kicked and beaten that it dare not. It seemed
held in suspense by the equal overmastering impulses, fear and
hunger. And Jean Liotard stared back. The lost, as it were
despairing, look of the dog began to penetrate his brain. He
held out his hand, and said: "*Viens!*" But at the sound the
little dog only squirmed away a few paces, then again sat down
and resumed its stare. Again Jean Liotard uttered that queer
laugh. If the good God were to hold out His hand and say to
him, "*Viens!*" he would do exactly as that little beast; he
would not come, not he! What was he too but a
starved and beaten dog—a driven wretch, kicked to hell! And
again, as if experimenting with himself, he held out his
hand and said: "*Viens!*" and again the beast squirmed a
little further away, and again sat down and stared. Jean
Liotard lost patience. His head drooped till his forehead
touched the ground. He smelt the parched herbs, and a faint
sensation of comfort stole through his nerves. He lay unmoving, trying to fancy himself dead and out of it all. The hum
of summer, the smell of grasses, the caress of the breeze going
over! He pressed the palms of his outstretched hands on the
warm soil, as one might on a woman's breast. If only it were
really death, how much better than life in this butcher's shop!
But death—his death, was waiting for him away over there, under the moaning shells, under the whining bullets, at the end of
a steel spike—a mangled, fœtid death. Death—his death, had
no sweet scent and no caress—save the kisses of rats and crows.

Life and death, what were they? Nothing but the preying of
creatures the one on the other—nothing but that; and love,
the blind instinct which made these birds and beasts of prey.
Bon sang de bon sang! The Christ hid his head finely nowadays! That cross up there on the mountain top, with the sun
gleaming on it—they had been right to put it up where no
man lived, and not even a dog roamed to be pitied! ' Fairy
tales!' he thought: ' Those who drive and those who are
driven, those who eat and those who are eaten—we are all poor
devils together. There is no pity, no God!' And the flies
drummed their wings above him. And the sun, boring into his
spine through his thin shirt, made him reach for his jacket.
The little dog, still sitting on its base twenty yards away, cowered and dropped its ears when he moved; and he thought:
' Poor beast! Someone has been doing the devil's work on
you not badly!' There were some biscuits in the pocket of his
jacket, and he held one out. The dog shivered, and its thin
pink tongue lolled out, panting with desire and fear. Jean
Liotard tossed the biscuit gently about half-way. The dog
cowered back a step or two, crept forward three, and again
squatted. Then very gradually it crept up to the biscuit, bolted
it, and regained its distance. The soldier took out another.
This time he threw it five paces only in front of him. Again
the little beast cowered, slunk forward, seized the biscuit, devoured it; but this time it only recoiled a pace or two, and
seemed, with panting mouth and faint wagging of the tail, to
beg for more. Jean Liotard held a third biscuit as far out in
front of him as he could, and waited. The creature crept forward and squatted just out of reach. There it sat, with saliva
dripping from its mouth; seemingly it could not make up its
mind to that awful venture. The soldier sat motionless; his
outstretched hand began to tire, but he did not budge—he
meant to conquer its fear. At last it snatched the biscuit. Jean
Liotard instantly held out a fourth. That too was snatched,
but at the fifth he was able to touch the dog. It cowered almost into the ground at touch of his fingers, and then lay, still
trembling violently, while the soldier continued to stroke its head
and ears. And suddenly his heart gave a twitter, the creature
had licked his hand. He took out his last biscuit, broke it up,
and fed the dog slowly with the bits, talking all the time;
when the last crumb was gone he continued to murmur and
crumple its ears softly. He had become aware of something

happening within the dog—something in the nature of conversion, as if it were saying: "My master, my new master—I worship, I love you!" The creature came gradually closer, quite close; then put up its sharp black nose and began to lick his face. Its little hot rough tongue licked and licked, and with each lick the soldier's heart relaxed, just as if the licks were being given there and something licked away. He put his arms round the thin body and hugged it, and still the creature went on feverishly licking at his face and neck and chest, as if trying to creep inside him. The sun poured down, the lizards rustled and whisked among the pebbles; the kissing never ceased up there among the willow and aspen leaves, and every kind of flying thing went past drumming its wings. There was no change in the summer afternoon. God might not be there, but pity had come back; Jean Liotard no longer had "*cafard*." He put the little dog gently off his lap, got up, and stretched himself. "*Voyons, mon brave, faut aller voir les copains! Tu es à moi.*" The little dog stood up on its hind legs, scratching with its forepaws at the soldier's thigh, as if trying to get at his face again; as if begging not to be left; and its tail waved feverishly, half in petition, half in rapture. The soldier caught the paws, set them down, and turned his face for home, making the noises that a man makes to his dog; and the little dog followed, close as he could get to those moving ankles, lifting his snout and panting with anxiety and love.

1917.

THE RECRUIT

SEVERAL times since that fateful fourth of August he had said:
" I sh'll 'ave to go."

And the farmer and his wife would look at him, he with a
sort of amusement, she with a queer compassion in her heart,
and one or the other would reply smiling: " That's all right,
Tom; there's plenty Germans yet. Yu wait a bit."

His mother, too, who came daily from the lonely cottage in
the little combe on the very edge of the big hill to work in the
kitchen and farm dairy, would turn her dark, taciturn head,
with still plentiful black hair, towards his face, which for all
its tan was so weirdly reminiscent of a withered baby, pinkish
and light-lashed with forelock and fair hair thin and rumpled,
and small blue eyes; and she would mutter:

" Don't yu never fret, boy. They'll come for 'ee fast enough
when they want 'ee." No one, least of all perhaps his mother,
could take quite seriously that little square, short-footed man,
born when she was just seventeen. Sure of work because he
was first-rate with every kind of beast, he was not yet looked
on as being quite " all there." He could neither read nor
write, had scarcely ever been outside the parish, and then only
in a shandrydan on a club treat, and knew no more of the
world than the native of a small South Sea Island. His life
from school age on had been passed, year in, year out, from
dawn till dark, with the cattle and their calves, the sheep, the
horses and the wild moor ponies; except when hay or corn harvest, or any exceptionally exacting festival absorbed him for the
moment. From shyness he never went into the bar of the inn,
and so had missed the greater part of village education. He
could, of course, read no papers; a map was to him but a mystic
mass of marks and colours; he had never seen the sea, never a
ship; no water broader than the parish streams; until the war
had never met anything more like a soldier than the constable
of the neighbouring village. But he had once seen a Royal
Marine in uniform. What sort of creatures these Germans were

to him, who knows? They were cruel—he had grasped that.
Something noxious, perhaps, like the adders whose backs he
broke with his stick; something dangerous, like the chained dog
at Shapton Farm, or the bull at Vannacombe. When the war
first broke out, and they had called the younger blacksmith (a
reservist and noted village marksman) back to his regiment, the
little cowman had smiled and said: " Wait till regiment gets to
front; Fred'll soon shoot 'em up."

But weeks and months went by, and it was always the Germans, the Germans; Fred had clearly not yet shot them up.
And now one and now another went off from the village, and
two from the farm itself; and the great Fred returned slightly
injured for a few weeks' rest, and, full of whisky from morning till night, made the village ring; and finally went off again
in a mood of manifest reluctance. All this weighed dumbly
on the mind of the little cowman, the more heavily that because of his inarticulate shyness he could never talk that weight
away, nor could anyone by talk relieve him, no premises of
knowledge or vision being there. From sheer physical con-
tagion he felt the grizzly menace in the air, and a sense of being left behind when others were going to meet that menace
with their fists, as it were. There was something proud and
sturdy in the little man, even in the look of him, for all that he
was " poor old Tom," who brought a smile to the lips of all.
He was passionate, too, if rubbed up the wrong way; but it
needed the malevolence and ingenuity of human beings to annoy him—with his beasts he never lost his temper, so that they
had perfect confidence in him. He resembled herdsmen of the
Alps, whom one may see in dumb communion with their creatures up in those high solitudes; for he too dwelt in a high solitude cut off from real fellowship with men and women by lack
of knowledge, and by the supercilious pity in them. Living
in such a remote world his talk—when he did say something—
had ever the surprising quality attaching to the thoughts of
those by whom the normal proportions of things are quite unknown. His short square figure, hatless and rarely coated in
any weather, dotting from foot to foot, a bit of stick in one
hand and often a straw in the mouth—he did not smoke—was
familiar in the yard where he turned the handle of the separator, or in the fields and cowsheds, from daybreak to dusk,
save for the hours of dinner and tea, which he ate in the farm
kitchen, making sparse and surprising comments. To his pecu-

liar whistles and calls the cattle and calves, for all their rumina-
tion and stubborn shyness, were amazingly responsive. It was
a pretty sight to see them pushing against each other round
him—for, after all, he was as much the source of their persistence, especially through the scanty winter months, as a mother
starling to her unfledged young.

When the Government issued their request to householders
to return the names of those of military age ready to serve if
called on, he heard of it, and stopped munching to say in his
abrupt fashion: " I'll go—fight the Germans." But the farmer
did not put his name down, saying to his wife:

" Poor old Tom! 'Twidden be 'ardly fair—they'd be makin'
game of 'un."

And his wife, her eyes shining with motherliness, answered:
" Poor lad, he's not fit-like."

The months went on—winter passing to spring, and the slow
decking of the trees and fields began with leaves and flowers,
with butterflies and the songs of birds. How far the little cowman would notice such a thing as that no one could ever have
said, devoid as he was of the vocabulary of beauty, but like all
the world his heart must have felt warmer and lighter under his
old waistcoat, and perhaps more than most hearts, for he could
often be seen standing stock-still in the fields, his browning
face turned to the sun.

Less and less he heard talk of Germans—dogged acceptance
of the state of war having settled on that far countryside—the
beggars were not beaten and killed off yet, but they would be in
good time. It was unpleasant to think of them more than could
be helped. Once in a way a youth went off and " 'listed," but,
though the parish had given more perhaps than the average,
a good few of military age still clung to life as they had known
it. Then some bright spirit conceived the notion that a county
regiment should march through the remoter districts to rouse
them up.

The cuckoo had been singing five days; the lanes and fields,
the woods and the village green were as Joseph's coat, so varied
and so bright the foliage, from golden oak-buds to the brilliant
little lime-tree leaves, the feathery green shoots of larches, and
the already darkening bunches of the sycamores. The earth was
dry—no rain for a fortnight—when the cars containing the
brown-clad men and a recruiting band drew up before the inn.
Here were clustered the farmers, the innkeeper, the grey-haired

postman; by the church gate and before the schoolyard were
knots of girls and children, schoolmistress, schoolmaster, parson; and down on the lower green a group of likely youths, an
old labourer or two, and apart from human beings, as was his
wont, the little cowman in brown corduroys tied below the knee
and an old waistcoat, the sleeves of his blue shirt dotted with
pink rolled up to the elbows of his brown arms; so he stood,
his brown neck and shaven-looking head quite bare, with his
bit of stick wedged between his waist and the ground, staring
with all his light-lashed water-blue eyes under the thatch of his
forelock.

The speeches rolled forth glib; the khaki-clad men drank their
second fill that morning of coffee and cider; the little cowman
stood straight and still, his head drawn back. Two figures—
officers, men who had been at the front—detached themselves
and came towards the group of likely youths. These wavered a
little, were silent, sniggered, stood their ground—the khaki-clad
figures passed among them. Hackneyed words, jests, the touch
of flattery changing swiftly to chaff—all the customary performance, hollow and pathetic; and then the two figures re-
emerged, their hands clenched, their eyes shifting here and there,
their lips drawn back in fixed smiles. They had failed and
were trying to hide it. They must not show contempt—the
young slackers might yet come in when the band played.

The cars were filled again, the band struck up: " It's a long,
long way to Tipperary."

And at the edge of the green, within two yards of the car's
dusty passage, the little cowman stood apart and stared. His
face was red. Behind him they were cheering—the parson and
farmers, schoolchildren, girls, even the group of youths. He
alone did not cheer, but his face grew still more red. When
the dust above the road and the distant blare of " Tipperary "
had dispersed and died he walked back to the farm, dotting from
one to other of his short feet. All that afternoon and evening
he spoke no word; but that flush seemed to have settled in his
face for good and all. He milked some cows, but forgot to
bring the pails up. Two of his precious cows he left unmilked
till their distressful lowing caused the farmer's wife to go down
and see. There he was, standing against a gate moving his
brown neck from side to side like an animal in pain, oblivious,
seemingly, of everything. She spoke to him:

" What's matter, Tom? " All he could answer was:

" I'se goin', I'se goin'." She milked the cows herself.

For the next three days he could settle to nothing, leaving his jobs half done, speaking to no one save to say:

" I'se goin'; I'se got to go." Even the beasts looked at him surprised.

On the Saturday the farmer, having consulted with his wife, said quietly:

" Well, Tom, ef yu want to go, yu shall. I'll drive 'ee down Monday. Us won't du nothin' to keep yu back."

The little cowman nodded. But he was restless as ever all through that Sunday, eating nothing.

On Monday morning, arrayed in his best clothes, he got into the dog-cart. There, without good-bye to anyone, not even to his beasts, he sat staring straight before him, square, and jolting up and down beside the farmer, who turned on him now and then a dubious, almost anxious eye.

So they drove the eleven miles to the recruiting station. He got down, entered, the farmer with him.

" Well, my lad," they asked him, " what d'you want to join? "

" Royal Marines."

It was a shock, coming from the short square figure of such an obvious landsman. The farmer took him by the arm.

" Why, yu'm a Devon man, Tom; better take county regiment. An't they gude enough for yu? "

Shaking his head he answered: " Royal Marines." ·

Was it the glamour of the words or the Royal Marine he had once seen that moved him to wish to join that outlandish corps? They took him to the recruiting station for the Royal Marines.

Stretching up his short square body and blowing out his cheeks to increase his height, he was put before the reading board. His eyes were splendid; little that passed in hedgerows, or the heavens, in woods, or on the hillsides, could escape them. They asked him to read the print.

Staring, he answered: " L."

" No, my lad, you're guessing."

" L."

The farmer plucked at the recruiting officer's sleeve, his face was twitching, and he whispered hoarsely:

" 'E don't know 'is alphabet."

The officer turned and contemplated that short square figure with the browned face so reminiscent of a withered baby, and the little blue eyes staring out under the dusty forelock. Then he grunted, and going up to him, laid a hand on his shoulder.

"*Your* heart's all right, my lad, but you can't pass."

The little cowman looked at him, turned, and went straight out. An hour later he sat again beside the farmer on the way home, staring before him and jolting up and down.

"They won't get me," he said suddenly: "I can fight, but I'se not goin'." A fire of resentment seemed to have been lit within him. That evening he ate his tea, and next day settled down again among his beasts. But whenever, now, the war was mentioned he would look up with his puckered smile which seemed to have in it a resentful amusement, and say:

"They ain't got me yet."

His dumb sacrifice passing their comprehension had been rejected—or so it seemed to him. He could not understand why they had spurned him—he was as good as they! His pride was hurt. No! They should not get him now!

1917.

COMPENSATION

IF, as you say (said Ferrand), there is compensation in this life for everything, do tell me where it comes in here.

Two years ago I was interpreter to an hotel in Ostend, and spent many hours on the Plage waiting for the steamers to bring sheep to my slaughter. There was a young man about that year who had a stall of cheap jewellery; I don't know his name, for among us he was called Tchuk-Tchuk; but I knew *him*—for we interpreters know everybody. He came from Southern Italy and called himself an Italian, but by birth he was probably an Algerian Jew; an intelligent boy, who knew that, except in England, it is far from profitable to be a Jew in these days. After seeing his nose and his beautiful head of frizzly hair, however, there was little more to be said on the subject. His clothes had been given him by an English tourist—a pair of flannel trousers, an old frock coat, a bowler hat. Incongruous? Yes, but think, how cheap! The only thing that looked natural to him was his tie; he had unsewn the ends and wore it without a collar. He was little and thin, which was not surprising, for all he ate a day was half a pound of bread, or its equivalent in macaroni, with a little piece of cheese, and on a feast day a bit of sausage. In those clothes, which were made for a fat man, he had the appearance of a scarecrow with a fine, large head. These "Italians" are the Chinese of the West. The conditions of life down there being impossible, they are driven out like locusts or the old inhabitants of Central Asia —a regular invasion. In every country they have a kind of Society which helps them to make a start. When once provided with organs, jewellery, or whatever their profession, they live on nothing, drink nothing, spend no money. Smoke? Yes, they smoke; but you have to give them the tobacco. Sometimes they bring their women; more often they come alone— they make money more quickly without. The end they have in view is to scrape together a treasure of two or three hundred pounds and go back to Italy rich men. If you're accustomed to the Italian at home, it will astonish you to see how he works when he's out of his own country, and how provident he is— a regular Chinaman. Tchuk-Tchuk was alone, and he worked like a slave. He was at his stand, day in, day out; if the sun burned, if there was a gale; he was often wet through, but no one could pass without receiving a smile from his teeth and a hand stretched out with some gimcrack or other. He always tried to impress the women, with whom he did most of his business—especially the *cocotterie*. Ah! how he looked at them with his great eyes! Temperamentally, I dare say, he was vicious enough; but, as you know, it costs money to be vicious, and he spent no money. His expenses were twopense a day for food and fourpence for his bed in a *café* full of other birds of his feather—sixpence a day, three shillings and sixpence a week. No other sort of human creature can keep this up long. My minimum is tenpence, which is not a bed of roses; but, then, I can't do without tobacco (to a man in extreme poverty a single vice is indispensable). But these " Italians " do without even, that. Tchuk-Tchuk sold; not very hard work, you say? Try it for half an hour; try and sell something good—and Tchuk-Tchuk's things were rubbish—flash coral jewellery, Italian enamels made up into pins and brooches, celluloid gimcracks. In the evenings I've often seen him doze off from sheer fatigue, but always with his eyes half-open, like a cat. His soul was in his stall; he watched everything—but only to sell his precious goods, for nothing interested him; he despised all the world around him—the people, the sea, the amusements; they were ridiculous and foreign. He had his stall, and he lived to sell. He was like a man shut up in a box—with not a pleasure, not a sympathy, nothing wherewith to touch this strange world in which he found himself.

"I'm of the South," he would say to me, jerking his head at the sea; " it's hard there. Over there I got a girl. She wouldn't be sorry to see me again; not too sorry! Over there one starves; name of a Saint " (he chose this form of oath, no doubt, because it sounded Christian), " it's hard there! "

I am not sentimental about Tchuk-Tchuk; he was an egoist to the bottom of his soul, but that did not in the least prevent his suffering for the want of his South, for the want of his sunshine, and his girl—the greater the egoism the greater the suffering. He craved like a dumb animal; but, as he remarked, " Over there one starves! " Naturally he had not waited for that. He had his hopes. "Wait a bit!" he used to say. "Last year I was in Brussels. Bad business! At the end they take away all my money for the Society, and give me this stall. This is all right—I make some money this season."

He had many clients among "women of morals," who had an eye for his beautiful head of hair, who know, too, that life is not all roses; and there was something pathetic in the persistency of Tchuk-Tchuk and the way his clothes hung about him like sacks; nor was he bad-looking, with his great black eyes and his slim, dirty hands.

One wet day I came on the Estacade when hardly a soul was there. Tchuk-Tchuk had covered his stall with a piece of old tarpaulin. He was smoking a long cigar.

"Aha! Tchuk-Tchuk," I said, "smoking?"

"Yes," says he, "it's good!"

"Why not smoke every day, you miser? It would comfort you when you're hungry."

He shook his head. "Costs money," says he. "This one cost me nothing. A kind of an individual gave it me—a red-faced Englishman—said he couldn't smoke it. He knew nothing, the idiot—this is good, I tell you!"

But it was Tchuk-Tchuk who knew nothing—he had been too long without the means of knowledge. It was interesting to see the way he ate, drank, inhaled, and soaked up that rank cigar—a true revel of sensuality.

The end of the season came, and all of us birds who prey on the visitors were getting ready to fly; but I stayed on, because I liked the place—the gay-coloured houses, the smell of fish in the port, the good air, the long green seas, the dunes; there's something of it all in my blood, and I'm always sorry to leave. But after the season is over—as Tchuk-Tchuk would say——"Name of a saint—one starves over there!"

One evening, at the very end, when there were scarcely twenty visitors in the place, I went as usual to a certain *café,* with two compartments, where everyone comes whose way of living is dubious—bullies, comedians, off-colour actresses, women of morals, "Turks," "Italians," "Greeks"—all such, in fact, as play the game of stealing—a regular rag-shop of cheats and gentlemen of industry—very interesting people, with whom I am well acquainted. Nearly everyone had gone; so that evening there were but few of us in the restaurant, and in the inner room three Italians only. I passed into that.

Presently in came Tchuk-Tchuk, the first time I had ever seen him in a place where one could spend a little money. How thin he was, with his little body and his great head! One would have said he hadn't eaten for a week. A week? A year! Down he sat, and called for a bottle of wine; and at once he began to chatter and snap his fingers.

"Ha, ha!" says one of the Italians; "look at Tchuk-Tchuk. What a nightingale he has become all of a sudden. Come, Tchuk-Tchuk, give us some of your wine, seeing you're in luck!"

Tchuk-Tchuk gave us of his wine, and ordered another bottle.

"Ho, ho!" says another Italian, "must have buried his family, this companion!" We drank—Tchuk-Tchuk faster than all. Do you know that sort of thirst, when you drink just to give you the feeling of having blood in the veins at all? Most people in that state can't stop—they drink themselves dead drunk. Tchuk-Tchuk was not like that. He was careful, as always, looking to his future. Oh! he kept his heart in hand; but in such cases a little goes a long way; he became cheerful —it doesn't take much to make an Italian cheerful who has been living for months on water and half-rations of bread and macaroni. It was evident, too, that he had reason to feel gay. He sang and laughed, and the other Italians sang and laughed with him. One of them said: "It seems our Tchuk-Tchuk has been doing good business. Come, Tchuk-Tchuk, tell us what you have made this season!"

But Tchuk-Tchuk only shook his head.

"Eh!" said the Italian, "the shy bird. It ought to be something good. As for me, comrades, honestly, five hundred francs is all I've made—not a centime more—and the half of that goes to the patron."

And each of them began talking of his gains, except Tchuk-Tchuk, who showed his teeth, and kept silence.

"Come, Tchuk-Tchuk," said one, "don't be a bandit—a little frankness!"

"He won't beat my sixteen hundred!" said another.

"Name of a Saint!" said Tchuk-Tchuk suddenly, "what do you say to four thousand?"

But we all laughed.

"La la!" said one, "he mocks us!"

Tchuk-Tchuk opened the front of his old frockcoat.

"Look!" he cried, and he pulled out four bills—each for a thousand francs. How we stared!

" See," said he, " what it is to be careful—I spend nothing—every cent is here! Now I go home—I get my girl; wish me good journey!" He set to work again to snap his fingers.

We stayed some time and drank another bottle. Tchuk-Tchuk paying. When we parted nobody was helpless, only, as I say, Tchuk-Tchuk on the road to the stars, as one is after a six months' fast. The next morning I was drinking a " bock " in the same *café*, for there was nothing else to do, when all of a sudden who should come running in but this same Tchuk-Tchuk! Ah! but he was no longer on the road to the stars. He flung himself down at the table, with his head between his hands, and the tears rolled down his cheeks.

" They've robbed me," he cried, " robbed me of every sou; robbed me while I slept. I had it here, under my pillow; I slept on it; it's gone—every sou!" He beat his breast.

" Come, Tchuk-Tchuk," said I, " from under your pillow? That's not possible! "

" How do I know? " he groaned; " it's gone, I tell you—all my money, all my money. I was heavy with the wine——" All he could do was to repeat again and again: " All my money, all my money! "

" Have you been to the police? "

He had been to the police. I tried to console him, but without much effect, as you may imagine. The boy was beside himself.

The police did nothing—why should they? If he had been a Rothschild it would have been different, but seeing he was only a poor devil of an Italian who had lost his all——!

Tchuk-Tchuk had sold his stall, his stock, everything he had, the day before, so he had not even the money for a ticket to Brussels. He was obliged to walk. He started—and to this day I see him starting, with his little hard hat on his beautiful black hair, and the unsewn ends of his tie. His face was like the face of the Devil thrown out of Eden!

What became of him I cannot say, but I do not see too clearly in all this the compensation of which you have been speaking.

And Ferrand was silent.

1904.

CONSCIENCE

TAGGART sat up. The scoop under the ranger's fence, cannily selected for his sleeping-place, was overhung by branches, and the birds of Hyde Park were at matins already. His watch had gone the way of his other belongings during the last three months, and he could only assume from the meagre light that it was but little after dawn. He was not grateful to the birds; he would be hungry long before a breakfast coming from he hardly knew where. But he listened to them with interest. This was the first night he had passed in the open, and, like all amateurs, he felt a kind of triumph at having achieved vagrancy in spite of the law, the ranger, and the dew. He was a Northumbrian too, and his " tail still up," as he expressed it. Born in a town, Taggart had not much country lore—at sparrows, blackbirds, thrushes, his knowledge stopped; but he enjoyed the bobbery the little beggars were kicking up, and, though a trifle stiff perhaps, he felt " fine."

He lit his pipe, and almost at once his brain began to revolve the daily problem of how to get a job, and of why he had lost the one he had.

Walking, three months ago, burly, upright, secure and jolly, into the room of his chief at the offices of " Conglomerated Journals Ltd.," he had been greeted with:

" Morning, Taggart. Georgie Grebe is to give us an article for *The Lighthouse*. He won't have time to write it, of course. I want you just to do us a column he could sign—something Grebeish. I'm anxious for a feature of that sort every week now in *The Lighthouse;* got half a dozen really good names. We must get it on its legs with the big Public."

Taggart smiled. Georgie Grebe! The name was a household word—tophole idea to get him!

" Did he ever write a line in his life, sir? "

" Don't suppose so—but you know the sort of thing he *would* write; he gets nothing for it but the Ad. The week after I've got Sir Cutman Kane—you'll want to be a bit careful there;

but you can get his manner from that book of his on murder
trials. He hasn't got a minute—must have it devilled; but he'll
sign anything decently done. I'm going to *make* 'em buy *The
Lighthouse,* Taggart. Get on to the Grebe article at once, will
you?"

Taggart nodded, and drawing from his pocket some type-
written sheets of paper, laid them on the bureau.

"Here's your signed leader, sir; I've gingered it a bit too
much, perhaps."

"Haven't time to look at it; got to catch the boat train,
Taggart."

"Shall I tone it down a little?"

"Better perhaps; use your judgment. Sit here, and do it
right now. Good-bye; back on Friday."

Reaching for his soft hat, assisted into his coat by Taggart,
the chief was gone.

Taggart sat down to pencil the signed leader.

"Good leader," he thought, " pity nobody knows I write 'em."

This devilling was quite an art, and, not unlike art, poorly
enough paid—still, not bad fun feeling you were the pea and
the chief only the shell—the chief, with his great name and controlling influence. He finished pencilling; O.K.'d the sheets;
thought: 'Georgie Grebe! What the deuce shall I write
about?' and went back to his room.

It was not much of a room, and there was not much in it
except Jimmy Counter, smoking a pipe and writing furiously.
Taggart sat down too, lit his own pipe, took a sheet of paper
and scrawled the words: "Georgie Grebe Article" across the
top.

Georgie Grebe! It *was* a scoop! The chief had a wonderful
flair for just the names that got the Public. There was something rather beautifully simple about writing an article for a
man who had never written a line—something virginal in the
conception. And when you came to think of it, something
virginal in the Public's buying of the article to read the thoughts
of their idol, Georgie Grebe. Yes, and what were the thoughts
of their idol, Georgie Grebe? If he, Taggart, didn't know,
nobody would, not even Georgie Grebe! Taggart smiled, then
felt a little nervous. Georgie Grebe—celebrated clown—probably he hadn't any thoughts! Really, there was something very
trustful about the Public! He dipped his pen in ink and sat
staring at the nib. Trustful! The word had disturbed the

transparency of his mental process, as a crystal of peroxide will disturb and colour a basinful of water. Trustful! The Public would pay their pennies to read what they thought were the thoughts of Georgie Grebe. But Georgie Grebe had no thoughts! Taggart bit into the pipe stem. Steady! He was getting on too fast. Of course Georgie Grebe had thoughts if he signed! By writing his name he adopted them—didn't he? His name would be reproduced in autograph, with the indispensable portrait. People would see by his features that Georgie Grebe must have had those thoughts. Trustful! Was the Public so very trustful—when there was such evidence? Besides, Grebe would read his thoughts—fraudulent! Bosh! This was just devilling; there was nothing fraudulent about "devilling" —everybody did it! Fraudulent! You might as well say those signed leaders written for the chief were fraudulent. Of course they weren't—they were only devilled. The Public paid for the thoughts of the chief, and they were the thoughts of the chief, since he signed them. Devilled thoughts! And yet! Would the Public pay if those leaders were signed A. P. Taggart? The thoughts would be the same—very good thoughts. They ought to pay—but—would they? He struck another match, and wrote:

"I am no writer, ladies and gentlemen. I am—believe me —a simple clown. In balancing this new pole upon my nose I am conscious of a certain sense of fraud——"

He crossed out the paragraph. That word again—must keep it from buzzing senselessly round his brain like this! He was only devilling; hold on to the word devilling; it was his living to devil—more or less—just earning his living—getting nothing out of it! Neither was Georgie Grebe—only the Ad! Then who was getting something out of it? "Conglomerated Journals"! out of Georgie Grebe's name; out of the chief's name below the devilled leaders—a pretty penny! But was there any harm in making the most of a big name? Taggart frowned. Suppose a man went into a shop and bought a box of pills, marked "Holloway," made up from a recipe of "Tompkins"—did it matter that the man thought they were Holloway's, if they were just as good pills, perhaps better? Taggart laid down his pen and took his pipe out of his mouth. 'Gosh!' he thought; 'never looked at it this way before! I believe it does matter. A man ought to get the exact article he pays for. If not, any fraud is possible. New Zealand mutton can be sold as Eng-

lish. Jaeger stuffs can have cotton in them. This Grebe article's a fraud.' He relit his pipe. With the first puff his English hatred of a moral attitude, or "swank" of any sort beset
him. Who was he to take stand against a custom? Didn't secretaries write the speeches of Parliamentary "big-bugs"?
Weren't the opinions of eminent lawyers often written by their
juniors, read over and signed? Weren't briefs and pleadings
devilled? Yes; but all that was different. In such cases the
Public weren't paying for expression, they were paying for
knowledge; the big lawyer put his imprimatur on the knowledge, not on the expression of it; the Cabinet Minister en-
dorsed his views, whether he had written them out or not, and
it was his views the Public paid for, not the expression of
them. But in this Grebe article the Public would not be paying
for any knowledge it contained, nor for any serious views; it
would pay for a peep into the mind of their idol. 'And his
mind will be mine!' thought Taggart; 'but who'd spend his
money to peep into my mind, if he *knew* it was my mind?'
He got up, and sat down again.

With a Public so gullible—what did it matter? They lapped
up anything and asked for more. Yes! But weren't the gullible
the very people who oughtn't to be gulled? He rose again and
toured the dishevelled room. The man at the other table raised
his head.

"You seem a bit on your toes."

Taggart stared down at him.

"I've got to write some drivel in *The Lighthouse* for Georgie
Grebe to sign. It's just struck me that it's a fraud on the Public. What do you say, Jimmy?"

"In a way. What about it?"

"If it is, I don't want to do it—that's all."

His colleague whistled.

"My dear chap, here am I writing a racing article, 'From
the Man in the Paddock'—I haven't been on a race-course
for years."

"Oh! well—that's venial."

"All's venial in our game. Shut your eyes and swallow.
You're only devilling."

"Ga!" said Taggart. "Give a thing a decent label, and
it is decent."

"I say, old man, what did you have for breakfast?"

"Look here, Jimmy, I'm inclined to think I've struck a snag. It never occurred to me before."

"Well, don't let it occur to you again. Think of old Dumas. I've heard he put his name to sixty volumes in one year. Has that done him any harm?"

Taggart rumpled his hair, reddish and rather stiff.

"Damn!" he said.

Counter laughed.

"You get a fixed screw for doing what you're told. Why worry? Papers must be sold. Georgie Grebe—that's some stunt."

"Blast Georgie Grebe!"

He took his hat and went out; a prolonged whistle followed him. All next day he spent doing other jobs, trying to persuade himself that he was a crank, and gingerly feeling the mouths of journalists. All he got was: Fuss about nothing! What was the matter with devilling? With life at such pressure, what else could you have? But for the life of him he could not persuade himself to go on with the thoughts of Georgie Grebe. He remembered suddenly that his father had changed the dogmas of his religion at forty-five, and thereby lost a cure of souls. He was very unhappy; it was like discovering that he had inherited tuberculosis. On Friday he was sent for by the chief.

"Morning, Taggart; I'm just back. Look here, this leader for to-morrow—it's nothing but a string of statements. Where's my style?"

Taggart shifted his considerable weight from foot to foot.

"Well, sir," he said, "I thought perhaps you'd like to put that in yourself, for a change. The facts are all right."

The chief stared.

"My good fellow, do you suppose I've got time for that? Anybody could have written this; I can't sign it as it stands. Tone it up."

Taggart took the article from the chief's hand.

"I don't know that I can," he said; "I'm——" and stopped.

The chief said kindly:

"Are you ill?"

Taggart disclaimed.

"Private trouble?"

"No."

"Well, get on with it, then. How's the Grebe article turned out?"

"It hasn't."

"How d'you mean?"

Taggart felt his body stiffening.

"Fact is I can't write it."

"Good gracious, man, any drivel will do, so long as it's got a flavour of some sort to carry the name."

Taggart swallowed.

"That's it. Is it quite playing the game with the Public, sir?"

The chief seemed to loom larger suddenly.

"I don't follow you, Taggart."

Taggart blurted out: "I don't want to write anyone else's stuff in future, unless it's just news or facts."

The chief's face grew very red.

"I pay you to do certain work. If you don't care to carry out instructions, we can dispense with your services. What's the matter with you, Taggart?"

Taggart replied with a wry smile:

"Suffering from a fit of conscience, sir. Isn't it a matter of commercial honesty?"

The chief sat back in his swivel chair and gazed at him for quite twenty seconds.

"Well," he said at last in an icy voice, "I have never been so insulted. Good-morning! You are at liberty."

Taggart laid down the sheets of paper, walked stiffly to the door, and turned.

"Awfully sorry, sir; can't help it."

The chief bowed distantly, and Taggart went out.

For three months he had enjoyed liberty. Journalism was overstocked; his name not well known. Too shy and proud to ask for recommendation from "Conglomerated Journals," he could never bring himself to explain why he had "got the hoof." Claim a higher standard of morality than his fellows—not he. For two months he had carried on pretty well, but the last few weeks had brought him low indeed. Yet the more he brooded, the more he felt he had been right, and the less inclined he was to speak of it. Loyalty to the chief he had insulted by taking such an attitude, dislike of being thought a fool, beyond all, dread of "swanking" kept him silent. When asked why he had left "Conglomerated Journals" he returned the answer always: "Disagreement on a point of principle," and refused to enter into details. But a feeling had got about that he was a bit of a crank; for though no one at "Con-glomerated Journals" knew exactly why he had vanished, Counter had spread the news that he had blasted Georgie Grebe, and refused to write his article. Someone else had done it. Taggart read the production with irritation. It was jolly bad. Inefficient devilling still hurt one who had devilled long and efficiently without a qualm. When the article which had not been written by Sir Cutman Kane appeared—he swore aloud. It was no more like the one Sir Cutman would have signed if Taggart had written it, than the boots of Taggart were like the boots of the chief, who seemed to wear a fresh pair every day, with cloth tops. He read the chief's new leaders with melancholy, spotting the many deficiencies of style supplied to the chief by—whoever it was now wrote them. His square red cheerful face had a bitter look while he was reading; and when he had finished, he would rumple his stiff hair. But he was sturdy, and never got so far as calling himself a fool for his pains, though week by week he felt more certain that his protest had been vain.

Sitting against the ranger's paling, listening to the birds, he had a dreamy feeling about it all. Queer creatures, human beings! So damned uncritical! Had he not been like that himself for years and years? The power of a label—that was what struck him, sitting there. Label a thing decently, and it *was* decent! Ah! but, "Rue by any other name would smell as sour!" Conscience!—it was the devil!

1922.

ONCE MORE

Awakened by the tiny kicks of her baby, she straightened his limbs on her breast, and lay staring up at the dirty ceiling. The first light of the March morning, through a window which had but a ragged piece of muslin over the lower half, spread its pale glimmer in the little room. It was, like all the little back rooms of that street, deserted by Hope; neither was there anything in it of beauty or value except the remains of her stock of violets in the round brown-wicker basket.

Soothed by the warmth of her chest and arms, the baby was sleeping again, with his down-covered tiny head snuggled into the hollow of her neck; and, just above that head, the mother's face was like that of a little sphinx.

Two days before, her husband had left her, saying that he was not coming back, but this had not dismayed her, for with the strange wisdom of those who begin to suffer young, she had long ago measured her chances with and without him. She made more than he did in their profession of flower-selling, because sometimes a " toff " gave her a fancy price, touched perhaps by the sight of her tired, pretty face, and young figure bent sideways by the weight of her baby. Yes, he took more money off her than she did off him; besides, he had left her twice before in the same way, and twice come back. The feeling in her heart was due to another discovery. Last evening, going home dead-tired, she had seen him on an omnibus with his arm round a woman's waist. At that sight a flame had leaped up in her; burdened with baby and basket, she had run after the 'bus; but it went too fast for her, she was soon left behind. And long, huddled over her fire, she had sat, seeing him with that other woman. And when the fire went out, getting into bed, had lain sleepless, still seeing, and hearing, and shivering with the cold. So, that was where he went! Was she going to put up with it any more? Thus she lay brooding, avoiding all extravagance, matter-of-fact, sphinx-like, even in thought.

The room grew light; she got up, went to the little cracked
mirror, and looked long at her face. If she had ever known
that she was pretty, the life she led with her boy-husband,
sometimes ill-treated, always scantily clothed, and more or less
in want, had bereft her of this knowledge. The woman round
whose waist she had seen his arm looked well-fed and had
feathers in her hat. And in that mirror she tried desperately
to find something which might weigh against those full cheeks
and those feathers. But she seemed to herself all eyes, there
was no colour in her cheeks; she seemed sad to herself. Turning
from that glass of little comfort, she lit the fire, and, taking up
her baby, sat down to feed it. With her bare feet to the flame,
and feeling the movement of the baby's lips against her, she had
the first sensation of warmth since the omnibus had passed her.
To her, striving so hard but so unconsciously for any thought
that would assuage her jealousy, there came a recollection that
was almost pleasant. Last evening a " toff," entering his garden
gate, had bought from her a single bunch of violets for half-a-
crown. Why had he smiled, and given her that half-crown?
With each tug of the baby's lips the sensation of warmth grew,
and with it began to be mingled a feeling of excitement. He
would not have looked at her so long, would not have smiled
—unless he had thought her pretty! But suddenly the baby's
lips ceased to move; the feeling of excitement died. Wrapping
the little thing in her shawl, she laid him back on the bed;
then, heating a little water, began to wash with unwonted care.
She had a passionate desire to make herself finer than that
woman with feathers in her hat. No " toff " would have smiled
at *her,* even though she had not had to pawn her clothes. Her
little brain, frozen with brooding, flaming with jealousy, ran
riot amongst clothes. There hung on two nails driven into the
wall—all her wardrobe—a ragged skirt, torn jersey, and black
straw hat. She put on her one undergarment, and went up to
them. Looking at those dim clothes, she was vaguely conscious
of the irony in things. Three weeks ago she had " put away "
her best suit for four shillings and sixpence, to renew her
husband's stock of flowers, which rain had ruined. She had
pawned her attractions to give him the chance to go after that
woman! From the secret place where she kept her wealth,
from those many pawn-tickets, she selected one, and put it
between her teeth; then, from a broken cup, where, under a
ragged cloth, she stored her money, she took the " toff's " half-

crown, and five pennies. It was all she had, and the week's rent was owing. She looked round the room; her blankets were in pawn; there was nothing left except her shawl. It was a thick shawl, good for eighteenpence. With interest three-pence, she would still need fourpence to redeem her suit. She went to her flower-basket and lifted the piece of dirty sacking. The bunches were withered. In her rage and disturbance over-night, she had forgotten to damp them. She sat down on her bed, and for full quarter of an hour stayed there unmoving, more like a little sphinx than ever, with her short, ivory-coloured face, black eyes, straight brows and closed red lips. Suddenly she got up; took off her undergarment and examined it. There were no holes! Wrapping it tightly in her shawl, she put on skirt and jersey, pinned her hat to her black hair, took pawn-ticket and her money, and went down the dirty stairs, out into the cold.

She made her way to the small shop which was the centre of her universe. No one was there, for the door had only just been opened; and she waited, stolid, amongst those innumerable goods, each one of which had been brought there wrapped in the stuff of human life. The proprietor caught sight of her presently through the glass of the inner door. He was a dark, strong man, and his quick eye, which had in it a sort of cring-ing hardness, instantly marked her shawl.

"I've had that before, I think, eighteenpence, ain't it?" From its recesses he took the undergarment. He looked at this critically; it was very plain, thick, and had no frills, but it was strangely new. "Sixpence on that, 'alfpenny off for the washing." Then, as if something in the nature of this trans-action had moved him, he added: "Let you off the washing." She silently held out to him her small rough hand, with her money and the pawn-ticket. He scrutinised both, and said: "I see; that'll be tuppence I owe you on the deal."

With the twopence and her suit, she journeyed home. She put on the suit over her skirt and jersey, for the sake of the warmth, and because that woman had full cheeks; stood for some minutes smoothing her hair and rubbing her face, goose-fleshed with the cold; then, leaving her baby with the woman on the ground floor, she went out towards the road where the omnibus had passed. Her heart was dry with longing to meet that woman; to be avenged on her, and *him*. All the morning she walked up and down. Now and again a youth stopped her, and tried to enter into conversation; but he soon desisted, as if something in her face had withered his good intentions. With the twopence she bought a sausage-roll, ate it, went home, fed her baby, and again came out. It was now afternoon, but she still wandered up and down, always driven on by that longing; and every now and then smiling up at some man. What she thought to gain by these smiles cannot be told, for no one could have answered them, so mirthless were they; and yet they gave her a queer dead pleasure, as if she felt that they ministered to her vengeance. A strong wind drove the clouds over a clear blue sky, and in this wind the buds and few crocuses in the gardens were trembling. In some of the Squares, too, pigeons were cooing; and all the people seemed hurrying with happiness. But for that young wife, for ever walking and loitering down the long road where the omnibus had passed, spring travelled the air in vain.

At five o'clock, moved by yet another obscure impulse of her longing for revenge, she branched off her beat to the white house where she had seen the "toff" enter last evening. She hesitated long before ringing the bell, and then very stolidly asked to see "the gentleman," in a voice a little thick and hoarse from the many colds she caught selling her flowers. While the maid went to see if this were possible, she waited in the hall. There was a mirror there; but she did not look at herself, standing quite still with her eyes fixed on the ground.

She was shown into a room, lighter, warmer, more strange than any room she had ever been in; giving her a feeling as though a plateful of Christmas pudding, soft, dark, and rich, had been placed before her. The walls were white and the woodwork white, and there were brown velvet curtains, and gold frames round the pictures.

She went in smiling, as at the men in the street. But the smile faded from her lips at once. On a sofa was a lady in a white dress; and she wished to turn and go away, for she felt at once that they must know she had no undergarment beneath her new suit. The gentleman asked her to sit down. She sat down, therefore; and in answer to questions, told them that her stock was spoiled, that she owed a week's rent, that her husband had left her and the baby! But even while speaking, she felt that this was not what she had come to say. They seemed to ask the questions over and over again, as if they did not understand her. And she told them suddenly that her husband had gone with another woman. When she said that, the lady made soft sounds, as if she understood and was sorry. She noticed what pretty small ears the lady had. The gentleman was afraid he did not know what could be done for her: Did she wish to leave her husband? She answered quickly: "I couldn't stay with him now, of course." And the lady murmured: "No, no; of course not." What then—the gentleman said—did she propose to do? She remained silent, staring at the carpet. It seemed to her suddenly that they were thinking: 'She's come for money.' The gentleman took out a sovereign, and said: "Will that be any good to you?" She made a little bob, and took the sovereign, clutching it very tight. It seemed to her that they wanted her to go away. She got up, therefore, and went to the door. The gentleman went with her; and as he opened the front door he smiled. She did not smile back, for she saw that he had only meant to be kind, yesterday. And this hurt her, as if suddenly there had slipped away from her part of her revenge.

She went home, still clutching the unchanged sovereign; so weak and faint that she could hardly feed her baby. She made up her fire and sat down beside it. It was past six, and nearly dark. Twice before, he had come back on the third day, about this time. If he were to come back now!

She crouched nearer to the fire. It grew quite dark. She looked at her baby; he was asleep, with his tiny fists crumpled against his cheeks. She made up the fire, and went back to her beat along the road where the omnibus had passed.

Two or three men stopped her, but she no longer smiled at them, and they soon sheered off. It was very clear, very cold; but she did not feel the cold. Her eyes were fastened on those great vans of warmth, the motor omnibuses. Long before each had borne its burden close, her eyes had begun searching. Long after they had rumbled by, her gaze followed them from under the brim of her black straw hat. But that for which she was looking never appeared. In the midst of the roar and the sudden hushes, of the stir and confusion of lamplight and shadow, the stir and confusion and blackness in her own heart, she thought of her baby, and hurried away. He was still sleeping, the fire still alight. Without undressing, she crept into bed, exhausted. If she was like a little sphinx awake, she was more so than ever under the mystery of sleep, with her black lashes resting on her cheeks, and her lips just parted. In her dreams she twisted her hands and moaned. She woke at midnight.

By the light of the still live fire she saw her husband moving past the foot of the bed. He neither spoke, nor looked at her, but sat down before the fire, and began to take off his boots. The sight of that domestic act roused her to fury. So he could come in when he liked—after going where he had gone, after being what he had been, the——! But no fierce sound came; she could form no word bad enough to call him by. After three days—after what she had seen—after all her waiting—and walking—and suffering—taking off his boots! Stealthily she raised herself in bed, the better to watch that act. If she had opened her mouth it would have been to utter a scream; no lesser cry could have relieved her heart. And still he neither spoke nor looked at her. She saw him slide down off the wooden chair, as if he would creep right into the fire. And she thought: 'Let him burn, the——!' A vile word clung in her brain and would not come forth. She could just see his figure hunched now all in a heap; she could hear his teeth chattering, and the sound gave her pleasure. Then he was quite silent, and she, too, held her breath. Was he asleep? The thought of this sleep, while she lay there consumed with rage, was too much for her. She uttered a little furious sound. He did not look up, but his foot moved, and a loosened cinder fell; there was again silence. She began creeping to the foot of the bed. Crouching there, with loins curved, and her face bent down between her stretched-out arms, she was close above his huddled figure; so close that with her hands she could have seized and twisted back his head. In fancy she was already doing this, putting her eyes close to his, setting her teeth in his forehead—so vividly that she had the taste of blood in her mouth. Suddenly she recoiled, burying her face between her arms, on the ragged bed coverlet. For some minutes she stayed thus, crouched like a wild cat on a branch. There was a dreadful sore feeling within her. She was thinking of the first night they had come home to that room; she was remembering his kisses. Something clicked in her throat. She no longer wished to tear and bite, and she raised her face. He had not stirred. She could just see the outline of his cheeks and chin; beardless, of a boy, utterly still, as if dead. She felt cold, and afraid. What was this silence? She could not even hear him breathe. She slid down on the floor. His eyes were open, very colourless, staring at the dying fire; his cheeks were hollow, his lips seemed to have no blood in them. But they moved, shivering desperately. So he was not dead! Only frozen and starved as he had been when he came back to her those two other times. The mask of her face let nothing be seen of her thoughts and feelings, but her teeth bit into her lower lip. So this was how he had come back to her once more!

The last of the fuel in the grate suddenly flickered into flame. He turned his head towards her. By the light of that feeble fire his eyes were like the eyes of her baby; they seemed to ask her for something; they looked so helpless; all his shuddering form seemed helpless. He muttered something; but his shivering choked the words, so that all that came to her was a sound such as her baby made. And at that sound something in her heart gave way; she pulled his head down on her breast, and with all her strength clutched him to her. And as the fire died, she still held him there, rocking him and sobbing, and once more trying to give him of the warmth of her little body.

1910.

BLACKMAIL

I

THE affectionate if rather mocking friend who had said of Charles Granter:*" Ce n'est pas un homme, c'est un bâtiment,"* seemed justified, to the thin dark man following him down Oakley Street, Chelsea, that early October afternoon. From the square foundations of his feet to his square fair beard and the top of his head under a square black bowler, he looked very big, solid as granite, indestructible—steel-clad, too, for his grey clothes increased his bulk in the mild sunlight; too big to be taken by the board—only fit to be submarined. And the man, dodging in his wake right down to the Embankment, ran up once or twice under his counter and fell behind again, as if appalled by the vessel's size and unconsciousness. Considering the heat of the past summer, the plane-trees were still very green, and few of their twittering leaves had dropped or turned yellow —just enough to confirm the glamorous melancholy of early Fall. Granter, though he lived with his wife in some mansions close by, went out of his way to pass under those trees and look at the river. This seeming disclosure of sensibility, perhaps, determined the shadowy man to dodge up again and become stationary close behind. Ravaged and streaked, as if he had lived submerged, he stood carefully noting with his darting dark eyes that they two were quite alone; then, swallowing violently so that the strings of his lean neck writhed, he moved stealthily up beside Granter, and said in a hurried, hoarse voice: " Beg pardon, Mister—ten pounds, and I'll say nothin'."

The face which Granter turned towards that surprising utterance was a good illustration of the saying, " And things are not what they seem." Above that big building of a body it quivered, ridiculously alive, and complex, as of a man full of nerves, humours, sarcasms; and a deep continuous chinking sound arose —of Charles Granter jingling coins in his trouser pocket. The

quiver settled into raised eyebrows, into crows' feet running out
on to the broad cheekbones, into a sarcastic smile drooping the
corners of the lips between moustache and beard. He said in
his rather high voice:

"What's the matter with you, my friend?"

"There's a lot the matter with me, Mister. Down and out I
am. I know where you live, I know your lady; but—ten pound
and I'll say nothin'."

"About what?"

"About your visitin' that gell, where you've just come from.
Ten pound. It's cheap—I'm a man of me word."

With lips still sarcastically drooped, Granter made a little
derisive sound.

Blackmail, by George!

"Come on, Guv'nor—I'm desperate; I mean to have that ten
pounds. You give it me here at six o'clock this evenin', if you
'aven't got it on you." His eyes flared suddenly in his hungry
face. "But no tricks! I ain't killed Huns for nothin'."

Granter surveyed him for a moment, then turned his back
and looked at the water.

"Well, you've got two hours to get it in—six o'clock, Mister;
and no tricks—I warn you."

The hoarse voice ceased, the sound of footsteps died away;
Granter was alone. The smile still clung to his lips, but he
was not amused; he was annoyed, with the measured indignation
of a big man highly civilised and innocent. Where had this
ruffian sprung from? To be spied on, without knowing it, like
this! His ears grew red. The damned scoundrel!

The thing was too absurd to pay attention to. And, instantly,
his highly-sophisticated consciousness began to pay attention.
How many visits had he made to this distressed flower-girl?
Three? And all because he didn't like handing over the case
to that Society which always found out the worst. They said
private charity was dangerous. Apparently it was! Blackmail! A consideration came, perching like a crow on the
branches of his mind: why hadn't he mentioned the flower-girl
to his wife, and made *her* do the visiting? Why! Because
Olga would have said the girl was a fraud. And perhaps she
was! A put-up job! Would the scoundrel have ventured on
this threat at all if the girl were not behind him? She might
support him with lies! His wife might believe them—— She

—she had such a vein of cynicism! How sordid, how domestically unpleasant!

Granter felt quite sick. Every decent human value seemed suddenly in question. And a second crow came croaking. Could one leave a scoundrel like this to play his tricks with impunity? Oughtn't one to go to the police? He stood extraordinarily still—a dappled leaf dropped from a plane-tree and lodged on his bowler hat; at the other end of him a little dog mistook him for a lamp-post. This was no joke! For a man with a reputation for humanity, integrity and commonsense—no joke at all! A Police Court meant the prosecution of a fellow-creature; getting him perhaps a year's imprisonment, when one had always felt that punishment practically never fitted crime! Staring at the river, he seemed to see cruelty hovering over himself, his wife, Society, the flower-girl, even over that scoundrel—naked cruelty, waiting to pounce on one or all. Whichever way one turned, the thing was dirty, cruel. No wonder blackmail was accounted such a heinous crime. No other human act was so cold-blooded, spider-like, and slimy; none plunged so deadly a dagger into the bowels of compassion, so eviscerated humanity, so murdered faith! And it would have been worse, if his conscience had not been clear. But was it so extremely clear? Would he have taken the trouble to go to that flower-girl's dwelling, not once, but three times, unless she had been attractive, unless her dark brown eyes had been pretty, and her common voice so soft? Would he have visited the blowsy old flower-woman at that other corner, in circumstances, no doubt, just as strenuous? His honesty answered: No. But his sense of justice added that, if he did like a pretty face, he was not vicious—he was fastidious and detested subterfuge. But then Olga was so cynical; she would certainly ask him why he hadn't visited the old flower-woman as well, and the lame man who sold matches, and all the other stray unfortunates of the neighbourhood. Well, there it was; and a bold course always the best! But what was the bold course? To go to the police? To his wife? To that girl, and find out if she were in this ramp? To·wait till six o'clock, meet the ruffian, and shake the teeth out of him? Granter could not decide. All seemed equally bold—would do equally well. And a fifth course presented itself which seemed even bolder: Ignore the thing!

The tide had just turned, and the full waters below him were in suspense, of a sunlit soft grey colour. This stillness of the river restored to Charles Granter something of the impersonal mood in which he had crossed the Embankment to look at it. Here, by the mother stream of this great town, was he, tall, strong, well-fed, and, if not rich, quite comfortable; and here, too, were hundreds of thousands like that needy flower-girl and this shadowy scoundrel, skating on the edge of destitution. And here this water was—to him a source of æsthetic enjoyment —to them a possible last refuge. The girl had talked of it— beggar's patter, perhaps, like the blackmailer's words: " I'm desperate—I'm down and out."

One wanted to be just! If he had known all about them— but there it was, he knew nothing!

' I can't believe she's such an ungrateful little wretch! ' he thought; ' I'll go back and see her again.' . . .

He retraced his way up Oakley Street to the Mews which she inhabited, and, ascending a stairway scented with petrol, knocked on a half-open door, whence he could see her baby, of doubtful authorship, seated in an empty flower-basket—a yellow baby, who stared up at him with the placidity of one recently fed. That stare seemed to Granter to be saying: " You look out that you're not taken for my author. Have you got an alibi, old man? " And almost unconsciously he began to calculate where he had been about fourteen or fifteen months ago. Not in London—thank goodness! in Brittany with his wife—all that July, August, and September. Jingling his money, he contemplated the baby. It seemed more, but it *might* be only four months old! The baby opened its mouth in a toothless smile. " Ga! " it said, and stretched out a tiny hand. Granter ceased to jingle the coins and gazed round the room. The first time he came, a month ago, to test her street-corner story, its condition had been deplorable. His theory that people were never better than their environments had prompted the second visit, and that of this afternoon. He had, he told himself, wanted to know that he was not throwing away his money. And there certainly was some appearance of comfort now in a room so small that he and the baby and a bed almost filled it. But the longer he contemplated them, the greater fool he felt for ever having come there even with those best intentions which were the devil. And, turning to go, he saw the girl herself coming up the stairs, with a paper bag in her hand and an evident bull's-eye in her mouth, for a scent of peppermint preceded her. Surely her cheekbones were higher than he had thought,

her eyebrows more oblique—a gipsy look! Her eyes, dark and
lustrous as a hound puppy's, smiled at him, and he said in his
rather high voice:

"I came back to ask you something."

"Yes, sir."

"Do you know a dark man with a thin face and a slight
squint, who's been in the Army?"

"What's his name, sir?"

"I don't know; but he followed me from here, and tried
to blackmail me on the Embankment. You know what blackmail is?"

"No, sir."

Feline, swift, furtive, she had passed him and taken up her
baby, slanting her dark glance at him from behind it. Granter's
eyes were very round just then, the corners of his mouth very
drawn down. He was experiencing a most queer sensation.
Really it was as if—though he disliked poetic emphasis—as if he
had suddenly seen something pre-civilised, pre-human, snake-
like, cat-like, monkey-like too, in those dark sliding eyes and
that yellow baby. Sure, as he stood there, she was in it; or, if
not in it, she knew of it!

"A dangerous game, that," he said. "Tell him—for his
own good—he had better drop it."

And, while he went, very square, downstairs, he thought:
' This is one of the finest opportunities you ever had for getting
to the bottom of human nature, and you're running away from
it.' So strongly did this thought obsess him that he halted,
in two minds, outside. A chauffeur, who was cleaning his car,
looked at him curiously. Charles Granter moved away.

II

When he reached the little drawing-room of their flat, his wife
was making tea. She was rather short, with a good figure, and
brown eyes in a flattish face, powdered and by no means un-
attractive. She had Slav blood in her—Polish; and Granter
never now confided to her the finer shades of his thoughts and
conduct because she had long made him feel he was her superior
in moral sensibility. He had no wish to feel superior—it
was often very awkward; but he could not help it. In view of
this attempt at blackmail, it was more than awkward. For it

is extraordinarily unpleasant to fall from a pedestal on which you do not wish to be.

He sat down, very large, in a lacquered chair with black cushions, spoke of the leaves turning, saw her look at him and smile, and felt that she knew he was disturbed.

"Do you ever wonder," he said, tinkling his tea-spoon, "about the lives that other people live?"

"What sort of people, Charles?"

"Oh—not our sort; matchsellers, don't you know, flower-sellers, people down and out?"

"No, I don't think I do."

If only he could tell her of this monstrous incident without slipping from his pedestal!

"It interests me enormously; there are such queer depths to reach, don't you know."

Her smile seemed to answer: "You don't reach the depths in me." And it was true. She was very Slav, with the warm gleam in her eyes and the opaque powdered skin of her flat comely face. An enigma—flatly an enigma! There were deep waters below the pedestal, like—like Phylæ, with columns still standing in the middle of the Nile Dam. Absurd!

"I've often wondered," he said, "how I should feel if I were down and out."

"You? You're too large, Charles, and too dignified, my dear; you'd be on the Civil List before you could turn round." Granter rose from the lacquered chair, jingling his coins. The most vivid pictures at that moment were, like a film, unrolled before his mind—of the grey sunlit river, and that accosting blackguard with his twisted murky face, and lips uttering hoarse sounds; of the yellow baby, and the girl's gipsy-dark glance from behind it; of a Police Court, and himself standing there and letting the whole cartload of the Law fall on them. And he said suddenly:

"I was blackmailed this afternoon, on the Embankment."

She did not answer, and turning with irritation, he saw that her fingers were in her ears.

"I do wish you wouldn't jingle your money so!" she said.

Confound it! She had not heard him.

"I've had an adventure," he began again. "You know the flower-girl who stands at that corner in Tite Street?"

"Yes; a gipsy baggage."

"H'm! Well, I bought a flower from her one day, and she

told me such a pathetic story that I went to her den to see if it was true. It seemed all right, so I gave her some money, don't you know. Then I thought I'd better see how she was spending it, so I went to see her again, don't you know."

A faint " Oh! Charles! " caused him to hurry on.

" And—what d'you think—a blackguard followed me to-day and tried to blackmail me for ten pounds on the Embankment."

A sound brought his face round to attention. His wife was lying back on the cushions of her chair in paroxysms of soft laughter.

It was clear to Granter, then, that what he had really been afraid of was just this. His wife would laugh at him—laugh at him slipping from the pedestal! Yes! it was that he had dreaded—not any disbelief in his fidelity. Somehow he felt too large to be laughed at. He *was* too large! Nature had set a size beyond which husbands——!

" I don't see what there is to laugh at! " he said frigidly; " there's no more odious crime than blackmail."

His wife was silent; two tears were trickling down her cheeks.

" Did you give it him? " she said in an extinguished voice.

" Of course not."

" What was he threatening? "

" To tell you."

" But what? "

" His beastly interpretation of my harmless visits."

The tears had made runlets in her powder, and he added viciously: " He doesn't know you, of course."

His wife dabbed her eyes, and a scent of geranium arose.

" It seems to me," said Granter, " that you'd be even more amused if there were something in it! "

" Oh! no, Charles, but—perhaps there is."

Granter looked at her fixedly.

" I'm sorry to disappoint you, there is not."

He saw her cover her lips with that rag of handkerchief, and abruptly left the room.

He went into his study and sat down before the fire. So it was funny to be a faithful husband? And suddenly he thought: ' If my wife can treat this as a joke, what—what about herself?' A nasty thought! An unconscionable thought! Really, it was as though that blackmailing scoundrel had dirtied human nature, till it seemed to function only from low motives. A church clock chimed. Six already! The ruffian would be back there on the Embankment, waiting for his ten pounds. Granter rose. His duty was to go out and hand him over to the police.

'No!' he thought viciously, 'let him come here! I'd very much like him to come here. I'd teach him!'

But a sort of shame beset him. Like most very big men, he was quite unaccustomed to violence—had never struck a blow in his life, not even in his school-days—had never had occasion to. He went across to the window. From there he could just see the Embankment parapet through the trees, in the failing light, and presently—sure enough—made out the fellow's figure slinking up and down like a hungry dog. And he stood, watching, jingling his money—nervous, sarcastic, angry, very interested. What would the rascal do now? Would he beard this great block of flats? And was the girl down there too—the girl, with her yellow baby? He saw the slinking figure cross from the far side and vanish under the loom of the mansions. In that interesting moment Granter burst through the bottom of one of his trousers pockets: several coins jingled on to the floor and rolled away. He was still looking for the last when he heard the door-bell ring—he had never really believed the ruffian would come up! Straightening himself abruptly, he went out into the hall. Service was performed by the mansions staff, so there was no one in the flat but himself and his wife. The bell rang again, and she, too, appeared.

"This is my Embankment friend who amuses you so much. I should like you to see him," he said grimly. He noted a quizzical apology on her face and opened the hall door.

Yes! there stood the man! By electric light, in upholstered surroundings, more " down and out " than ever. A bad lot, but a miserable poor wretch, with his broken boots, his thin, twisted, twitching face, his pinched shabby figure—only his hungry eyes looked dangerous.

"Come in," said Granter. "You want to see my wife, I think."

The man recoiled.

"I don't want to see 'er," he muttered, "unless you force me to. Give us *five* pound, Guv'nor, and I won't worry you again. I don't want to cause trouble between man and wife."

"Come in," repeated Granter; "she's expecting you."

The man stood, silently passing a pale tongue over a pale

upper lip, as though conjuring some new resolution from his embarrassment.

"Now, see 'ere, Mister," he said suddenly, "you'll regret it if I come in—you will, straight."

"I shall regret it if you don't. You're a very interesting fellow, and an awful scoundrel."

"Well, who made me one?" the man burst out; "you answer me that."

"Are you coming in?"

"Yes, I am."

He came, and Granter shut the door behind him. It was like inviting a snake or a mad dog into one's parlour; but the memory of having been laughed at was so fresh within him that he rather welcomed the sensation.

"Now," he said, "have the kindness!" and opened the drawing-room door.

The man slunk in, blinking in the stronger light.

Granter went towards his wife, who was standing before the fire.

"This gentleman has an important communication to make to you, it seems."

The expression of her face struck him as peculiar—surely she was not frightened! And he experienced a kind of pleasure in seeing them both look so exquisitely uncomfortable.

"Well," he said ironically, "perhaps you'd like me not to listen." And, going back to the door, he stood leaning against it with his hands up to his ears. He saw the fellow give him a furtive look and go nearer to her; his lips moved rapidly, hers answered, and he thought: 'What on earth am I covering my ears for?' As he took his hands away, the man turned round and said:

"I'm goin' now, Mister; a little mistake—sorry to 'ave troubled you."

His wife had turned to the fire again; and with a puzzled feeling Granter opened the door. As the fellow passed, he took him by the arm, twisted him around into the study, and, locking the door, put the key into his pocket.

"Now, then," he said, "you precious scoundrel!"

The man shifted on his broken boots. "Don't you hit me, Guv'nor. I got a knife here."

"I'm not going to hit you. I'm going to hand you over to the police."

The man's eyes roved, looking for a way of escape, then rested, as if fascinated, on the glowing hearth.

"What's ten pound?" he said suddenly. "You'd never ha' missed it."

Granter smiled.

"You don't seem to realise, my friend, that blackmail is the most devilish crime a man can commit." And he crossed over to the telephone.

The man's eyes, dark, restless, violent, and yet hungry, began to shift up and down the building of a man before him.

"No," he said suddenly, with a sort of pathos, "don't do that, Guv'nor!"

Something—the look of his eyes or the tone of his voice—affected Granter.

"But if I don't," he said slowly, "you'll be blackmailing the next person you meet. You're as dangerous as a viper."

The man's lips quivered; he covered them with his hand, and said from behind it:

"I'm a man like yourself. I'm down and out—that's all. Look at me!"

Granter's glance dwelt on the trembling hand. "Yes, but you fellows destroy all belief in human nature," he said vehemently.

"See 'ere, Guv'nor; you try livin' like me—you try it! My Gawd! You try my life these last six months—cadgin' and crawlin' for a job!" He made a deep sound. "A man 'oo's done 'is bit, too. Wot life is it? A stinkin' life, not fit for a dawg, let alone a 'uman bein'. An' when I see a great big chap like you, beggin' your pardon, Mister—well fed, with everything to 'is 'and—it was regular askin' for it. It come over me, it did."

"No, no," said Granter grimly; "that won't do. It couldn't have been sudden. You calculated—you concocted this. Blackmail is sheer filthy cold-blooded blackguardism. You don't care two straws whom you hurt, whose lives you wreck, what faiths you destroy." And he put his hand on the receiver.

The man squirmed.

"Steady on, Guv'nor! I've gotta find food. I've gotta find clothes. I can't live on air. I can't go naked."

Granter stood motionless, while the man's voice continued to travel to him across the cosy room.

"Give us a chawnce, Guv'nor! Ah! give us a chawnce! You

can't understand my temptations. Don't 'ave the police to me. I won't do this again—give you me word—so 'elp me! I've got it in the neck. Let me go, Guv'nor!"

In Granter, motionless as the flats he lived in, a really heavy struggle was in progress—not between duty and pity, but between revengeful anger and a sort of horror at using the strength of prosperity against so broken a wretch.

"Let me go, Mister!" came the hoarse voice again. "Be a sport!"

Granter dropped the receiver, and unlocked the door.

"All right; you can go."

The man crossed swiftly.

"Christ!" he said; "good luck! And as to the lady—I take it back. I never see 'er. It's all me eye."

He was across the hall and gone before Granter could say a word; the scurrying shuffle of his footsteps down the stairs died away. "And as to the lady—I take it back—I never see her. It's all me eye!" Good God! The scoundrel, having failed with him, had been trying to blackmail his wife—his wife, who had laughed at his fidelity!—his wife who had looked—frightened! "All me eye!" Her face started up before Granter—*scared* under its powder, with a mask drawn over it. And he had let that scoundrel go! Scared! That was the meaning! . . . Blackmail—of all poisonous human actions! . . . His wife! . . . But . . . what now . . . !

1921.

TWO LOOKS

THE old director of the " Yew Trees " Cemetery walked slowly across from his house to see that all was ready.

He had seen pass into the square of earth committed to his charge so many to whom he had been in the habit of nodding, so many whose faces even he had not known. To him it was the everyday event; yet this funeral, one more in the countless tale, disturbed him—a sharp reminder of the passage of time.

For twenty years had gone by since the death of Septimus Godwin, the cynical, romantic doctor who had been his greatest friend; by whose cleverness all had sworn, of whose powers of fascination all had gossiped! And now they were burying his son!

He had not seen the widow since, for she had left the town at once; but he recollected her distinctly—a tall, dark woman with bright brown eyes, much younger than her husband, and only married to him eighteen months before he died. He remembered her slim figure standing by the grave at that long-past funeral, and the look on her face which had puzzled him so terribly—a look of—a most peculiar look!

He thought of it even now, walking along the narrow path toward his old friend's grave—the handsomest in the cemetery, commanding from the topmost point the whitened slope and river that lay beyond. He came to its little private garden. Spring flowers were blossoming; the railings had been freshly painted; and by the door of the grave wreaths awaited the new arrival. All was in order.

The old director opened the mausoleum with his key. Below, seen through a thick glass floor, lay the shining coffin of the father; beneath, on the lower tier, would rest the coffin of the son.

A gentle voice, close behind him, said:

" Can you tell me, sir, what they are doing to my old doctor's grave ? "

The old director turned and saw before him a lady well past middle age. He did not know her face, but it was pleasant, with faded rose-leaf cheeks, and silvered hair under a shady hat.

" Madam, there is a funeral here this afternoon."

" Ah! Can it be his wife?"

" Madam, his son; a young man of only twenty."

" His son! At what time did you say?"

" At two o'clock."

" Thank you; you are very kind."

With uplifted hat he watched her walk away. It worried him to see a face he did not know.

All went off beautifully; but, dining that same evening with his friend, a certain doctor, the old director asked:

" Did you see a lady with grey hair hovering about this afternoon?"

The doctor, a tall man, with a beard still yellow, drew his guest's chair nearer to the fire.

" I did," he answered.

" Did you remark her face? A very odd expression—a sort of—what shall I call it? Very odd indeed! Who is she? I saw her at the grave this morning."

The doctor shook his head.

" Not so very odd, I think."

" Come! What do you mean by that?"

The doctor hesitated. Then, taking the decanter, he filled his old friend's glass, and answered:

" Well, sir, you were Godwin's greatest chum—I will tell you, if you like, the story of his death. You were away at the time, if you remember."

" It is safe with me," said the old director.

" Septimus Godwin," began the doctor slowly, " died on a Thursday about three o'clock, and I was only called in to see him at two. I found him far gone, but conscious now and then. It was a case of—but you know the details, so I needn't go into that. His wife was in the room, and on the bed at his feet lay his pet dog—a terrier; you may recollect, perhaps, he had a special breed. I hadn't been there ten minutes, when a maid came in and whispered something to her mistress. Mrs. Godwin answered angrily, ' See him? Go down and say she ought to know better than to come here at such a time!' The maid went, but soon came back. Could the lady see Mrs. Godwin for just a moment? Mrs. Godwin answered that she could not leave her husband. The maid looked frightened and went away again. She came back for the third time. The lady had said she must see Dr. Godwin; it was a matter of life and death! 'Death—indeed!' exclaimed Mrs. Godwin. 'Shameful! Go down and tell her, if she doesn't go immediately I will send for the police!'"

"The poor maid looked at me. I offered to go down and see the visitor myself. I found her in the dining-room, and knew her at once. Never mind her name, but she belongs to a county family not a hundred miles from here. A beautiful woman she was then; but her face that day was quite distorted.

"'For God's sake, doctor,' she said, 'is there any hope?'

"I was obliged to tell her there was none.

"'Then I must see him,' she said.

"I begged her to consider what she was asking. But she held me out a signet ring. Just like Godwin—wasn't it—that sort of Byronism, eh!

"'He sent me this,' she said, 'an hour ago. It was agreed between us that if ever he sent that, I must come. If it were only myself I could bear it—a woman can bear anything; but he'll die thinking I wouldn't come, thinking I didn't care—and I would give my life for him this minute!'

"Now, a dying man's request is sacred. I told her she should see him. I made her follow me upstairs and wait outside his room. I promised to let her know if he recovered consciousness. I have never been thanked like that, before or since.

"I went back into the bedroom. He was still unconscious and the terrier whining. In the next room a child was crying —the very same young man we buried to-day. Mrs. Godwin was still standing by the bed.

"'Have you sent her away?'

"I had to say that Godwin really wished to see her. At that she broke out:

"'I won't have her here—the wretch!'

"I begged her to control herself, and remember that her husband was a dying man.

"'But I'm his wife,' she said, and flew out of the room."

The doctor paused, staring at the fire. He shrugged his shoulders, and went on: "I'd have stopped her fury, if I could! A dying man is not the same as the live animal, that he must needs be wrangled over. And suffering's sacred, even to us doctors. I could hear their voices outside. Heaven knows what they said to each other. And there lay Godwin with his white face and his black hair—deathly still—fine-looking fellow he always was! Then I saw that he was coming to! The women had begun again outside—first the wife, sharp and scornful; then the other, hushed and slow. I saw Godwin lift his finger and point it at the door. I went out and said to the woman, ' Dr. Godwin wishes to see you; please control yourself.'

" We went back into the room. The wife followed. But Godwin had lost conciousness again. They sat down, those two, and hid their faces. I can see them now, one on each side of the bed, their eyes covered with their hands, each with her claim on him, all murdered by the other's presence; each with her torn love. H'm! What they must have suffered, then! And all the time the child crying—the child of one of them that might have been the other's! "

The doctor was silent, and the old director turned towards him his white-bearded, ruddy face, with a look as if he were groping in the dark.

" Just then, I remember," the doctor went on suddenly, " the bells of St. Jude's close by began to peal out for the finish of a wedding. That brought Godwin back to life. He just looked from one woman to the other with a queer, miserable sort of smile, enough to make your heart break. And they both looked at him. The face of the wife—poor thing!—was as bitter hard as a cut stone, but she sat there, without ever stirring a finger. As for the other woman—I couldn't look at her. Godwin beckoned to me; but I couldn't catch his words, the bells drowned them. A minute later he was dead.

" Life's a funny thing! You wake in the morning with your foot firm on the ladder—one touch, and down you go! You snuff out like a candle. And it's lucky when your flame goes out if only one woman's flame goes out too.

" Neither of those women cried. The wife stayed there by the bed. I got the other one away to her carriage, down the street. And so she was there to-day! That explains, I think, the look you saw."

The doctor ceased; and in silence the old director nodded. Yes! That explained the look he had seen on the face of that unknown woman, the deep, unseizable, weird look. That explained the look he had seen on the wife's face at the funeral twenty years ago!

And peering wistfully, he said:

"They looked—they looked—almost triumphant!"

Then, slowly, he rubbed his hands over his knees, with the secret craving of the old for warmth.

1904.

A LONG-AGO AFFAIR

HUBERT MARSLAND, the landscape painter, returning from a
day's sketching on the river in the summer of 1921, had occasion
to stay the progress of his two-seater about ten miles from
London for a minor repair, and while his car was being seen to,
strolled away from the garage to have a look at a house where
he had often spent his holidays as a boy. Walking through a
gateway and passing a large gravel-pit on his left, he was soon
opposite the house, which stood back a little in its grounds.
Very much changed! More pretentious, not so homely as when
his Uncle and Aunt lived there, and he used to play cricket
on this warren opposite, where the cricket ground, it seemed,
had been turned into a golf course. It was late—the dinner-
hour, nobody playing, and passing on to the links he stood
digesting the geography. Here must have been where the old
pavilion was. And there—still turfed—where he had made
that particularly nice stroke to leg, when he went in last and
carried his bat for thirteen. Thirty-nine years ago—his six-
teenth birthday. How vividly he remembered his new pads!
A. P. Lucas had played against them and only made thirty-
two—one founded one's style on A. P. Lucas in those days—
feet in front of the bat, and pointed a little forward, elegant;
you never saw it now, and a good thing too—one could sacrifice
too much to style! Still, the tendency was all the other way;
style was too much " off," perhaps!

He stepped back into the sun and sat down on the grass.
Peaceful—very still! The haze of the distant downs was visible
between his Uncle's old house and the next; and there was the
clump of elms on the far side behind which the sun would be
going down just as it used to then. He pressed the palms of
his hands to the turf. A glorious summer—something like
that summer of long ago. And warmth from the turf, or
perhaps from the past, crept into his heart and made it ache a
little. Just here he must have sat, after his innings, at Mrs.

Monteith's feet peeping out of a flounced dress. Lord! The
fools boys were! How headlong and uncalculating their devotions! A softness in voice and eyes, a smile, a touch or two
—and they were slaves! Young fools, but good young fools.
And, standing behind her chair—he could see him now—that
other idol Captain MacKay, with his face of browned ivory—
just the colour of that elephant's tusk his Uncle had, which
had gone so yellow—and his perfect black moustache, his white
tie, check suit, carnation, spats, Malacca cane—all so fascinating!
Mrs. Monteith, "the grass widow" they had called her! He
remembered the look in people's eyes, the tone in their voices.
Such a pretty woman! He had "fallen for her" at first sight,
as the Yanks put it—her special scent, her daintiness, her voice!
And that day on the river, when she made much of him, and
Captain MacKay attended Evelyn Curtiss so assiduously that
he was expected to propose. Quaint period! They used the
word courting then, wore full skirts, high stays; and himself a
blue elastic belt round his white-flannelled waist. And in the
evening afterwards, his Aunt had said with an arch smile:
"Good-night, *silly* boy!" Silly boy indeed, with a flower the
grass widow had dropped pressed by his cheek into his pillow!
What folly! And that next Sunday—looking forward to Church
—passionately brushing his top hat; all through the service
spying at her creamy profile, two pews in front on the left,
between goat-bearded old Hallgrave her Uncle, and her pink,
broad, white-haired Aunt; scheming to get near her when she
came out, lingering, lurking, getting just a smile and the rustle
of her flounces. Ah, ha! A little went a long way then! And
the last day of his holidays and its night with the first introduction to reality. Who said the Victorian Age was innocent?

Marsland put his palm up to his cheek. No! the dew was
not yet falling! And his mind lightly turned and tossed his
memories of women, as a man turns and tosses hay to air it;
but nothing remembered gave him quite the feeling of that
first experience.

His Aunt's dance! His first white waistcoat, bought *ad hoc,*
from the local tailor, his tie laboriously imitating the hero—
Captain MacKay's. All came back with such freshness in the
quiet of the warren—the expectancy, the humble shy excitement, the breathless asking for a dance, the writing "Mrs.
Monteith" twice on his little gilt-edged programme with its
tiny tasselled white pencil; her slow-moving fan, her smile.

And the first dance when it came; what infinite care not to tread on her white satin toes; what a thrill when her arm pressed his in the crush—such holy rapture, about all the first part of that evening, with yet another dance to come! If only he could have twirled her and "reversed" like his pattern, Captain MacKay! Then delirium growing as the second dance came near, making him cut his partner—the cool grass-scented air out on the dark terrace, with the chafers booming by, and in the starshine the poplars wondrously tall; the careful adjustment of his tie and waistcoat, the careful polishing of his hot face! A long breath then, and into the house to find her! Ballroom, supper-room, stairs, library, billiard-room, all drawn blank—"Estudiantina" going on and on, and he a wandering, white-waistcoated young ghost. Ah! The conservatory—and the hurrying there! And then the moment which had always been, was even now, such a blurred confused impression. Smothered voices from between a clump of flowers: "I saw her." "Who was the man?" A glimpse, gone past in a flash, of an ivory face, a black moustache! And then her voice: "Hubert"; and her hot hand clasping his, drawing him to her; her scent, her face smiling, very set! A rustling behind the flowers, those people spying; and suddenly her lips on his cheek, the kiss sounding in his ears, her voice saying, very softly: "Hubert, dear boy!" The rustle receded, ceased. What a long silent minute, then, among the ferns and blossoms in the dusk with her face close to his, pale, perturbed, before she led him out into the light, while he was slowly realising that she had made use of him to shelter her. A boy—not old enough to be her lover, but old enough to save her name and that of Captain MacKay! Her kiss—the last of many—but not upon *his* lips, *his* cheeks! Hard work realising that! A boy—of no account —a boy, who in a day would be at school again, kissed that *he* and *she* might renew their intrigue unsuspected!

How had he behaved the rest of that evening of romance bedrabbled? He hardly knew. Betrayed with a kiss! Two idols in the dust! And did they care what he was feeling? Not they! All they cared for was to cover up their tracks with him! But somehow—somehow—he had never shown her that he knew. Only, when their dance was over, and someone came and took her for the next, he escaped up to his little room, tore off his gloves, his waistcoat; lay on his bed, thought bitter thoughts. A boy! There he had stayed, with the thrum of the music in his ears, till at last it died away for good and the carriages were gone, and the night was quiet.

Squatting on the warren grass, still warm and dewless, Marsland rubbed his knees. Nothing like boys for generosity! And, with a little smile, he thought of his Aunt next morning, half-arch and half-concerned: "It isn't nice, dear, to sit out in dark corners, and—well, perhaps, it wasn't your fault, but still, it isn't nice—not—quite——" and of how suddenly she had stopped, looking in his face, where his lips were curling in his first ironic laugh. She had never forgiven him that laugh—thinking him a cynical young Lothario? And Marsland thought: 'Live and learn! Wonder what became of those two? Victorian Age! Hatches were battened down in those days! But, innocent—my hat!'

Ah! The sun was off, dew falling! He got up, rubbing his knees to take the stiffness out of them. Pigeons in the wood beyond were calling. A window in his Uncle's old home blazed like a jewel in the sun's last rays between the poplar trees. Heh! dear—a little long-ago affair!

1922.

THE FIRST AND THE LAST

I

"So the last shall be first, and the first last."—HOLY WRIT.

IT was a dark room at that hour of six in the evening, when just
the single oil reading-lamp under its green shade let fall a
dapple of light over the Turkey carpet; over the covers of
books taken out of the book-shelves, and the open pages of the
one selected; over the deep blue and gold of the coffee service
on the little old stool with its Oriental embroidery. Very dark
in the winter, with drawn curtains, many rows of leather-bound
volumes, oak-pannelled walls and ceiling. So large, too, that
the lighted spot before the fire where he sat was just an oasis.
But that was what Keith Darrant liked, after his day's work—
the hard early morning study of his " cases," the fret and strain
of the day in court; it was his rest, these two hours before
dinner, with books, coffee, a pipe, and sometimes a nap. In
red Turkish slippers and his old brown velvet coat, he was well
suited to that framing of glow and darkness. A painter would
have seized avidly on his clear-cut, yellowish face, with its black
eyebrows twisting up over eyes—grey or brown, one could hardly
tell, and its dark grizzling hair still plentiful, in spite of those
daily hours of wig. He seldom thought of his work while he
sat there, throwing off with practised ease the strain of that
long attention to the multiple threads of argument and evidence
to be disentangled—work profoundly interesting, as a rule, to
his clear intellect, trained to almost instinctive rejection of all but
the essential, to selection of what was legally vital out of the
mass of confused tactical and human detail presented to his
scrutiny; yet sometimes tedious and wearing. As for instance
to-day, when he had suspected his client of perjury, and was
almost convinced that he must throw up his brief. He had
disliked the weak-looking, white-faced fellow from the first,

691

and his nervous, shifty answers, his prominent startled eyes—
a type too common in these days of canting tolerations and
weak humanitarianism; no good, no good!

Of the three books he had taken down, a volume of Voltaire
—curious fascination that Frenchman had, for all his destructive irony!—a volume of Burton's travels, and Stevenson's
"New Arabian Nights," he had pitched upon the last. He felt,
that evening, the want of something sedative, a desire to rest
from thought of any kind. The court had been crowded,
stuffy; the air, as he walked home, soft, sou'-westerly, charged
with coming moisture, no quality of vigour in it; he felt relaxed, tired, even nervy, and for once the loneliness of his house
seemed strange and comfortless.

Lowering the lamp, he turned his face towards the fire. Perhaps he would get a sleep before that boring dinner at the
Tellassons'. He wished it were vacation, and Maisie back from
school. A widower for many years, he had lost the habit of a
woman about him; yet to-night he had a positive yearning
for the society of his young daughter, with her quick ways, and
bright, dark eyes. Curious what perpetual need of a woman
some men had! His brother Laurence—wasted—all through
women—atrophy of willpower! A man on the edge of things;
living from hand to mouth; his gifts all down at heel! One
would have thought the Scottish strain might have saved him;
and yet, when a Scotsman did begin to go downhill, who could
go faster? Curious that their mother's blood should have worked
so differently in her two sons. He himself had always felt he
owed all his success to it.

His thoughts went off at a tangent to a certain issue troub-
ling his legal conscience. He had not wavered in the usual
assumption of omniscience, but he was by no means sure that he
had given right advice. Well! without that power to decide and
hold to decision in spite of misgiving, one would never have
been fit for one's position at the Bar, never have been fit for
anything. The longer he lived, the more certain he became of
the prime necessity of virile and decisive action in all the affairs of life. A word and a blow—and the blow first! Doubts,
hesitation, sentiment—the muling and puking of this twilight
age——! And there welled up on his handsome face a smile
that was almost devilish—the tricks of firelight are so many!
It faded again in sheer drowsiness; he slept. . . .

He woke with a start, having a feeling of something out beyond the light, and without turning his head said: " What's that? " There came a sound as if somebody had caught his breath. He turned up the lamp.

" Who's there? "

A voice over by the door answered:

" Only I—Larry."

Something in the tone, or perhaps just being startled out of sleep like this, made him shiver. He said:

" I was asleep. Come in! "

It was noticeable that he did not get up, or even turn his head, now that he knew who it was, but waited, his half-closed eyes fixed on the fire, for his brother to come forward. A visit from Laurence was not an unmixed blessing. He could hear him breathing, and became conscious of a scent of whisky. Why could not the fellow at least abstain when he was coming here! It was so childish, so lacking in any sense of proportion or of decency! And he said sharply:

" Well, Larry, what is it? "

It was always something. He often wondered at the strength of that sense of trusteeship, which kept him still tolerant of the troubles, amenable to the petitions of this brother of his; or was it just " blood " feeling, a Highland sense of loyalty to kith and kin; an old-time quality which judgment and half his instincts told him was weakness, but which, in spite of all, bound him to the distressful fellow? Was he drunk now, that he kept lurking out there by the door? And he said less sharply:

" Why don't you come and sit down? "

He was coming now, avoiding the light, skirting along the walls just beyond the radiance of the lamp, his feet and legs to the waist brightly lighted, but his face disintegrated in shadow, like the face of a dark ghost.

" Are you ill, man? "

Still no answer, save a shake of that head, and the passing up of a hand, out of the light, to the ghostly forehead under the dishevelled hair. The scent of whisky was stronger now; and Keith thought:

" He really is drunk. Nice thing for the new butler to see! If he can't behave——"

The figure against the wall heaved a sigh—so truly from an overburdened heart that Keith was conscious with a certain dismay of not having yet fathomed the cause of this uncanny

silence. He got up, and, back to the fire, said with a brutality
born of nerves rather than design:

"What is it, man? Have you committed a murder, that you
stand there dumb as a fish?"

For a second no answer at all, not even of breathing; then,
just the whisper:

"Yes."

The sense of unreality which so helps one at moments of disaster enabled Keith to say vigorously:

"By Jove! You *have* been drinking!"

But it passed at once into deadly apprehension.

"What do you mean? Come here, where I can see you.
What's the matter with you, Larry?"

With a sudden lurch and dive, his brother left the shelter
of the shadow, and sank into a chair in the circle of light.
And another long, broken sigh escaped him.

"There's nothing the matter with me, Keith! It's true!"

Keith stepped quickly forward, and stared down into his
brother's face; and instantly he saw that it *was* true. No one
could have simulated the look in those eyes—of horrified wonder, as if they would never again get on terms with the face to
which they belonged. To see them squeezed the heart—only
real misery could look like that. Then that sudden pity became
angry bewilderment.

"What in God's name is this nonsense?"

But it was significant that he lowered his voice; went over
to the door, too, to see if it were shut. Laurence had drawn
his chair forward, huddling over the fire—a thin figure, a worn,
highcheek-boned face with deep-sunk blue eyes, and wavy hair
all ruffled, a face that still had a certain beauty. Putting a hand
on that lean shoulder, Keith said:

"Come, Larry! Pull yourself together, and drop exaggera-
tion."

"It's true, I tell you; I've killed a man."

The noisy violence of that outburst acted like a douche. What
was the fellow about—shouting out such words! But suddenly Laurence lifted his hands and wrung them. The gesture
was so utterly painful that it drew a quiver from Keith's face.

"Why did you come here," he said, "and tell *me* this?"

Larry's face was really unearthly sometimes, such strange
gleams passed up on to it!

" Whom else should I tell? I came to know what I'm to do,
Keith? Give myself up, or what?"

At that sudden introduction of the practical, Keith felt his
heart twitch. Was it then as real as all that? But he said,
very quietly:

" Just tell me—— How did it come about, this—affair?"

That question linked the dark, gruesome, fantastic nightmare
on to actuality.

" When did it happen?"

" Last night."

In Larry's face there was—there had always been—something
childishly truthful. He would never stand a chance in court!
And Keith said:

" How? Where? You'd better tell me quietly from the beginning. Drink this coffee; it'll clear your head."

Laurence took the little blue cup and drained it.

" Yes," he said. " It's like this, Keith. There's a girl I've
known for some months now——"

Women! And Keith said between his teeth: " Well?"

" Her father was a Pole who died over here when she was
sixteen, and left her all alone. A man called Walenn, a mongrel American, living in the same house, married her, or pretended to—she's very pretty, Keith—he left her with a baby
six months old, and another coming. That one died, and she
did nearly. Then she starved till another fellow took her on.
She lived with him two years; then Walenn turned up again,
and made her go back to him. The brute used to beat her
black and blue, all for nothing. Then he left her again. When
I met her she'd lost her elder child, too, and was taking anybody who came along."

He suddenly looked up into Keith's face.

" But I've never met a sweeter woman, nor a truer, that I
swear. Woman! She's only twenty now! When I went to her
last night that brute—that Walenn—had found her out again;
and when he came for me, swaggering and bullying—— Look!"
he touched a dark mark on his forehead—" I took his throat in
my hands, and when I let go——"

" Yes?"

" Dead. I never knew till afterwards that she was hanging
on to him behind."

Again he made that gesture—wringing his hands.

In a hard voice Keith said:

" What did you do then? "

" We sat by it a long time. Then I carried it on my back down the street, round a corner to an archway."

" How far? "

" About fifty yards."

" Was anyone—did anyone see? "

" No."

" What time? "

" Three."

" And then? "

" Went back to her."

" Why—in Heaven's name? "

" She was lonely and afraid; so was I, Keith."

" Where is this place? "

" Forty-two, Borrow Street, Soho."

" And the archway? "

" Corner of Glove Lane."

" Good God! Why—I saw it in the paper! "

And seizing the journal that lay on his bureau, Keith read again that paragraph: " The body of a man was found this morning under an archway in Glove Lane, Soho. From marks about the throat suspicions of foul play are entertained. The body had apparently been robbed, and nothing was discovered leading to identification."

It was real earnest, then. Murder! His own brother! He faced round and said:

" You saw this in the paper, and dreamed it. Understand —you dreamed it! "

The wistful answer came:

" If only I had, Keith—if only I had! "

In his turn, Keith very nearly wrung his hands.

" Did you take anything from the—body? "

" This dropped while we were struggling."

It was an empty envelope with a South American post-mark addressed: " Patrick Walenn, Simon's Hotel, Farrier Street, London." Again with that twitching in his heart, Keith said:

" Put it in the fire."

Then suddenly he stooped to pluck it out. By that command—he had—identified himself with this—this——— But he did not pluck it out. It blackened, writhed, and vanished. And once more he said:

" What in God's name made you come here and tell *me?* "

"You know about these things. I didn't mean to kill him.
I love the girl. What shall I do, Keith?"

Simple! How simple! To ask what he was to do! It was
like Larry! And he said:

"You were not seen, you think?"

"It's a dark street. There was no one about."

"When did you leave this girl the second time?"

"About seven o'clock."

"Where did you go?"

"To my rooms."

"In Fitzroy Street?"

"Yes."

"Did anyone see you come in?"

"No."

"What have you done since?"

"Sat there."

"Not been out?"

"No."

"Not seen the girl?"

"No."

"You don't know, then, what she's done since?"

"No."

"Would she give you away?"

"Never."

"Would she give herself away—hysteria?"

"No."

"Who knows of your relations with her?"

"No one."

"No one?"

"I don't know who should, Keith."

"Did anyone see you going in last night, when you first went
to her?"

"No. She lives on the ground floor. I've got keys."

"Give them to me. What else have you that connects you
with her?"

"Nothing."

"In your rooms?"

"No."

"No photographs. No letters?"

"No."

"Be careful."

"Nothing."

" No one saw you going back to her the second time? "

" No."

" No one saw you leave her in the morning? "

" No."

" You were fortunate. Sit down again, man. I must think."

Think! Think out this accursed thing—so beyond all thought, and all belief. But he could not think. Not a coherent thought would come. And he began again:

" Was it his first reappearance with her? "

" Yes."

" She told you so? "

" Yes."

" How did he find out where she was? "

" I don't know."

" How drunk were you? "

" I was not drunk."

" How much had you drunk? "

" About a bottle of claret—nothing."

" You say you didn't mean to kill him? "

" No—God knows! "

" That's something. What made you choose the arch? "

" It was the first dark place."

" Did his face look as if he had been strangled? "

" Don't! "

" Did it? "

" Yes."

" Very disfigured? "

" Yes."

" Did you look to see if his clothes were marked? "

" No."

" Why not? "

" Why not? My God! If you had done it——! "

" You say he was disfigured. Would he be recognisable? "

" I don't know."

" When she lived with him last—where was that? "

" I don't know for certain. Pimlico, I think."

" Not Soho? "

" No."

" How long has she been at the Soho place? "

" Nearly a year."

" Always the same rooms? "

" Yes."

" Is there anyone living in that house or street who would be likely to know her as his wife? "

" I don't think so."

" What was he? "

" I should think he was a professional ' bully.' "

" I see. Spending most of his time abroad, then? "

" Yes."

" Do you know if he was known to the police? "

" I haven't heard of it."

" Now listen, Larry. When you leave here go straight home, and don't go out till I come to you, to-morrow morning. Promise that! "

" I promise."

" I've got a dinner engagement. I'll think this out. Don't drink. Don't talk! Pull yourself together."

" Don't keep me longer than you can help, Keith! "

That white face, those eyes, that shaking hand! With a twinge of pity in the midst of all the turbulence of his revolt, and fear, and disgust, Keith put his hand on his brother's shoulder, and said:

" Courage! "

And suddenly he thought: ' My God! Courage! I shall want it all myself! '

II

Laurence Darrant, leaving his brother's house in the Adelphi, walked northwards, rapidly, slowly, rapidly again. For, if there are men who by force of will do one thing only at a time, there are men who from lack of will do now one thing, now another, with equal intensity. To such natures, to be gripped by the Nemesis which attends the lack of self-control is no reason for being more self-controlled. Rather does it foster their pet feeling: " What matter? To-morrow we die! " The effort of will required to go to Keith had relieved, exhausted and exasperated him. In accordance with those three feelings was the progress of his walk. He started from the door with the fixed resolve to go home and stay there quietly till Keith came. He was in Keith's hands; Keith would know what was to be done. But he had not gone three hundred yards before he felt so utterly weary, body and soul, that if he had but had a pistol in his pocket he would have shot himself in the street. Not even the thought of the girl—this young unfortunate with her strange devotion, who had kept him straight these last five months, who had roused in him a depth of feeling he had never known before—would have availed against that sudden black dejection. Why go on—a waif at the mercy of his own nature, a straw blown here and there by every gust which rose in him? Why not have done with it for ever, and take it out in sleep?

He was approaching the fatal street, where he and the girl, that early morning, had spent the hours clutched together, trying in the refuge of love to forget for a moment their horror and fear. Should he go in? He had promised Keith not to. Why had he promised? He caught sight of himself in a chemist's lighted window. Miserable, shadowy brute! And he remembered suddenly a dog he had picked up once in the streets of Pera, a black-and-white creature—different from the other dogs, not one of their breed, a pariah of pariahs, who had strayed there somehow. He had taken it home to the house where he was staying, contrary to all custom of the country; had got fond of it; had shot it himself, sooner than leave it behind again to the mercies of its own kind in the streets. Twelve years ago! And those sleeve-links made of little Turkish coins he had brought back for the girl at the hairdresser's in Chancery Lane where he used to get shaved—pretty creature, like a wild rose. He had asked of her a kiss for payment. What queer emotion when she put her face forward to his lips —a sort of passionate tenderness and shame, at the softness and warmth of that flushed cheek, at her beauty and trustful gratitude. She would soon have given herself to him—that one! He had never gone there again! And to this day he did not know why he had abstained; to this day he did not know whether he were glad or sorry not to have plucked that rose. He must surely have been very different then! Queer business, life— queer, queer business!—to go through it never knowing what you would do next. Ah! to be like Keith, steady, buttoned-up in success; a brass pot, a pillar of society! Once, as a boy, he had been within an ace of killing Keith, for sneering at him. Once in Southern Italy he had been near killing a driver who was flogging his horse. And now, that dark-faced, swinish bully who had ruined the girl he had grown to love—he had done it! Killed him! Killed a man!

He who did not want to hurt a fly. The chemist's window confronted him with the sudden thought that he had at home

that which made him safe, in case they should arrest him. He
would never again go out without some of those little white
tablets sewn into the lining of his coat. Restful, even ex-
hilarating thought! They said a man should not take his own
life. Let *them* taste horror—those glib citizens! Let them live
as that girl had lived, as millions lived all the world over, under their canting dogmas! A man might rather even take his
life than watch their cursed inhumanities.

He went into the chemist's for a bromide; and, while the
man was mixing it, stood resting one foot like a tired horse.
The "life" he had squeezed out of that fellow! After all, a
billion living creatures gave up life each day, had it squeezed
out of them, mostly. And perhaps not one a day deserved
death so much as that loathly fellow. Life! a breath—a flame!
Nothing! Why, then, this icy clutching at his heart?

The chemist brought the draught.

"Not sleeping, sir?"

"No."

The man's eyes seemed to say: "Yes! Burning the candle
at both ends—I know!" Odd life, a chemist's; pills and pow-
ders all day long, to hold the machinery of men together!
Devilish odd trade!

In going out he caught the reflection of his face in a mirror;
it seemed too good altogether for a man who had committed
murder. There was a sort of brightness underneath, an amiability lurking about its shadows; how—how could it be the face
of a man who had done what he had done? His head felt
lighter now, his feet lighter; he walked rapidly again.

Curious feeling of relief and oppression all at once! Frightful—to long for company, for talk, for distraction; and—to be
afraid of it! The girl—the girl and Keith were now the only
persons who would not give him that feeling of dread. And,
of those two—Keith was not——! Who could consort with
one who was never wrong, a successful, righteous fellow; a chap
built so that he knew nothing about himself, wanted to know
nothing, a chap all solid actions? To be a quicksand swallowing up one's own resolutions was bad enough! But to be like
Keith—all will-power, marching along, treading down his own
feelings and weaknesses!—— No! One could not make a comrade of a man like Keith, even if he were one's brother? The
only creature in all the world was the girl. She alone knew
and felt what he was feeling; would put up with him and love

him whatever he did, or was done to him. He stopped and took shelter in a doorway, to light a cigarette.

He had suddenly a fearful wish to pass the archway where he had placed the body; a fearful wish that had no sense, no end in view, no anything; just an insensate craving to see the dark place again. He crossed Borrow Street to the little lane. There was only one person visible, a man on the far side with his shoulders hunched against the wind; a short, dark figure which crossed and came towards him in the flickering lamplight. What a face! Yellow, ravaged, clothed almost to the eyes in a stubbly greyish growth of beard, with blackish teeth, and haunting bloodshot eyes. And what a figure of rags—one shoulder higher than the other, one leg a little lame, and thin! A surge of feeling came up in Laurence for this creature, more unfortunate than himself. There were lower depths than his!

"Well, brother," he said, " *you* don't look too prosperous! "

The smile which gleamed out on the man's face seemed as unlikely as a smile on a scarecrow.

"Prosperity doesn't come my way," he said in a rusty voice. " I'm a failure—always been a failure. And yet—you wouldn't think it, would you?—I was a minister of religion once."

Laurence held out a shilling. But the man shook his head.

"Keep your money," he said. "I've got more than you to-day, I daresay. But thank you for taking a little interest. That's worth more than money to a man that's down."

"You're right."

"Yes," the rusty voice went on; "I'd as soon die as go on living as I do. And now I've lost my self-respect. Often wondered how long a starving man could go without losing his self-respect. Not so very long. You take my word for that." And without the slightest change in the monotony of that creaking voice he added:

"Did you read of the murder? Just here. I've been looking at the place."

The words, " So have I! " leaped up to Laurence's lips; he choked them down with a sort of terror.

"I wish you better luck," he said. "Good-night!" and hurried away. A sort of ghastly laughter was forcing its way up in his throat. Was everyone talking of the murder he had committed? Even the very scarecrows?

III

There are some natures so constituted that, due to be hung at ten o'clock, they will play chess at eight. Such men invariably rise. They make especially good bishops, editors, judges, impresarios, Prime Ministers, money-lenders, and generals; in fact, fill with exceptional credit any position of power over their fellow-men. They have spiritual cold storage, in which are preserved their nervous systems. In such men there is little or none of that fluid sense and continuity of feeling known under those vague terms, speculation, poetry, philosophy. Men of facts and of decision switching imagination on and off at will, subordinating sentiment to reason. . . . one does not think of them when watching wind ripple over cornfields, or swallows flying.

Keith Darrant had need for being of that breed during his dinner at the Tellasson's. It was just eleven when he issued from the big house in Portland Place and refrained from taking a cab. He wanted to walk that he might better think. What crude and wanton irony there was in his situation! To have been made father-confessor to a murderer, he—well on towards a judgeship! With his contempt for the kind of weakness which landed men in such abysses, he felt it all so sordid, so "impossible," that he could hardly bring his mind to bear on it at all. And yet he must, because of two powerful instincts— self-preservation and blood-loyalty.

The wind had still the sapping softness of the afternoon, but rain had held off so far. It was warm, and he unbuttoned his fur overcoat. The nature of his thoughts deepened the dark austerity of his face, whose thin, well-cut lips were always pressing together, as if, by meeting, to dispose of each thought as it came up. He moved along the crowded pavements glumly. That air of festive conspiracy, which drops with the darkness on to lighted streets, galled him. He turned off on a darker route.

This ghastly business! Convinced of its reality, he yet could not see it. The thing existed in his mind, not as a picture, but as a piece of irrefutable evidence. Larry had not meant to do it, of course. But it was murder, all the same. Men like Larry—weak, impulsive, sentimental, introspective creatures—did they ever mean what they did? This man, this

Walenn, was, by all accounts, better dead than alive; no need to waste a thought on him! But, crime—the ugliness—Justice unsatisfied! Crime concealed—and his own share in the concealment! And yet—brother to brother! Surely no one could demand action from him! It was only a question of what he was going to advise Larry to do. To keep silent, and disappear? Had that a chance of success? Perhaps—if the answers to his questions had been correct. But this girl! Suppose the dead man's relationship to her were ferreted out, could she be relied on not to endanger Larry? These women were all the same, unstable as water, emotional, shiftless—pests of society. Then, too, a crime untracked, dogging all his brother's after life; a secret following him wherever he might vanish to; hanging over him, watching for some drunken moment, to slip out of his lips. It was bad to think of. A clean breast of it? But his heart twitched within him. " Brother of Mr. Keith Darrant, the well-known King's Counsel "—visiting a woman of the town, strangling with his bare hands the woman's husband! No intention to murder, but—a dead man! A dead man carried out of the house, laid under a dark archway! Provocation! Recommended to mercy—penal servitude for life! Was that the advice he was going to give Larry to-morrow morning?

And he had a sudden vision of shaven men with clay-coloured features, run, as it were, to seed, as he had seen them once in Pentonville, when he had gone there to visit a prisoner. Larry! whom, as a baby creature, he had watched straddling; whom, as a little fellow, he had fagged; whom he had seen through scrapes at college; to whom he had lent money time and again, and time and again admonished in his courses. Larry! Five years younger than himself; and committed to his charge by their mother when she died. To become for life one of those men with faces like diseased plants; with no hair but a bushy stubble; with arrows marked on their yellow clothes! Larry! One of those men herded like sheep; at the beck and call of common men! A gentleman, his own brother, to live that slave's life, to be ordered here and there, year after year, day in, day out. Something snapped within him. He could not give that advice. Impossible! But, if not, he must make sure of his ground, must verify, must know. This Glove Lane— this archway? It would not be far from where he was that very moment. He looked for someone of whom to make enquiry. A policeman was standing at the corner, his stolid face illumined by a lamp; capable and watchful—an excellent officer, no doubt; but, turning his head away, Keith passed him without a word. Strange to feel that cold, uneasy feeling in presence of the law! A grim little driving home of what it all meant! Then, suddenly, he saw that the turning to his left was Borrow Street itself. He walked up one side, crossed over, and returned. He passed Number Forty-two, a small house with business names printed on the lifeless windows of the first and second floors; with dark-curtained windows on the ground floor, or was there just a slink of light in one corner? Which way had Larry turned? Which way under that grisly burden? Fifty paces of this squalid street—narrow, and dark, and empty, thank heaven! Glove Lane! Here it was! A tiny runlet of a street. And here——! He had run right on to the arch, a brick bridge connecting two portions of a warehouse, and dark indeed.

"That's right, gov'nor! That's the place!" He needed all his self-control to turn leisurely to the speaker. "'Ere's where they found the body—very spot—leanin' up 'ere. They ain't got 'im yet. Lytest—me lord!"

It was a ragged boy holding out a tattered yellowish journal. His lynx eyes peered up from under lanky wisps of hair, and his voice had the proprietary note of one making "a corner" in his news. Keith took the paper and gave him twopence. He even found a sort of comfort in the young ghoul's hanging about there; it meant that others besides himself had come morbidly to look. By the dim lamplight he read: "Glove Lane garrotting mystery. Nothing has yet been discovered of the murdered man's identity; from the cut of his clothes he is supposed to be a foreigner." The boy had vanished, and Keith saw the figure of a policeman coming slowly down this gutter of a street. A second's hesitation, and he stood firm. Nothing obviously could have brought him here save this "mystery," and he stayed quietly staring at the arch. The policeman moved up abreast. Keith saw that he was the one whom he had passed just now. He noted the cold offensive question die out of the man's eyes when they caught the gleam of white shirt-front under the opened fur collar. And holding up the paper, he said:

"Is this where the man was found?"

"Yes, sir."

"Still a mystery, I see?"

" Well, we can't always go by the papers. But I don't fancy they do know much about it, yet."

" Dark spot. Do fellows sleep under here? "

The policeman nodded. " There's not an arch in London where we don't get 'em sometimes."

" Nothing found on him—I think I read? "

" Not a copper. Pockets inside out. There's some funny characters about this quarter. Greeks, Hitalians—all sorts."

Queer sensation this, of being glad of a policeman's confidential tone!

" Well, good-night! "

" Good-night, sir. Good-night! "

He looked back from Borrow Street. The policeman was still standing there holding up his lantern, so that its light fell into the archway, as if trying to read its secret.

Now that he had seen this dark, deserted spot, the chances seemed to him much better. " Pockets inside out! " Either Larry had had presence of mind to do a very clever thing, or someone had been at the body before the police found it. That was the more likely. A dead backwater of a place. At three o'clock—loneliest of all hours—Larry's five minutes' grim excursion to and fro might well have passed unseen! Now, it all depended on the girl; on whether Laurence had been seen coming to her or going away; on whether, if the man's relationship to her were discovered, she could be relied on to say nothing. There was not a soul in Borrow Street now; hardly even a lighted window; and he took one of those rather desperate decisions only possible to men daily accustomed to the instant taking of responsibility. He would go to her, and see for himself. He came to the door of Forty-two, obviously one of those which are only shut at night, and tried the larger key. It fitted, and he was in a gas-lighted passage, with an oil-clothed floor, and a single door to his left. He stood there undecided. She must be made to understand that he knew everything. She must not be told more than that he was a friend of Larry's. She must not be frightened, yet must be forced to give her very soul away. A hostile witness—not to be treated as hostile —a matter for delicate handling! But his knock was not answered.

Should he give up this nerve-racking, bizarre effort to come at a basis of judgment; go away, and just tell Laurence that he could not advise him? And then—what? Something *must* be done. He knocked again. Still no answer. And with that impatience of being thwarted, natural to him, and fostered to the full by the conditions of his life, he tried the other key. It worked, and he opened the door. Inside all was dark, but a voice from some way off, with a sort of breathless relief in its foreign tones, said:

"Oh! then it's you, Larry! Why did you knock? I was so frightened. Turn up the light, dear. Come in!"

Feeling by the door for a switch in the pitch blackness, he was conscious of arms round his neck, a warm thinly clad body pressed to his own; then withdrawn as quickly, with a gasp, and the most awful terror-stricken whisper:

"Oh! Who is it?"

With a glacial shiver down his own spine, Keith answered:

"A friend of Laurence. Don't be frightened!"

There was such silence that he could hear a clock ticking, and the sound of his own hand passing over the surface of the wall, trying to find the switch. He found it, and in the light which leaped up he saw, stiffened against a dark curtain evidently screening off a bedroom, a girl standing, holding a long black coat together at her throat, so that her face with its pale brown hair, short and square-cut and curling up underneath, had an uncanny look of being detached from any body. Her face was so alabaster pale that the staring, startled eyes, dark blue or brown, and the faint rose of the parted lips, were like colour stainings on a white mask; and it had a strange delicacy, truth, and pathos, such as only suffering brings. Though not susceptible to æsthetic emotion, Keith was curiously affected. He said gently:

"You needn't be afraid. I haven't come to do you harm— quite the contrary. May I sit down and talk?" And, holding up the keys, he added: "Laurence wouldn't have given me these, would he, if he hadn't trusted me?"

Still she did not move, and he had the impression that he was looking at a spirit—a spirit startled out of its flesh. Nor at the moment did it seem in the least strange that he should conceive such an odd thought. He stared round the room— clean and tawdry, with its tarnished gilt mirror, marble-topped side-table, and plush-covered sofa. Twenty years and more since he had been in such a place. And he said:

"Won't you sit down? I'm sorry to have startled you."

But still she did not move, whispering:

" Who are you, please ? "

And, moved suddenly beyond the realm of caution by the
terror in that whisper, he answered:

" Larry's brother."

She uttered a little sigh of relief which went to Keith's heart,
and, still holding the dark coat together at her throat, came
forward and sat down on the sofa. He could see that her feet,
thrust, into slippers, were bare; with her short hair, and those
candid startled eyes, she looked like a tall child. He drew up a
chair and said:

" You must forgive me coming at such an hour; he's told me,
you see."

He expected her to flinch and gasp; but she only clasped her
hands together on her knees, and said:

" Yes ? "

Then horror and discomfort rose up in him afresh.

" An awful business ! "

Her whisper echoed him:

" Yes, oh! yes! Awful—it is awful ! "

And suddenly realising that the man must have fallen dead
just where he was sitting, Keith became stock silent, staring
at the floor.

" Yes," she whispered; " just there. I see him now always
falling ! "

How she said that! With what a strange gentle despair !
In this girl of evil life, who had brought on them this tragedy,
what was it which moved him to a sort of unwilling compassion ?

" You look very young," he said.

" I am twenty."

" And you are fond of—my brother ? "

" I would die for him."

Impossible to mistake the tone of her voice, or the look in her
eyes, true deep Slav eyes; dark brown, not blue as he had
thought at first. It was a very pretty face—either her life had
not eaten into it yet, or the suffering of these last hours had
purged away those marks; or perhaps this devotion of hers to
Larry. He felt strangely at sea, sitting there with this child
of twenty; he, over forty, a man of the world, professionally
used to every side of human nature. But he said, stammering
a little:

" I—I have come to see how far you can save him. Listen, and just answer the questions I put to you."

She raised her hands, squeezed them together, and murmured:

" Oh! I will answer anything."

" This man, then—your—your husband—was he a bad man? "

" A dreadful man."

" Before he came here last night, how long since you saw him? "

" Eighteen months."

" Where did you live when you saw him last? "

" In Pimlico."

" Does anybody about here know you as Mrs. Walenn? "

" No. When I came here, after my little girl died, I came to live a bad life. Nobody knows me at all. I am quite alone."

" If they discover who he was, they will look for his wife? "

" I do not know. He did not let people think I was married to him. I was very young; he treated many, I think, like me."

" Do you think he was known to the police? "

She shook her head. " He was very clever."

" What is your name now? "

" Wanda Livinska."

" Were you known by that name before you were married? "

" Wanda is my Christian name. Livinska—I just call myself."

" I see; since you came here."

" Yes."

" Did my brother ever see this man before last night? "

" Never."

" You had told him about his treatment of you? "

" Yes. And that man first went for him."

" I saw the mark. Do you think anyone saw my brother come to you? "

" I do not know. He says not."

" Can you tell if anyone saw him carrying the—the thing away? "

" No one in this street—I was looking."

" Nor coming back? "

" No one."

" Nor going out in the morning? "

" I do not think it."

" Have you a servant? "

" Only a woman who comes at nine in the morning for an hour."

" Does she know Larry? "

" No."

" Friends, acquaintances? "

" No; I am very quiet. And since I knew your brother, I see no one. Nobody comes here but him for a long time now."

" How long? "

" Five months."

" Have you been out to-day? "

" No."

" What have you been doing? "

" Crying."

It was said with a certain dreadful simplicity, and pressing her hands together she went on:

" He is in danger because of me. I am so afraid for him."

Holding up his hand to check that emotion, he said:

" Look at me! "

She fixed those dark eyes on him, and in her bare throat, from which the coat had fallen back, he could see her resolutely swallowing down her agitation.

" If the worst comes to the worst, and this man is traced to you, can you trust yourself not to give my brother away? "

Her eyes shone. She got up and went to the fireplace:

" Look! I have burned all the things he has given me— even his picture. Now I have nothing from him."

Keith, too, got up.

" Good! One more question: Do the police know you, be- cause—because of your life? "

She shook her head, looking at him intently with those mourn- fully true eyes. And he felt a sort of shame.

" I was obliged to ask. Do you know where he lives? "

" Yes."

" You must not go there. And he must not come to you here."

Her lips quivered; but she bowed her head. Suddenly he found her quite close to him, speaking almost in a whisper:

" Please do not take him from me altogether. I will be so careful. I will not do anything to hurt him; but if I cannot see him sometimes I shall die. Please do not take him from me." And catching his hand between her own she pressed it desperately. It was several seconds before Keith said:

"Leave that to me. I will see him. I shall arrange. You must leave that to me."

"But you will be kind?"

He felt her lips kissing his hand. And the soft moist touch sent a queer feeling through him, protective, yet just a little brutal, having in it a shiver of sensuality. He withdrew his hand. And as if warned that she had been too pressing, she recoiled humbly. But suddenly she turned, and stood absolutely rigid; then almost inaudibly whispered: "Listen! Someone out—out there!" And darting past him she turned out the light.

Almost at once came a knock on the door. He could feel—actually feel the terror of this girl beside him in the dark. And he, too, felt terror. Who could it be? No one came but Larry, she had said. Who else then could it be? Again came the knock, louder! He felt the breath of her whisper on his cheek; "If it is Larry! I must open." He shrank back against the wall, heard her open the door and say faintly: "Yes. Please! Who?"

Light painted a thin moving line on the wall opposite, and a voice which Keith recognised answered:

"All right, miss. Your outer door's open here. You ought to keep it shut after dark."

God! That policeman! And it had been his own doing, not shutting the outer door behind when he came in. He heard her say timidly in her foreign voice: "Thank you, sir!" the policeman's retreating steps, the outer door being shut, and felt her close to him again. That something in her youth and strange prettiness had touched and kept him gentle, no longer blunted the edge of his exasperation, now that he could not see her. They were all the same, these women; could not speak the truth! And he said brusquely:

"You told me they didn't know you!"

Her voice answered like a sigh:

"I did not think they did, sir. It is so long I was not out in the town, not since I had Larry."

The repulsion which all the time seethed deep in Keith welled up at those words. His brother—son of *his* mother, a gentleman—the property of this girl, bound to her, body and soul, by this unspeakable event! But she had turned up the light. Had she some intuition that darkness was against her? Yes, she *was* pretty with that soft face, colourless save for its lips and dark eyes, with that face somehow so touching, so unaccountably good, and like a child's.

"I am going now," he said. "Remember! He mustn't come here; you mustn't go to him. I shall see him to-morrow. If you are as fond as him as you say—take care, take care!"

She sighed out, "Yes! oh, yes!" and Keith went to the door. She was standing with her back to the wall, and to follow him she only moved her head—that dove-like face with all its life in eyes which seemed saying: "Look into us; nothing we hide; all—all is there!"

And he went out.

In the passage he paused before opening the outer door. He did not want to meet that policeman again; the fellow's round should have taken him well out of the street by now, and, turning the handle cautiously, he looked out. No one in sight. He stood a moment, wondering if he should turn to right or left, then briskly crossed the street. A voice to his right hand said:

"Good-night, sir."

There in the shadow of a doorway the policeman was standing. The fellow must have seen him coming out! Utterly unable to restrain a start, and muttering "Good-night!" Keith walked on rapidly.

He went full quarter of a mile before he lost that startled and uneasy feeling in sardonic exasperation that he, Keith Darrant, had been taken for a frequenter of a lady of the town. The whole thing—the whole thing!—a vile and disgusting business! His very mind felt dirty and breathless; his spirit, drawn out of sheath, had slowly to slide back before he could at all focus and readjust his reasoning faculty. Certainly, he had got the knowledge he wanted. There was less danger than he thought. That girl's eyes! No mistaking her devotion. She would not give Larry away. Yes! Larry must clear out—South America—the East—it did not matter. But he felt no relief. The cheap, tawdry room had wrapped itself round his fancy with its atmosphere of murky love, with the feeling it inspired, of emotion caged within those yellowish walls and the red stuff of its furniture. That girl's face! Devotion; truth, too, and beauty, rare and moving, in its setting of darkness and horror, in that nest of vice and of disorder! . . . The dark archway; the street arab, with his gleeful: "They 'ain't got 'im yet!"; the feel of those bare arms round his neck; that whisper of horror in the darkness; above all, again, her child face looking into his, so truthful! And suddenly he stood quite still in the street. What in God's name was he about? What grotesque juggling amongst shadows, what strange and ghastly eccentricity was all this? The forces of order and routine, all the actualities of his daily life, marched on him at that moment and swept everything before them. It was a dream, a nightmare—not real! It was ridiculous! That he—*he* should thus be bound up with things so black and bizarre!

He had come by now to the Strand, that street down which every day he moved to the Law Courts, to his daily work; his work so dignified and regular, so irreproachable and solid. No! The thing was all a monstrous nightmare! It would go, if he fixed his mind on the familiar objects around, read the names on the shops, looked at the faces passing. Far down the thoroughfare he caught the outline of the old church, and beyond, the loom of the Law Courts themselves. The bell of a fire-engine sounded, and the horses came galloping by, with the shining metal, rattle of hoofs, and hoarse shouting. Here was a sensation, real and harmless, dignified and customary! A woman flaunting round the corner looked up at him and leered out: " Good-night! " Even that was customary, tolerable. Two policemen passed, supporting between them a man the worse for liquor, full of fight and expletives; the sight was soothing, an ordinary thing which brought passing annoyance, interest, disgust. It had begun to rain; he felt it on his face with pleasure—an actual thing, not eccentric, a thing which happened every day!

He began to cross the street. Cabs were going at furious speed now that the last omnibus had ceased to run; it distracted him to take this actual, ordinary risk run so often every day. During that crossing of the Strand, with the rain in his face and the cabs shooting past, he regained for the first time his assurance, shook off this unreal sense of being in the grip of something, and walked resolutely to·the corner of his home turning. But passing into that darker stretch, he again stood still. A policeman had also turned into that street on the other side. Not—surely not——! Absurd! They were all alike to look at —those fellows! Absurd! He walked on sharply, and let himself into his house. But on his way upstairs he could not for the life of him help raising a corner of a curtain and looking from the staircase window. The policeman was marching solemnly, about twenty-five yards away, paying apparently no attention to anything whatever.

IV

Keith woke at five o'clock, his usual hour, without remembrance. But the grisly shadow started up when he entered his study, where the lamp burned, and the fire shone, and the coffee was set ready, just as when yesterday afternoon Larry had stood out there against the wall. For a moment he fought against realisation; then, drinking off his coffee, sat down sullenly at the bureau to his customary three hours' study of the day's cases.

Not one word of his brief could he take in. It was all jumbled with murky images and apprehensions, and for full half an hour he suffered mental paralysis. Then the sheer necessity of knowing something of the case which he had to open at half-past ten that morning forced him to a concentration which never quite subdued the *malaise* at the bottom of his heart. Nevertheless, when he rose at half-past eight and went into the bathroom, he had earned his grim satisfaction in this victory of will-power. By half-past nine he must be at Larry's. A boat left London for the Argentine to-morrow. If Larry was to get away at once, money must be arranged for. And then at breakfast he came on this paragraph in the paper:

" SOHO MURDER

" Enquiry late last night established the fact that the police have discovered the identity of the man found strangled yesterday morning under an archway in Glove Lane. An arrest has been made."

By good fortune he had finished eating, for the words made him feel physically sick. At this very minute Larry might be locked up, waiting to be charged—might even have been arrested before his own visit to the girl last night. If Larry were arrested she must be implicated. What, then, would be his own position? Idiot to go and look at that archway, to go and see the girl! Had that policeman really followed him home? Accessory after the fact! Keith Darrant, King's Counsel, man of mark! He forced himself by an effort, which had something of the heroic, to drop this panicky feeling. Panic never did good. He must face it and see. He refused even to hurry, calmly collected the papers wanted for the day, and attended to a letter or two before he set out in a taxi-cab to Fitzroy Street.

Waiting outside there in the grey morning for his ring to be answered, he looked the very picture of a man who knew his mind, a man of resolution. But it needed all his will-power to ask without tremor: " Mr. Darrant in? " to hear without sign of any kind the answer: " He's not up yet, sir."

" Never mind; I'll go in and see him. Mr. Keith Darrant."

On his way to Laurence's bedroom, in the midst of utter relief, he had the self-possession to think: ' This arrest is the best thing that could have happened. It'll keep their noses on a wrong scent till Larry's got away. The girl must be sent off too, but not with him.' Panic had ended in quite hardening his resolution. He entered the bedroom with a feeling of disgust. The fellow was lying there, his bare arms crossed behind his tousled head, staring at the ceiling, and smoking one of many cigarettes whose ends littered a chair beside him, whose sickly reek tainted the air. That pale face, with its jutting cheekbones and chin, its hollow cheeks and blue eyes far sunk back —what a wreck of goodness!

He looked up at Keith through the haze of smoke and said quietly: " Well, brother, what's the sentence? ' Transportation for life, and then to be fined forty pounds'? "

The flippancy revolted Keith. It was Larry all over! Last night horrified and humble, this morning, " Don't care " and feather-headed. He said sourly:

" Oh! You can joke about it now? "

Laurence turned his face to the wall.

" Must."

Fatalism! How detestable were natures like that!

" I've been to see her," he said.

" You? "

" Last night. She can be trusted."

Laurence laughed.

" That I told you."

" I had to see for myself. You must clear out at once, Larry. She can come out to you by the next boat; but you can't go together. Have you any money? "

" No."

" I can foot your expenses, and lend you a year's income in

advance. But it must be a clean cut; after you get out there your whereabouts must only be known to me."

A long sigh answered him.

"You're very good to me, Keith; you've always been very good. I don't know why."

Keith answered drily:

"Nor I. There's a boat to the Argentine to-morrow. You're in luck; they've made an arrest. It's in the paper."

"What?"

The cigarette end dropped, the thin pyjama'd figure writhed up and stood clutching at the bedrail.

"What?"

The disturbing thought flitted through Keith's brain: "I was a fool. He takes it queerly; what now?"

Laurence passed his hand over his forehead and sat down on the bed.

"I hadn't thought of that," he said. "It does me!"

Keith stared. In his relief that the arrested man was not Laurence, this had not occurred to him. What folly!

"Why?" he said quickly; "an innocent man's in no danger. They always get the wrong man first. It's a piece of luck, that's all. It gives us time."

How often had he not seen that expression on Larry's face, wistful, questioning, as if trying to see the thing with his—Keith's—eyes, trying to submit to better judgment? And he said, almost gently:

"Now, look here, Larry; this is too serious to trifle with. Don't worry about that. Leave it to me. Just get ready to be off. I'll take your berth and make arrangements. Here's some money for kit. I can come round between five and six and let you know. Pull yourself together, man. As soon as the girl's joined you out there, you'd better get across to Chile, the further the better. You must simply lose yourself. I must go now, if I'm to get to the Bank before I go down to the courts." And looking very steadily at his brother, he added:

"Come! You've got to think of me in this matter as well as of yourself. No playing fast and loose with the arrangements. Understand?"

But still Larry gazed up at him with that wistful questioning, and not till he had repeated, "Understand?" did he receive "Yes" for answer.

Driving away, he thought: 'Queer fellow! I don't know

him, shall never know him!' and at once began to concentrate
on the practical arrangements. At his bank he drew out £400;
but waiting for the notes to be counted he suffered qualms.
A clumsy way of doing things! If there had been more time!
The thought 'Accessory after the fact!' now infected everything. Notes were traceable. No other way of getting him
away at once, though. One must take lesser risks to avoid
greater. From the bank he drove to the office of the steamship
line. He had told Larry he would book his passage. But that
would not do! He must only ask anonymously if there were ac-
commodation. Having discovered that there were vacant berths,
he drove on to the Law Courts. If he could have taken a morning off, he would have gone down to the police court and seen
them charge this man. But even that was not too safe, with a
face so well known as his. What would come of this arrest?
Nothing, surely! The police always took somebody up to keep
the public quiet. Then, suddenly, he had again the feeling
that it was all a nightmare; Larry had never done it; the police
had got the right man! But instantly the memory of the girl's
awe-stricken face, her figure huddling on the sofa, her words:
"I see him always falling!" came back. God! What a business!

He felt he had never been more clear-headed and forcible than
that morning in court. When he came out for lunch he bought
the most sensational of the evening papers. But it was yet too
early for news, and he had to go back into court no whit wiser
concerning the arrest. When at last he threw off wig and gown,
and had got through a conference and other necessary work,
he went out to Chancery Lane, buying a paper on the way.
Then he hailed a cab and drove once more to Fitzroy Street.

V

Laurence had remained sitting on his bed for many minutes.
An innocent man in no danger! Keith had said it—the celebrated lawyer! Could he rely on that? Go out 8,000 miles, he
and the girl, and leave a fellow-creature perhaps in mortal
peril for an act committed by himself?

In the past night he had touched bottom, as he thought:
become ready to face anything. When Keith came in he would
without murmur have accepted the advice: "Give yourself up!"
He was prepared to pitch away the end of his life as he pitched

from him the fag-ends of his cigarettes. And the long sigh
he had heaved, hearing of reprieve, had been only half relief.
Then, with incredible swiftness there had rushed through him
a feeling of unutterable joy and hope. Clean away—into a new
country, a new life! The girl and he! Out there he wouldn't
care, would rejoice even to have squashed the life out of such a
noisome beetle of a man. Out there! Under a new sun, where
blood ran quicker than in this foggy land, and people took
justice into their own hands. For it had been justice on that
brute even though he had not meant to kill him. And then to
hear of this arrest! They would be charging the man to-day.
He could go and see the poor creature accused of the murder
he himself had committed! And he laughed. Go and see how
likely it was that they might hang a fellow-man in place of himself? He dressed, but too shaky to shave himself, went out to
a barber's shop. While there he read the news which Keith
had seen. In this paper the name of the arrested man was
given: "John Evan, no address." To be brought up on the
charge at Bow Street. Yes! He must go. Once, twice, three
times he walked past the entrance of the court before at last
he entered and screwed himself away among the tag and bob-
tail.

The court was crowded; and from the murmurs round he
could tell that it was his particular case which had brought so
many there. In a dazed way he watched charge after charge
disposed of with lightning quickness. But were they never going to reach his business? And then suddenly he saw the little
scarecrow man of last night advancing to the dock between two
policemen, more ragged and miserable than ever by light of
day, like some shaggy, wan, grey animal surrounded by sleek
hounds.

A sort of satisfied purr was rising all round; and with horror
Laurence perceived that this—this was the man accused of what
he himself had done—this queer, battered unfortunate to whom
he had shown a passing friendliness. Then all feeling merged
in the appalling interest of listening. The evidence was very
short. Testimony of the hotelkeeper where Walenn had been
staying, the identification of his body, and of a snake-shaped
ring he had been wearing at dinner that evening. Testimony
of a pawnbroker, that this same ring was pawned with him the
first thing yesterday morning by the prisoner. Testimony of a
policeman that he had noticed the man Evan several times in

Glove Lane, and twice moved him on from sleeping under that arch. Testimony of another policeman that, when arrested at midnight, Evan had said: "Yes; I took the ring off his finger. I found him there dead. . . . I know I oughtn't to have done it. . . . I'm an educated man; it was stupid to pawn the ring. I found him with his pockets turned inside out."

Fascinating and terrible to sit staring at the man in whose place he should have been; to wonder when those small bright-grey bloodshot eyes would spy him out, and how he would meet that glance. Like a baited raccoon the little man stood, screwed back into a corner, mournful, cynical, fierce, with his ridged, obtuse yellow face, and his stubbly grey beard and hair, and his eyes wandering now and again amongst the crowd. But with all his might Laurence kept his face unmoved. Then came the word "Remanded"; and, more like a baited beast than ever, the man was led away.

Laurence sat on, a cold perspiration thick on his forehead. Someone else, then, had come on the body and turned the pockets inside out before John Evan took the ring. A man such as Walenn would not be out at night without money. Besides, if Evan had found money on the body he would never have run the risk of taking that ring. Yes, someone else had come on the body first. It was for that one to come forward and prove that the ring was still on the dead man's finger when he left him, and thus clear Evan. He clung to that thought; it seemed to make him less responsible for the little man's position; to remove him and his own deed one step further back. If they found the person who had taken the money, it would prove Evan's innocence. He came out of the court in a sort of trance. And a craving to get drunk attacked him. One could not go on like this without the relief of some oblivion. If he could only get drunk, keep drunk till this business was decided and he knew whether he must give himself up or no. He had now no fear at all of people suspecting him; only fear of himself —fear that he might go and give himself up. Now he could see the girl; the danger from that was as nothing compared with the danger from his own conscience. He had promised Keith not to see her. Keith had been decent and loyal to him —good old Keith! But he would never understand that this girl was now all he cared about in life; that he would rather be cut off from life itself than be cut off from her. Instead of becoming less and less, she was becoming more and more to him

—experience strange and thrilling! Out of deep misery she had grown happy—through him; out of a sordid, shifting life recovered coherence and bloom, through devotion to him—*him,* of all people in the world! It was a miracle. She demanded nothing of him, adored him, as no other woman ever had—it was this which had anchored his drifting barque; this—and her truthful mild intelligence, and that burning warmth of a woman who, long treated by men as but a sack of sex, now loves at last.

And suddenly, mastering his craving to get drunk, he made towards Soho. He had been a fool to give those keys to Keith. She must have been frightened by his visit; and, perhaps, doubly miserable since, knowing nothing, imagining everything! Keith was sure to have terrified her. Poor little thing!

Down the street where he had stolen in the dark with the dead body on his back, he almost ran for the cover of her house. The door was opened to him before he knocked, her arms were round his neck, her lips pressed to his. The fire was out, as if she had been unable to remember to keep warm. A stool had been drawn to the window, and there she had evidently been sitting, like a bird in a cage, looking out into the grey street. Though she had been told that he was not to come, instinct had kept her there; or the pathetic, aching hope against hope which lovers never part with.

Now that he was there, her first thoughts were for his comfort. The fire was lighted. He must eat, drink, smoke. There was never in her doings any of the "I am doing this for you, but you ought to be doing that for me" which belongs to so many marriages and *liaisons.* She was like a devoted slave, so in love with the chains that she never knew she wore them. And to Laurence, who had so little sense of property, this only served to deepen tenderness, and the hold she had on him. He had resolved not to tell her of the new danger he ran from his own conscience. But resolutions with him were but the opposite of what was sure to come; and at last the words, "They've arrested someone," escaped him.

From her face he knew she had grasped the danger at once; had divined it, perhaps, before he spoke. But she only twined her arms round him and kissed his lips. And he knew that she was begging him to put his love for her above his conscience. Who would ever have thought that he could feel as he did to this girl who had been in the arms of so many! The stained

and suffering past of a loved woman awakens in some men only
chivalry; in others, more respectable, it rouses a tigerish itch,
a rancorous jealousy of what in the past was given to others.
Sometimes it will do both. When he had her in his arms he felt
no remorse for killing the coarse, handsome brute who had ruined
her. He savagely rejoiced in it. But when she laid her head in
the hollow of his shoulder, turning to him her white face with
the faint colour-staining on the parted lips, the cheeks, the
eyelids; when her dark, wide-apart, brown eyes gazed up in the
happiness of her abandonment—he felt only tenderness and protection.

He left her at five o'clock, and had not gone two streets' length
before the memory of the little grey vagabond, screwed back
in the far corner of the dock like a baited raccoon, of his dreary,
creaking voice, took possession of him again; and a kind of
savagery mounted in his brain against a world where one could
be so tortured without having meant harm to anyone.

At the door of his lodgings Keith was getting out of a cab.
They went in together, but neither of them sat down; Keith
standing with his back to the carefully shut door, Laurence
with his back to the table, as if they knew there was a tug
coming. And Keith said:

"There's room on that boat. Go down and book your berth
before they shut. Here's the money!"

"I'm going to stick it, Keith."

Keith stepped forward and put a roll of notes on the table.

"Now look here, Larry. I've read the police-court proceedings. There's nothing in that. Out of prison, or in prison for
a few weeks, it's all the same to a night-bird of that sort.
Dismiss it from your mind—there's not nearly enough evidence
to convict. This gives you your chance. Take it like a man,
and make a new life for yourself."

Laurence smiled; but the smile had a touch of madness and
a touch of malice. He took up the notes.

"Clear out, and save the honour of brother Keith. Put
them back in your pocket, Keith, or I'll put them in the fire.
Come, take them!" And, crossing to the fire, he held them to
the bars. "Take them, or in they go!"

Keith took back the notes.

"I've still got some kind of honour, Keith; if I clear out I
shall have none, not the rag of any, left. It may be worth more
to me than that—I can't tell yet—I can't tell."

There was a long silence before Keith answered:

"I tell you you're mistaken; no jury will convict. If they did, a judge would never hang on it. A ghoul who can rob a dead body *ought* to be in prison. What he did is worse than what you did, if you come to that!"

Laurence lifted his face.

"Judge not, brother," he said; "the heart is a dark well."

Keith's yellowish face grew red and swollen, as though he were mastering the tickle of a bronchial cough.

"What are you going to do, then? I suppose I may ask you not to be entirely oblivious of our name; or is such a consideration unworthy of your honour?"

Laurence bent his head. The gesture said more clearly than words: "Don't kick a man when he's down!"

"I don't know what I'm going to do—nothing at present. I'm awfully sorry, Keith; awfully sorry."

Keith looked at him, and without another word went out.

VI

To any, save philosophers, reputation may be threatened almost as much by disgrace to name and family as by the disgrace of self. Keith's instinct was always to deal actively with danger. But this blow, whether it fell on him by discovery or by confession, could not be countered. As blight falls on a rose from who knows where, the scandalous murk would light on him. No repulse possible! Not even a wriggling from under! Brother of a murderer hung or sent to penal servitude! His daughter niece to a murderer! His dead mother—a murderer's mother! And to wait day after day, week after week, not knowing whether the blow would fall, was an extraordinary atrocious penance, the injustice of which, to a man of rectitude, seemed daily the more monstrous.

The remand had produced evidence that the murdered man had been drinking heavily on the night of his death, and further evidence of the accused's professional vagabondage and destitution; it was shown, too, that for some time the archway in Glove Lane had been his favourite night haunt. He had been committed for trial in January. This time, despite misgivings, Keith had attended the police court. To his great relief Larry was not there. But the policeman who had come up while he was looking at the archway, and given him afterwards that scare in the girl's rooms, was chief witness to the way the accused man haunted Glove Lane. Though Keith held his silk hat high, he still had the uncomfortable feeling that the man had recognised him.

His conscience suffered few, if any, twinges for letting this man rest under the shadow of the murder. He genuinely believed that there was not evidence enough to convict; nor was it in him to appreciate the tortures of a vagabond shut up. The scamp deserved what he had got for robbing a dead body; and in any case such a scarecrow was better off in prison than sleeping out under archways in December. Sentiment was foreign to Keith's character, and his justice that of those who subordinate the fates of the weak and shiftless to the needful paramountcy of the strong and well established.

His daughter came back from school for the Christmas holidays. It was hard to look up from her bright eyes and rosy cheeks and see this shadow hanging above his calm and ordered life, as in a glowing room one's eye may catch an impending patch of darkness drawn like a spider's web across a corner of the ceiling.

On the afternoon of Christmas Eve they went, by her desire, to a church in Soho, where the Christmas Oratorio was being given; and coming away passed, by chance of a wrong turning, down Borrow Street. Ugh! How that startled moment, when the girl had pressed herself against him in the dark, and her terror-stricken whisper: "Oh! Who is it?" leaped out before him! Always that business—that ghastly business! After the trial he would have another try to get them both away. And he thrust his arm within his young daughter's, hurrying her on, out of this street where shadows filled all the winter air.

But that evening when she had gone to bed he felt uncontrollably restless. He had not seen Larry for weeks. What was he about? What desperations were hatching in his disorderly brain? Was he very miserable; had he perhaps sunk into a stupor of debauchery? And the old feeling of protectiveness rose up in him; a warmth born of long ago Christmas Eves, when they had stockings hung out in the night stuffed by a Santa Claus whose hand never failed to tuck them up, whose kiss was their nightly waft into sleep.

Stars were sparkling out there over the river; the sky frosty-clear, and black. Bells had not begun to ring as yet. And obeying an obscure, deep impulse, Keith wrapped himself once

more into his fur coat, pulled a motoring cap over his eyes, and
sallied forth.

In the Strand he took a cab to Fitzroy Street. There was no
light in Larry's windows, and on a card he saw the words "To
Let." Gone! Had he after all cleared out for good? But
how—without money? And the girl? Bells were ringing now
in the silent frostiness. Christmas Eve! And Keith thought:
'If only this wretched business were off my mind! Monstrous
that one should suffer for the faults of others!'

He took a route which led him past Borrow Street. Solitude brooded there, and he walked resolutely down on the far
side, looking hard at the girl's window. There was a light. The
curtains just failed to meet, so that a thin gleam shone through.
He crossed; and after glancing swiftly up and down, deliberately
peered in.

He only stood there perhaps twenty seconds, but visual records gleaned in a moment sometimes outlast the visions of hours
and days. The electric light was not burning; but, in the
centre of the room the girl was kneeling in her night-gown before a little table on which were four lighted candles. Her
arms were crossed on her breast; the candle-light shone on her
fair cropped hair, on the profile of cheek and chin, on her bowed
white neck. For a moment he thought her alone; then behind
her saw his brother in a sleeping suit, leaning against the wall,
with arms crossed, watching. It was the expression on his
face which burned the whole thing in, so that always afterwards
he was able to see that little scene—such an expression as
could never have been on the face of one even faintly conscious
that he was watched by any living thing on earth. The whole
of Larry's heart and feeling seemed to have come up out of
him. Yearning, mockery, love, despair! The depth of his
feeling for this girl, his stress of mind, fears, hopes; the flotsam
good and evil of his soul, all transfigured there, exposed and
unforgettable. The candle-light shone upward on to his face,
twisted by the strangest smile; his eyes, darker and more wistful than mortal eyes should be, seemed to beseech and mock the
white-clad girl, who, all unconscious, knelt without movement,
like a carved figure of devotion. The words seemed coming
from his lips: "Pray for us! Bravo! Yes! Pray for us!"
And suddenly Keith saw her stretch out her arms and lift her
face with a look of ecstasy, and Laurence starting forward.
What had she seen beyond the candle flames? It is the un-

expected which invests visions with poignancy. Nothing more strange could Keith have seen in this nest of the murky and illicit. But in sheer panic lest he might be caught thus spying he drew back and hurried on.

So Larry was living there with her! When the moment came he could still find him.

Before going in, he stood full five minutes leaning on the terrace parapet before his house, gazing at the star-frosted sky, and the river cut by the trees into black pools, oiled over by gleams from the Embankment lamps. And, deep down, behind his mere thoughts, he ached—somehow, somewhere ached. Beyond the cage of all that he saw and heard and thought, he had perceived something he could not reach. But the night was cold, the bells silent, for it had struck twelve. Entering his house, he stole upstairs.

VII

If for Keith those six weeks before the Glove Lane murder trial came on were fraught with uneasiness and gloom, they were for Laurence almost the happiest since his youth. From the moment when he left his rooms and went to the girl's to live, a kind of peace and exaltation took possession of him. Not by any effort of will did he throw off the nightmare hanging over him. Nor was he drugged by love. He was in a sort of spiritual catalepsy. In face of fate too powerful for his will, his turmoil, anxiety, and even restlessness had ceased; his life floated in the ether of " what must come, will." Out of this catalepsy, his spirit sometimes fell headlong into black waters. In one such whirlpool he was struggling on the night of Christmas Eve. When the girl rose from her knees he asked her:

" What did you see? "

Pressing close to him, she drew him down on to the floor before the fire; and they sat, knees drawn up, hands clasped, like two children trying to see over the edge of the world.

" It was the Virgin I saw. She stood against the wall and smiled. We shall be happy soon."

" When we die, Wanda," he said, suddenly, " let it be together. We shall keep each other warm out there."

Huddling to him she whispered: " Yes, oh, yes! If you die, I could not go on living."

It was this utter dependence on him, the feeling that he had rescued something, which gave him sense of anchorage. That, and his buried life in the retreat of these two rooms. Just for an hour in the morning, from nine to ten, the charwoman would come, but not another soul all day. They never went out together. He would stay in bed late, while Wanda bought what they needed for the day's meals; lying on his back, hands clasped behind his head, recalling her face, the movements of her slim, rounded, supple figure, robing itself before his gaze; feeling again the kiss she had left on his lips, the gleam of her soft eyes, so strangely dark in so fair a face. In a sort of trance he would lie still till she came back. Then get up to breakfast about noon off things she had cooked, drinking coffee. In the afternoon he would go out alone and walk for hours, anywhere, so long as it was East. To the East there was always suffering to be seen, always that which soothed him with the feeling that he and his troubles were only a tiny part of trouble; that while so many other sorrowing and shadowy creatures lived he was not cut off. To go West was to encourage dejection. In the West all was like Keith, successful, immaculate, ordered, resolute. He would come back tired out, and sit watching her cook their little dinner. The evenings were given up to love. Queer trance of an existence, which both were afraid to break. No sign from her of wanting those excitements which girls who have lived her life, even for a few months, are supposed to need. She never asked him to take her anywhere; never, in word, deed, look, seemed anything but almost rapturously content. And yet he knew, and she knew, that they were only waiting to see whether Fate would turn her thumb down on them. In these days he did not drink. Out of his quarter's money, when it came in, he had paid his debts—their expenses were very small. He never went to see Keith, never wrote to him, hardly thought of him. And from those dread apparitions —Walenn lying with the breath choked out of him, and the little grey, driven animal in the dock—he hid, as only a man can who must hide or be destroyed. But daily he bought a newspaper, and feverishly, furtively scanned its columns.

VIII

Coming out of the Law Courts on the afternoon of January 28, at the triumphant end of a desperately fought will case,

Keith saw on a poster the words: "Glove Lane Murder: Trial and Verdict"; and with a rush of dismay he thought: 'Good God! I never looked at the paper this morning!' The elation which had filled him a second before, the absorption he had felt for two days now in the case so hardly won, seemed suddenly quite sickeningly trivial. What on earth had he been doing to forget that horrible business even for an instant? He stood quite still on the crowded pavement, unable, really unable, to buy a paper. But his face was like a piece of iron when he did step forward and hold his penny out. There it was in the "Stop Press"! "Glove Lane Murder. The jury returned a verdict of Guilty. Sentence of death was passed."

His first sensation was simple irritation. How had they come to commit such an imbecility? Monstrous! The evidence ——! Then the futility of even reading the report, of even considering how they had come to record such a verdict struck him with savage suddenness. There it was, and nothing he could do or say would alter it; no condemnation of this idiotic verdict would help reverse it. The situation was desperate, indeed! That five minutes' walk from the Law Courts to his chambers was the longest he had ever taken.

Men of decided character little know beforehand what they will do in certain contingencies. For the imaginations of decided people do not endow mere contingencies with sufficient actuality. Keith had never really settled what he was going to do if this man were condemned. Often in those past weeks he had said to himself: 'Of course, if they bring him in guilty, that's another thing!' But, now that they had, he was beset by exactly the same old arguments and feelings, the same instincts of loyalty and protection towards Laurence and himself, intensified by the fearful imminence of the danger. And yet, here was this man about to be hung for a thing he had not done! Nothing could get over that! But then he was such a worthless vagabond, a ghoul who had robbed a dead body. If Larry were condemned in his stead, would there be any less miscarriage of justice? To strangle a brute who had struck you, by the accident of keeping your hands on his throat a few seconds too long, was there any more guilt in that—was there even as much as in deliberate theft from a dead man? Reverence for order, for justice, and established fact, will often march shoulder to shoulder with Jesuitry in natures to whom success is vital.

In the narrow stone passage leading to his staircase a friend
called out: "Bravo, Darrant! That was a squeak! Congratulations!" And with a bitter little smile Keith thought:
'Congratulations! I!'

At the first possible moment he hurried back to the Strand,
and, hailing a cab, he told the man to put him down at a turning
near to Borrow Street.

It was the girl who opened to his knock. Startled, clasping
her hands, she looked strange to Keith in her black skirt and
blouse of some soft velvety stuff the colour of faded roses. Her
round, rather long throat was bare; and Keith noticed fretfully
that she wore gold earrings. Her eyes, so pitch dark against
her white face, and the short fair hair which curled into her
neck, seemed both to search and to plead.

"My brother?"

"He is not in, sir, yet."

"Do you know where he is?"

"No."

"He is living with you here now?"

"Yes."

"Are you still as fond of him as ever, then?"

With a movement, as though she despaired of words, she
clasped her hands over her heart. And he said:

"I see."

He had the same strange feeling as on his first visit to her,
and when through the chink in the curtains he had watched
her kneeling—of pity mingled with some faint sexual emotion.
And crossing to the fire he asked:

"May I wait for him?"

"Oh! Please! Will you sit down?"

But Keith shook his head. And with a catch in her breath
she said:

"You will not take him from me. I should die."

He turned round on her sharply.

"*I* don't want him taken from you. I want to help you
keep him. Are you ready to go away at any time?"

"Yes. Oh, yes!"

"And he?"

She answered almost in a whisper:

"Yes; but there is that poor man."

"That poor man is a graveyard thief; a hyena; a ghoul—not

worth consideration." And the rasp in his own voice surprised him.

"Ah!" she sighed. "But I am sorry for him. Perhaps he was hungry. I have been hungry—you do things then that you would not. And perhaps he has no one to love; if you have no one to love you can be very bad. I think of him often—in prison."

Between his teeth Keith muttered: "And Laurence?"

"We do never speak of it; we are afraid."

"He's not told you, then, about the trial?"

Her eyes dilated.

"The trial! Oh! He was strange last night. This morning, too, he got up early. Is it—is it over?"

"Yes."

"What has come?"

"Guilty."

For a moment Keith thought she was going to faint. She had closed her eyes, and swayed so that he took a step and put his hands on her arms.

"Listen!" he said. "Help me, don't let Laurence out of your sight. We must have time. I must see what they intend to do. They can't be going to hang this man. I must have time, I tell you. You must prevent his giving himself up."

She stood, staring in his face, while he still held her arms, gripping into her soft flesh through the velvety sleeves.

"Do you understand?"

"Yes—but if he has already!"

Keith felt the shiver which ran through her. And the thought rushed into his mind: ' My God! Suppose the police come round while I'm here!' If Larry had indeed gone to them! If that policeman who had seen him here the night after the murder should find him here again just after the verdict! He said almost fiercely:

"Can I trust you not to let Larry out of your sight? Quick! Answer!"

Clasping her hands to her breast, she answered humbly:

"I will try."

"If he hasn't already done this, watch him like a lynx! Don't let him go out without you. I'll come to-morrow morning early. You're a Catholic, aren't you? Swear to me that you won't let him do anything till he's seen me again."

She did not answer, looking past him at the door; and Keith

heard a key in the latch. There was Laurence himself, holding
in his hand a great bunch of pink lilies and white narcissi. His
face was pale and haggard. He said quietly:

" Hallo, Keith ! "

The girl's eyes were fastened on Larry's face; and Keith,
looking from one to the other, knew that he had never had
more need for wariness.

" Have you seen? " he said.

Laurence nodded. His expression, as a rule so tell-tale of
his emotions, baffled Keith utterly.

" Well? "

" I've been expecting it."

" The thing can't stand—that's certain. But I must have
time to look into the report. I must have time to see what I
can do. D'you understand me, Larry?—I must have time."
He knew he was talking at random. The only thing was to get
them away at once out of reach of confession; but he dared
not say so.

" Promise me that you'll do nothing, that you won't go out
even till I've seen you to-morrow morning."

Again Laurence nodded. And Keith looked at the girl.
Would she see that he did not break that promise? Her eyes
were still fixed immovably on Larry's face. And with the
feeling that he could get no further, Keith turned to go.

" Promise me," he said.

Laurence answered: " I promise."

He was smiling. Keith could make nothing of that smile, nor
of the expression in the girl's eyes. And saying: " I have your
promise, I rely on it ! " he went.

IX

To keep from any woman who loves, knowledge of her lover's
mood, is as hard as to keep music from moving the heart. But
when that woman has lived in suffering, and for the first time
knows the comfort of love, then let the lover try as he may to
disguise his heart—no use ! Yet by virtue of subtler abnegation
she will often succeed in keeping it from him that she knows.

When Keith was gone the girl made no outcry, asked no
questions, managed that Larry should not suspect her intuition ;
all that evening she acted as if she knew of nothing preparing
within him, and through him, within herself.

His words, caresses, the very zest with which he helped her
to prepare the feast, the flowers he had brought, the wine he
made her drink, the avoidance of any word which could spoil
their happiness, all—all told her. He was too inexorably gay
and loving. Not for her—to whom every word and every kiss
had uncannily the desperate value of a last word and kiss—not
for her to deprive herself of these by any sign or gesture which
might betray her prescience. She took all, and would have taken
more, a hundredfold. She did not want to drink the wine he
kept tilting into her glass, but, with the acceptance learned
by women who have lived her life, she did not refuse. She had
never refused him anything.

Laurence drank deeply. The wine gave an edge to these few
hours of pleasure, an exaltation of energy. It dulled his sense
of pity, too. It was pity he was afraid of—for himself and
for this girl. To make even this tawdry room look beautiful,
with firelight and candlelight, dark amber wine in the glasses,
tall pink lilies spilling their saffron, exuding their hot perfume
—she and even himself must look their best. Not even music
was lacking to their feast. Someone was playing a pianola
across the street, and the sound, very faint, came stealing—swelling, sinking, festive, mournful; having a far-off life of its own,
like the flickering fire-flames before which they lay embraced,
or the lilies delicate between the candles. Listening to that
music, tracing with his finger the tiny veins on her breast, he
lay like one recovering from a swoon. No parting. None!
But sleep, as the firelight sleeps when flames die; as music sleeps
on its deserted strings!

And the girl watched him.

It was nearly ten when he bade her go to bed. And after she
had gone obedient into the bedroom, he brought ink and paper
down by the fire. The drifter, the unstable, the good-for-
nothing—did not falter. He had thought, when it came to
the point, he would fail himself; but a sort of rage bore him
forward. If he lived on and confessed, they would shut him
up, take from him the one thing he loved, cut him off from
her; sand up his only well in the desert. Curse them! And
he wrote by firelight which mellowed the white sheets of paper;
while, against the dark curtain, the girl, in her nightgown, unconscious of the cold, stood watching.

A man, when he drowns, remembers his past. Like the lost
poet he had " gone with the wind." Now it was for him to be

true in his fashion. A man may falter for weeks and weeks, consciously, subconsciously, even in his dreams, till there comes that moment when the only thing impossible is to go on faltering. The black cap, the little driven grey man looking up at it with a sort of wonder—faltering had ceased!

He had finished now, and was but staring into the fire.

The fire, the candles, and the fire—no more the flame and flicker!

And, by the dark curtain, the girl watched.

X

Keith went, not home, but to his club; and in the room devoted to the reception of guests, empty at this hour, he sat down and read the report of the trial. The fools had made out a case that looked black enough. And for a long time, on the thick soft carpet which let out no sound of footfall, he paced up and down, thinking. He might see the defending counsel, might surely do that as an expert who thought there had been miscarriage of justice. They must appeal; a petition, too, might be started in the last event. The thing could—must be put right yet, if only Larry and that girl did nothing!

He had no appetite, but the custom of dining is too strong. And while he ate, he glanced with irritation at his fellow-members. They looked so at their ease. Unjust—that this black cloud should hang over one blameless as any of them! Friends, connoisseurs of such things—a judge among them—came specially to his table to express their admiration of his conduct of that will case. To-night he had real excuse for pride, but he felt none. Yet, in this well-warmed quietly glowing room, filled with decorously eating, decorously talking men, he gained insensibly some comfort. This surely was reality; that shadowy business out there only the drear sound of a wind one must and did keep out—like the poverty and grime which had no real existence for the secure and prosperous. He drank champagne. It helped to fortify reality, to make shadows seem more shadowy. And down in the smoking-room he sat before the fire, in one of those chairs which embalm after-dinner dreams. He grew sleepy there, and at eleven o'clock rose to go home. But when he had once passed down the shallow marble steps, out through the revolving door which let in no draughts, he was visited by fear, as if he had drawn it in with the breath of the January wind. Larry's face; and the girl watching it! Why had she watched like that? Larry's smile; the flowers in his hand? Buying flowers at such a moment! The girl was his slave—whatever he told her, she would do. But she would never be able to stop him. At this very moment he might be rushing to give himself up!

His hand, thrust deep into the pocket of his fur coat, came in contact suddenly with something cold. The keys Larry had given him all that time ago. There they had lain forgotten ever since. The chance touch decided him. He turned off towards Borrow Street, walking at full speed. He could but go again and see. He would sleep better if he knew that he had left no stone unturned. At the corner of that dismal street he had to wait for solitude before he made for the house which he now loathed with a deadly loathing. He opened the outer door and shut it to behind him. He knocked, but no one came. Perhaps they had gone to bed. Again and again he knocked, then opened the door, stepped in, and closed it carefully. Candles lighted, the fire burning; cushions thrown on the floor in front of it and strewn with flowers! The table, too, covered with flowers and with the remnants of a meal. Through the half-drawn curtain he could see that the inner room was also lighted. Had they gone out, leaving everything like this? Gone out! His heart beat. Bottles! Larry had been drinking!

Had it really come? Must he go back home with this murk on him; knowing that his brother was a confessed and branded murderer? He went quickly to the half-drawn curtains and looked in. Against the wall he saw a bed, and those two in it. He recoiled in sheer amazement and relief. Asleep with curtains undrawn, lights left on? Asleep through all his knocking! They must both be drunk. The blood rushed up in his neck. Asleep! And rushing forward again, he called out: " Larry! " Then, with a gasp he went towards the bed. " Larry! " No answer! No movement! Seizing his brother's shoulder, he shook it violently. It felt cold. They were lying in each other's arms, breast to breast, lips to lips, their faces white in the light shining above the dressing-table. And such a shudder shook Keith that he had to grasp the brass rail above their heads. Then he bent down, and, wetting his finger, placed it close to their joined lips. No two could ever swoon so utterly as that;

not even a drunken sleep could be so fast. His wet finger felt
not the faintest stir of air, nor was there any movement in the
pulses of their hands. No breath! No life! The eyes of the
girl were closed. How strangely innocent she looked! Larry's
open eyes seemed to be gazing at her shut eyes; but Keith saw
that they were sightless. With a sort of sob he drew down the
lids. Then, by an impulse that he could never have explained,
he laid a hand on his brother's head, and a hand on the girl's
fair hair. The clothes had fallen down a little from her bare
shoulder; he pulled them up, as if to keep her warm, and caught
the glint of metal; a tiny gilt crucifix no longer than a thumb-
nail, on a thread of steel chain, had slipped down from her
breast into the hollow of the arm which lay round Larry's neck.
Keith buried it beneath the clothes and noticed an envelope
pinned to the coverlet; bending down he read: "Please give
this at once to the police.—LAURENCE DARRANT." He thrust
it into his pocket. Like elastic stretched beyond its uttermost,
his reason, will, faculties of calculation and resolve snapped
to within him. He thought with incredible swiftness: 'I
must know nothing of this. I must go!' And, almost before
he knew that he had moved, he was out again in the street.

He could never have told of what he thought while he was
walking home. He did not really come to himself till he was
in his study. There, with a trembling hand, he poured himself
out whisky and drank it off! If he had not chanced to go there,
the charwoman would have found them when she came in the
morning, and given that envelope to the police! He took it out.
He had a right—a right to know what was in it! He broke
it open.

"I, Laurence Darrant, about to die by my own hand, declare
that this is a solemn and true confession. I committed what
is known as the Glove Lane Murder on the night of November
the 27th last in the following way"—on and on to the last
words—"We didn't want to die; but we could not bear separation, and I couldn't face letting an innocent man be hung for me.
I do not see any other way. I beg that there may be no *post-
mortem* on our bodies. The stuff we have taken is some of that
which will be found on the dressing-table. Please bury us
together.

"LAURENCE DARRANT.

"*January the 28th,* about ten o'clock p.m."

Full five minutes Keith stood with those sheets of paper in his hand, while the clock ticked, the wind moaned a little in the trees outside, the flames licked the logs with the quiet click and ruffle of their intense far-away life down there on the hearth. Then he roused himself, and sat down to read the whole again.

There it was, just as Larry had told it to him—nothing left out, very clear; even to the addresses of people who could identify the girl as having once been Walenn's wife or mistress. It would convince. Yes! It would convince.

The sheets dropped from his hand. Very slowly he was grasping the appalling fact that on the floor beside his chair lay the life or death of yet another man; that by taking this confession he had taken into his own hands the fate of the vagabond lying under sentence of death; that he could not give him back his life without incurring the smirch of this disgrace, without even endangering himself. If he let this confession reach the authorities he could never escape the gravest suspicion that he had known of the whole affair during these two months. He would have to attend the inquest, be recognised by that police-man as having come to the archway to see where the body had lain, as having visited the girl the very evening after the murder. Who would believe in the mere coincidence of such visits on the part of the murderer's brother? But apart from that suspicion, the fearful scandal which so sensational an affair must make would mar his career, his life, his young daughter's life! Larry's suicide with this girl would make sensation enough as it was; but nothing to that other. Such a death had its romance; involved him in no way save as a mourner, could per-haps even be hushed up! The other—nothing could hush that up, nothing prevent its ringing to the house-tops. He got up from his chair, and for many minutes roamed the room unable to get his mind to bear on the issue. Images kept starting up before him. The face of the man who handed him wig and gown each morning, puffy and curious, with a leer on it he had never noticed before; his young daughter's lifted eyebrows, mouth drooping, eyes troubled; the tiny gilt crucifix glinting in the hollow of the dead girl's arm; the sightless look in Larry's unclosed eyes; even his own thumb and finger pulling the lids down. And then he saw a street and endless people passing,

turning to stare at him. And, stopping in his tramp, he said
aloud: "Let them go to hell! Seven days' wonder!" Was
he not trustee to that confession! Trustee! After all he had
done nothing to be ashamed of, even if he had kept knowledge
dark. A brother! Who could blame him? And he picked up
those sheets of paper. But, like a great murky hand, the
scandal spread itself about him; its coarse malignant voice
seemed shouting: "Paiper! . . . Paiper! . . . Glove Lane
Murder! . . . Suicide and confession of brother of well-known
K.C. . . . Well-known K.C.'s brother. . . . Murder and suicide.
. . . Paiper!" Was he to let loose that flood of foulness? Was
he, who had done nothing, to smirch his own little daughter's
life; to smirch his dead brother, their dead mother—himself,
his own valuable, important future? And all for a sewer rat!
Let him hang, let the fellow hang if he must! And that was
not certain. Appeal! Petition! He might—he should be saved!
To have got thus far and then, by his own action, topple himself
down!

With a sudden darting movement he thrust the confession in
among the burning coals. And a smile licked at the folds in
his dark face, like those flames licking the sheets of paper, till
they writhed and blackened. With the toe of his boot he dispersed their scorched and crumbling wafer. Stamp them in!
Stamp in that man's life! Burnt! No more doubts, no more
of this gnawing fear! Burnt? A man—an innocent—sewer
rat! Recoiling from the fire he grasped his forehead. Burning
hot.

Well, it was done! Only fools without will or purpose regretted. And suddenly he laughed. So Larry had died for
nothing! He had no will, no purpose, and was dead! He and
that girl might now have been living, loving each other in the
warm night, away at the other end of the world, instead of
lying dead in the cold night here! Fools and weaklings
regretted, suffered from conscience and remorse. A man trod
firmly, held to his purpose, no matter what came of it!

He went to the window and drew back the curtain. What
was that? A gibbet in the air, a body hanging? Ah! Only the
trees—the dark trees—the winter skeleton trees! Recoiling, he
returned to his armchair and sat down before the fire. It had
been shining like that, the lamp turned low, his chair drawn up,
when Larry came in that afternoon two months ago. Bah!

He had never come at all! It was a nightmare. He had been asleep. How his head burned! And leaping up, he looked at the calendar on his bureau. " January the 28th ! " No dream ! His face hardened and darkened. On! Not like Larry! On!

1914.

HAD A HORSE

I

SOME quarter of a century ago, there abode in Oxford a small bookmaker called James Shrewin—or more usually "Jimmy," a run-about and damped-down little man, who made a precarious living out of the effect of horses on undergraduates. He had a so-called office just off the "Corn," where he was always open to the patronage of the young bloods of Bullingdon, and other horse-loving coteries, who bestowed on him sufficient money to enable him to live. It was through the conspicuous smash of one of them—young Gardon Colquhoun—that he became the owner of a horse. He had been far from wanting what was in the nature of a white elephant to one of his underground habits, but had taken it in discharge of betting debts, to which, of course, in the event of bankruptcy, he would have no legal claim. She was a three-year-old chestnut filly, by Lopez out of Calendar, bore the name Calliope, and was trained out on the Downs near Wantage. On a Sunday afternoon, then, in late July "Jimmy" got his friend, George Pulcher, the publican, to drive him out there in his sort of dog-cart.

"Must 'ave a look at the bilkin' mare," he had said: "that young 'Cocoon' told me she was a corker; but what's third to Referee at Sandown, and never ran as a two-year-old? All I know is, she's eatin' 'er 'ead off!"

Beside the plethoric bulk of Pulcher, clad in a light-coloured box cloth coat with enormous whitish buttons and a full-blown rose in the lapel, "Jimmy's" little, thin, dark-clothed form, withered by anxiety and gin, was, as it were, invisible; and compared with Pulcher's setting sun, his face, with shaven cheeks sucked-in, and smudged-in eyes, was like a ghost's under a grey bowler. He spoke off-handedly about his animal, but he was impressed, in a sense abashed, by his ownership. 'What the 'ell?' was his constant thought. Was he going to race her, sell her—what? How, indeed, to get back out of her the sum he had been fool enough to let "young Cocoon" owe him, to say nothing of her trainer's bill? The notion, too, of having to confront that trainer with his ownership was oppressive to one whose whole life was passed in keeping out of the foreground of the picture. Owner! He had never owned even a white mouse, let alone a white elephant. And an 'orse would ruin him in no time if he didn't look alive about it!

The son of a small London baker, devoted to errandry at the age of fourteen, "Jimmy" Shrewin owed his profession to a certain smartness at sums, a dislike of baking, and an early habit of hanging about street corners with other boys, who had their daily pennies on an 'orse. He had a narrow calculating head, which pushed him towards street corner books before he was eighteen. From that time on he had been a surreptitious nomad, till he had silted up at Oxford, where, owing to Vice-Chancellors, an expert in underground life had greater scope than elsewhere. When he sat solitary at his narrow table in the back room near the "Corn"—for he had no clerk or associate—eyeing the door, with his lists in a drawer before him, and his black shiny betting book ready for young "bloods," he had a sharp, cold, furtive air, and but for a certain imitated tightness of trousers, and a collar standing up all round, gave no impression of ever having heard of the quadruped called horse. Indeed, for "Jimmy" "horse" was a newspaper quantity with figures against its various names. Even when, for a short spell, hanger-on to a firm of cheap-ring bookmakers, he had seen almost nothing of horse; his racecourse hours were spent ferreting among a bawling, perspiring crowd, or hanging round within earshot of tight-lipped nobs, trainers, jockeys, anyone who looked like having "information." Nowadays he never went near a race-meeting—his business, of betting on races, giving him no chance—yet his conversation seldom deviated for more than a minute at a time from that physically unknown animal the horse. The ways of making money out of it, infinite, intricate, variegated, occupied the mind in all his haunts, to the accompaniment of liquid and tobacco. Gin and bitters was "Jimmy's" drink; for choice he smoked cheroots; and he would cherish in his mouth the cold stump of one long after it had gone out, for the homely feeling it gave him, while he talked, or listened to talk on horses. He was of that vast number, town bred, who, like crows round a carcase, feed on that which to them is not alive. And now he had a horse!

The dog-cart travelled at a clinking pace behind Pulcher's bob-tail. "Jimmy's" cheroot burned well in the warm July air; the dust powdered his dark clothes and pinched, sallow face. He thought with malicious pleasure of that young spark "Cocoon's" collapse—high-'anded lot of young fools, thinking themselves so knowing; many were the grins, and not few the grittings of his blackened teeth he had to smother at their swagger. "Jimmy, you robber!" "Jimmy, you little black-guard!" Young sparks—gay and languid—well, one of 'em had gone out!

He looked round with his screwed-up eyes at his friend George Pulcher, who, man and licensed victualler, had his bally in-dependence; lived remote from "the Quality" in his Paradise, "The Green Dragon"; had not to kow-tow to anyone; went to Newbury, Gatwick, Stockbridge, here and there, at will. Ah! George Pulcher had the ideal life—and looked it: crimson, square, full-bodied. Judge of a horse, too, in his own estima-tion; a leery bird—for whose judgment "Jimmy" had respect —who got "the office" of any clever work as quick as most men! And he said:

"What am I going to do with this blinkin' 'orse, George?"

Without moving its head the oracle spoke, in a voice rich and raw: "Let's 'ave a look at her first, Jimmy! Don't like her name—Calliope; but you can't change what's in the Stud-book. This Jenning that trains 'er is a crusty chap."

"Jimmy" nervously sucked-in his lips. The cart was mount-ing through the hedgeless fields which fringed the Downs; larks were singing, the wheat was very green, and patches of char-lock brightened everything; it was lonely, few trees, few houses, no people, extreme peace, just a few rooks crossing under a blue sky.

"Wonder if he'll offer us a drink?" said "Jimmy."

"Not he; but help yourself, my son."

"Jimmy" helped himself from a large wicker-covered flask. "Good for you, George—here's how!"

The large man shifted the reins and drank, in turn, tilting up a face whose jaw still struggled to assert itself against chins and neck.

"Well, here's your bloomin' horse," he said. "She can't win the Derby now, but she may do us a bit of good yet."

II

The trainer, Jenning, coming from his Sunday afternoon round of the boxes, heard the sound of wheels. He was a thin man, neat in clothes and boots, medium in height, with a slight limp, narrow grey whiskers, thin shaven lips, eyes sharp and grey.

A dog-cart stopping at his yard-gate and a rum-looking couple of customers!

"Well, gentlemen?"

"Mr. Jenning? My name's Pulcher—George Pulcher. Brought a client of yours over to see his new mare. Mr. James Shrewin, Oxford city."

"Jimmy" got down and stood before his trainer's uncompromising stare.

"What mare's that?" said Jenning.

"Calliope."

"Calliope—Mr. Colquhoun's?"

"Jimmy" held out a letter.

"DEAR JENNINGS,

"I have sold Calliope to Jimmy Shrewin, the Oxford bookie. He takes her with all engagements and liabilities, including your training bill. I'm frightfully sick at having to part with her, but needs must when the devil drives.

"GARDON COLQUHOUN."

The trainer folded the letter.

"Got proof of registration?"

"Jimmy" drew out another paper.

The trainer inspected it, and called out: "Ben, bring out Calliope. Excuse me a minute," and he walked into his house.

"Jimmy" stood, shifting from leg to leg. Mortification had set in; the dry abruptness of the trainer had injured even a self-esteem starved from youth.

The voice of Pulcher boomed. "Told you he was a crusty devil. 'And 'im a bit of his own."

The trainer was coming back.

"My bill," he said. "When you've paid it you can have the mare. I train for gentlemen."

"The hell you do!" said Pulcher.

"Jimmy" said nothing, staring at the bill—seventy-eight

pounds three shillings! A buzzing fly settled in the hollow of his cheek, and he did not even brush it off. Seventy-eight pounds!

The sound of hoofs roused him. Here came his horse, throwing up her head as if enquiring why she was being disturbed a second time on Sunday! In the movement of that small head and satin neck was something free and beyond present company.

"There she is," said the trainer. "That'll do, Ben. Stand, girl!"

Answering to a jerk or two of the halter, the mare stood kicking slightly with a white hind foot and whisking her tail. Her bright coat shone in the sunlight, and little shivers and wrinklings passed up and down its satin because of the flies. Then, for a moment, she stood still, ears pricked, eyes on the distance.

"Jimmy" approached her. She had resumed her twitchings, swishings, and slight kicking, and at a respectful distance he circled, bending as if looking at crucial points. He knew what her sire and dam had done, and all the horses that had beaten, or been beaten by them; could have retailed by the half-hour the peculiar hearsay of their careers; and here was their offspring in flesh and blood, and he was dumb! He didn't know a thing about what she ought to look like, and he knew it; but he felt obscurely moved. She seemed to him "a picture."

Completing his circle, he approached her head, white-blazed, thrown up again in listening, or scenting, and gingerly he laid his hand on her neck, warm and smooth as a woman's shoulder. She paid no attention to his touch, and he took his hand away. Ought he to look at her teeth or feel her legs? No, he was not buying her, she was his already; but he must say something. He looked round. The trainer was watching him with a little smile. For almost the first time in his life the worm turned in "Jimmy" Shrewin; he spoke no word and walked back to the cart.

"Take her in," said Jenning.

From his seat beside Pulcher, "Jimmy" watched the mare returning to her box.

"When I've cashed your cheque," said the trainer, "you can send for her"; and, turning on his heel, he went towards his house. The voice of Pulcher followed him.

"Blast your impudence! Git on, bob-tail, we'll shake the dust off 'ere."

Among the fringing fields the dog-cart hurried away. The

sun slanted, the heat grew less, the colour of young wheat and of the charlock brightened.

"The tyke! By Gawd, 'Jimmy,' I'd 'ave hit him on the mug! But you've got one there. She's a bit o' blood, my boy; and I know the trainer for her, Polman—no blasted airs about 'im."

"Jimmy" sucked at his cheroot.

"I ain't had your advantages, George, and that's a fact. I got into it too young, and I'm a little chap. But I'll send the . . . my cheque to-morrow. I got my pride, I 'ope." It was the first time that thought had ever come to him.

III

Though not quite the centre of the Turf, the Green Dragon had nursed a *coup* in its day, nor was it without a sense of veneration. The ownership of Calliope invested "Jimmy" Shrewin with the importance of those out of whom something can be had. It took time for one so long accustomed to beck and call, to mole-like procedure, and the demeanour of young bloods to realise that he had it. But slowly, with the marked increase of his unpaid-for cheroots, with the way in which glasses hung suspended when he came in, with the edgings up to him, and a certain tendency to accompany him along the street, it dawned on him that he was not only an out-of-bounds bookie, but a man. So long as he had remained unconscious of his double nature he had been content with laying the odds, as best he might, and getting what he could out of every situation, straight or crooked. Now that he was also a man, his complacency was ruffled. He suffered from a growing headiness connected with his horse. She was trained, now, by Polman, further along the Downs, too far for Pulcher's bob-tail; and though her public life was carried on at the Green Dragon, her private life required a train journey over night. "Jimmy" took it twice a week—touting his own horse in the August mornings up on the Downs, without drink or talk, or even cheroots. Early morning, larks singing, and the sound of galloping hoofs! In a moment of expansion he confided to Pulcher that it was "bally 'olesome."

There had been the slight difficulty of being mistaken for a tout by his new trainer Polman, a stoutish man with the look of one of those large sandy Cornish cats, not precisely furtive because reticence and craft are their nature. But, that once over, his personality swelled slowly. This month of August was one of those interludes, in fact, when nothing happens, but which shape the future by secret ripening.

An error to suppose that men conduct finance, high or low, from greed, or love of gambling; they do it out of self-esteem, out of an itch to prove their judgment superior to their neighbours', out of a longing for importance. George Pulcher did not despise the turning of a penny, but he valued much more the consciousness that men were saying: " Old George, what 'e says goes—knows a thing or two—George Pulcher! "

To pull the strings of " Jimmy " Shrewin's horse was a rich and subtle opportunity absorbingly improvable. But first one had to study the animal's engagements, and, secondly, to gauge that unknown quantity, her " form." To make anything of her this year they must " get about it." That young " toff," her previous owner, had of course flown high, entering her for classic races, high-class handicaps, neglecting the rich chances of lesser occasions.

Third to Referee in the three-year-old race at Sandown Spring —two heads—was all that was known of her, and now they had given her seven two in the Cambridgeshire. She might have a chance, and again she might not. He sat two long evenings with " Jimmy " in the little private room off the bar, deliberating this grave question.

" Jimmy " inclined to the bold course. He kept saying: " The mare's a flyer, George—she's the 'ell of a flyer! "

" Wait till she's been tried," said the oracle.

Had Polman anything that would give them a line?

Yes, he had The Shirker (named with that irony which appeals to the English), one of the most honest four-year-olds that ever looked through bridle, who had run up against almost every animal of mark—the one horse that Polman never interfered with, for if interrupted in his training, he ran all the better; who seldom won, but was almost always placed—the sort of horse that handicappers pivot on.

" But," said Pulcher, " try her with The Shirker, and the first stable money will send her up to tens. That 'orse is so darned regular. We've got to throw a bit of dust first, ' Jimmy.' I'll go over and see Polman."

In " Jimmy's " withered chest a faint resentment rose—it

wasn't George's horse; but it sank again beneath his friend's bulk and reputation.

The "bit of dust" was thrown at the ordinary hour of exercise over the Long Mile on the last day of August—the five-year-old Hangman carrying eight stone seven, the three-year-old Parrot seven stone five; what Calliope was carrying nobody but Polman knew. The forethought of George Pulcher had secured the unofficial presence of the Press. The instructions to the boy on Calliope were to be there at the finish if he could, but on no account to win. "Jimmy" and George Pulcher had come out over night. They sat together in the dog-cart by the clump of bushes which marked the winning-post, with Polman on his cob on the far side.

By a fine, warm light the three horses were visible to the naked eye in the slight dip down by the start. And, through the glasses, invested in now that he had a horse, "Jimmy" could see every movement of his mare with her blazed face— rather on her toes, like the bright chestnut and "bit o' blood" she was. He had a pit-patting in his heart, and his lips were tight pressed. Suppose she was no good after all, and that young "Cocoon" had palmed him off a pup! But mixed in with his financial fear was an anxiety more intimate, as if his own value were at stake.

From George Pulcher came an almost excited gurgle.

"See the tout! See 'im behind that bush. Thinks we don't know 'e's there, wot oh!"

"Jimmy" bit into his cheroot. "They're running," he said.

Rather wide, the black Hangman on the far side, Calliope in the middle, they came sweeping up the long mile. "Jimmy" held his tobaccoed breath. The mare was going freely—a length or two behind—making up her ground! Now for it!——

Ah! she 'ad the 'Angman beat, and ding-dong with this Parrot! It was all he could do to keep from calling out. With a rush and a cludding of hoofs they passed—the blazed nose just behind the Parrot's bay nose—dead heat all but, with the Hangman beat a good length!

"There 'e goes, 'Jimmy'! See the blank scuttlin' down the 'ill like a blinkin' rabbit. That'll be in to-morrow's paper, that trial will. Ah! but 'ow to read it—that's the point."

The horses had been wheeled and were sidling back; Polman was going forward on his cob.

"Jimmy" jumped down. Whatever that fellow had to say,

he meant to hear. It was his horse! Narrowly avoiding the hoofs of his hot, fidgeting mare, he said sharply:

" What about it? "

Polman never looked you in the face; his speech came as if not intended to be heard by anyone:

" Tell Mr. Shrewin how she went."

" Had a bit up my sleeve. If I'd hit her a smart one, I could ha' landed by a length or more."

" That so? " said " Jimmy " with a hiss. " Well, *don't* you hit her; she don't want hittin'. You remember that."

The boy said sulkily: " All right! "

" Take her home," said Polman. Then, with that reflective averted air of his, he added: " She was carrying eight stone, Mr. Shrewin; you've got a good one there. She's the Hangman at level weights."

Something wild leaped up in " Jimmy "—the Hangman's form unrolled itself before him in the air—he had a horse—he dam' well had a horse!

IV

But how delicate is the process of backing your fancy! The planting of a commission—what tender and efficient work before it will flower! That sixth sense of the racing man, which, like the senses of savages in great forests, seizes telepathically on what is not there, must be dulled, duped, deluded.

George Pulcher had the thing in hand. One might have thought the gross man incapable of such a fairy touch, such power of sowing with one hand and reaping with the other. He intimated rather than asserted that Calliope and the Parrot were one and the same thing. " The Parrot," he said, " couldn't win with seven stone—no use thinkin' of this Calliope."

Local opinion was the rock on which, like a great tactician, he built. So long as local opinion was adverse, he could dribble money on in London; the natural jump-up from every long shot taken was dragged back by the careful radiation of disparagement from the seat of knowledge.

" Jimmy " was the fly in his ointment of those balmy early weeks while snapping up every penny of long odds, before suspicion could begin to work from the persistence of enquiry. Half-a-dozen times he found the " little cuss within an ace of blowing the gaff on his own blinkin' mare "; seemed unable to

run his horse down; the little beggar's head was swellin' !
Once " Jimmy " had even got up and gone out, leaving a gin
and bitters untasted on the bar. Pulcher improved on his absence in the presence of a London tout.

"Saw the trial meself! 'Jimmy' don't like to think he's
got a stiff 'un."

And next morning his London agent snapped up some thirty-
threes again.

According to the trial the mare was the Hangman at seven
stone two, and really hot stuff—a seven-to-one chance. It was
none the less with a sense of outrage that, opening the *Sporting
Life* on the last day of September, he found her quoted at 100-8.
Whose work was this?

He reviewed the altered situation in disgust. He had invested about half the stable commission of three hundred pounds
at an average of thirty-to-one, but, now that she had " come "
in the betting, he would hardly average tens with the rest.
What fool had put his oar in?

He learned the explanation two days later. The rash, the
unknown backer, was " Jimmy " ! He had acted, it appeared,
from jealousy; a bookmaker—it took one's breath away!

" Backed her on your own just because that young ' Cocoon '
told you he fancied her ! "

" Jimmy " looked up from the table in his " office," where he
was sitting in wait for the scanty custom of the Long Vacation.

" She's not *his* horse," he said sullenly. " I wasn't going to
have *him* get the cream."

" What did you put on? " growled Pulcher.

" Took five hundred to thirty, and fifteen twenties."

" An' see what it's done—knocked the bottom out of the
commission. Am I to take that fifty as part of it? "

" Jimmy " nodded.

" That leaves an 'undred to invest," said Pulcher, somewhat
mollified. He stood, with his mind twisting in his thick still
body. " It's no good waitin' now," he said; " I'll work the rest
of the money on to-day. If I can average tens on the balance,
we'll 'ave six thousand three hundred to play with and the
stakes. They tell me Jenning fancies this Diamond Stud of
his. *He* ought to know the form with Calliope, blast him!
We got to watch that."

They had! Diamond Stud, a four-year-old with eight stone
two, was being backed as if the Cambridgeshire were over. From

fifteens he advanced to sevens, thence to favouritism at fives.
Pulcher bit on it. Jenning *must* know where he stood with
Calliope! It meant—it meant she couldn't win! The tactician
wasted no time in vain regret. Establish Calliope in the betting
and lay off. The time had come to utilise The Shirker.

It was misty on the Downs—fine-weather mist of a bright
October. The three horses became spectral on their way to the
starting-point. Polman had thrown the Parrot in again, but
this time he made no secret of the weights. The Shirker was
carrying eight seven, Calliope eight, the Parrot seven stone.

Once more, in the cart, with his glasses sweeping the bright
mist, " Jimmy " had that pit-patting in his heart. Here they
came! His mare leading—all riding hard—a genuine finish!
They passed—The Shirker beaten, a clear length, with the
Parrot at his girth. Beside him in the cart, George Pulcher
mumbled:

" She's The Shirker at eight stone four, ' Jimmy ' ! "

A silent drive, big with thought, back to a river inn; a silent
breakfast. Over a tankard at the close the Oracle spoke.

" The Shirker, at eight stone four, is a good 'ot chance, but
no cert, ' Jimmy.' We'll let 'em know this trial quite open,
weights and all. That'll bring her in the betting. And we'll
watch Diamond Stud. If he drops back we'll know Jenning
thinks he can't beat us now. If Diamond Stud stands up,
we'll know Jenning thinks he's still got our mare safe. Then
our line'll be clear: we lay off the lot, pick up a thousand or
so, and 'ave the mare in at a nice weight at Liverpool."

" Jimmy's " smudged-in eyes stared hungrily.

" How's that ? " he said. " Suppose she wins ! "

" Wins! If we lay off the lot, she *won't* win."

" Pull her ! "

George Pulcher's voice sank half an octave with disgust.

" Pull her! Who talked of pullin' ? She'll run a bye, that's
all. We shan't ever know whether she could 'a won or not."

" Jimmy " sat silent; the situation was such as his life during
sixteen years had waited for. They stood to win both ways with
a bit of handling.

" Who's to ride ? " he said.

" Polman's got a call on Docker. He can just ride the weight.
Either way he's good for us—strong finisher, and a rare judge
of distance; knows how to time things to a T. Win or not, he's
our man."

"Jimmy" was deep in figures. Laying-off at sevens, they would still win four thousand and the stakes.

"I'd like a win," he said.

"Ah!" said Pulcher. "But there'll be twenty in the field, my son; no more uncertain race than that bally Cambridgeshire. We could pick up a thou——as easy as I pick up this pot. Bird in the 'and, 'Jimmy,' and a good 'andicap in the bush. If she wins, she's finished. Well, we'll put this trial about and see 'ow Jenning pops."

Jenning popped amazingly. Diamond Stud receded a point, then re-established himself at nine to two. Jenning was clearly not dismayed.

George Pulcher shook his head, and waited, uncertain still which way to jump. Ironical circumstance decided him.

Term had begun; "Jimmy" was busy at his seat of custom. By some miracle of guardianly intervention, young Colquhoun had not gone broke. He was "up" again, eager to retrieve his reputation, and that little brute "Jimmy" would not lay against his horse! He merely sucked in his cheeks, and answered: "I'm not layin' my own 'orse." It was felt that he was not the man he had been; assertion had come into his manner, he was better dressed. Someone had seen him at the station looking quite a "toff" in a blue box-cloth coat standing well out from his wisp of a figure, and with a pair of brown race-glasses slung over the shoulder. Altogether the "little brute was getting too big for his boots."

And this strange improvement hardened the feeling that his horse was a real good thing. Patriotism began to burn in Oxford. Here was a "snip" that belonged to them, as it were, and the money in support of it, finding no outlet, began to ball.

A week before the race—with Calliope at nine to one, and very little doing—young Colquhoun went up to town, taking with him the accumulated support of betting Oxford. That evening she stood at sixes. Next day the public followed on.

George Pulcher took advantage. In this crisis of the proceedings he acted on his own initiative. The mare went back to eights, but the deed was done. He had laid off the whole bally lot, including the stake money. He put it to "Jimmy" that evening in a nutshell.

"We pick up a thousand, and the Liverpool as good as in our pocket. I've done worse."

"Jimmy" grunted out: "She could 'a won."

"Not she. Jenning knows—and there's others in the race. This Wasp is goin' to take a lot of catchin', and Deerstalker's not out of it. He's a hell of a horse, even with that weight."

Again "Jimmy" grunted, slowly sucking down his gin and bitters. Sullenly he said:

"Well, I don't want to put money in the pocket of young 'Cocoon' and his crowd. Like his impudence, backin' my horse as if it was his own."

"We'll 'ave to go and see her run, 'Jimmy.'"

"Not me," said "Jimmy."

"What! First time she runs! It won't look natural."

"No," repeated "Jimmy." "I don't want to see 'er beat."

George Pulcher laid his hand on a skinny shoulder.

"Nonsense, 'Jimmy.' You've got to, for the sake of your reputation. You'll enjoy seein' your mare saddled. We'll go up over night. I shall 'ave a few pound on Deerstalker. I believe he can beat this Diamond Stud. And you leave Docker to me; I'll 'ave a word with him at Gatwick to-morrow. I've known 'im since he was that 'igh; an' 'e ain't much more now."

"All right!" growled "Jimmy."

V

The longer you can bet on a race the greater its fascination. Handicappers can properly enjoy the beauty of their work; clubmen and oracles of the course have due scope for reminiscence and prophecy; bookmakers in lovely leisure can indulge a little their own calculated preferences, instead of being hurried to soulless conclusions by a half-hour's market on the course; the professional backer has the longer in which to dream of his fortune made at last by some hell of a horse—spotted somewhere as interfered with, left at the post, running green, too fat, not fancied, backward—now bound to win this hell of a race. And the general public has the chance to read the horses' names in the betting news for days and days; and what a comfort that is!

"Jimmy" Shrewin was not one of those philosophers who justify the great and growing game of betting on the ground that it improves the breed of an animal less and less in use. He justified it much more simply—he lived by it. And in the whole of his career of nearly twenty years since he made hole-and-corner books among the boys of London, he had never stood so utterly on velvet as that morning when his horse must win him five hundred pounds by merely losing. He had spent the night in London anticipating a fraction of his gains with George Pulcher at a music-hall. And, in a first-class carriage, as became an owner, he travelled down to Newmarket by an early special. An early special key turned in the lock of the carriage door, preserved their numbers at six, all professionals, with blank, rather rolling eyes, mouths shut or slightly fishy, ears to the ground; and the only natural talker a red-faced man, who had " been at it thirty years." Intoning the pasts and futures of this hell of a horse or that, even he was silent on the race in hand; and the journey was half over before the beauty of their own judgments loosened tongues thereon.   George Pulcher started it.

" I fancy Deerstalker," he said : " he's a hell of a horse."

" Too much weight," said the red-faced man.   " What about this Calliope ? "

" Ah ! " said Pulcher.   " D'you fancy your mare, ' Jimmy '? ? "

With all eyes turned on him, lost in his blue box-cloth coat, brown bowler, and cheroot smoke, " Jimmy " experienced a subtle thrill. Addressing the space between the red-faced man and Pulcher, he said :

" If she runs up to 'er looks."

" Ah ! " said Pulcher, " she's dark—nice mare, but a bit light and shelly."

" Lopez out o' Calendar," muttered the red-faced man. " Lopez didn't stay, but he was the hell of a horse over seven furlongs. The Shirker ought to 'ave told you a bit."

" Jimmy " did not answer. It gave him pleasure to see the red-faced man's eye trying to get past, and failing.

" Nice race to pick up. Don't fancy the favourite meself ; he'd nothin' to beat at Ascot."

" Jenning knows what he's about," said Pulcher.

Jenning !   Before " Jimmy's " mind passed again that first sight of his horse, and the trainer's smile, as if he—Jimmy Shrewin, who owned her—had been dirt. Tyke ! To have the mare beaten by one of his ! A deep, subtle vexation had oppressed him at times all these last days since George Pulcher had decided in favour of the mare's running a bye. D—n George Pulcher ! He took too much on himself ! Thought he had " Jimmy " Shrewin in his pocket ! He looked at the block of crimson opposite. Aunt Sally! If George Pulcher could tell what was passing in his mind!

But driving up to the Course he was not above sharing a sandwich and a flask. In fact, his feelings were unstable and gusty—sometimes resentment, sometimes the old respect for his friend's independent bulk. The dignity of ownership takes long to establish itself in those who have been kicked about.

"All right with Docker," murmured Pulcher, sucking at the wicker flask. "I gave him the office at Gatwick."

"She could 'a won," muttered "Jimmy."

"Not she, my boy; there's two at least can beat 'er."

Like all oracles, George Pulcher could believe what he wanted to.

Arriving, they entered the grand-stand enclosure, and over the dividing railings "Jimmy" gazed at the Cheap Ring, already filling up with its usual customers. Faces and umbrellas—the same old crowd. How often had he been in that Cheap Ring, with hardly room to move, seeing nothing, hearing nothing but "Two to one on the field!" "Two to one on the field!" "Threes Swordfish!" "Fives Alabaster!" "Two to one on the field!" Nothing but a sea of men like himself, and a sky overhead. He was not exactly conscious of criticism, only of a dull "Glad I'm shut of that lot" feeling.

Leaving George Pulcher deep in conversation with a crony, he lighted a cheroot and slipped out on to the Course. He passed the Jockey Club enclosure. Some early "toffs" were there in twos and threes, exchanging wisdom. He looked at them without envy or malice. He was an owner himself now, almost one of them in a manner of thinking. With a sort of relish he thought of how his past life had circled round those "toffs," slippery, shadowlike, kicked about; and now he could get up on the Downs away from "toffs," George Pulcher, all that crowd, and smell the grass, and hear the bally larks, and watch his own mare gallop!

They were putting the numbers up for the first race. Queer not to be betting, not to be touting round; queer to be giving it a rest! Utterly familiar with those names on the board, he was utterly unfamiliar with the shapes they stood for.

'I'll go and see 'em come out of the paddock,' he thought, and moved on, skimpy in his bell-shaped coat and billycock with flattened brim. The clamour of the Rings rose behind him while he was entering the paddock.

Very green, very peaceful, there; not many people, yet! Three horses in the second race were being led slowly in a sort of winding ring; and men were clustering round the further gate where the horses would come out. "Jimmy" joined them, sucking at his cheroot. They were a picture! Damn it! he didn't know but that 'orses laid over men! Pretty creatures!

One by one they passed out of the gate, a round dozen. Selling platers, but pictures for all that!

He turned back towards the horses being led about; and the old instinct to listen took him close to little groups. Talk was all of the big race. From a tall "toff" he caught the word Calliope.

"Belongs to a bookie, they say."

Bookie! Why not? Wasn't a bookie as good as any other? Ah! and sometimes better than these young snobs with everything to their hand! A bookie—well, what chance had he ever had?

A big brown horse came by.

"That's Deerstalker," he heard the "toff" say.

"Jimmy" gazed at George Pulcher's fancy with a sort of hostility. Here came another—Wasp, six stone ten, and Deerstalker nine stone—top and bottom of the race!

'My 'orse'd beat either o' them,' he thought stubbornly. 'Don't like that Wasp.'

The distant roar was hushed. They were running in the first race! He moved back to the gate. The quick clamour rose and dropped, and here they came—back into the paddock, darkened with sweat, flanks heaving a little!

"Jimmy" followed the winner, saw the jockey weigh in.

"What jockey's that?" he asked.

"That? Why, Docker!"

"Jimmy" stared. A short, square, bow-legged figure, with a hardwood face! Waiting his chance, he went up to him and said:

"Docker, you ride my 'orse in the big race."

"Mr. Shrewin?"

"The same," said "Jimmy." The jockey's left eyelid dropped a little. Nothing responded in "Jimmy's" face. "I'll see you before the race," he said.

Again the jockey's eyelid wavered, he nodded and passed on.

"Jimmy" stared at his own boots; they struck him suddenly

as too yellow and not at the right angle. But why, he couldn't say.

More horses now—those of the first race being unsaddled, clothed, and led away. More men—three familiar figures: young "Cocoon" and two others of his Oxford customers.

"Jimmy" turned sharply from them. Stand their airs?— not he! He had a sudden sickish feeling. With a win, he'd have been a made man—on his own! Blast George Pulcher and his caution! To think of being back in Oxford with those young bloods jeering at his beaten horse! He bit deep into the stump of his cheroot, and suddenly came on Jenning standing by a horse with a star on its bay forehead. The trainer gave him no sign of recognition, but signed to the boy to lead the horse into a stall, and followed, shutting the door. It was exactly as if he had said: "Vermin about!"

An evil little smile curled "Jimmy's" lips. The tyke!

The horses for the second race passed out of the paddock gate, and he turned to find his own. His ferreting eyes soon sighted Polman. What the cat-faced fellow knew, or was thinking, "Jimmy" could not tell. Nobody could tell.

"Where's the mare?" he said.

"Just coming round."

No mistaking her; fine as a star; shiny-coated, sinuous, her blazed face held rather high! Who said she was "shelly"? She was a picture! He walked a few paces close to the boy.

"That's Calliope. . . . H'm! . . . Nice filly! . . . Looks fit. . . . Who's this James Shrewin? . . . What's she at? . . . I like her looks."

His horse! Not a prettier filly in the world!

He followed Polman into her stall to see her saddled. In the twilight there he watched her toilet; the rub-over; the exact adjustments; the bottle of water to the mouth; the buckling of the bridle—watched her head high above the boy keeping her steady with gentle pulls of a rein in each hand held out a little wide, and now and then stroking her blazed nose; watched her pretence of nipping at his hand: he watched the beauty of her exaggerated in this half-lit isolation away from the others, the life and litheness in her satin body, the wilful expectancy in her bright soft eyes.

Run a bye! This bit o' blood—this bit o' fire! This horse of his! Deep within that shell of blue box-cloth against the stall

partition a thought declared itself: 'I'm——if she shall! She
can beat the lot! And she's——well going to!'

The door was thrown open, and she led out. He moved alongside. They were staring at her, following her. No wonder!
She was a picture, his horse—his! She had gone to "Jimmy's"
head.

They passed Jenning with Diamond Stud waiting to be
mounted. "Jimmy" shot him a look. Let the——wait!

His mare reached the palings and was halted. "Jimmy"
saw the short square figure of her jockey, in the new magenta
cap and jacket—*his* cap, *his* jacket! Beautiful they looked, and
no mistake!

"A word with you," he said.

The jockey halted, looked quickly round.

"All right, Mr. Shrewin. I know."

"Jimmy's" eyes smouldered at him; hardly moving his lips,
he said, intently: "You——well don't! You'll——well ride
her to win. Never mind *him!* If you don't, I'll have you off
the turf. Understand me! You'll——well ride 'er to win."

The jockey's jaw dropped.

"All right, Mr. Shrewin."

"See it is," said "Jimmy" with a hiss. . . .

"Mount jockeys!"

He saw magenta swing into the saddle. And suddenly, as if
smitten with the plague, he scuttled away.

VI

He scuttled to where he could see them going down—seventeen. No need to search for his colours; they blazed, like George
Pulcher's countenance, or a rhododendron bush in sunlight,
above that bright chestnut with the white nose, curveting a
little as she was led past.

Now they came cantering—Deerstalker in the lead.

"He's a hell of a horse, Deerstalker," said someone behind.

"Jimmy" cast a nervous glance around. No sign of George
Pulcher!

One by one they cantered past, and he watched them with
a cold feeling in his stomach. Still unused to sight of the
creatures out of which he made his living, they *all* seemed to him
hells of horses.

The same voice said:

" New colours! Well, you can see 'em, and the mare too. She's a showy one. Calliope? She's goin' back in the bettin', though."

" Jimmy " moved up through the Ring.

" Four to one on the field! " " Six Deerstalker! " " Sevens Magistrate! " " Ten to one Wasp! " " Ten to one Calliope! " " Four to one Diamond Stud! " " Four to one on the field! "

Steady as a rock, that horse of Jenning, and his own going back!

" Twelves Calliope! " he heard, just as he reached the stand. The telepathic genius of the Ring missed nothing—almost!

A cold shiver went through him. What had he done by his words to Docker? Spoiled the golden egg laid so carefully? But perhaps she couldn't win even if they let her! He began to mount the stand, his mind in the most acute confusion.

A voice said: " Hullo, ' Jimmy ' ! Is she going to win? " One of his young Oxford sparks was jammed against him on the stairway!

He raised his lip in a sort of snarl, and, huddling himself, slipped through and up ahead. He came out and edged in close to the stairs where he could get play for his glasses. Behind him one of those who improve the shining hour among backers cut off from opportunity, was intoning the odds a point shorter than below. " Three to one on the field." " Fives Deerstalker." " Eight to one Wasp."

" What price Calliope? " said " Jimmy," sharply.

" Hundred to eight."

" Done! " Handing him the eight, he took the ticket. Behind him the man's eyes moved fishily, and he resumed his incantation.

" Three to one on the field . . . three to one on the field. Six to one ·Magistrate."

On the wheeling bunch of colours at the start " Jimmy " trained his glasses. Something had broken clean away and come half the course—something in yellow.

" Eights Magistrate. Eight to one Magistrate," drifted up. So they had spotted that! Precious little they didn't spot! Magistrate was round again, and being ridden back. " Jimmy " rested his glasses a moment, and looked down. Swarms in the Cheap Ring, Tattersalls, the stands—a crowd so great you could lose George Pulcher in it. Just below a little man was making

silent, frantic signals with his arms across to someone in the
Cheap Ring. "Jimmy" raised his glasses. In line now—
magenta third from the rails!

"They're off!" The hush, you could cut it with a knife!
Something in green away on the right—Wasp! What a bat
they were going! And a sort of numbness in "Jimmy's" mind
cracked suddenly; his glasses shook; his thin, weasley face
became suffused and quivered. Magenta—magenta—two from
the rails! He could make no story of the race such as he would
read in to-morrow's paper—he could see nothing but magenta.

Out of the dip now, and coming fast—green still leading—
something in violet, something in tartan, closing.

"Wasp's beat!"   "The favourite—the favourite wins!"
"Deerstalker—Deerstalker wins!"   "What's that in pink on
the rails?"

It was *his* in pink on the rails! Behind him a man went
suddenly mad.

"Deerstalker—Come on with 'im, Stee! Deerstalker 'll win
—Deerstalker 'll win!"

"Jimmy" sputtered venomously: "Will 'e? Will 'e?"

Deerstalker and his own out from the rest—opposite the
Cheap Ring—neck and neck—Docker riding like a demon.

"Deerstalker! Deerstalker!"   "Calliope wins! She wins!"

Gawd! His horse! They flashed past—fifty yards to go, and
not a head between 'em!

"Deerstalker! Deerstalker!"   "Calliope!"

He saw his mare shoot out—she'd won!

With a little queer sound he squirmed and wriggled on to
the stairs. No thoughts while he squeezed, and slid, and hurried—only emotion—out of the Ring, away to the paddock. His
horse!

Docker had weighed in when he reached the mare. All right!
He passed with a grin. "Jimmy" turned almost into the body
of Polman standing like an image.

"Well, Mr. Shrewin," he said to nobody, "she's won."

'Damn you!' thought "Jimmy." 'Damn the lot of you!'
And he went up to his mare. Quivering, streaked with sweat,
impatient of the gathering crowd, she showed the whites of her
eyes when he put his hand up to her nose.

"Good girl!" he said, and watched her led away.

'Gawd! I want a drink!' he thought.

Gingerly, keeping a sharp lookout for Pulcher, he returned to the Stand to get it, and to draw his hundred. But up there by the stairs the discreet fellow was no more. On the ticket was the name O. H. Jones, and nothing else. " Jimmy " Shrewin had been welshed! He went down at last in a bad temper. At the bottom of the staircase stood George Pulcher. The big man's face was crimson, his eyes ominous. He blocked " Jimmy " into a corner.

" Ah! " he said; " you little crow! What the 'ell made you speak to Docker? "

" Jimmy " grinned. Some new body within him stood there defiant. " She's my 'orse," he said.

" You—Gawd-forsaken rat! If I 'ad you in a quiet spot I'd shake the life out of you! "

" Jimmy " stared up, his little spindle legs apart, like a cocksparrow confronting an offended pigeon.

" Go 'ome," he said, " George Pulcher; and get your mother to mend your socks. You don't know 'ow! Thought I wasn't a man, did you? Well, now you——well know I am. Keep off my 'orse in future."

Crimson rushed up on crimson in Pulcher's face; he raised his heavy fists. " Jimmy " stood, unmoving, his little hands in his bell-coat pockets, his withered face upraised. The big man gulped as if swallowing back the tide of blood; his fists edged forward and then—dropped.

" That's better," said " Jimmy," " hit one of your own size."

Emitting a deep growl, George Pulcher walked away.

" Two to one on the field—I'll back the field—Two to one on the field." " Threes Snowdrift—Fours Iron Dook."

" Jimmy " stood a moment mechanically listening to the music of his life, then edging out, he took a fly and was driven to the station.

All the way up to town he sat chewing his cheroot with the glow of drink inside him, thinking of that finish, and of how he had stood up to George Pulcher. For a whole day he was lost in London, but Friday saw him once more at his seat of custom in the " Corn." Not having laid against his horse, he had had a good race in spite of everything; yet, the following week, uncertain into what further quagmires of quixotry she might lead him, he sold Calliope.

But for years betting upon horses that he never saw, underground like a rat, yet never again so accessible to the kicks of fortune, or so prone before the shafts of superiority, he would think of the Downs with the blinkin' larks singin', and talk of how once he—had a horse.

1923.